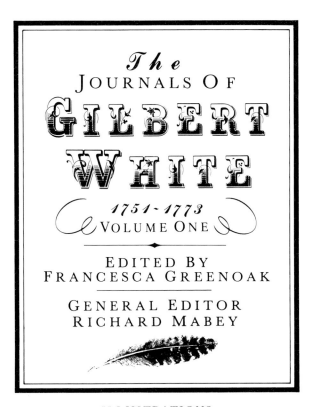

The
JOURNALS OF
GILBERT WHITE

1751 - 1773

VOLUME ONE

EDITED BY
FRANCESCA GREENOAK

GENERAL EDITOR
RICHARD MABEY

ILLUSTRATIONS
BY CLARE ROBERTS

CENTURY
LONDON · MELBOURNE · AUCKLAND
JOHANNESBURG

'Dutch Net' – an old variety
of cantaloup melon.
Trial greenhouses of E·W·King,
Seed Merchants, Essex.
19 August.

Art Direction and Design by
Bob Hook

First published in 1986 by Century
Hutchinson Ltd,
Brookmount House, 62–65 Chandos Place,
Covent Garden, London WC2N 4NW

Century Hutchinson Australia Pty Ltd,
PO Box 496, 16–22 Church Street,
Hawthorn, Victoria 3122,
Australia

Century Hutchinson New Zealand Ltd,
PO Box 40-086, Glenfield, Auckland 10,
New Zealand

Century Hutchinson South Africa Pty Ltd,
PO Box 337, Bergvlei, 2012 South Africa

Set in Caslon Old Face and Caslon Open
Face
Printed and bound in Great Britain by
Butler and Tanner Ltd, Frome, Somerset

British Library Cataloguing in Publication
Data

White, Gilbert
The Gilbert White Journals, 1751–73.
Vol. 1
1. White, Gilbert 2. Naturalists—
England—Selborne (Hampshire)—
Biography
I. Title II. Greenoak, Francesca
508'.092'4   QH31.W58

ISBN 0 7126 1294 7

CONTENTS

4
ACKNOWLEDGEMENTS

5
FOREWORD

6
INTRODUCTION

12
GILBERT WHITE'S GARDEN
by David Standing

15
NOTES ON THE TEXT

18
GARDEN KALENDAR

188
FLORA SELBORNIENSIS

223
NATURALIST'S JOURNAL

480
NOTES

500
GLOSSARY · INDEX

530
BIBLIOGRAPHY

Also by Richard Mabey
GILBERT WHITE
A biography of the author of
The Natural History of Selborne

Acknowledgements

I should like to thank Robin McIntosh for her painstaking
work in transcribing the hand-written manuscript, and
Moyna Kitchin for copy editing. I am grateful to Dr June
Chatfield and David Standing of the Gilbert White
Museum, Selborne, whose knowledge and work I have
drawn upon. The staff of the British Museum (Natural
History) were extremely helpful in establishing the identity
of most of the butterfly species, and many of the insect
species mentioned by Gilbert White. I should also like to
thank Dr Anita McConnell of the Science Museum and
David Elliston Allen who corresponded with me on specific
matters in the text. Finally, my thanks to the publishing
team at Century Hutchinson for their support and to Bob
Hook for his excellent design.

F. G.

F o r e w o r d

Gilbert White is often described as the founding father of natural history and his book *The Natural History of Selborne* is one of the most frequently published titles in the English language. Increasingly White is also being recognised as an important literary figure, who played a key role in the development of descriptive writing about place and nature.

Despite this, his *Journals*, which span more than forty years of observation, have never been published in full. As well as being the source of raw material for *The Natural History*, they are a unique record in their own right, and have a vividness and intimacy of style that was not to be seen again in English journal writing for another fifty years.

These two volumes cover the entire range of White's journals, from the early notes in a *Garden Kalendar* in 1751 to the final *Naturalist's Journal* entries in 1793. They are fully transcribed for the first time, and include all the detailed daily weather data of the original. As editor, Francesca Greenoak's chief aim throughout has been to make these remarkable manuscripts accessible to a wider audience. Annotation has therefore been kept to the minimum necessary for clarity and understanding.

In keeping with a tradition that has grown up around various editions of *The Natural History* of including illustrations of Selborne contemporary with the edition, these two volumes of *Journals* have been augmented by original drawings by Clare Roberts. Her pictures and field notes echo the detail and intimacy of White's writing, and were all drawn in the parish of Selborne and the surrounding countryside during 1985 and 1986.

Richard Mabey

INTRODUCTION

In 1750, Gilbert White's good friend and faithful correspondent John Mulso wrote to him:

> You are now I suppose to be found . . . ranging your Trees and nursing your Plants . . . I wish you joy of the arrival of the swallows and the swifts and the nightingales. I hope you will send me word how your nurseries go on, and the true state of Selborne Hanger . . .

By this time, at the age of thirty, a year after having been ordained, Gilbert had an evident interest in gardening and in the fauna and flora of his home village, and this was to be steadily extended and amplified throughout the rest of his life. Starting in 1751, he began to keep yearly journals in which he wrote perceptive notes on gardening and natural history, continuing this practice over forty-three years and ceasing to write entries only eleven days before his death. These journals prove his quite remarkable observational skills and, more clearly than any of his other writings, show a man whose scientific curiosity about the natural world incorporated a deep affection for plants and animals, particularly those of his native parish.

The journals fall into two distinct groupings, which differ more in form than content. The *Garden Kalendar*, continued between the years 1751 and 1767, comprise mostly but not exclusively gardening notes, written intermittently on blank quarto sheets. The *Naturalist's Journal* was a printed diary-notebook, each volume holding a year's observations, and Gilbert kept up these journals from the year 1768 until 1793. There was in addition a notebook-journal, the *Flora Selborniensis*, in which he wrote botanical observations during the year 1766.

Keeping regular notes of observations on horticultural, meteorological and natural history matters was a fairly widespread practice among gentlemen of Gilbert White's day. Robert Marsham, who corresponded with Gilbert after the publication of the *Natural History of Selborne*, wrote that he had kept a journal for more than fifty years. Coincidentally, Marsham seems to have been encouraged into the diary habit by Dr Stephen Hales, the notable scientist and botanist, Rector of Faringdon (a parish close to Selborne) and also a friend of the White family. Another friend of Robert Marsham was Benjamin Stillingfleet, in his latter years a gardener and botanist of considerable repute, who in 1759 published the influential *Miscellaneous Tracts relating to Natural History, Husbandry and Physick*. In the printed preface to the *Naturalist's Journal*, its originator Daines Barrington made several references to Stillingfleet's ideas, especially his recommendation of the keeping of daily records and observations. Thomas Barker of Rutland, who resided near Gilbert's uncle and aunt Mr and Mrs Isaacs at Whitwell Rectory, also kept a journal between the years 1736 and 1801. In its initial year, there were two spring-time notes initialled GW, one on wild geese flying northwards, and another on the sound of the cuckoo. It seems, however, that Gilbert did not keep a continuous journal of his own until he returned and settled back into life in his home village of Selborne, following his degree and ordination.

Gilbert White was a keen experimental gardener, and in 1747 bought for himself the most important horticultural work of the time, Philip Miller's great *Gardener's Dictionary*. Later he was to correspond with Miller, to meet him and exchange seeds. The Wakes, the family home of the White family, has its frontage right on the main street, with a considerable garden to the rear, backed by a field and the great beech hanger of Selborne. The garden was augmented and landscaped by Gilbert and his brothers and they adopted the Hanger itself into their schemes as part of the garden vista. Some of the their work is still evident today: the lime trees to the front of the house, part of the fruit wall, the ha-ha at the end of the garden, and the two paths up the Hanger – the steep Zig-zag and the gentler Bostal.

The *Garden Kalendar* and the later years of the *Naturalist's Journal* give considerable detail about the plants in the garden of the Wakes. The cottage garden flowers which

Gilbert grew in his borders are now once again in fashion – hollyhocks, larkspur, asters, lilies, fritillaries. He also planted trees and shrubs and several experimental crops such as sweet corn, sea kale and certain 'small beans' from Oxfordshire, 'never sowed but once in England'. In tune with the horticultural preoccupations of his time, Gilbert spent a great deal of energy maintaining hot-beds for melons and cucumbers. Yet the innovator, even one of dedication and skill, is, just like any gardener, at risk from the upredictable English weather. Gilbert White's hot-beds sometimes reached baking point and burned the plants or lost heat completely so that they perished of cold. An entry for 1754 notes bleakly 'uncommon severe winter. Most things in the garden destroyed.'

The beautiful garden upon which his friend Mulso heaped high compliments in later years was won by hard labour and planning. The intractable Selborne soil was improved with cartloads of dung, and good loamy soil was brought over from nearby Dorton. Small parcels of land were bought bit by bit from neighbours, to enlarge the grounds. The 'picturesque' was the prevailing concept of the late eighteenth century, and entering into its spirit, Gilbert made a bastion and a mound. He hung a series of gates, artificially sized and placed to make a vista. He set up oil jars to mimic urns, and made up a two-dimensional board to look from a distance like a statue. He also built alcoves (small summerhouses) at places where the view was especially attractive.

Nearly all the observations in the *Garden Kalendar* are concerned with cultivated plants, but in the 1760s Gilbert was becoming increasingly interested in wild plants. He purchased an important botanical work: William Hudson's *Flora Anglica* in 1765, and amended the title page of the *Kalendar* of that year to include notes on the wild flora also. This was not entirely satisfactory, and in 1766 he kept both a *Garden Kalendar* and a notebook which he called *Flora Selborniensis*, which is a catalogue of his wild plant observations. This was a year of botanical groundwork.

In 1768, he received as a gift a journal devised by the

Honourable Daines Barrington and published by Gilbert's brother Benjamin. *The Naturalist's Journal* was a standardised diary for the kind of observations that gentlemen of a scientific inclination had been making informally on the subject of natural history. At first Gilbert observed the formalities of the columns, which designated set spaces for the first trees in leaf, flowers to bloom, birds appearing and so on, but it took only a few years for most of the information to be written all over the page in sometimes quite lengthy paragraphs. Towards the end of the 1770s, he began inserting blank pages on which to write pieces of more extended observation. The only records he continued to keep in columns were the figures for the barometer and thermometer readings, and notes on wind and rain.

Gilbert White has long been acclaimed for several important discoveries. It was he who first distinguished between the three leaf warblers, who gave us the first and still revealing description of the harvest mouse. He observed the yearly appearance and reappearance of a 'large bat', giving us the earliest notes on the behaviour of the noctule bat in Britain, and he made many pioneering observations on his favourites among the birds: swifts, martins and swallows.

Yet it is not for these achievements alone that Gilbert White is revered and regarded nationally with affection, and his *Natural History of Selborne*, never out of print. Under his serious and affectionate scrutiny, the parish, one of the most ancient units of human community in England, was extended conceptually to include plants and animals – presented not as specimens, but co-existing within an intimate landscape. A follower in White's footsteps will note obvious losses – kites, bustards, the playful ravens over the Hanger – and one has to search for glow-worms or wrynecks. Yet it is significant that walking around Selborne today one may see, as Gilbert White did, a nuthatch in the churchyard, marsh marigolds brightening the church meadow, toothwort on the hazel bank, hellebores in the hollow lanes and along the quiet country roads, and an astonishingly rich mixture of woodland plants: daffodils, golden saxifrage, ferns and even the shy rarity, herb Paris.

As a writer, Gilbert was far from flamboyant. Indeed, so great was his reticence that even in the journals the personal pronoun rarely intrudes itself. None the less, there is a strong sense of the man behind the observations. The arrival of swallows is accompanied in the journal by exclamation marks!! Snow is lying 'shoe-deep' or reaching to a horse's chest; and there are 'cracks in the ground deeper than the length of a walking stick'. These tell a story of the naturalist watching the skies, tentatively trying the snow or barging through drifts on horseback, prodding the dried-out ground enquiringly with his stick. He drew on the resources of English and classical poetry, prose and science as he wrote the apparently simple journal notes which read so vividly:

> May 2nd 1765: No vegetation seems to stir at present.
> May 3rd : This evening the vehement east-west wind seems
> to be abated; & the air is soft, & cloudy. Ground
> bound like stone.

As the years passed, Gilbert became more confident and relaxed. He was corresponding with and meeting some of the foremost scientists and naturalists of the period, and it is clear that he recognised the original contribution that he could make to the state of knowledge of the time. He wrote two papers which were read at meetings of the Royal Society, and had, by the mid-1770s, decided to write a book about the natural history of his native parish which was to be a distillation of his enquiries and observations. Gilbert White had a fine critical faculty, and one senses an impatience with headlong and insufficiently substantiated natural history writing. As early as 1770, he was writing to Daines Barrington:

> Though there is endless room for observation in the field of
> nature which is boundless, yet investigation (where a man
> endeavours to be sure of his facts) can make but slow
> progress; and all that one could collect in many years would
> go into a very narrow compass.

What sets Gilbert White apart from other naturalists is not simply a matter of unusual perception. The clear-sightedness of his observations arises from a continuous endeavour to strike through conventional interpretations or misleading appearances to reach the truth of whatever subject he was considering. He took immense pains with style, not just as a matter of pride, but because he rightly saw a fundamental correlation between precision of thought and exactness of expression. The *Naturalist's Journals* are both field notes and a working manuscript for *The Natural History of Selborne*. They are by no means hasty jottings, but already accomplished and polished notes, many of which were transposed to the published book with only minimal editing, and they provide a close insight into the life-long interests of this remarkable naturalist.

GILBERT WHITE'S GARDEN

THESE NOTES ARE USED BY KIND PERMISSION OF
DAVID STANDING, GARDENER AT THE WAKES
(THE GILBERT WHITE MUSEUM).

The garden of Gilbert White's house, the Wakes, looked out over fields to the steep tree-covered hillside, the great beech hanger. Immediately to the south of the Wakes was a yard and stable block, and beyond this, higher ground known as Baker's Hill. When (about 1730) John and Anne White, Gilbert's parents, moved to the house, then called 'late Wakes' after the previous owner (subsequently, it became known simply as 'Wakes') it seems that the property had only a small garden, which John White began to lay out. Over the years to come, a number of other plots were acquired and used variously for flowers, vegetables and fruit, separated from each other by wicket fences and evergreen hedges near the house, and by tall hedges towards the Hanger.

By the 1750s the gardens had evolved into a reversed L shape, the long arm of the L stretching south over Baker's Hill, behind other cottages in the main street. Later, in the 1760s, the grounds expanded in the opposite direction, with the purchase of Lassam's orchard and other fields behind the house.

The Individual Gardens

Six main areas of the garden may be identified from the *Garden Kalendar*.

(1) Turner's Garden and
(2) The Field Garden

These were large vegetable plots on Baker's Hill. Crops grown included beans, cabbages, celery, carrots, radishes, turnips, leeks and cucumbers. Potatoes were also grown, a crop uncommon locally at that time. Turner's garden was adjacent to White's orchard, from which it was separated by a quickset hedge. The Field Garden contained a 'melonry' – hot beds on which White grew melons. These consisted of mounds of fermenting manure covered with a layer of rich soil in which were planted the melon seedlings and covered with glass frames.

(3) Orchard, Quincunx and Flower Bank

These were also on Baker's Hill: the orchard and shrubbery appear to have been located close to the house and yard. The orchard contained filbert, apple, plum and pear trees, a Dutch medlar and cherries. Between the trees ran a grass walk edged with lilies, tulips, hollyhocks, wallflowers and columbines.

Further up the hill White had arranged fir trees as a quincunx (one in each corner and one in the centre of a square). Around this was a hedge, within which beans, turnips, and peas were grown. Near the quincunx, he erected an ornamental oil jar vase on a pedestal nine feet high, and constructed his first ha-ha or sunken fence of wooden piles (now destroyed). From here a flower bank ran down the side of Baker's Hill. On this were planted lilies, crown imperials, rockets and evening primroses. White built an alcove on the north-western corner of the hill.

(4) The Outer Fields

In his outer garden White carried out various landscaping improvements of the type suggested by William Kent the landscape gardener who proposed that urns, obelisks and statues be placed in a romantic, natural setting. White made a mount five feet high at the bottom of the great mead, and constructed a smaller one under the great oak tree. In the Ewell, a small narrow field on his north west boundary he erected the first oil jar vase, the second being near the quincunx. He also cut a vista through the tall hedges, terminating with a figure of Hercules painted on a board 12 feet high to represent a statue.

One particular field was set aside as a flower garden. Here a wide range of ornamental plants were grown in 'basons' – holes filled with light fertile soil. Some were reserved for annuals – including balsams, marigolds, and love-in-a-mist, whilst others contained perennials such as lupins, irises and hollyhocks. Shrubs and trees were also planted – roses, elders, jasmines and lilacs.

(5) The Little Garden and Borders around the House

Close to the house was a small ornamental garden with lilies, crown imperials, crocuses, scarlet lychnis and pinks. Covering the walls of the house were vines, roses, figs and passion flowers, whilst borders under the window contained snowdrops, tulips, rockets and solomons seal.

(6) The New Garden

From the name we can deduce that this garden was an addition to the existing grounds. It lay to the north of the cottage, and adjoined the main street, in a position now occupied by the billiard room, corridor, library, and originally, the great parlour (built in 1777).

The garden was divided into ornamental and kitchen sections. In the flower garden were planted French and African marigolds, larkspur, sweet peas, campanulas and foxgloves. There was also a bed of roses, interplanted with hollyhocks. In the vegetable garden a range of leaf and root crops were grown, with asparagus beds, plots of annual fennel (finochia) and horseradish, and cucumbers. Dutch honeysuckles scrambled over a trellis.

In June 1760 White agreed to purchase a neighbouring plot, an old orchard, which nearly doubled the area of the garden behind the house. After grubbing out the trees, the ground was levelled and a second ha-ha, this time of stone, was built in 1761. A sun dial was erected on the turf above the wall, which White called the terrace.

This second new garden was then laid out with six big rectangular beds, separated by turf paths. A fruit wall was erected along the northern side of the plot, against which were planted five vines, three nectarines, two peach trees and an apricot, with a passion flower at each end.

The border in front of the fruit wall provided a valuable south-facing site, and in addition to the fruit trees, early crops of lettuces and radishes were grown. The ha-ha, sundial and a small section of fruit wall can still be seen in the Wakes garden today, this part of the grounds having changed little since the time of Gilbert White.

N O T E S
O N T H E T E X T

This is the first time that Gilbert White's journals have been printed in full. His forty-three years of notes and observations are published here in two volumes:

Volume I   *The Garden Kalendar; Flora Selborniensis; Naturalist's Journal (1768–73)*.

Volume II   *Naturalist's Journal (1774–93)*.

Garden Kalendar

The manuscript of Gilbert White's *Garden Kalendar*, kept between the years 1751 and 1767, is at the British Library. It consists of quarto sheets of letter paper which were subsequently stitched together. The work has appeared in print in a facsimile edition with an introduction and notes by John Clegg (Scolar Press, 1975).

Flora Selborniensis

Flora Selborniensis was written by Gilbert White during the year 1766. It consists of a number of quarto sheets of notes principally about the wild flowers in the environs of Selborne. It is now owned by the Selborne Society. A facsimile *Flora Selborniensis* was published by the Society in a limited edition.

Naturalist's Journal

Between the years 1768 and the year of his death 1793, Gilbert White made an entry almost every day in his *Naturalist's Journal*, taking it with him on his journeys away from home. The format for these annual journals had been devised by Daines Barrington and published by Gilbert's brother Benjamin White, and were in the form of blank diaries split into printed columns headed with items relevant to those with an interest in natural history. A selection of the entries, edited by Walter Johnson, appeared in 1931, but the complete journals have never been published in full. For this purpose, a transcription was made from the microfilm held by the British Library, where the manuscript journals are kept.

Any editor of Gilbert White's works begins with the immediate benefit of the orderliness of the author's method. The writing is clear copperplate, and there are very few indecipherable words. The arrangement of entries is generally easy to follow.

The two main principles behind the presentation and annotation of these manuscripts are maintaining the authenticity of the text, and endeavouring to present it in the way most accessible to the reader. Notes have been kept to a minimum and are intended simply to explain names or terms which would be unfamiliar to a present-day reader, or to indicate instances where the present status of plants and creatures mentioned by Gilbert White has changed dramatically. The variable spelling and the punctuation of the originals have been retained wherever possible, and most of the few crossings-out have been annotated. Gilbert sometimes used archaisms for effect and, as his interest in antiquities grew, drew also on vernacular Hampshire names for topographical details and for plants and animals. Interestingly, the English common names for plants have changed less than the scientific names over the last two hundred years.

Gilbert used the standard English flora of the early eighteenth century, John Ray's great work *Synopsis methodica stirpium Britannicarium* in its third edition of 1724 edited by J. J. Dillenius, and from 1765 he referred also to Hudson's *Flora Anglica*. He was familiar with the work of Linnaeus and, after 1768, many of the scientific names used are Linnaean ones. On the title-page of some of his journals he appends the information that 'the plants are named according to the sexual system [the Linnaean method], the birds according to Ray, the Insects according to Linnaeus'. Every attempt has been made in the glossary/index of this edition to identify the species noted by Gilbert White. Translations of Latin or Greek quotations are to be found under the note for that day.

In the course of putting Gilbert White's written notes into a printed form editorial requirements have dictated a kind of design which differs from the original. While the guiding principle has been to maintain the authenticity of the work, the aim has also been to achieve a result which is more accessible and easier to follow than the original, which was, after all, not intended for publication.

For the *Garden Kalendar* and the *Flora Selborniensis*, a simple format consisting of date, followed by notes, reproduces that of the originals. In the case of the *Naturalist's Journal* a different procedure has been adopted, and this is outlined on page 223 at the beginning of that section.

All scientific names have been italicised. Punctuation, including the use of colons where modern usage would dictate semi-colons or full stops, has been reproduced exactly as in the manuscripts. Gilbert White's short forms y^e and Bro^r have also been retained, as has the form *it's* for the possessive.

Key to symbols

The Editor's notes on the text are indicated thus ¶ and the notes themselves are grouped at the end of the book under the relevant dates. They are also identified by date in the glossary/index.

Gilbert's own notes are marked with asterisks, as in the manuscripts, and included in the text.

Editorial footnotes relating to the position or authorship of certain passages are indicated by a dagger sign†.

Comments or notes added by Gilbert at a date later than the adjacent entry are set in a different typeface.

GARDEN KALENDAR
— 1751 —

JANUARY 7. Two rows of early Spanish-Beans¶ in Turner's plot.¶ The four other rows were set in ye middle of November.

14. Earthed-up a row of Celery.

23. Planted 250 loaf-Cabbage¶ plants in Turner's plot.

24. Sowed first Crop of Radishes turnip, & common; lettuce; & onions under the pales in the little Garden.¶

24. Planted-out five bulbs of the Crown Imperial (which I had from a Seedsman in London) in the middle plot of the little Garden.

24. Planted three slips of the Passion-flower, sent me by Mr Newlin, in the little Garden.

FEBRUARY 23. Planted 14 Cuttings of the large, white, Dutch-Currants¶ (which I brought from Godalming) in the little Garden.

27. New staked the Espaliers.

MARCH 7. Planted five young passion-flower plants, which I had from Oxōn. Gave my U: White¶ four.

8. Sowed a Crop of Asparagus seed: & seven rows of pease in the new Garden for the first Crop.

9. Set a Layer of Persian-Jessamin, which came from Mr Budd's.

15. Earthed-up the two last rows of Celery.

D^o Layed-down three twigs of the mulberry-tree.

21. Made first Hot-bed: cleared the strawberry, & raspberry beds.

22. Sowed in the Hot-bed* Cucumber,¶ Melon, Squashes, & Mays-seed.¶ Planted-out Holy-oaks, down the field, & in the Garden-border, & before the House: the seed from the Grange.¶ Sowed a Crop of Carrots, Parsneps, Beets, Radishes, Lettuce, Leeks, Onions; a small crop of Salsafy; red Cabbage-seed, Dutch parsley, & Chardoons.¶ There had been a Glut of wet for five weeks, & the Ground was rather too moist; but worked pretty well.

23. In the Hot-bed, two rows of African, & French Marigold seed.

27. Planted four rows of Winsor-beans¶ in the field-Garden in ground just turned in from Grass.

APRIL 1. Sowed in the field-garden four rows of marrow-fat pease.¶

2: 3. Planted four Asparagus-beds with plants of my own raising in the new Garden: sowed a thin Crop of Onions upon them. The Ground was well sanded, & trenched deep with good rotten Dung, but wet when planted.

2. Earthed-up the two last rows of Celeri the last time.

---

*This bed by means of the great rains lost it's Heat, so that the Cucumbers, Melons, & Squashes never came-up.

4. Sowed a crop of common, & curled Parsley: & planted 13 Holy-oaks in the orchard, & yard.

6. Sowed a full Crop of Carrots, Salsafy, Skirret, Scorzonera,¶ Lettuce, Radishes, Beet. Sowed the seed of a remarkable large leek. Sowed a large bed of sea-cale,*¶ which I brought from the South-hams of Devon. Sliped,¶ & dressed the artichoke-beds. A small crop of Onions under Kelsey's Hedge for picklers. The Ground still wet.

13. Made a second Hot-bed: sowed within the frame, common Cucumbers, Horn D.º Squashes, Melons, Balsams, French Marygolds, purslain:¶ without the frame; Common Celeri, Celeriac, or turnip-rooted Celeri, Nasturtium, Sun-flowers, & purslain. Made a cover of oiled paper¶ for the first bed.

18. Sowed nine rows of marrowfat pease in the plot just without the field Garden.

23. Planted 300 of Cabbages in the field-garden. Sowed Holy-oak, Oriental-Mallow, & Nasturtium, & Larkspur-seed in the common Ground. Let an old Barrel with the Head beat-out into the Ground to hold water for the Hot-beds, &c.

26. Cut Asparagus for the first time.

27. Made a new Hot bed: transplanted the melon-plants into it: sowed some Cucumber-seed in it: & sowed common Celeri, & Sunflowers without the frame. Transplanted the Mays into the border next Lassams:¶ transplanted the African Marrygolds in the beds, & some of the Cucumbers: sowed 2 rows of Garden Cress, & two of Wh: Mustard on an old bed. Dug-up the last parcel of blanched Celeri.

MAY   3. Pulled the first Radishes.

7. Sowed a Crop of Parsneps, (the first failed) with radishes, & Lettuce. The first Crop of curled Endive, green, & white. The first Crop of French-Beans, two rows in the new-garden.

9. Second Crop of Skirret;* the first failing.

14. Crop of Common Beans in the field-Garden.

23. Pricked-out the red Cabbages. Sowed flowering Lupines of several Sorts, & Lady-pease in the basons¶ in the Field, & the border in the Garden.*

24. Pricked-out the Chardons: sowed five basons with Cucumber-seed in the natural Ground. Transplanted one Holy-oak into the border in the Field.

---

*The Sea-cale lay a long while in the Ground before it appeared; six weeks at least.
*The Skirret all run to seed.
*No fine weather, but constant wind, wet, & frost till the 18th of May. Then very dry, & hot.

25. Planted-out the Melons for the last time, & covered them with oiled papers. Sowed a plot of Roman, & a plot of white Broccoli-seed;* & shaded them well with boughs. Sowed some Common, & curled parsley; & some purslane.

27. Planted-out three squashes.

28. Crop of Common Celeri.

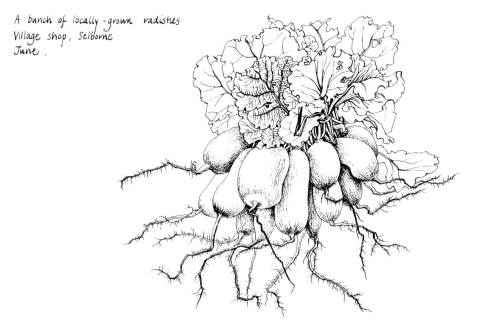

A bunch of locally-grown radishes
Village shop, Selborne
June.

JUNE 11: 13. Row & half of Marrowfats; & D° of French-beans.

20. Gathered first pease.

21. Planted-out Nasturtiums, Sunflowers, Balsams, & French, & African Marrigolds in the field, & new Garden.

24. Pricked-out a large Quantity of white, & Roman Broccoli.

25. Planted-out curled white, & green Endive in rows: pricked out three plots of Celeri: planted-out red Cabbages; & a plot of Leeks from the Giant Leek. Sowed a Crop of Endive (second Crop) both sorts.

26. Planted out the Holy-oaks sown in ye Spring.

27. Gathered first beans, little spanish, set in November.*

AUGUST 27. Earthed-up the first planted Chardons; planted out more: trenched 6 rows of Celeri. Sowed a small plot of turnip-radishes. Planted out several rows of Broccoli.

---

*A prodigious Crop of Broccoli by shading, & watering.
*Latter end of July sowed a large bed of Spinage, & radishes. Came-up very well.

SEPTEMBER 9.   Earthed-up the first row of Chardons for the last time in pots with the bottoms out.

12.   Basketed-up the second row of Chardons: sowed a large bed of Spinage.

OCTOBER   5.   Planted Stock-gilliflowers¶ from Bradley down the Field. Dug up the two first Chardons.

11.   Trenched-out a row of Celery in the field Garden: earthed-up the last Chardons the first time.

14.   Sow'd three rows of early Spanish Beans in the field garden.

23.   Added one row more of small beans from Oxōn, never sowed but once in England.

26.   Planted seven spruce firs from North-warnboro' in Baker's Hill: some flowering shrubs in the lower part next the walk: a Quince-tree in the old orchard. Earthed-up the new asparagus-beds in the new Garden.

NOVEMBER 2.   Finished the Shrubery. A severe frost for planting. Earthed--up the old asparagus-beds.

6.   Planted in a border in the old Orchard several cuttings of Gooseberries, Currants, Honey-suckles, & Scorpion Sennas.¶ Earthed-up the Celery in the new Garden.

DECEMBER 2:   Trenched some Ground against spring. Earthed-up Artichoke-
3.   beds¶ for the winter. Earthed-up the last Chardons; & the Celery.

The Year 1751 was one of the wettest Years in the memory of Man. There were constant Storms & Gluts of rain from the 20th of Feb: to the 20th of May. Part of May, & all June were very dry, & burning. But all July, & great part of August were as wet as ever: so that nothing in Gardens in a clayey soil grew to any size: & nothing came to bear 'till five or six weeks later than usual.

— 1752 —

MIDDLE OF   two rows of Beans, & nine of early pease in the field-Garden.
FEBRUARY.

MARCH   4.   Hot-bed in the field-Garden: the dung had been cast a fortnight, & mixed with Coal-cynders. 3 hundred of Cabbage-plants in the new, & Turner's Garden.

5.   Mulched, & banked-up the Quincunx of firs¶ on Baker's Hill. Dressed the Raspberry-beds, & planted a new one in the new Garden. Sowed a Crop of Celeri on the outside of the Cucumber-frame. Sowed a crop of carrots, Parsneps, Leeks, Onions, Skirrets, Beets, Radishes, Lettuce, fine Coss sort. A large Plot of fine Asparagus-seed from Chalgrave in the new Garden. Sowed

Flower bason by buck path
The WaRes.
August

in the new Garden Frenchoneysuckles, Columbines, & Everlasting-pease.

6. Weeded Sea-Cale-bed. Sowed Holy-oak seed, & Oriental-Mallow, a good large bed in the new Garden. Sowed two rows of forward pease in the Garden in the field.

7. Sowed in the Hot-bed Cucumbers, French Marrigolds, African D.º Indian wheat; & Nasturtiums on the outside.* Dressed strawberry-beds. Planted a row of Esshallots. Planted Holy-oaks down the field. New-dug the border at the bench in the Field. Made a screen for the Hot-bed with pease-haulm.

10. Plashed, & banked-up the Quickset-hedge¶ between Turner's, & the Orchard. Planted Holy-oaks in the New-garden. Sowed poppy-seed, & Larkspur-seed in the Borders of the new Garden: Dressed Asparagus-beds: earthed-up the late row of Celeri in the field-Garden. Mended the Sea-Cale with seed, where it was wanting.

11. Dunged, & dug-up some Ground in the new Garden. Dug the flower-basons in the field. Sowed the ground in the little mead (lately cleared from nettles) with Grass-seeds. Prepared two basons, one on each side the street-door, for passion-flowers. Thinned the young bed of Spinage.

11. Sowed seven rows of broad beans in the Quincunx on the top of Baker's Hill. Planted in the new Garden three of the large Dutch-Currant-trees, which I brought in cuttings from Godalming last Year.

APRIL 8. †Planted water'd & shaded the *Laurestinus* near the Bench in the Field & the Passion flower on each side the Street door. Sowed a Row of Laburnum Seed from Ringmer.

10. †Put sixteen Concumber plants under the Hand Glasses.¶

11. †Plant'.ᵈ six Concumb. plants from W. Wells in the Old Hot Bed.

13. †Transplanted the Indian Corn in the Cups¶ in the field by the Brickwalk in Bakers Hill & in the Oats towards Willis's. Planted each Corner of Bakers Hill within the Rod Hedge¶ with Beans.

15. †Sow'd three Rows of French Beans in the field Gardⁿ, first Row from the Tub in the Barn second from the paper bag in the Kitchen third from the Chaise.
†Mem. made a Bed of Sand for the seed.

15. †Planted some yellow Indian Corn in the New hot Bed without the Glasses, to supply those that fail in the Cups.

16. †Sowed a Row of purple double stocks from London & half a Row of Brampton Stocks from Ringmer. Sowed in the New Garden on the Border by the Brick Walk, Love lies a Bleeding,

---

*Appeared all above ground on the 11ᵗʰ. The bed heats well, without being too fierce.
†Note inserted here: Thomas White's writing – GW.

Painted Lady Peas, Larkspurs, Yellow Lupines, & Double
Poppies.
†Mem. Sowed Radishes with the Stocks as Miller directs.¶

MAY   14. Planted some Indian-Corn, & French & African Marrigolds
        down the basons in the field. Some D⁹ Marrigolds in the new
        Garden.
      16. Made a new hot-bed in the field-Garden: made a ridge with 10
        cups in the new Garden for Cucumbers in the natural Ground, &
        sowed them with seed.
      18. Sowed a Crop of Broccoli, parsley, & Finochia¶ in the new-
        Garden.
      19. Removed four plants,¶ with fruit set on them, into the new hot-
        bed.
      20. Planted-out Sunflowers, & Nasturtiums down the field; sowed a
        row of dwarf white french-beans in the field-Garden; mended the
        early rows of french-beans in D⁹

JULY   23. Planted 200 white, & Roman Broccoli-plants (which I brought
        from Oxōn) in the new, & field Garden. Planted 200 Savoys in
        the field Garden.
      27. Sowed a crop of winter-spinage, with some turnep-radishes, in
        the new Garden.
      29. Sowed a Crop of turneps, for spring-Greens,¶ in the field-
        Garden. A Crop of D⁹ among the firs on Baker's Hill.

'Painted Lady' sweet peas
Annual garden
the Wakes.
30 May.

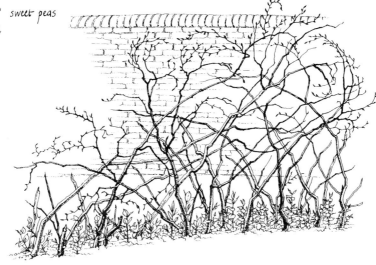

AUGUST 3. Trenched six rows of Celeri in the field-Garden. Sowed a Crop of
        Coss Lettuce, & endive.
SEPTEMBER
      15. N: S.¶ Tyed-up several large Endive.
      16. Sowed a plot of Rhubarb; & two late Crops of Spinage.

29. Tyed-up the remaining Endive.

OCTOBER 19. Six rows of early, African Beans, in the field-Garden.
24. Trenched two rows of Celery in the field-Garden.

— 1753 —

JANUARY 1. Planted three rows of small African Beans in the Quincunx-garden.
2. Sowed a crop of Asparagus-seed, of our own saving, in the new Garden.
16. Two rows of broad beans in the fir-quincunx, & two in Turner's Garden.
19. Five rows of forward pease in Turner's Garden.
23. Planted five Bushels of turneps for greens.
24. Thinned-out the raspberry-beds.
26. Sowed a long drill of parsley in New Gard.ⁿ & a Crop of Asparagus seed in D.º

OCTOBER 25. 1753. Seven rows of early African-Beans in the field-Garden. Three rows of early pease in Turner's Garden. Laid-down several Branches of the Laurus-tinus¶ in yᵉ little Garden: & some boughs of the Mulberry-tree. Pease destroyed, & most of the beans.

— 1754 —

An uncommon severe winter: most things in the Garden destroyed.

FEBRUARY Latter end. A crop of early pease in Turner's: & crop of broad beans in the field-Garden.

MARCH 5. Made a very deep hot-bed: half the dung cast before hand, & half from dunghill at once. The season uncommonly dry, & fine. Sowed a large Crop of spinage in the field-garden to supply the general destruction made by the severe winter. A wonderful large, useful Crop.
6. Sowed larkspurs, painted ladies, & Columbines in the borders in the new Garden: & a Crop of Parsley.
12. Sowed two pots of melons in the Hot-bed, & one pot of cockscombs: backed-up the bed to the top of the frame, the frost being very extream.
19. Sowed two pots of M.ʳ Missen's melon-seeds; one pot of early Cucumber-seeds; one pot of Gibson's Capsicums. The bed in fine order, but the frost very severe. One pot more of Cockscombs.
    The first-sown Cockscombs appear'd about the 21. came-up very thick: the first-sown melons about 23. very strong. Raised the pots as soon as they appeared.
26. Sowed a row of Bosworth's early melons in the hot bed without

		pots: a row of my own Cucum: seed: & two rows of Bosworth's white-Dutch Cucum: seed,* never sowed before in England.
	29.	Cast eleven Cart-loads of Hot dung in the field-garden for melon-beds, & Cucum.ʳ ridges.
	29.	Sowed a Crop of Carrots, radishes, white Coss, & <u>green</u> Coss lettuce, Parsneps, Beets, leeks, Holyoaks, & Onions. Planted-out some Laburnums raised in 1752 from seeds in Baker's Hill.
APRIL	4.	Made a very large hot-bed for my two-light melon-frame.¶ The Dung very warm.
	5.	Made four rows of the broken rows of early beans. Laid fine earth 6 inches thick between the Hot-bed; sowed some radishes, & a crop of Celeri.
	8.	Laid-on the earth on the great Melon-bed. Bed heats finely: wonderful fine weather.
	9.	Sowed a large Crop of marrow-fats in Turner's.
	10.	Planted three large, forward Cucumber-plants, given me by Mʳ Johnson, in my first Hot-bed.
		Planted six Laurels near the pitching in the old orchard;¶ two Larches on the bank near the Ewel-gate; a Scotch, & silver fir in the upper end of the Ewel-close.
	11.	Made a melon-hot-bed with 14 barrows of dung, for my smallest frame covered with a paper-light.¶ Made my ridge for three hand-glasses.
	12.	Transplanted three of my forwardest melon plants (four leaves each) into each of the lights of my great frames: one to be taken away from each hill, when they are settled. Mem: the earth would not turn-out, till the pots were broken. The bed in a fine heat. The plants had fill'd the pots with their fibres. Made a slight hot-bed in the new garden with 8 barrows of dung for hardy annuals: put-on my old frame, & old oil'd paper. Sowed a Crop of Carrots & lettuce in the shady quarter of the new garden; spots of Sunflowers, & Nasturtiums in the borders of Dᵒ six rows of broad beans in the field gardens.
		Planted-out some cucumber-plants (sadly wire-drawn) under two of the Hand-glasses; & sowed six of Mʳ Burrough's melon-seeds under an other; the ridge in a fine heat. The early melon-plants from Mʳ Burrough's seed. Those to be put in the paper-frame from Mʳ Missen's.
	14.	Sowed in the new-garden hot-bed, rows of African Marygolds, & Indian Corn: planted 20 shallot-bulbs, & 12 Garlick Dᵒ in new Gard:
	17.	Planted a pot of Mʳ Missen's melons in the small frame under the paper light.
	15.	Brought 4 white cucumber-plants from Waltham; put them under a Hand-glass.
	19.	Very thick Ice, & the Ground froze hard. Frequent showers of

*Never came up.

snow, & hail. The Hot-beds maintain their Heat well: the melon-beds too apt to steam; & the air too cold to be admitted in any great degree.

24.   Pinch'd my early melon's for the first time: & added a good depth of fine mould, mixed with sand, so as to fill the frames half way up.

   The paper-light torn by a storm, & the melon plants damag'd.

25.   Planted-out about 20 of the best Cockscombs on the upper side of the Cucumber, & two-light melon-frames.

   Planted a pot of Missen's melons in the small frame; the other pot being damaged by a storm which tore the paper light. Planted some large french Lupines from Mͬ͠ Budd in the new Garden.

MAY   2.   Sowed some Cucumber-seeds under an Hand-glass in the natural Ground, for a natural Crop. Prick'd-out a small bed of early Celeri, just in the first leaf, for early trenches.

8.   Earthed-up the melon-beds a good depth more: took-off a joint with a knife that had been omitted; stopp'd some of the runners: the plants in good vigour, & offering for fruit, & bloom.

   The cucumber plants show fruit; but none yet set.

   The Cockscombs wonderful forward, & stocky; & have showed bloom ever since the end of April.

9. 10.   Dressed the Artichoke-beds; & sowed three long rows of large, white french-beans in the field Garden.

21.   Made a good strong hot-bed to finish-off the Cockscombs with: plunged 10 large pots in the bed, & half-filled them with fine earth.

   Lined-out & earth'd very deep the melon-beds for the last time; & rais'd all the frames to the top of the earth. Planted some Capsicums, & pendulous Amaranths from Waltham in smaller pots: & 24 Cauliflowers from Soberton in new Garden.

22.   Made a wattle hedge,¶ about 18 inches high, round the melon-beds, to widen out the beds.

   Moved ten of the best Cockscombs into the large pots in the new beds: the plants were taken-up with a sheet of tin with a good deal of earth, & well water'd. The plants very fine, & forward, & in good bloom; & 22 inches high. Two old frames placed one on the other: & the bed beginning to heat well.

22.   The forwardest bason of Burrough's melons shewed for fruit. The weather uncommonly dry & sultry. Planted some forward Celeri from Mͬ͠ Beaver's. A large parcel more of my own Celeri in new Garden.

22.   Sowed a Crop of turnep-seed in field garden, & new-Garden after a soaking shower.

25.   Planted 300 of backward Cabbage plants.

JUNE   5.   The Cockscombs full 28 inches high; the combs very broad, &
                        the stems very stocky.

                5.   Planted 100 of fine Savoys in the place of the two Asparagus-beds
                        grubb'd-up in the new Garden. Sowed a crop of Coss-lettuce, &
                        endive green, & white.

                6.   Planted-out a Crop of Leeks in field-Garden.

                15.   †Cut first Cucumber. Cockscombs 3 foot high the tallest, widest
                        Comb 3¼ Inches.

                28.   Lin'd the Cockscomb-bed,¶ which began to grow cool, with 9
                        barrows of very hot dung:

                28.   Only five melons set; those very large, & in the two-light frame.
                        Missens plants still cast their fruit; not one set.

JULY   2.   The best Comb five inches & half wide: the melons swell apace.
                        The cockscomb-bed very hot with the new lining. Shady,
                        showery weather for these last 3 weeks, & not kind for the
                        melons.

*Catmint and cockscombs
flowering outside the garden door.
The Wakes.
18 July.*

                6.   Trench'd-out four rows of Celeri in yᵉ field-Garden: planted a
                        large bed of late-sown Coss-lettuce in yᵉ New-Garden.

                        †Thomas White's handwriting.

	17.	Planted a large Crop of Broccoli-plants from Captain Gwyn's; with Endives between.
	23.	Cut-away a vast deal of the melon-vines, which were shot-out beyond all bounds: none of Missen's set yet; & no more of Burrough's. Put a brick under some of the Melons. No kind Melon-weather since the beginning of June; but a constant cloudy, windy season, but not much rain. Missen's Melons shew plenty of fruit, but it all drops-off. The melon's earth too rich; which occasion'd such an abundance of vine: besides the seed was but one year old.
	23.	Took the Cockscombs out of their frame: the best comb full seven Inches wide; the leaves very large, & green; & the largest Stems two inches & a quarter round: the Combs well indented: That Amaranth that was suffered to run to many heads, looks very fine, & makes a pleasing variety. The wind is very apt to snap-off the leaves when the plants are first set-out, before the air has hardened them: heavy rains do the same. The tallest plant about three feet four inches. †Mem. the constant wet Weather rotted several of the Heads of those that stood abroad.
	25.	Cut first natural Cucumber.
AUGUST	7.	†Cut first Melon wt. 4½ lb. it was firm & thick fleshed & better tasted than could be expected after such a continuance of Shade & wonderful wet Weather. The best Combs grow mouldy.
	14.	Missen's plants too vigorous to let any fruit set. Fine weather: cut away the vines from the melons to let in the full Sun.
	15.	Sowed a Crop of Spinage, & Radishes in the field-Garden.
MARCH	12. 1752.	Mem: Left the three new Cucumber-frames, taken to pieces, in the old barn, in the straw-bey, leaning against the boards of the new stable. Put the glass-frames belonging to them (but with no Glass in them) in the lumber-garret: & the oaken-pins in a deal-box in the lumber-Garret. Mem: Seven very full cart-loads of dung make an exact suitable hot-bed for my great two-light frame: & five D.° for my four hand-glasses.
SEPTEMBER		
	13.	Collected Mushroom-spawn, & laid it up to dry.
	20.	Laid-down Baker's Hill with white clover-seed; & rolled it well. A long dry fit of 6 weeks.
	28.	Made an Horse-radish-bed in the new-Garden: planted the buds 10 inches deep. †Transplanted a Row of Mint, one of Balm and one of Pennyroyal.

---

†Thomas White's handwriting.

30.   †Parted the Lilly roots in the Little Garden & planted the large ones in the Field Basons, & the offsets in the Orchard, with the Tulips &c that if any of them are worth preserving they may be markt when in bloom & remov'd into the Garden. Transplanted Sweet Williams from Waltham into the Little Garden from the New Garden with a few Stocks.

OCTOBER 1.   Carryed ten loads of virgin-earth from Dorton into the little mead for the melon-frames.

9.   A thorough soaking rain, after an uninterrupted fit of above six weeks dry weather.

15.   †Planted a Bason of Double Perr! Sunflower   No. 6
                Single D°   No. 7
                Double Ragged Robin   No. 8
         two Roots of Campan. Pyram. in pots
         two Peach leav'd D?   No. 9
            Canterbury Bells   No. 11
         two Roots Double Scarlet Lychnis, one in little Gard? the other in the field   No. 12
         Two yellow Lillies ⎱ in little Garden
         Two fiery D° ⎰

21.   †Planted some Yellow & purple Crocus' for Borders in the Little Garden. Planted Slips of Pinks & Cloves¶ in the Little Garden & in some of the field Basons.

22.   †Planted Fox: Gloves Mulleins, Wood laurel & Bearsfoot from the Wood & Soap Wort from Gale's Garden Hedge. Planted three Opulus' from Berrimans.

24.   †Sow'd three New Basons with Larkspur seeds   N? 5
Sow'd a Row of Laburnum seed in the Seedling Bed in New Gard.   N? 1
           Fraxinella seed in D?   N? 2
           Persicaria   N? 3
Planted Golden Rod & S! Peter's Wort¶ from D? Bristow's.
         Mem. some offsets in seedling Bed.
Planted some Xyphiums or Bulbous Iris' in the Little Garden.   No. 10
Planted some Tuberous rooted Iris' in the field. Mem. the Xyphiums were sent by Mistake.
Planted a *Spiraea Frutex* from M? Budd.

NOVEMBER 5.   †Transplanted a Row of Laurustines into the Gate from the Little Garden.

6.   †Moved the Layers of *Laurustinus* into the Nursery Bed in the Orchard.

9.   †Planted four Box Trees (which came from behind the old Pales)

---

†Thomas White's handwriting.

in the vista at the upper end of ye field.

†Removed four Rose Trees into one Bason in the Fields. Very wet Weather, but not very cold.

20. Planted 9 rows of Mazagon beans¶ in Turner's Garden. Earth'd Asparagus-beds.

21. Made, earth'd, & thatch'd a musroom-bed seven feet long according to Miller.¶

21. Altered the square-plot behind where the old pales stood, & threw it into a grass plot, with two very wide borders, one towards the street, & one towards Kelsey's Gate.

Planted-out 3 doz of Coss lettuce under two old frames to stand the winter in the new Garden near the melon-beds.

DECEMBER 17. †Put the Spawn into the Mushroom Beds.

31. Earth'd up the second Crop of Celeri.

— 1755 —

JANUARY 6. Sowed a row of Holly-berries behind the Filberts against Kelsey's Yard.

FEBRUARY 7. Made an Hot-bed with the small frame for White-mustard &c: & an other with an hand-glass for Celeri. Sowed it last week in Feb:

19. Sowed half a pound of spinage in the field-Garden: 6 rows of forward pease in Turner's D? Planted 200 of Cabages in Field D?

20. Sowed a Gallon & half of broad beans in ye field-Garden. Very severe frost.

21. Made an Hot-bed for early radishes, hoop'd it over, & cover'd it with a large mat.

MARCH 12. Very deep snow, 7 inches on plain ground.

13. Made a very deep & large Hot-bed for my melon-seeds; &c: with seven cart-loads of dung: thatch'd the edges of the bed without the frame.

14. Made slight Hot-bed for the *Arbutus*-seed.

15. Sowed two pots of Mr Garnier's Cantaleoupe-Melons 1753: two pots of Mr Hunter's of Waverly D? 1752: two pots of Cockscombs: one pot of pendulous Amaranths: one pot of sensitive-plant-seed: one pot of *Arbutus*-seed: two pots of my own large Andalusian-Melons: Mem: Carry'd Mr Garnier's Cantaleupe-seed (being but two years old) in my Breeches-pocket 6 or 8 weeks.¶ Sad snowy, wet, cold weather.

17. Scattered the overplus of the *Arbutus*-seed among the new-planted Filberts in the orchard.

Mem: To observe if any grow.

17. Hot-bed heats well.

---

†Thomas White's handwriting.

19.   Sowed five rows of Marrow-fat-pease in field-G:
20.   Planted 74 Laurels from Waverly down Baker's Hill with two *Ilex*-acrons between each two: one portugal-laurel, one weeping-willow, one parsley, one black mountain-Virginian-Elder, one flowering-Rasp: two stoneless barberies,¶ 6 roses, down the basons in the field: 2 Dutch Honey-suckles against the Trellis in new Garden: & some Pine, & Chili-Strawberries¶ in new Garden.
21.   Sowed 12 seeds of Cedar of Libanus, a Crop of Larches, Weymouth-Pines, & Cluster-pines in two Boxes standing to the morning sun in the field-garden; & hoop'd & netted y^m.
     Planted Ivy round the little-house,¶ & a Bed of Rasps at the north end of the House:
     Planted a fine Mulberry-tree, of my own raising from a layer, in the new opening in the new-Garden.
27.   †Sowed more Melons in the Pots that fail'd.
31.   †Sowed one pot of Mr Garnier's Cantalupe 1753, one pot of Ld Lincolns Green Cantalupe 1751. one pot of Mr Hunter's Yellow Cantalupe 1752 and one pot of Miller's very fine old seed.

APRIL   1.   Sowed a Crop of Carrots, Coss-lettuce, & parsneps in the New-Garden.
           2.   Cast 20 Cart-loads of Dung in the melon ground.
           3.   Planted 13 Laurels round the necessary,¶ & against the street.
14: 15:   Made a large melon-bed with 20 loads of dung for six lights in the field-garden. The weather wet, & unfavourable. The melon-seeds in the pots came-up weak, & poor, the season not favouring.
         16.   Sowed a pot of Romania-Melon -seed 1753: & a pot of Zatta 1751: a pot of three-thorned-*Acacia*-seed;¶ & a pot of seed mark'd only *Acacia*: Evergreen-Oak Acrons: Bird-cherry-seed: cut-leaf'd tulip-tree seed: Boorcole, red & green: savoy seed: *Campanula Pyrimidalis*: Scarlet Lychniss: Holy-oak-seed: leeks: Beets, parsley, & onions.
         17.   Sowed Basons of Double-China-Aster, Double-Larkspurs, Nasturtiums, Nigella Romana, Venetian-poppies, Oriental-mallows, Venus-Lookinglass, Candy-Tuft, & Chrysanthemums in the new borders in the Garden; & in the Basons in the field. Sowed some Orange-gourds, & long-Gourds under the *Arbutus* mat. Painted-Ladies in the New-Garden.
         19.   Planted some foxglove-roots from London in the shady Border in the new-garden.
         19.   Turn'd-out two pots of Cantaleupe, & two pots of Andalusian-melons into the two great frames. The plants in thriving condition, but the bed hardly shews any signs of Heat. The weather uncommonly dry, sunny, & sultry.
         20.   The Romania, & Zatta-melons appeared out of the Ground.
         21.   Turn'd-out two pots of Cantaleupe-melons into the two single lights, the one Glass, the other paper.

---

†Note inserted in the text: John White's handwriting.

Seedlings of the cantaloup melon 'Dutch Net'. Early May

22. Made an Hot-bed for two Hand-glasses, & one paper light, with seven loads of Farmer Parsons's dung: earth'd the basons with Dorton-mould.¶ The *Acacia*-seeds appeared to day. Sultry weather. Cut a good mess of Asparagus for the first time.

23. Planted large plot of Artichokes from Dʳ Bristow's in the new-garden; & sowed a Crop of Coss-lettuce between. Made a slight hot-bed with 1 load of dung for sunflowers, African-Marrigolds, double Asters, & Celeri; & hoop'd, & matted it.¶ Made Cucumber-ridge with two loads of dung for two Hand-glasses.

25. Transplanted out of their pots some Zatta-Melon-plants in the paper-light; & some Romania-Melon-plants under the two hand-glasses: the bed heats very finely. Transplanted some Cucumber-plants under the two other Hand glasses. Showry, warm weather.

26. Turn'd out a pot of Cantaleupe-Melons into the original seed-bed, & earth'd it up a great depth.

28. Planted-out 6 Acacias in 6 penny-pots: very long tap-roots.

29. Transplanted some Cockscomb-plants, not very forward, into one of the two-light melon-frames. Transplanted three Orange-gourd-plants under the melon-ground-Hedge. Planted two Storax-trees, from Guernsey, sent me by Will: Yalden,¶ in one of the basons of the field.

JUNE 23. Cut the first Cucumber.

JULY 17. Planted-out plots of Endive-plants. Turn'd-out remarkably fine & large.

18. Only six brace of melons set. The Acacias in the pots very fine. A fine Crop of Cluster-pines: 10 or 12 Weymouth-pines: 2 Cedars of Libanus: not one Larch, nor *Arbutus*.

An uncommon hot, dry summer to this time.

18. About 500 savoys-plants, & about 6 score boor-cole plants, all of our own raising, in Turner's Garden.

AUGUST 1. †Cut the first Melon. Mem: It hung too long & was mealy. This was intended for a Cantaleupe, but proved a common sort.

26. Gather'd the first Mushrooms from spawn put into a bed last Decemʳ yᵉ 17th.

---

†Unidentified handwriting.

Herb Garden
The Wakes
12 July

Only six brace of melons set: hinder'd in their ripening by a long run of cold, shady weather.

28. Planted-out a great many Holy-oaks in the new-Garden, Yard, & field.

28. Tyed-up 30 Good Endive-plants. More should be ty'd-up about the 18th of Septem^r with different-coloured Yarn.

SEPTEMBER 1. Planted a plot in New-Garden with Pine-strawberries brought from Waverly. Those planted in the spring dyed.

2. Cut two Cantaleupe-Melons: the biggest weigh'd 3 p^{ds} 5 oun: they were perfectly dry, & high-flavour'd, notwithstanding the weather had been shady, & cool for three weeks: & uncommonly wet & stormy for the last week.

Made a large Musroom-bed, eight feet long; used eleven Barrows of hot dung with no layers of earth intermix'd.

15. †Planted the mushroom spawn brought from Dean on the new made bed, it was moderately warm. the larger lumps were set on the ridge, the smaller earth near the bottom. NB I planted the SE side & Thomas the NW.

19. Tyed-up more Endive: those tyed-up before not well blanch'd, for want of being ty'd with double yarn, & in two places.

The new Musroom-bed heats gently.

The double China-asters make a fine show.

Mem: the green-Endive, by being so much longer, tyes-up, & blanches much better than the white.

23. Put the Acacias in their winter-quarters in a frame under the Hedge of the melon-ground: planted some lettuce to stand the winter in the same frame, & along the border: placed an old frame for a Quart^r of an Hund: of Cauliflower-plants: put the two boxes of the seedling-pines under the sunny-hedge. Sowed a Crop of persicaria-seed, & green-Coss-lettuce on the same border. Sowed a Crop of Belvedere on the same border.

OCTOBER 6. Sent the Cauliflowers from Dene.

30. Planted two basons in the field with Canterbury-bells. Planted a Nursery of some Scorpion-sena, & *Spiraea*-suckers in the New-Garden.

NOVEMBER 2. Planted ten rows of Mazagan-beans (never planted in England) in the field-garden.

Planted four Pyramidal-Campanulas in four large pots, & plunged them in the Border under the melon-screen.

Planted 30 full-grown perennial-sunflower-roots in the border against the street, & Kelsey's Yard; & in the upper part of the basons in ye field.

2. Planted some slips from the perennial-sunflowers in a nursery.

---

†Note inserted in the text: John White entry? [By no means certain: it is not in the same hand as the entry for 27 March.]

Fine settled weather for 9, or 10 days before: the only good weather since July.

The Campanulas, & sunflowers lay in the ware-house in London, & were somewhat damaged by the closeness of the Box.

6. Sowed two more patches of ye last year's persicaria-seed under the melon-hedge. One plant of the last sowing come-up very strong.

11. Most uncommon frost for one night, & considering the season of the Year: Ice near an inch thick, & the dirt hard enough to bear an Horse.

6. Planted 12 cuttings of Tamarisk sent down from London with the Peren! Sunflowers, &c.

24. Turn'd the Horse-path at the Bottom of Baker's-Hill, & continu'd-out the Quincunx-basons & prepar'd them for shrubs.

25. Staked & tyed the Quincunx of Firs that were much loosen'd by the late violent rains, & winds.

DECEMBER 1. Earth'd up the Artichoke-beds for the winter.
Eleven evergreen-oaks alive down Baker's-Hill.

27. Finished two large three-light Melon-frames, each ten feet & an half long, & five wide in the clear; & containing 97 feet of Glass in ye lights, & an half foot.

A terrible winter for Earthquakes, Inundations, Tempests, & continual Rains. No frost worth mentioning except on the 11th & 12th of Novem^r

— 1756 —

JANUARY 23. Made an hot-bed on the dung-hill in the Yard, with Mr Johnson's frame, for white-mustard, & cress.

30. Earth'd-up the backward Celeri.

31. Planted two Cuttings from the weeping-willow in the New-Garden.

FEBRUARY 14. Planted 200 of Cabbage-plants in ye field-garden.

14. Made a Melonry in the Field-Garden 45 feet long, & lin'd it at ye back very warm, & secure with some damaged rushes of John Berriman's: lin'd ye two side-screens in the same manner; & in particular that towards ye Cucumber-bed, that it's Farina might not mix with ye melons.¶

Mem: The winter-Coss-lettuce, which stood very safe under frames during the severe dry frosty winter 1754: are this winter rotted by dampness, tho' there have been no frosts at all to touch y^m

18. Snowed very hard from morning to night: by ye evening the snow lay 14 inches deep on plain-Ground; & lodged so heavy on the Hedges that it broke y^m down in several places; & weigh'd all the shrubs flat to the Ground. Went-off with a gentle thaw without any rain.

23. Cast eight of our little Cart-loads of hot dung in the field-garden

for yᵉ melon seed-bed.

24. Sowed quartᵣ of a pound of spinage in the field-garden.

25. Planted six rows of large Winsor-beans in yᵉ field-Garden: six rows of Marrow-fat-pease in Turner's Garden.

27. Planted a row, & an half more of broad-beans.

28. Made the melon-seedling-Hot-bed with the whole eight loads of dung, except a little for the Celeri. Weather very fine, & the Ground in good dry order.

    Made a Celeri-Hot-bed for an hand glass, & sowed the Celeri-seed.

    Planted some lilac-suckers from Bradley in Turner's; & some Cuttings of the parsley, & Mountain-Elder. Planted a large lilac-sucker in a field-bason.

MARCH 1. Sowed ten pots of Mᵣ Hunter's red-seeded Cantaleupes 1752: & two pots of Mᵣ Hunter's white-seeded Cantaleupes 1754.

    Sowed a pot of early prickly Cucumbers. Fine weather; & bed heats well.

    Sprinkled the bed with quick-lime to kill the small snails, & grubs.

2. Raised the fence of the Cucumber-Ground equal with that of the melon-Ground, & lined it with pease-haulm: so the two fences screen the whole North-end of the field-garden the length of 70 feet.

6. Removed the two Larches from the Ewel-Close, where one had been damaged by yᵉ Horses, into the Basons in Baker's Hill.

    Cucumbers began to appear.

    Removed one of the Laburnums into a gap in the Orchard-hedge. Planted some layers of Jasmine in Turner's Garden.

7. The Melon-plants began to appear.

8. Sowed 12 basons in the field with double Larkspur-seed. One ounce will sow 8 basons very thick.

    Sprinkled more quick-lime round the young Melon-plants.

9. Sowed a box of Polyanth-seed: cleansed the moss & filth from off the *Acacia*-pots, & sifted-on a little fine earth. Sifted a little fine Earth over the seedling Cedars of Lib: & pines in the boxes.

10. Sowed a Crop of Carrots in the New-Garden & mixed with it some radishes, onions, & coss-lettuce both green, & white.

11. Sowed one pot of Mᵣ Hunter's White-seeded Cantaleupes 1752.

    Forked the Asparagus-beds; & raked yᵐ for yᵉ first time.

    Made a rod-hedge round the Quincunx of firs. Very dry March-like weather: no rain since the great Snow Feb: 18.

13. Hot, sunny days, & fierce frosts at night. Thick Ice.

15. Brought a four-wheel'd post-chaise to yᵉ Door¶ at that early time of Year.

16. Cast 15 good Dung-carts of hot dung for the melon-bed: 9 of our own dung, & 6 of Farmer Parsons's. The Ground as dry as at Midsumᵣ

17. Sowed an ounce of Onion-seed in yᵉ New-Garden. Transplanted

the Cucumber-plants from the pot, to the full Ground in the
frame. Planted some very large potatoes from Swarraton in
Turner's Garden. The Ground was double-trenched in the
winter; & some rotten dung, & old thatch were dug-in at
planting.

18. Sowed two pots of *Arbutus*-seed, & one pot of *Magnolia*-seed, &
plunged them in the Hot-bed.

19. Sowed hard almost all day. Several of yᵉ Melon-plants go-off
with a mouldiness that spreads on the leaves.

20. Received a large Cargo of Shrubs, & flower-roots from Brothᵣ
Thomas in London.

22. Planted in the Basons in the field, a Moss-provence, & some
damask, Monday, & red roses; *Spiraea frutex*; blue, & white
lilacs; Syringa;¶ early golden-rod; sumach; *Althaea frutex*;
guelder-rose; *coccigrya*; female dogwood; double flowering-
thorn; & Persian Jasmine. In the New-Garden forward-
honeysuckle; Lavender cotton;¶ golden-sage; double, & single
Lychnis; blue, & white Campanulas; catchflies; blue, & peach-
bloom Mich: daisies; striped bulbous *Iris*; ribbon-grass; double,
& variegated perriwinkle: & fruit-bearing Passion-flower near
the brew-house-door. Snowy, frosty, untoward weather for
planting. Four new hand-glasses fᵐ Alton.

23. Backed-up the seedling-bed, which began to lose almost all it's
heat, with seven barrows of hot dung.
　　Drew a parcel of the cast-dung from the side of the heap, &
made an Hot-bed for an Hand-glass: sowed three pots with
Yellow, & white-seeded Cantaleupes 1752: & several cucumber-
seeds round the pots for the ridge-hand-glasses. The first Melon-
plants continue to go-off with mouldiness. Danger of a scarcity of
plants for the frames. The Cucumᵣ plants in the same frame very
healthy. Storms of Hail, & rain all day.

24. Hard frost, & thick Ice.

27. Frost so fierce that it damaged the flowers, & shrubs very much:
Ice near an Inch thick: heavy snow all the morning.

29. Dress'd the Rasberry-bed.

31. Planted four limes in the Butcher's Yard, to hide the sight of
Blood, & filth from yᵉ Windows.

APRIL 2. Planted out of their winter-box a bed of Cauliflower-plants.
Sowed two pots of Larch-seed; two pots of China-Arbor-Vitae; &
a pot of Arbor-Judae-seed.

3. Made my great ten-light melon-bed with fifteen dung-carts of
hot-dung. Laid an Hillock of Dorton-earth in the middle of each
light; & cover'd the whole bed about two inches thick with earth.
The earth wet & cloddy, & not in condition for the purpose.
Supply'd the Artichoke-bed (which had lost most of it's plants)
with very good slips from Dᵣ Bristow's.

5. Sowed a large Quantity of Holy-oak-seed, with some radishes for
the bugs;¶ crop of parsneps; crop of Leeks; row of parsley: row of

Larch, & Judas-tree-seed in the common-ground; four rows of Evergreen-oak-acrons; plot of Tree mallow, & curled mallow; some Honesty-seed; Date stones; crop of red-beet: & some cress, & white mustard.

6.   Made a Cucumber-bed for three Hand-glasses with two dung-carts of Parsons's Dung. The trench 16 feet long, two & an half broad, & one & half deep: the dung did not reach to the level of the Ground by some Inches.

    Made a slight Hot-bed for hardy annuals with seven barrows of dung: laid fine earth over it five inches deep.

    Sowed the border against Parsons's Yard with Sunflowers, Lady-pease, Venetian Mallow, ¶ Nasturtium, Larkspurs, Candytuft.

10.   Sowed in the annual Bed Sunflowers, African Marrigolds, Orange-Gourds, Double-China Aster, Marvel of Peru, Celeriac.

10.   Turned-out eight pots of Yellow-seeded Cantaleupes, & two of white into my ten great Lights. The white-seeded under the tiled lights. One pretty good plant under each light. The bed but in indifferent condition by reason of the continual rains, & black cloudy weather.

10.   Sowed some Yellow-seeded, & white-seeded Cantaleupes in the old seed-Bed, for fear some plants in the lights should miscarry: some Romania-melon-seeds in D? for ye Hand-glass-ridge.

    Mem: Those melon-plants that were once seized with a mouldiness constantly dy'd-away by degrees, 'till they were quite devour'd by it; except those plants on which I tryed the experiment of clipping-off the infected part with a pair of scissors: when they recover'd, & afterwards grew pretty well. The only method I can find of preventing the earth from falling from the melon-plants in turning them out of their pots, is by plaistering-down a cake of wet Clay over the mouth of the pots. Those pots turn-out best that have two or three plants; because there are more roots to hold the earth together.

    No snail ever comes near a place well sprinkled with quick-lime, especially in a frame where the wet is kept-off. And what is very strange, quick lime, tho' plentifully shaken upon them, will not injure the youngest, or tenderest plant.

12.   Sowed a plot of Savoy-seed, very good Sort: & plot of Borecole red, & green: some Pendulous Amaranth in Annual bed.

    Planted quart^t of Hund: of laurels against the street in the new-Garden to thicken ye screen; & down Baker's-hill, where the turkeys had destroyed them.

13.   Planted some Laurestines down Baker's-Hill, where the Laurels were dead. Constant heavy rains day, & night.

    Six rows of Marrowfats in Turner's Gard^n

    This April thro' a most surprizing Season for wet, & frost. The 20th was a vast rain: but on the 26th it rain'd for 22 Hours without ceasing, & brought on such a vast flood as has seldom been seen; the meadows round Oxōn being entirely cover'd a great depth.

MAY   1.   Received from Broth.ʳ Thomas an *Arbutus*, common Cypress, Portugal-Laurel, Cluster-pine, Silver-fir, Swedish-Juniper, Evergreen *Cytisus*, Passion-flower, & some small evergreen Creepers. Fine plants, & most of them turn'd-out of pots & sent down with all their earth about yᵐ.

My ten-light Cantaleupe-bed so flooded by those vast rains that all the plants are dead.

Planted yᵉ evergreens in the basons in the field.

     4.   Heavy storms of snow, & thunder.

     5.   Frost so hard that the dirt carryed.

     6.   Broke-up my ten-light Cantaleupe-bed, & work'd it up with five dung-carts more of hot-dung. Sensible heat remaining in the bed, tho' it had been so flooded.

Put earth into the boxes in good dry order. Soft mild shower.

7: 8: 9.   Very wet season.

     10.   Planted my ten-light melon-bed a second time with Waverley-Cantaleupe, & Romania-melons. Bed in fine order for Heat.

Pollarded limes planted in front of former butcher's shop.
Selborne.
10 May.

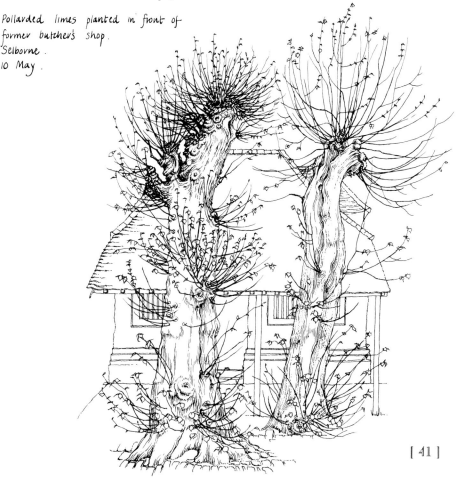

Planted-out the seedling Cedar of Libanus in a penny-pot.

Four lights of Cantaleupes, & six of Romagna-Melons.

11. Violent rain, snow, & hail: Ice in the night.

12. Made a ridge for five handglasses with four dung-carts of dung.

Received from Kensington one Holly-leaved Oak, one Olive-leav'd D̲o̲ one red Cedar of Virginia, one White D̲o̲ one Spanish-Evergreen-Creeper, one Balm of Gilead-Fir, two Weymouth-pines, one Acacia-leaved-Cypress. All nicely pack'd with a deal of earth about their roots; & about a foot & half high.

From Williamson Nursery-man at Kensington.

14. Sowed some common green, & White-Dutch Cucumber-seeds under an Hand-Glass.

Set up my first Oil-Jar Vase¶ at the bottom of the Ewel-Close with a pannel only in front: Mount, pedestal, & Vase nine feet high.

Dripping season still.

15. No one Day so much as spring like before: now absolute Summer.

Sowed a crop of Green-Coss-lettuce among the New-planted Artichokes.

Planted three of the Hand-glasses with Cucumber plants, three plants in a Glass.

17. Pricked-out the seedling Weymouth, & Cluster-pines in the New-Garden.

Prick'd-out a plot of Celeri in Turner's.

18. Planted 300 & quart̲s̲ of Cabbage-plants in the field-Garden.

Very hot sunshine with a cold East-wind.

19. Set-up my second Oil-jar vase at the top of the broad walk, with a face to the cross-walk. Mount, pedestal, & Jar some inches above nine feet high.

19. Pinch'd my melons to make them throw-out runners: the melons, for want of having been in pots, a long while in taking to y̲e̲ Ground.

20. Planted six rows of large White Dutch Kidney-beans as long as the Spinage will permit.

24. Earth'd-up the melon-hillocks for y̲e̲ first time with Dorton-Mould. Mould in fine order.

28. Bright sunshine, & smart frosts for this fortnight past, with a cutting East-Wind most part of the time: now a small shower. Ground strangely bound, & parched. Cucumbers begin to set.

31. Cut the first Cucumber: 3 more almost grown on the same plant.

Planted all the Handglasses with cucumber-plants, white, & green. Planted some basons in the field with Sunflowers.

Bright, settled dry weather, the Ground bound as hard as a stone.

JUNE 1. Five of the melon-plants have runners with two Joints.

3. Pinched the forwardest of the melons at the third Joint: & pinch'd-off all the small buds about their stems. Best Cantaleupe

knit for bloom.¶

7. Three weeks & three days drought, except a shower once for a few minutes. Now moderate showers.

10. Earth'd Melons second time with Dorton-earth: second runners show second Joint. The Glazier cemented the large lights, which drip wretchedly: mended but not cured. Frequent Showers.

16. Prick'd out five Hund: of Savoys; & 175 of Bore-cole. Length'ned-out rows of French-beans. Melons throw-out plenty of fruit; & Male-bloom full blown. Hot, dripping weather, which makes the melons grow wonderfully. Prick'd-out more Celeri.

19. Lin'd-out the melon-bed with 8 dung-carts of Dung; & laid-on the full thickness of earth without, & within the frames. Earth'd the frames twice with Dorton-mould, & the last time with common Garden-mould.

27. Gather'd Mazagan Beans.
Several Melons set.
Sowed Crop of Endive.

JULY

24. Full twenty Brace of Melons, most of them well-grown: the plants in great vigour.

26. Planted-out Crop of Endive in the field-Garden.

27. Planted-out first plot of Savoys.

29. Planted-out Borecole, & rest of Savoys.

AUGUST

2. Cut first Melon, a Romania: very early, considering the first bed was destroy'd.

3. Cut brace & half more of Romania: turn'd, & tiled the rest,¶ which was much wanting.
Cut 70 Cucumbers.

4. Trenched-out 8 rows of Celeri: planted some of the Borders in the New-Garden with Polyanths of my own raising.
Cut four brace & half of Melons this week.

15. Had cut eleven brace of Romania-Melons: one from the plant that was put a seed into one of the great frames on May ye 10.

18. Planted six pots with Cuttings of Geraniums.
Mushroom-bed bears pretty well at one end.

18. Sowed Crop of Turneps in the Quincunx, & among the Savoys.

21. Sowed half pound of spinage; & with it turnep-radish seed; & brown dutch, & green-Capuchin-Lettuce to stand the Winter.

22. Cut the first Cantaleupe, a very small one: it was almost cleft in two: was high-flavour'd, & vastly superior to any of the Romanias. This Melon set the first of any; & was full 8 weeks in ripening. The plant on which this grew was one of the first crop, the only one that survived; & was moved in a careless manner back into the seedling-bed; & brought back again when the bed was new-worked-up.
Constant heavy rains for a week: the wheat that is down begins to grow.

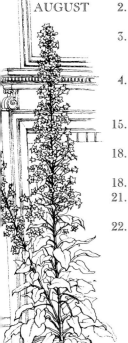

Pyramidal Campanula
brought indoors to flower
beside fireplace in great parlour.
10 August.

Annual garden,
the Wakes,
July.

24. Cut second Cantaleupes, the largest in y^e Boxes; weigh'd 3 p^ds. 7 oun: sent it to London to Broth^r Tom. Turn'd colour before it began to smell, which is unusual.¶

25. Planted-out Holy-oaks in the New-Garden next the street; & among the limes in the Butcher's Yard.

26: 27: 28. Cut a brace & half of Mr Hunter's Cantaleupes: a brace were not much emboss'd on their Rind, & not so high flavoured as might be expected: the other was very rough, very firm fleshed, high flavoured, & very weighty for it's size. N.B. All the Cantaleupes yet have chang'd colour, & smelt without cracking at the Stalk.

28. True fine Harvest-weather. Wheat much grown about the Country; some grew as it stood.

29. Cut one Waverly, & one Miller's Cantaleupe: sent the Waverly one to Bradley.

    Miller's tho' it promised well was very abominable; being about an Inch thick in the Rind, without any flesh or flavour. The rind was finely emboss'd, & the shape Compressed like a Turnep.

    Brought the only flowering Pyram: Campan. into the parlour: it produced only a single stalk.

SEPTEMBER 2. Tyed up 30 Endives: first tying.

7. French-beans so backward that not above three boilings have been gathered yet.

11. Cut the other Miller's Cantaleupe: turn'd out as execrable as the former.

16. Brought a large Cantaleupe from Waverly, weight 3 p^ds 9 oun: turn'd-out very high-flavoured, & curious: saved the seed.

18. Tyed-up the Endives in the new-Garden. [Crossed out.]

25. Planted 300 laurel-Cuttings in Turner's.

OCTOBER 3. Cut brace & half of Romania-melons: good for latter Crop.

9. Set nine Hyacinths, given me by Mr Frinley, to blow in Glasses in ye parlour.

25. Cut last melon: the 41st.

NOVEMBER 9. Planted ten rows & half of Mazagan-beans in the field-garden.

    One Quart of true small mazagan-beans will plant eleven good rows.

9: 10: 11: 12. Extream hard frost, & bearing Ice. From the 18th to ye 25: uncommon fierce frost, & some snow.

†Mem: Put the pins belonging to my new melon-frame in the small leathern trunk in the man's room.
Pins in a box in the lumber-garret.
†Spring 1755. Borrowed seven of our Cart-loads of Hot-dung of Farmer Parsons.
†March 1756. Borrowed six good Dung-carts of hot dung of Farmer Parsons.

---

†These notes, added on a spare page, were crossed out.

†April 6. Borrowed two dung-Carts more of Parsons's dung.
†May 6. Borrowed seven loads of dung of John Berriman.
†June 18. Borrowed of Berriman four loads of Dung.

— 1757 —

JANUARY   1.   Planted a row of Tulips & Ranunculus's, given me by my Broth.ʳ
Thomas, in the Border in the New-Garden next the street. Dug-
out the soil, & filled the trench with earth well-mixed with lime-
rubbish.

         3.   Planted the Fir-Quincunx with five rows of Winsor-beans:
dunged the ground, that was very poor, with ten wheel-barrows
of very rotten dung. After the beans the ground to be trenched
with Celeri.

             Levelled, & widen'd the Area of yᵉ Melon-Ground; having
made an underground Drain to prevent it's being flooded any
more.

         4.   A most extraordinary dry season for wheeling-out the dung of the
old Hot-beds; & for trenching the ground for Crops.

             On the 2.ⁿᵈ began a frost, which on yᵉ 3.ʳᵈ & 4.ᵗʰ by means of a
strong East wind, became very severe, so as to freeze-up all the
pools & ponds: the ground, which had been quite drained before
by a fortnight's dry weather, look'd white & dusty, & was not the
least relaxed or greasy at noon for many days together. On the
10.ᵗʰ came a thaw, & a little snow. The Laurustines, & other
tender Evergreens began to suffer a little, especially on the severe
windy days. Frozen-up again, & lasted (tho' there were frequent
hasty showers) without the frost ever being out of the Ground 'till
Feb: 6.ᵗʰ Great Quantities of snow fell, which being half melted
by the rain made the Country slippery to a strange degree. The
frost penetrated deep into the ground, & seems to have been the
severest since that in 1740. Seems to have done no material
damage to vegetation; but has made the Ground very light, &
mellow.

FEBRUARY 10.   Sowed half a pound of spinage in the field-Garden, with some
Browndutch, & Capuchin-lettuce; some common, & white
turnep Radishes.

         11.   Several of the Hyacinths are tall, & just ready to blow.

         12.   Planted six rows of Hotspur-pease, & two of Marrowfats in the
field-Garden. Summer-like weather: the ground by means of the
frost perfectly mellow. Sowed a crop of parsley in the New
Garden.

         17.   Made an Hot-bed in the Yard with 16 wheel-barrows
of dung, only to raise yᵉ Cucumber-plants, & a little Cress,
& white-mustard. To be taken away, & work'd-up in a
future Bed.

         18.   One of the Sunbury Jacinths (yᵉ only one not decay'd) in full
bloom. Those from M.ʳ Budd drawn-up very tall, but not blown.

19.	Sowed some early Cucumber-seeds under one of the Handglasses.
21.	Planted 100 of Cabbages in Turner's: sowed hand-glasses in the Yard with Cress, & white-mustard.
24.	Carryed eight of our little Cart-loads of dung into the field-garden for a seedling melon-bed.
28.	Made a very stout hot-bed above three feet thick for the melon-seeds, & to forward the Cucumber-plants, with 8 Cart-loads of dung: Saved about two barrows of dung, & made a Celeri-bed for one Handglass.

MARCH	2.	Sowed the New Hot-bed with Yellow-seeded Waverley Cantaleupe 1752: & White-seeded Waverly D? 1752 & 1754: with Dutch Cantaleupe (never sowed in England) 1754: & with John Bosworth's Zatta-melon from Florence 1754. Sowed also a few early Cucumber-seeds for fear the plants should fail.
		Sowed a small Hand-glass Hot-bed with Celeri, & Celeriac. Dress'd Rasp-bed: & hoed beans: but a thin Crop.
	4.	Sowed 14 basons in the field with double upright larkspur-seed; & bush'd¶ them well.
		Sunk a wine-Hog's head in the field-garden for a well.
		Sowed some Asparagus-seed to mend the beds that are decaying.
		Very dry weather, & severe frost.
	8.	The seedling melon-bed, tho' made so strong, would not come to any Heat: so I cut away the bed sloping-in on every side, & lined it very thick with four little cart-loads of dung just fresh from the stable.
	11.	Bed begins to heat very well: prick'd the cucumbers from under the Hand-glass into it. Melons not yet come-up. Lost about a week in the forwarding the Cucumber-plants by the bed's not heating. Sowed the Hand-glasses in the Yard with more Cress, & Mustard. That little bed keeps it's heat well still.
	14.	Sowed 22 Mazagan-beans, all worm-eaten, to try if the best will be fit to plant next year.
		Tyed the melon-bed, that crack'd & was like to bulge-out, with a strong cord, that seems to secure it.
		Made a melon paper-House¶ 8 feet long, & 5 feet wide: to be covered with the best writing paper.
		Planted two seedling white-Elders in the little mead.
	17.	Supplyed the basons where the shrubs were dead, with new ones.
		Melon-plants come-up very fast.
	18.	Planted a weeping-willow, a fine plant, one year from a Cutting, in one of the basons in the field: planted a black-Virginian-Mountain-Elder in the little mead.
	19.	Sowed 20 more Yellow Cantaleupe-seeds Selborn 1755: to supply the room of any plants that may fail.
		Sowed 9 basons in the border next Parsons's Yard with double Larkspurs. Some of the forward Cucumber-plants

		show a rough leaf.

21. Sowed Crop of Carrots, White & Green Coss-Lettuce, & common radishes in Turner's Garden. Headed-down the limes in the Butcher's Yard; & took several Cuttings from the Weeping-willow & planted them in the Nursery.

22. Sowed the Clover in the wheat;¶ & mixed with it the white-Dutch-Clover that had been in the House two or three years.

Sowed 40 of Murdoch Myddleton's white-Cucumber-seeds in the seedling-bed. Bed heats very well.

23. Raked, & weeded the Asparagus-beds.

24. Sowed 20 seeds of prickly Cucumbers just come from London.

26. Cast six loads (dungcarts) of hot dung in the field-garden for the cucumber-bed. Planted Quart: of Hund: of Cauliflowers in a well-dung'd plot in the field-Garden: from Preedy at Farnham.

28. Made a very stout Cucumber-bed five feet wide, two feet & half deep, & thirteen feet long for three lights, with the six loads of Dung: cut very deep holes in the middle of each light, & raised a hillock of fine earth to receive the plants: cut also a trench at the back of the frames, & plunged 12 pots to the brims to receive the melon-plants.

Sowed nine more basons of double-upright-Larkspurs in the border in the new-Garden against the street.

31. Planted the plants of Cucumbers in the new bed, three in an Hole: they shew each four leaves; but have not grown much for some days past. Bed gives a very strong Heat.

Planted a Quart of Marrot-fat-pease in three rows in the field-Garden.

APRIL 1. Planted out twelve pots of melons: five with yellow-seeded Cantaleupe plants, old seed from Waverley, with one D: new seed of my own saving in the same pot: three with new Yellow D: three with White-seeded Cantaleupes, old seed from Waverley: & one pot with Dutch Cantaleupe from Holland, never sowed in England. Left six Selborn Cantaleupes, & two Zatta-plants in the seedling bed.

Mem: to soak the earth well beforehand with water, or else the fine earth is very apt to crumble away, & leave the roots naked in moving.

2. Sowed two or three white Cantaleupe-seeds in each of the pots that contain the white Cantaleupe plants.

Sowed a good Quantity of the old green Cucumber seeds; & D: of Middleton's White D: in the one-light Cucumber-frame. The former sowing of Middleton's white Cucumber-seed, & of the new green D: from London came-up wretchedly.

Sad wet, cold weather, & constant high winds (some of them very terrible, & mischievous ones) for three weeks past.

New Cucumber-bed heats well; & Cucumber, & melon-plants have struck-root already.

5. Sowed a Crop of leeks, beets, parsneps,

turnep-radishes, & onions.

 Unusual hot weather this week: during which, John, who was but a very young Gardener, scorch'd up, & suffocated all his forward Cucumbers: & drawed his melon-plants in the pots, but has not spoiled them.

21. Snowed very hard for sixteen hours: the greatest snow that has fallen this Year; & must have been a foot deep had it not for the greatest part melted as it fell. Went away without any frost, & seems to have done no damage.

23. Made the melon-bed for the six large lights, & two of the small ones, with 18 dung-carts of dung, just 30 feet long, & about two & half high, & all above ground.

25. Dressed the border against Parsons's & sowed in it, Sunflowers, Candy tuft, Venetian-poppy, & Venus looking glass: sowed large plot of savoy-seed, plot of sweet William-seed, & some rows of sorrel, & parsley.

 Sowed some Celeri on the melon-bed between the frames; & some White-seeded Cantaleupes for the paper-House in one of the large lights.

 On examination it appeared that the earth in the Cucumber-bed was burnt by the fierce heat of the bed: dug it out of the basons, & put in fresh: One bason of the early Cucumbers will recover, the other two must be new-planted.

 My Polyanths, which I raised from seed given me by M.rs Snooke, & sowed last spring, make now a most beautiful appearance; many of them have large, upright stems, producing many flowers, which are large, beautifully striped, & open flat.

 Mark'd the finest blowers with sticks, intending to save seed from them.

26. Turned-out five pots of Waverley Yellow-seed Cantaleupes, & one Selborn D.o into my six great Lights: & only <u>one</u> pot of John Bosworth's Dutch Cantaleupe into the middle of <u>my two light</u> frame.

 All the pots were turned-out well except the Dutch-Cantaleupe, whose earth stuck to the pot, & pull'd-off many of it's fibres.

 Sowed Crop of Borecole green & red; & vast plot of Holy-oak-seed: & a row of tree-mallow seed.

26. Sowed four rows of dwarf white Battersea-kidney-beans in the New Garden. An handful of beans left out of one pint. Ground in good dry order.

 Supplyed the two basons of Cucumbers that were burnt, with some white, & green prickly plants.

MAY 9. Made an Hot-bed for my melon-paper-house with four loads of dung joined-on to the former bed.

 Made hot-bed for seedling-annuals with three barrows of weeds, & four of dung.

 Early Cucumbers shew nothing but male bloom.

 Planted two rows of large white Dutch-Kidney-beans.

Gold laced polyanthus,
by the brick path,
the Wakes
3 May.

10.   Sowed Annual-bed with African & French Marrigolds, Marvel
      of Peru, Gourds, & double China-Asters.
          Sowed some rows of Sunflower-seed.
          Plants shew some few Cucumbers. Some of the melon-plants
      decaying in their seedling-leaves: turned-out some more pots into
      the basons. Shall save but one Waverly melon-plant; all the rest
      Selborn seed, except the two White-seeded plants under the
      paper, that are Waverly.

12.   Sowed an Hand-glass on ye cold ground with several sorts of
      white Dutch-Cucumbers; & a few green prickly Cucum^{rs}
          Sowed a late Crop of green, & white Coss-lettuce. Prick'd-out
      some rows of Capuchin-Lettuce.

13.   Earthed-up the melon-hillocks for ye first time with Dorton-
      earth. The reason that ye first melon-plants that were turned-out
      did not succeed, seems to be, that the earth in the pots was press'd
      down too hard, so that the fibres could not push thro'. Laid-on the
      hillocks upon the new-made melon-bed; & put-on the paper-
      house. Earth'd the forward Cucumbers, & water'd them all over.

16.   Pinch'd, & turned-out two pots of white-seeded Wav:
      Cantaleupes under the paper-house: the bed very hot. The plants
      strangely rooted for their age. One of the plants under the two-
      light-frame has got a runner with two joints.

18.   Mended-out the Artichokes that were decayed with some plants
      from Johnson's.
          Very hot, sunny weather: no rain for five weeks; the ground
      very much burnt.

20.   Pinched one of the melon-runners at the third Joint. The weather

		full fierce for hot-beds under Glass.
	23.	Earth'd melon-hillocks the second time with garden-mould, which had been turn'd & prepared on purpose, & is in excellent order. The melon-plants in general weak, & puny: pinch'd some of their runners at the second, & some at the third Joint according to their strength.

        Sowed three rows more of large Dutch-Kidney-beans in the field: garden; the sowing of White dwarf D.º seems to be rotten in the Ground, notwithstanding the great dryness of the Ground.

24.   Sowed an other Hand-glass with white-Dutch-Cucumbers in the cold Ground.

26.   Planted 200 of Cabbage-plants in the Field-Garden.

27.   Earth'd-up the melons under the paper-house the first time: the plants thriving.

29.   Cut first Cucumber. Several more set. Fine soaking shower after six weeks drought.

JUNE   1.   Prick'd-out first bed of Celeri: & transplanted from their seedling-bed a large Crop of leeks. Ground thoro'ly moisten'd by a long gentle rain.

2.   Planted-out the natural Cucumbers under the hand-glasses. Planted some variegated Gourds in the Corner near the Brewhouse-door. Sowed a row more of large French-beans in the field-Garden.

3.   Widened-out the early Cucumber-bed with the dung of the seedling-bed, & laid-on a good depth of stiff earth.

6.   Sowed five rows of dwarf White-kidney-beans in the new-Garden, where the early crop fail'd. Soak'd the beans over night in water, the weather & ground being extremely dry.

7.   Tyed-up a few of the best Coss-Lettuce: a fine Crop.
        Several of the melons show bloom, but are very weak in vine.
        Earth'd-up melons the third time.
        Weeded & thinn'd-out Carrots: a good Crop.

10.   Earth'd-up melons the fourth time: the boxes almost full of earth. Extream dry weather. Melons mend by more frequent watering.

11.   Staked the Holy-oaks in the Garden, & Butcher's Yard, & tyed them up.
        Water'd melons pretty much at a distance from their stems. Great drought. Melons shew fruit. They, & Cucumbers require constant shading from yᵉ fierce heat.

13.   Prick'd-out second crop of Celeri in Turner's Garden.
        Earth'd-out the melon-frames with their full depth of earth: & watered them well.
        Extream hot weather. Melons improve every day, & shew several fruit; but are still scanty in vine. Those under the paper-house thrive well.

17.   Gathered first pease.

19.   The Coss-lettuce, that were tyed-up, well-grown, & finely blanch'd.

20. Lined-out the melon-bed with 18 Dung-Carts of Dung, & earth'd it the full depth within, & without the boxes. Bed 13 feet wide, & contains 40 loads of Dung. Plants under the boxes still but weak; those under the paper-house very thriving. Gentle rain: the ground before burnt to ashes.

21: 22. Prick'd-out about 650 Savoys; & about 230 Bore-cole-plants.

24. Buried the stones, & rubbish from yᵉ Butcher's in the Yard to make it sound. Dry, scorching weather.

25. Watered melons well: burning season, & no signs of rain. Fruit in plenty; but none set.

27. Earth'd the melon-bed still deeper on account of the extream Heat; & pull'd the Lights quite off for the whole day, & covered the frame with mats. Plants draw very long without any fruit setting.

Cucumbers raised in the cold ground very forward, & thriving.

28. Planted several Basons in the field with Sunflowers.

30. Sowed a plot of Endive, & shaded it with a mat.

JULY 5. Pull'd-up the two melon-plants in the two-light-frame, which had never showed a fruit so far as to blow; & planted in their room two Selborn Cantaleupes, sown about the 21 of May, just shooting into runners.

Drought continues; & the Garden suffers greatly.

16. Planted-out, after waiting five or six weeks for a shower, the Af: & French Marrigolds, & double-China-Asters, in the midst of an unusual drought: the Earth quite dust spit-deep.

17. Gathered first natural Cucumber from a seed put into the cold Ground the 12ᵗʰ of May.

Double sunflowers
in the annual garden,
the Wakes
26 July.

20.   Great tempest of thunder & lightening, & vast rains after 13
       weeks drought. Frequent showers 'till the 15 of August, then
       sixteen days wet, & very bad Harvest weather.

AUGUST   22.   Found on my return from Sunbury six brace of moderate-sized
       Cantaleupes; & about the same number of small ones, that will
       ripen, if the season be favourable. No fruit would set 'till the
       rains came, & the intense heats were abated: & what did set was
       all on the third wood, the second casting it's fruit, & drawing
       very weak.
          Planted-out in my absence near a thousand savoys, & a large
       plot of Borecole; was sown a pound of spinage, mixed with
       turnep-radishes, & lettuce of many sorts: & trench'd-out eight
       good rows of Celeri.
          The Pyram: Campanula in beautiful bloom; but has only two
       stems.

29.   Planted-out 43 Holyoak-plants before & behind the melon-
       screen, & in the border of the New-Garden against the street.

SEPTEMBER

17.   Tyed-up about 25 Endives: they run very small this year.
18.   Cut first Cantaleupe, a small fig-shaped one, & not thick-flesh'd.
       The leaves of the plants unusually decayed.

19: 20: 21: 22.   Slip'd & new-planted the pinks in the Borders against the House:
       dug-up the Crocuss, & planted them in double rows before the
       pinks; they are encreased to near 500 roots; slip'd the best of the
       Polyanths, & planted them in two rows in the border against the
       broad walk: planted a border of seedling Sweet-Williams against
       Parsons's Yard: planted three rows of green-Capuchin, &
       Brown-Dutch-Lettuce the length of the melon-ground on a
       border just under the rush-screen to stand the winter: planted
       several Basons in the field with Sweet-Williams: took-up the
       yellow-lilys & a fine large Martagon under my Father's window,
       & planted them in a bason in the field: the two Xiphiums were
       encreased to a great number; planted some of them in the Basons
       round ye lilies; & some in a row under my Father's window:¶
       planted my Tulips in the same place; & a few Ranunculus, &
       Fritillarias: planted a row of Crocus-roots on each side as you go
       out of the new Garden:

27.   Put nine Hyacinths to blow in the Glasses over the Chimney.
       They were given me by Mr Frinley, & brought me by M^rs
       Mulso.¶

28.   Planted a row of Sweet Williams, & a row of Polyanths under the
       back of the melon-screen: some Polyanths along the dark walk in
       the orchard.
          Delicate Autumn-weather, & no rain for more than a month.
       Roads perfectly dry.
          Cantaleupes come-in apace: very high-flavoured, but small; as
       they were all on the third wood. The white-seeded sort very good.

Hollyhocks
in the rose garden.
The WaRes.
August.

OCTOBER 1: 2. Cut two very high-flavoured Cantaleupes, both under two p^{ds} in weight. They were very weighty for their size; & their coats very black, & embossed. Sent them to Lord Keeper.¶

11. Tyed-up second tying of Endives with red Yarn. Earth'd-up three rows of Celeri quite to the top.

Cut three Brace of Cantaleupes for Mangoes,¶ that were too backward to ripen. Left two brace & half, that may ripen tolerably well, if the season favours.

16. Received from my Broth^r Thomas 50 double snow-drop-roots; & six very large double *Narcissus*-roots.

17. Set three of the largest Narcissus's to blow in sand.

17. Sowed a large quantity of Laurel-berries in all the gaps of the Hedges; down Baker's Hill; at the top of Turner's Garden; & in the New-Garden against the street. Berries very large & ripe, from Mr Bridger's.

24. Planted in the Basons in ye field five double rockets, six scarlet Martagons, six Fraxinellas, 3 tallest purple Asters, 3 Dwarf D^o 2 German Goldylocks, 6 double Sunflowers, 3 tall smelling Sunflowers, 2 Carolina Sunflowers; from Murdoch Middleton. In the broad borders under my Father's window; 6 Solomon's seals, 6 double Narcissus's from Mur: Middleton: several double rockets from Mr Budd; striped *Epilobium* in the field.

Put two Jonquils to blow in the Glasses; & changed some of the Hyacinths that did not thrive for some of M: Myddleton's.

26. Finished digging-up a new piece of Garden-ground 60 feet by 30 in Baker's hill beyond the Field-Garden.

27. Sowed a large Quantity of Elder, Buckthorn, & dog-wood-berries in the ditch by the sand-walk.

28. Planted seven rows of small, early Beans in Turner's Garden.

Took away the two three-light frames. The Ground very dry, & in fine order.

29. Planted 50 snow-drops in three Clusters under my Father's window. Turn'd-out double.

Dunged, & earthed the Asparagus-beds.

30. Cut a melon; tolerable for the season.

31. Turn'd-off the earth from the melon-bed; & cut two brace of unripe fruit.

NOVEMBER 1. Planted in the Border next ye street 24 tulips from Mr Budd: 12 Hyacinths from D^o 5 Hyacinths from Murdoch Middleton: 12 Jonquils from D^o 8 Narcissus's from D^o 2 Dutch Narcissus's from Bro: Thomas: & two Groups of foxgloves from Mr Budd. Trenched the border well with lime-rubbish; & put the roots into the Ground in fine dry order.

Planted in a double-trench'd plot of Ground five rows of Horse-radish 10 inches deep.

Planted several slips of Mich: Daisies round the basons of Golden-rod; & in the new-planted basons of double-perennial-Sun-flowers. No rain for many weeks, & the ground as dry as in Summer.

Cast the Dorton melon-earth, & mixed some rotten Dung with it.

6. Cut-up a Cantaleupe that had been cut green, & laid in the Buffet to ripen.¶ It had a very good flavour, & was better than many a common melon ripened in the Height of the Season.

26. The early beans come-up very well. Mild growing weather as yet.

DECEMBER 1. Eat a Cantaleupe that had been a month in the House. It was firm, & well-flavoured.

9. Earth'd-up the Artichokes. Hoed the beans, that are grown pretty tall.

Very mild weather 'till this time.

26. Cut the last Cantaleupe, a very small one & not very good.

Very mild weather; hardly any frost yet.

The spring & summer 1757 were remarkably hot & dry. The dry weather began in passion-week, & continued-on without any Interruption except y* 29 of May 'till the 20th of July. The air was rather cold in April & May: but the sun, shining all day from a cloudless skie for many weeks, dryed the ground in a very uncommon manner: & the heats of June, & July quite burnt it to dust. I observed that our wet clay withstood the drought very well for many weeks: but when once it was thoro'ly parched (as it was more than spit deep) vegetation suffered more than in the gravelly soils. The barley, oats, & pease, having no rains to bring y[m] up, did not yield half a crop: but the wheat (which is never known to be injured by dry weather) turned-out very well. On y* twentieth of July fell a very heavy, & extensive thunder-shower: after which there were moderate rains, that restored a little verdure to the grass-fields. From the 16 of August set-in a very wet season for 15 or 16 days, which made people in some pain for the wheat that began to grow. About the beginning of Septem[r] began the most delicate Autumn, & lasted quite into Novem[r] with very little or no frost quite to the Close of the Year. On a large well-prepared melon-bed I could get no melons to set 'till the great rains fell; all the watering & shading not being sufficient to keep the plants from drawing. By my Brother Barker's account they had seasonable rains in the spring & summer; for their lent-crops in Rutland were very good.

— 1758 —

JANUARY 1; 2. Fierce black frost; went-off with an heavy rain.

9. Wheeled into the Cucumber-ground 17 barrows of very hot dung for seedling-Cucumb[rs].

Earth'd two rows of Celeri.

Very mild, spring-like weather.

10. Sowed a box of Polyanth-seed of my own saving, & set it under an Hedge where it could only have the morning-sun.

Hoed the beans, which are very prosperous, the second time.

13. Made a deep one-light Cucumber-bed, for my smallest frame.

16. Laid-on the earth three Inches thick: it was cold, & lumpish tho' mix'd-up with a good Quantity of rotten dung, & two spade's full of wood-ashes. Matted down the frame very close.

17. Finished an earth-house¶ in the melon-ground. It is worked in a circular shape with rods & coped over with the same, & then well thatched: is nine feet over & eight feet high; & has room to hold a good Quantity of mould, & a man at work without any inconvenience.

18. Sowed about 40 early Cucumber-seeds of the year 1752 in the hot-bed. Bed comes to it's heat very regularly. Hard frost, & great rime; & no sun for some days. The bed matted down a nights with three mats.

19. Carryed out three moderate dung-carts of ashes from the ash-house,¶ & sowed on Baker's Hill, which is now laid for natural Grass; & has been Clover for two Years past: spread also the upper part of it with the dung out of the melon-bed.

20. Turned all the melon-earth; & mixed it with a good proportion of the Dung of the last melon-bed. Dung hardly rotten enough.

20. Hot-bed works very well. Hard frost for two or three days: now ground covered with snow.

One of the Hyacinths in the glasses seems to promise to blow soon.

22. On this day, which was very bright, the sun shone very warm on the Hot-bed from a quarter before nine, to three quart^{rs} after two. Very hard frost.

24. Set-up about 20 Yards into the Hanger in a line with the six Gates, a figure of the Hesperian Hercules, painted on board, eight feet high, on a pedestal of four feet & an half. It looks like a statue, & shows well all over our out-let.

Cucumber-seeds swelled for sprouting, but not up yet: lined the end of the bed next the screen with two barrows of hot dung. Sort of thaw.

27. Finding the hot-bed scarce powerful enough to heat the three inches of earth thro', which was full wet when laid-on; I took-off the mould half the depth, & put the seeds in again. Some of the seeds sprouted. Sowed about 20 more. Earth very warm towards the bottom.

Planted about 40 Ranunculus-roots, given me by Mr Budd, in the Border against Parsons's, to blow after those that were put into the Ground in October.

29. Cucumber-plants come-up apace.

29. On this Day the mercury in the weather-glasses,¶ which had been mounting leisurely for many days, was got one full degree above settled-fair in the parlour, & within half a degree

Narcissus 'Paper white'
in hall window,
the Wakes.

of the same in the study.

My Father, who has been a nice observer of that up stairs for full 37 years, is certain that it never has been at that pitch before within that time. Very still, grey, close weather, with the wind at full east, & quite a thaw: tho' there has been somewhat of a frost for more than a fortnight past. Ground very dry; little rain having fallen for these three weeks past.

30. Mercury continues at the same height. Same still, gloomy weather.

Sent for 42 bushels of peat-ashes from the forest-side. Sowed fifteen bushels on the broad-mead, & 15 bushels on the Ewel-slip. Ashes very dry, & curiously preserved. Laid-up the remainder in ash-house.

Brought at the same time an old sandstone-roller from Mr Bridger's at Oakhanger. It was, it seems, formerly the property of Mr Xmass of Oakhanger, Father to Sarah Xmass; & may probably have been made these 60 or 70 Years; & yet is very little damaged by age or weather.

31. The Narcissus's, planted in sand in common blowing-glasses, have crammed the glasses so full, that tho' they budded very strongly at first, they have hardly advanced at all since in height for many weeks: one of ye Glasses, that was crack'd by accident, is quite split to pieces by the large, strong roots. Took it out of the Glass, & planted it in a pint-mug fill'd with sand.

FEBRUARY 2. Sowed about 20 more cucumber-seeds; the third sowing: the first, & second come-up very well, & begin to get some greenness.

4. Lined one end of the hot-bed with one Barrow of Dung. Bed declines in heat.

Sowed two samples of white-clover-seed, from different Seeds-men, in the Hot-bed.

6. Backed the hot-bed with six barrows of hot-dung.

Took away the suckers from the filberts against Parsons's; & planted some of them where they have failed against Turner's.

6: 7: 8. Trimm'd, & tack'd ye vines, (as much as old neglected trees could be reduced the first Year) according to Hitt's directions.¶ Covered many parts of the wall very well with horizontal wood. Left the disbudding till the budds are more swell'd. Trimmed ye figtree, which was full of young wood, & plies very well to the wall.

9. Put-in about 20 more Cucumber-seeds. Former sowings do not come-up well.

11. One of the Hyacinths in the glasses blown-out in several of it's buds.

Some in the Garden, thro' the mildness of the winter, budded for bloom.

	14.	Had 20 bushels of tan¶ from Alton for the Cucumber-bed.
23; 24; 25.		Made a cucumber-bed full fourteen feet long, & almost four feet deep at the back for my two two-light frames with ten Dung-carts of dung, which is very short this year on account of the scarcity of litter; & was very cold & wet by reason of the vast rains about that time. Covered the dung the space of one of the frames about five inches thick with tan, & filled a deep hole in the centre of each light with the same. Laid a leaden-pipe into the frame that has got the tin-chimney, (according to Dᵣ Hales's¶ proposal) up thro' the back of the bed, in order to convey-in a succession of fresh air a nights.

Made an hot-bed for a single hand-glass for Celeri.

Planted half hund: large forward cabbage plants.

	27.	Planted 100 brown-Dutch, & green Capuchin Lettuces from Bradley that had stood yᵉ winter, in the room of our own, which rotted thro' the wetness of the soil.
	28.	Sowed the Celeri-bed.
MARCH	1.	Great flood: wet for a long time.
	2.	Laid the hillocks of earth in the middle of each light. No earth fit to have been used, had it not been for the earth-house, thro' the vast rains.
	4.	Plunged nine melon-pots in the tan-frame, & three in the other frame. Contrived some wodden bottoms to the pots to make the earth turn-out more easily. Sowed plenty of Cucumber-seeds in a good depth of earth. Bed comes well to it's heat. Sad wet, stormy weather.
	6.	Sowed one melon-seed, from that curious Melon brought from Waverly in 1756, in each of the twelve pots. Bed heats well. Weather still so stormy, & wet, that there is no removing the Cucumber-plants. It has rained of late from all Quarters of the Skie.
	7.	Found an opportunity at last to plant-out the Cucumber-plants, three tolerable ones in each Hillock; some of which shew a rough leaf. Bed in fine warm order both in the tan, & dung part.

Sowed two more of the same Cantaleupe-seeds in nine of the pots.

	9.	Transplanted a large Laburnum into the Butcher's Garden. Planted half Hund: more Cabbage-plants.
	11.	Laid that part of the leaden-pipe, which comes-out behind the Cucumber-bed coiled up in a large box made out of yᵉ seed-box; & filled the box with about two barrows & half of Hot dung. The nose of the pipe comes-out about three inches beyond the box.
	13.	Planted 100 more Cabbage-plants, in all 200; the rows two feet apart, & the plants one foot from each other in the rows: every other plant to be pulled-up early in the summer.
	14.	Melon-plants begin to appear.
	16.	Planted Gallon of broad-beans in the lower field-garden, almost

seven rows. Sowed pound of spinage, with some common radishes, which ought to have been sowed 5 weeks before, but was prevented by the wet, in the upper field garden. Sowed some Celeriac between the Cucumber-boxes. Sowed eight basons in the field with double-upright-larkspurs; & the two lowest with large-single-branching D?

Perfect Summer for these two days.

18.   Earthed-up Cucumber-hillocks¶ the first time. Plants thrive, & many of them shew four leaves. Melons up some in every pot; they look healthy, & grow apace.

18.   Turned-out a large *Narcissus*, that was intended to blow within, into one of the borders. Planted some bunches of single snow-drops in bloom under my Father's window.

Sowed about 30 more green Cucumber-seeds in the Hot-bed. Filled-up the box, that contains the leaden pipe, with one more barrow of dung: the dung begins to heat in the box: the nose of the pipe hot in the morning, & cold towards the evening. Very wet afternoon.

19.   Vast heavy rains most part of yᵉ day.

21.   Great snow all the day, & most part of the night; which went off the next day in a stinking, wet fog. Very trying weather for Hot-beds, more like Jan: than March. No sun for many Days.

23.   Planted among the Holyoaks next the street in yᵉ New-Garden 2 Austrian Briars, 1 black Belgic-rose, 1 York & Lancaster D? 1 Marbled D? 1 monthly D? from Mʳ Budd:¶ & two large roots of the Aster-kind in the Border before the roses. A very late-blowing sort.

25.   Planted three more Provence-roses from Mʳ Budd in the same place. Forked Asparagus-beds: dressed Rasberry-bed: sowed the lower plot of the new field Garden with seven rows of marrow-fat pease at four feet asunder. Ground in a cold clammy Condition.

Tryed an experiment¶ late in yᵉ evening with a Candle on the two Cucumber-frames after they had been close covered-up some Hours. On putting the Candle down a few Inches into that frame that has leaded lights & no Chimney, the flame was extinguished at once three several times by the foul vapour: while the frame with the tiled lights, & Chimney was so free from vapour that it had no sensible effect on the flame. I then applyed the candle to the top of the Chimney, from whence issued so much steam as to affect the flame, tho' not put it out. Hence it is apparent that this Invention must be a benefit to plants in Hot-beds by preventing them from being stewed in the night time in the exhalations that arise from the dung, & yᵗ own leaves.

The melons confirm the matter, being unusually green & vigorous for their age. I applyed the Candle to the nose of the leaden pipe; but it had no effect on it: so that what air comes-up thro' it must be wholesome, & free from vapour.

28.   Planted 59 potatoes in Turners; not very large roots. Sowed the wheat with white Dutch Clover: Baker's Hill with Rye Grass, &

black-seed:¶ the vase-mount, & hollow-way into the Ewel with
D.º Fine weather. Set-up the vases: put-on two bold Handles to
the lower one; & two side-pannels to the pedestal. Sowed two
rows of parsley, & transplanted some mint.

APRIL   1. Unusual sunny, scorching weather for a week past. The heat
drew the forward Cucumbers, notwithstanding they were
constantly shaded; & would have spoiled the melons (as yᵉ same
kind of heat did this time twelvemonth) had not the pots been
raised. Forward Cucumbers weak; & begin to shew for bloom.

          3. Sowed 14 of John Bosworth's curious large white Cucumber-
seeds in one of the frames, in order to raise some plants for one of
the Hand-glasses to save seed from.

          4. Sowed almost an ounce of Carrot-seed, mixed with Coss-lettuce¶
green & white, & some common radishes, in Turner's Garden.
Sowed in the field-Garden ounce of onion-seed, half ounce of
Leek-seed, & a small Quantity of parsnep-seed.

          6. Made a one-light hot-bed for Annuals with six full barrows of
dung.

          9. Very dry weather for this fortnight past: for the last week fierce
frosts.

         10. Several basons of sunflower-seed sowed among the Holy-oaks in
the New-Garden against the street; & some among the Butcher's
Limes. Sowed the annual-bed with French & African-
Marrigolds; Double-China-asters, & single D.º & white Asters;
pendulous-Amaranths; & some Gourds for Dame Tyrrel.

          9. Saw two swallows:¶ one was seen in yᵉ village on the 3rd.

         11. Sowed in a seedling-bed in the field Garden Sunflowers, French-
Wallflower, Columbine, Sweet-Williams, Double-China-pinks
under two hand-glasses, Everlasting-pea, French-Honeysuckle,
Evergreen-*Cytisus*, & Holyoaks: in the new-Garden in the
broad-border, & against the apple tree, painted-Lady-pease;
Nigella romana; in the Kitchen part half ounce more of Leek-
seed, & small plot of red beet.

         12. Sowed third Crop of Marrow-fat-pease, one row in Turner's,
two rows in old field-garden, two rows in new field-garden.

         13. Worked-up a nine-light melon-bed with 18 good dung-carts of
fresh, hot dung, & 80 bushels of fresh tan. I had made this bed
just a week before, only two days after the materials were brought
in; but finding it to heat violently I ordered it to be pulled to
pieces, & cast back again, that it might spend it's violent Heat.
The bed is 36 feet long, six feet & an half wide, & about two feet
& half high. The tan makes a covering all over of about 8 inches
thick. In the middle of each light I laid a patch of rotten dung
about two inches thick, which I beat-down hard to keep-off the
fierce heat from the hillocks of earth.
      Fierce east-wind; & no rain for near three weeks: the ground,
& roads unusually dry.

         15. Raked-over the Asparagus-beds the second time: stuck the first

Crop of Marrowfat pease: filled the box that contains the leaden-pipe with hot dung the second time.

Cutting winds all day, & thick ice every night.

16. So fierce a frost with a South-wind as to freeze the steam which run out in water from between the panes of yᵉ Melon-frames into long Icicles on the Edges of the lights.

17. Prepared & dunged the basons in the field, which are to be planted with Annuals hereafter. Fine shower.

18. Put a barrow of fine mellow earth into each melon-light. Bed seems now to be very mild. More soft showers. Earth-house of great Use to keep a constant supply of fine mould dry & ready for the frames.

20. Found the melon-hillocks so hot that I durst not turn the plants into them: plunged the plants in the pots into the hillocks.

Turned-out some Hyacinths that were out of bloom from the blowing-glasses into the flower-border.

Sowed Crop of Boorcole green, & red.

Polyanths in full bloom; but not so fine as last Year. Several Hyacinths in the border very large & handsome. White & yellow Narcissuss with golden Cups blow very well both in glasses & abroad.

21. Found the melon-bed so hot still that I did not trust the plants out of the pots. Earthed the bed all over an inch thick to keep down the steam, which in the night had spoiled three of the plants. Bored some holes very deep in the back of the bed to let out the violent Heat. I find a moderate thickness of tan, when laid on a good strong bed of dung, to occasion a very dangerous, & unequal Heat, so that there is scarce any Judging when the earth is free from burning. For in shady weather it will appear very mild; but on a hot morning will rage again, as fierce as when it first came to it's full heat. Tan gives a mild & lasting heat by itself, but does not seem suitable with dung.

22. Took-out the tan the whole depth as wide as the Hillocks, & mixed-up the hillocks with a little fresh earth. Did not find the earth burnt, but much too hot. Filled the space whence the tan came with barrows of rotten dung trod down very hard, about four Inches thick.

Sowed four rows of dwarf kidney beans, the white sort; & a crop of Savoy-seed. Perfect Summer weather.

24. Ventured to turn-out yᵉ Melons, tho' some of the hillocks were full hot: mixed-up a good deal of fresh earth in each hillock, & set yᵉ plants as high as possible: left the wodden bottoms under some of the plants to see if they will prevent the roots from burning. Intend to cover the frames but slightly, while the bed is so hot.

Made an hot-bed for the smallest one-light frame, to prick the annuals in, with 5 barrows of dung, & two of Grass. Made two beds for two hand-glasses with two barrows of dung each to forward some of Bosworth's large white Cucumbers to save seed from.

Dressed Artichoke bed. Forked up yᵉ seedling Asparagus; only 16 plants to be found. Layed some boughs of Laurustines; & planted a Laurustine by yᵉ pitching.

27. Planted-out John Bosworth's large white Cucumbers, three under each Hand-glass, to make early plants to save some seed of that fine sort from: pricked-out the annuals in yᵉ two one-light frames, & sowed some more Afr: Marrigolds, & more of Bosworth's Cucumber-seeds. Weeded all the basons, & flower-borders. Melon-bed steams greatly; but seems to be past it's vehement Heat.

Fine soft showers all the Afternoon, & evening.

Disbudded the vines that were laid on the walls according to Hit.¶

MAY 1. Planted about 20 bulbs of Eschallots in the New-Garden.

Some melon-plants continue to fail, tho' the bed is very mild, & the mould sweet & unburnt.

Swallows over the church
Selborne
8 May

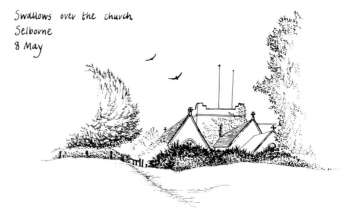

12. On my return from London I found several of the melon-plants very large & thriving; except in two of the basons, where they were puny, & withered: supply'd those two basons with some late-sowed Cantaleupe plants from Seed saved at Selborn 1755.

15. A most extraordinary dry season ever since the end of March: all our worst roads have been dryed-up many weeks. For this fortnight past the heats have been very great. Grass & lent-corn must suffer unless rain comes soon. Apples-trees finely blown. Bosworth's Cucumbers come-on well under the Hand-glasses.

17. Widened-out the Cucumber-bed four feet with the dung of the seedling-bed; & laid-on a thick covering of earth.

Prick'd-out a good plot of Celeriac. Vines trained according to Hit full of Bloom.

20. Sowed a Quart, four rows, of large white kidney-beans in the field-Garden: watered them well beforehand. Earthed the melons, & watered them stoutly: trod the earth round the stems

down very hard to keep-out the heat. Planted four Handglasses in the cold ground with M.ʳ Bosworth's large white Cucumber-plants raised in the annual-bed. Very hot, dry weather. Sowed some Cucumber-seeds under a hand-glass.

22.   Prick'd-out a plot of Celeri: sowed a Crop of Coss-lettuce green & white.

24.   Made a melon-bed for four Hills with six loads of dung in front of the large bed: it is five feet wide, & seventeen long.

25.   Turned-out a pot of Selborn Cantaleupes into each Hill, & covered them with Hand-glasses. Intend to cover the plants, when they spread, with the two two-light frames.

     Violent hot weather: no rain for some weeks. The ground burnt, & cracked to an unusual degree. Things in both fields, & Gardens suffer greatly. The fierce heat has lately damaged both melons, & Cucumbers, notwithstanding constant shading, & unusual watering.

26.   Planted 6 basons in the field with Indian-pinks: set the plants pretty near together. Fine soft rains all day: every thing greatly refresh'd after so tedious a drought. Sunny days & east winds for the most part ever since the last week in March.

29.   Weeded the Carrots, & Laurels, & hoed the potatoes: weeded the seedling-flowers.

     Tacked the Young wood of the vines all perpendicular, for the first time, according to Hit.

30: 31.   Raised & earthed the melon-frames almost their full quantity. Melon-bed very warm still. Many of the melon-plants very thriving; abound in vine, & shew male bloom, & fruit.

     Planted 100 of late Cabbages; & pricked-out some Broccoli plants given me by M.ʳ Budd. Shady moist weather for a week past: now frequent heavy showers that have well soaked the Ground down to the roots of Corn, & Garden-stuff.

JUNE   2.   Sowed four rows of large white-Kidney-beans, & one of dwarfs in y.ᵉ field-Garden: five rows of dwarf D.º in the Quincunx.

3.   Gathered first beans.

5.   Cut a brace of Cucumbers. Shady, moist weather.

6.   Earth'd the hand-glass melons the first time: the bed not earth'd all over yet. The plants are strong, & produce plenty of wood; but are strangely blistered in their second leaves by being exposed to y.ᵉ fierce sun while the night-dew was on them.

9.   Mulberry-tree shews several Blossoms for the first time. Fine summer-weather with now & then a shower. French-beans that had been watered all night, & were sown on the 2.ᵈ of June, began to appear on the 8.ᵗʰ

9.   Raised the Cucumber-frames the thickness of a brick above the mould: turned down y.ᵉ large white-Cucumbers from under the hand-glass; they are strong plants, & shew fruit.

10.   Went to raise the melon-frames, but found the melon-roots have extended themselves all along against the sides of the boxes, &

require room by lining.

Watered the Mulberry-tree well to make the fruit set.

12. Gathered first Marrowfats.

Soaking rain for ten Hours.

13: 14. Lined the melon-bed three feet on each side with eleven loads of dung; & laid-on a good depth of earth: raised the frames to the top of the earth. Lined the ends of the bed with one load of Dung: the bed is now full 40 feet long, & 12 feet wide. Earth'd it deep as far as the earth would last: run a slight hedge round the edges to keep up the earth.

15. Earth'd the Hills of the melons under ye Hand-glasses: stop'd some of the plants at the third Joint: plants very vigorous.

Sowed Crop of Endive.

Soft showery weather.

Prick'd-out 600 Savoys, & 350 Boor-cole-plants, green, & purple.

16. Planted-out all the leeks at six inches asunder: about 200.

Pricked-out a little more Celeri.

Planted-out a bed of small Coss-lettuce.

Sowed a row of parsley.

Wet, blowing weather.

17. Planted 100 Cabbage-plants in the room of those planted May 31st which were dead.

Tyed-up first Coss-lettuce.

Some of John Bosworth's long Cucumbers set.

20. Planted-out the greatest part of my Annuals, African & French-Marrigolds, Pendulous Amaranths, & China-Asters: They were pricked into a second bed, & are very forward, & large.

Pricked-out an 120 Roman-Broccoli-plants from Waverley.

Two Labourers have been working for 5 or 6 Days in the Garden, & have hoed & weeded all the Crops, & cleaned all the paths, & borders that were in a foul Condition.

22. Planted more Annuals, Sunflowers, & China-Asters, in field, & Garden.

27. Nailed, & trimmed the vines: the second time, according to Hit. The bunches in full bloom.

28. Earthed the hand-glass melon-bed the full depth, took away ye hand-glasses, & put the two two-light frames over the plants. Plants strong, but shew little fruit, or bloom.

Planted some of Murd: Middleton's white-Cucumber-plants under three hand-glasses.

JULY 1. Stuck the sticks to the large kidney-beans. Heavy thunder-showers. Melons swell apace. The late bed shews fruit. Dwarf kidney-beans in full bloom.

3. Lined-out the two-light melon-bed a yard wide with three loads of dung, & laid on earth very thick. Prick'd out a good many Sweet Williams. Planted out more annuals: sowed a small spot of Endive.

4. Pricked-out bed of Holy-oaks to put them in less room: pricked-out vast Quantities of Sweet Williams.
  Blowing, wet weather on to the 14: when there was quite a storm all night, & such quantities of rain as made quite a flood: the trees & flowers were much damaged by the wind.

15. Found on my return from Dene about thirteen brace of Cantleupes set; some very large. Plants in vast vigour with leaves near a foot in Diameter. More fruit setting every day. Those plants in the two-light frames seem to be full late; hardly any of their fruit blown-out yet. Two plants in new frame have 8 brace of fruit between y.^{m}

18: 19: 20. Showery, black weather. Trenched-out seven rows of Celeri. Planted-out second plot of Endive: first plot about a fortnight before. Planted large plot with Roman-Broccoli from Waverley.
  On examination it appeared that the Cantaleupe-fibres have run the full extent of the 12 feet bed: laid-on some more earth behind to secure their Roots from the Sun. Some of their branches, on which are large fruit, are attack'd with mouldiness this wet weather. Raised the frames behind, the thickness of a Brick to shoot-off the rain, that drips thro', & rots some of the Haulm.

21. Quite heavy showers to day, & strong wind.
Some of the melon-leaves measure 11 inches & three Quart^{rs} in diameter.

20. Gathered first French-beans; white dwarfs.

24. Stringed pine strawberries.¶
  Continual showers.

25. Dug-up Hyacinth, & tulip-roots: Hyacinths bloated with the wet weather. Planted in their room African & French-Marrigolds.
  Vast rains still.

26. Great rain.

28. Vast rains with Thunder.

29: 30. Dry weather: on 31st rain for 14 hours. The melon-vines suffer with the continual wet, which has continued now more than a month. Cut-off a full-grown Cantaleupe that was rotten.

AUGUST 1. Black, moist weather all day; vast rains at night.

2. Sultry, bright morning: turned the large Melons.

3. Tiled, & turned all the largest melons: full twenty brace set; tho' perhaps they may not all ripen.

4. Sowed half pound of spinage, & some white-turnep-radish-seed in the new field-Garden: began planting-out savoys, & Boorcole. Two hot, bright days.

5. Cut-off the small side-shoots from the bearing wood of the vines, leaving one joint on; according to Hitt's directions. Grapes pretty large. The fourth hot, dry day.

7. Drawed-out the boorcole, & savoy-bed to a foot & half apart, & planted the new field-Garden with D.^{o}

8. Brought in a doors the Pyramidal Campanula: it has seven Stems,

& just begins to shew some bloom.

11. Trenched two long rows more of Celeri. Vast rains the two days before.

12. Finished the hay-rick: hay-making was in hand just seven weeks. A deal of Hay much damaged.

13. Beautiful harvest-weather.

16. Tyed-up some of the forwardest endives.

Vast rains last night, & this evening.

The wheat is all cut, & must soon be damaged if this weather lasts. It has never been dry more than four days together, & that only twice, since the first of July: in general only two days together: & that but seldom. The Cantaleupes have had a very disadvantageous season; nothing but black, wet weather since they have been set. Sr Mat: Featherstone's Cantaleupes, I hear, have very little flavour.

19. Earth'd one row of Celeri half the way up. Planted a row of Savoys between every two rows of dwarf-kidney-beans in the Quincunx. Housed the wheat not in very good order.

21. Tyed-up more Endive.

22. Cut the first Cantaleupe, the largest of the Crop: weighed 3 p^{ds} 5 oun: & half. It proved perfectly delicate, dry, & firm notwithstanding the unfavourable weather ever since the time of setting. Saved the seed.

23. Cut second Cantaleupe: weighed 2 p^{ds} 5 oun: Fine, bright weather for five days.

24. Cut a brace more of Cantaleupes; one weighed 2 p^{ds} 6 oun: one 2 p^{ds} 4 ounces.

Great rain in the afternoon.

25. Sent a brace of the Cantaleupes to Lord Keeper: eat the third at Home, which turned out perfectly delicate; rather superior to ye first, eaten at the Hermitage.¶ Saved the seed.

26. Cut & set-up in the sun ye six large white seed-Cucumbers: the biggest weighed 2 p^{ds} 14 oun: & the longest measured 13 inch: in length.

Sowed a small plot of Coss, green Capuchin, & Brown-Dutch-Lettuce-seed, for plants to stand the winter.

28. Cut small Cantaleupe, weighed but 15 oun: vast rains all day, & a great flood.

29. Tyed-up about 30 more Endives.

31. Heavy rain for about 30 Hours, which coming upon the back of such vast showers before, occasioned an extraordinary flood, which ran over the foot-bridges, & was greater than any winter-flood for many years past. It filled James Knight's biggest pond, which had been fished this summer, brim full: & raised the Landsprings in ye fields, so as to damage the paths.

SEPTEMBER 5. Earth'd-up early row of Celeri to the top.

Eat a brace of Cantaleupes at the Hermitage: the black, rough one very high flavoured. Shady, showery weather. Saved the seed.

Pulled-up the Onions, & Eshallots, & laid them to dry. Onions begin to rot with ye wet.

7. Eat a very delicate Cantaleupe: it had a bottle-nose, & grew close to the stem. Sav'd ye seed. Shady, showery weather: now a vast rain.

8. Cut first Endives.
Vast rains still.

9. This day ten weeks the wet season began.

10. The Cantaleupes threaten to come all together. Cut two brace, & half to day.

12. Held a Cantaleupe-feast at ye Hermitage: cut-up a brace & an half of fruit among 14 people. Weather very fine ever since the ninth.

13. Planted-out two rows of Polyanths down the border next Lasham's. Should have been transplanted many weeks ago, if the wet weather had not prevented.

14. Eat a brace & half of Cantaleupes. Saved the seed of one that grew near the stem, & was very fine.
Tyed-up more Endives.

17. Had been dry for 8 days; now very wet.

18. Cut a Cantaleupe from one of the later plants: weighed 2 p^ds 5 oun: Esteemed very curious: saved ye seed.

26. Earthed about half way seven rows of Celeri.

27. Cut two Cantaleupes, & took away two of the frames: only one fruit remaining. Dug-up the Carrots, & Potatoes: the potatoes not a great Crop, nor very large. Dry, pleasant weather.

28. Continued the dug-ground down Baker's Hill for more Garden. Dug a border down the Shrubbery under the rod-hedge.

OCTOBER 2: 3. Chip'd the best of ye Polyanths¶ in ye broad shady walk, & planted two rows again in the same place.

4: 5: 6. Planted three beds of Pine-Strawberries, & two of scarlet D^o in the New Garden. Planted a few large strawberries call'd Collinson's, Nova Scotia, & white Strawberries sent me by Brother Thomas.

6. Cut last Cantaleupe: & housed the frame very dry. Firm, good-flavoured Fruit.

8. Fine still weather in general since the 9th of Septem^r now rain, & a vast storm of wind, that blew-down some shrubs, & beat to pieces all the flowers.

17. Transplanted about 100 Green Capuchin, & Brown-dutch Lettuce to Dame Tyrrels garden to stand ye winter. Dressed the border at ye back of ye melon-screen, & planted a row of Sweet Williams: planted a row of D^o in the border in the New-Garden against ye Street.

21. Received from Mur: Middleton 12 double blue Hyacinths, 12 early-blowing tulips, 6 Polyanth-Narcissus,¶ 6 double white-Hyacinths, Quart^r p^d of Anemonies, 50 good *Ranunculus*, two Moss-Provence-roses.

21. Planted the two Moss-Provence roses behind the border next yᵉ street in the New-Garden. Put to blow in the Glasses 3 double blue, & 3 double white Hyacinths; & one early Tulip.

27. Slip'd-out the buds of the Pyramidal Campanula, which blowed this Year, & planted them in several pots, four in a pot.

NOVEMBER 2. Saw a very unusual sight; a large flock of House-Martens¶ playing about between our fields, & the Hanger. I never saw any of the swallow-kind later than the old 10: of Octoᵇʳ The Hanger being quite naked of leaves made the sight the more extraordinary.

Warm wet weather for many days, with blowing nights, & sunny mornings.

The leaf fallen more than usual.

8. M: Middleton's large late *Aster* just blowing: a fine shewey flower of a beautiful purple.

8. Set to blow in Glasses four Polyanth-Narcissus, & two Hyacinths brought me by Brother Thomas.

14. Planted in the Butcher's Yard between yᵉ limes one white, & two purple lilacs.

16. Planted in broad border next Parsons's:

No: 1. Double blue Hyacinths.
2. Dᵒ White.
3. Early tulips.
4. Quarter of a pound of Anemonies.
5. 50 *Ranunculus*.
6. My own Hyacinths.
7. My own Tulips.
8. Bro: Tho: Polyanth-Narcissus, & Jonquils: some have been in Glasses.
9. Mʳ Budd's *Ranunculus*.
10. Mur. Middleton's *Narcissus*.
11. 16 Coronae Imperiales.
12. Mʳ Budd's *Narcissus*.

The border very dry, & in very fine order.

20. Planted four Damascene-plum-trees from North-Warnboro'.

24. Set up two wickets from yᵉ upper end of my Ewel-close thro' Parsons's field to the pound-field.¶

Planted 9 long rows, 3 pints of early beans, in the field-garden. Ground in very dry, good order.

25. Trenched & dunged very stoutly a piece of Ground for melon-earth next spring.

DECEMBER 14. Earthed up Artichokes.

The Spring, & Summer of 1758 were much in the extreams. From yᵉ last week in March to the first of July was one long dry fit, with very few showers between. At one time, I think, the Ground was more scorch'd than even in summer 1757: & the lent-corn began

to suffer greatly. But on the 1ˢᵗ of July the great rains began to set-
in, & continued with very little intermission till the 10 of Septemʳ.
The Autumn was moderately dry, & pleasant; & continued very
mild, one short frost excepted, to the end of yᵉ Year.

— 1759 —

JANUARY 19. Wheeled-in, & cast 18 barrows of hot dung for the seedling-
Cucumber-bed.

20. The season has continued uncommonly mild to this time. Many
kinds of flowers are got above ground some weeks before their
usual time: the snow-drops, & some Crocus's were in bloom
before old Decemʳ was out: & Farmer Knight complains that
several of his turneps are in blossom.

Covered the tulip, & Hyacinth-buds with a thin coat of tan
that is rotten.

Have got some mould in excellent order for the early
Cucumbers; it is a mixture of strong loam, ashes, & tan, tumbled
about & well incorporated all the winter.

The Glass has been very high for many days with a falling
mist, & blustering west-wind.

22. Turned the earth trench'd for yᵉ Melons, & gave it an other
sprinkle of very rotten dung: turned the Dorton-earth, & mixed
with it three barrows of rotten tan.

23. Made the Cucumber seedling-Hot-bed, turning the front to the
south west to take all the sun these short days.

Hard frost for two nights, & bearing Ice.

24. Laid-on the mould on the hot-bed; fill'd & plunged four pots for
Cucumber seeds.

Sowed a pot with Cucumber-seeds, & set it by the parlour-fire
for experiment-sake.*

26. Bed come to a kindly heat: sowed above an 100 Cucumber-seeds
within & without the pots.

30. Cucumber-plants begin to appear.

FEBRUARY 3. Sowed a small quantity of curious Polyanth-seed, given me by Mʳ
Hale of Hambleton, in a box; & set yᵉ box where it may receive
the morning-sun.

Sowed 20 more Cucumber-seeds in the frame. First plants
thrive, & look of a good Colour. Unusual sunny, fine weather.

Cucumbers in yᵉ pot by the fireside come-up very well.

5. Set in a nursery-bed a good parcel of Hyacinth, & Tulip-ofsets.

7. Finished trimming, & tacking the vines according to Hit. Took
away abundance of yᵉ old wood: The vines in one Year more will
be quite furnished with new.

Ashed the great mead, Clover-field, & part of the slip with

---

*These seeds came-up, but would not advance beyond the two first
leaves.

three dung-pots of ashes: quite cleared the House.

Cucumber-plants thrive so fast, that to day, the 12 day from sowing the seeds, many of the plants have got a rough leaf.

Fine dry weather, with a good deal of Sunshine; more like April, than old January. Paths quite firm.

8: 9: 10. Set-on three Labourers this fine weather to dig all my Ground ready for Crops: turn'd my plot of melon-earth the third time: & wheeled out of the way all the old rotten dung, & tan.

10. Sowed Gallon of early pease; & half pound of spinage: planted Gallon of Winsor beans, & 200 of Cabbage plants.

9. Turned-out of their pots, & planted in deep mould several of the best Cucumber plants: plants strong, & thriving.

Notwithstanding the long dry weather the Ground will just work decently.

12. Carried into the Hot-bed Ground eight loads (dung-carts) of hot dung for the forward Cucumbers.

Perfect summer: the air full of Gnats: & the surface of the Ground full of spiders webs, as in a fine day in August. The sun lay so hot on the frame that the Cucumber-plants wanted to be shaded. Some plants have a broad rough leaf.

13. Made the bank against the new-garden pretty fine, & smooth by the advantage of this fine weather. Planted it with flowers in two rows: the upper row was Columbines, French-honeysuckles, & rose Campions, at a Yard apart: the lower row all sweet-Williams, at a foot apart. Ordered the bank to be well-beat, & the water-table to be cut so deep, that no mould can tumble on the brick walk. The bank lays very handsome, on a hanging level.

15. Cucumber-plants thrive strangely. Some have got a fourth leaf quite expanded; & their first rough leaf as broad as a Crown-piece. No rain at all since this day month. Great fogs for these two days past, that hang 'till the afternoon: then bright sun-shine.

Planted Holyoaks in the new border under the rod-hedge down Baker's-hill; & mended-out the borders in our own, & the Butcher's Yard.

17. Received from Mr Philip Miller of Chelsea about 80 Mellon-seeds 1754: immediately from Armenia; which he finds to be better than those that have been first brought to Cantaleupe, & thence to England.

20. Made my early Cucumber-bed with 8 loads of dung; & cased it round well with a Coat of refuse hay, well sparred-on.

Black, rough, March-like weather: seems to threaten snow.

22. Laid-on the hills of earth on the Cucumber-bed. Now rain after many weeks dry weather.

23. Turned-out two pots of Cucumbers in one of the two-light frames: the Plants have got a fifth leaf, & a joint: the two first rough leaves are as broad as the palm of my Hand. This day month the seeds were put into the frame. Plunged 14 pots of Cantaleupes in the two two-light frames.

24. Sowed six of the pots with Cantaleupe-seed from Waverley 1756:

             & eight of the pots with Armenian-Cantaleupe 1754 from M.ʳ
Miller. Fierce, piercing East-wind with a low, sinking Glass.
The Glass has been up at, & above fair ever since new-Year's
day, 'till yesterday.

25.   Vast rain all night.

26.   Transplanted more Cucumbers in the other two light-frame. Bed
full hot.

27.   One pot of Miller's Cantaleupes begins to appear. Continual
heavy rain.

28.   Sowed one more Armenian seed in each of the six pots: so there
are three seeds in every pot. Plants came almost all up in general
last night: raised the pots allmost out of the mould.

MARCH   1.   Sowed some Cucumber-seeds to give away.

         3.   The Cantaleupes looking not quite right, I plunged the pots up to
their brims in the mould.

        4.   Cucumbers grow away, & put out long wires; have six leaves, &
three jonts.
        Sad heavy showers.
        Put-in a few more Cantaleupe-seeds into the worst-looking
pots.

        6.   Ventured to mat-down the Cucumber-frames untriged¶ for the
first time. Continual rain.

        7.   Bright sun-shine all day; scalded some of the Cucumber-leaves.

        8.   Continual rain all day.

        9.   Raised the frames the thickness of one brick. Cantaleupes look in
general very well: plenty of plants at present. Vast storm in the
Evening, & very heavy rain.

10.   Vast tempest all night, & this morning; which at noon blew-down
the weather-cock on the tower.

12.   This day 6 weeks the Cucumber-plants appeared above ground;
& have now five & six joints apiece, & are full of budds for
bloom, & fruit. Watered them gently for the first time over the
leaves with yᵉ watering-pot. Promises for dry, & cold.

13: 14.   Carted 20 loads of hot dung into the melon-ground for yᵉ
Cantaleupes: seven of my own, & thirteen borrowed.

15.   One of the Cucumber-plants has a Male-bloom fully expanded.
        The weather very wet, & stormy.
        Sowed yᵉ Celeri Hand-glass.

17.   Vast storms still.
        Cucumbers thrive, but not the Cantaleupes.

19.   Received from Brother Tho: three sorts of the double-flowering
Sweet Briar;¶ & two roots of the large tap-rooted *Lathyrus*; &
three roots of the Lathyrus-Earth-nut with a tuberose root.
        Vast rain most part of the day. Wind abated. The late storms
have done considerable damage among our ships.

20.   Cucumber-plants showed plenty of fruit for the first time; all on
the second wood. Black weather, & continual showers.

22.   Moved the seedling Cucumber-frame nearer to the two-light

frames, & sowed it with radishes on very deep mould. Beautiful day.

21. Mowed the grass-plot for the first time: a vast plenty of Grass, which lined the Cucumber-bed. Made two beds, with one barrow of dung each, for two handglasses, for White-mustard, & cress.

23. Planted 4 of the double-Briars in the new-Garden against the street, & one in the front of the House; & the two long *Lathyrus*-roots against the apple-tree next Parsons's. Grubb'd the orchard-walk, & planted it with Holy-oaks, & Wall-flowers. Potted some sweet-Williams. Removed the double jonquils, out of the orchard, under Lassam's hedge.

24. Dressed the Rasps. Removed half the Capuchin, & Brown-Dutch Lettuces from Dame Tyrrel's Garden back to the New-Garden. Sowed four Drills of Marrow-fat pease in Baker's hill. Sowed a drill of parsley. Yesterday a beautiful Summer's day.

Grafted my three Cantaleupe frames, & raised them 9 inches behind, & in proportion before. Hyacinths in bloom in the open air; & one *Narcissus*. Early Tulips have been blown above this fortnight.

25. First Cucumber-blossom fully expanded.

Still, grey weather, with a very high Barometer. Some fruit shows on the first runners of some plants. The lining of grass-mowings gives a great Heat to the Cucumber bed. Hyacinths abroad full as early, as those in ye Glasses.

26 Work'd-up the 20 loads of dung (brought in on the 14th) into a Cantaleupe-bed for the nine large lights. The bed is tucked to six feet & half broad, & 36 in length. Laid some very stiff loam all over about an inch thick; & put on the boxes, & lights. The bed is about two feet thick. Housed seven more barrows of dorton-loam; in all 14.

27. Sawed-down those two espalier-trees in ye New-Garden that bore angular apples: & employed John Lassam to graft the stems with some Cuttings from the Royal-russet in the Orchard. Grafted two of the Golden-pippins in the Orchard with Cuttings from the tree of the same sort.

28. Put the male-bloom to three of the first fruit-Cucumber-blossoms, that were just turning-in, in order to set them.

Sowed three pots more of Miller's, & three pots of Waverley-Cantaleupes, two seeds in a pot; to supply the hills in Case of any failure. Miller's marked as usual with sticks. Plunged the pots in one of the Cantaleupe-boxes.

29. Sowed half a Gallon more, four rows of Marrow-fats, in the lower field-garden: the rows are four feet apart; the former sowing five.

30. Put a brimful Barrow of Dorton-loam into each light of the Cantaleupe-bed. The Hills will require, now the boxes are raised, a barrow & half each at least. Bed comes slowly to it's heat; & is very mild yet.

31. Planted groups of Sweet-Williams in the border under the rod-

hedge down the Shrubbery.

Put half barrow more of loam to each Cantaleupe-Hill. Bed very mild.

Finished a bastion, & Haha, fenced with sharp'ned piles, in the vista from Baker's Hill to the Great mead: & a conical mount,¶ about six feet diameter at top, & five high, at the bottom of the great mead. Mount about eight days work; Haha about sixteen.

Fierce frost, & vast hoar-frost on the Grass: the ground continued very hard, & icy all day in the shade.

APRIL   2.   Sowed ounce of Carrots with green, & white Cos-Lettuce; ounce of Onions; & a few parsneps. Fine weather.

          3.   The Cantaleupe-bed not coming to a proper degree of Heat, I ordered it to be pulled to pieces, & worked-up with 10 loads of fresh hot dung just brought-in. The Labourers made-use of about 16 loads of the first bed again: so the new bed contains 26 loads. Laid some loam all over to keep-down the steam; & some turfs under the Hills. Put one barrow of loam to each Hill. Bed more than seven feet wide; & two feet & half thick behind.

          4.   Widened-out the Cucumber-bed in front three feet with about two loads of the dung, which came-out of the Cantaleupe-bed; & laid-on a thick covering of strong loam: lined it behind with Grass, & weeds. Some fruit set, that grows apace.

Planted some Everlasting-pease of my sowing last year; & some earth-Nut-Lathyruss under the rod-hedge against Parsons's. Planted more sweet-Williams, & some Columbines under the rod-hedge against the shrubbery. Planted 8 Laurels, with a sweetwilliam between each two, on the bank of the Bastion behind the seat. Planted Columbines in the Orchard-walk.

          5.   Raked down, & weeded the Asparagus-bed the first time.

          7.   On my return from Chilgrove, & Harting I found the Cantaleupe-bed come to a very fine degree of Heat. Turned-out the Cantaleupes into their Hills: the plants are healthy, & well-rooted; but a little drawn by the large rambling runners of ye Cucumbers. The three nearest hills are Waverley; the six farthest are Armenian Cantaleupes. Six pots left, which I plunged in the great boxes.

Sowed about 40 seeds of the great White-Dutch-Cucumber, saved last Year.

Six pots of Waverley, & Armenian-Cantaleupes just coming out of the mould, by way of supply, if wanted.

          8.   Vast rain from the East: & all day on ye 6th

          9.   Cut first Cucumber: it has a good flavour, & smell. Several more set. The seeds were put into the Ground 10 weeks, & two days ago.

Unusual heavy rain for 29 hours.

       11.   Vast rain great part of the day, & night.

The lining the Cantaleupe-bed between the frames with weeds cut from the orchard filled the bed with snails. Forced to take the weeds away, else the snails would have devoured all the plants. The water stands in the lining of the Cucumber-bed almost shoe-deep.

At a mark cut in the bark of the great Oak in the mead, between two & three feet from the ground, I measured that tree with a design to see how much the body may swell in one summer. It girted seven feet 5 inc:

12. Sowed about a peck of old bacon-salt in middle of the great mead.

Made half Hogsh: of raisin wine with a Hund: of Smyrnas, & half D⁰ of Malagas: put to them in the tun-tub 27 Gallons of water.

13. Made an Annual-bed for the biggest one-light frame with 6 barrows of hot dung, & one of weeds: laid on the mould six inches deep. Finished-off, & raked very smooth the bastion, & sowed it very thick with rye-grass, & white clover. Sowed yᵉ bare places in the fields, & orchard with the same. Planted two rows of slips of a very fine sort of double-bloody-wall-flower from my Dame Scot's of Harting. Made the ground very mellow with lime-rubbish. Sowed a plot of Holy-oak-seed, & leek-seed. Planted some rose-campions, & Columbines in the new Garden. A perfect summer's day, that fetched the beds finely to their heat after such gluts of rain.

Saw seven swallows, the first this Year, playing about James Knight's House.

My great Dutch-Cucumbers come-up in one of the Cantaleupe-boxes almost every seed.

14. Sowed the annual Bed with African, & French Marrygolds, purple, & white Asters, and pendulous Amaranths.

Planted a potatoe-bed with fine large potatoes cut in pieces, which came from Swarraton: three rows a Yard from each other. Put half barrow of loam into each Cantaleupe-light.

16. Cut brace of Cucumbers: the second time of cutting.

Sowed everlasting pease, & wild-*Lathyrus* from the Lythe; soaked the seeds in water two nights, & a day: Dwarf-sunflowers; Nasturtiums; Tree-primroses; Rhubarb; Boorcole, red, & green; & savoys.

Dressed Artichokes.

Earthed Cantaleupe hills for the first time: examined into the hills, & found the bed unexpectedly warm: no loam burnt, but very hot. Gave a pretty deal of water. Plants in general thrive, & throw-out runners. The turfs at bottow very useful.

Very cutting, March-like weather.

17. Cut brace of Cucumbers.

Very stormy, cold weather.

16. Heard the first nightingale in my fields.

On my return on the 28 from Oxōn I found the Cantaleupe-plants in good Condition; several of the runners had three or four Joints apiece. The three hills of Waverley-plants much more gross, & strong than any of the Armenian: tho' the last are in a

promising way. Stop'd-down the runners, & cut away some
plants, where very thick. The bed very hot. One hill quite
destroyed by a Grub: John destroyed the Grub, & transplanted-
out a fresh pot in the Hill.

Cut this day the twentieth Cucumber: many more growing in
succession.

Cutting east-wind for some days.

30. Made five hills in the new Garden for Hand-glasses, three with
two barrows of hot dung apiece, & two with two apiece, for the
large white-Dutch-Cucumbers.

Some of the Cantaleupes have a shew for bloom: their hills
have been earthed twice. Sowed more balsoms in pots: the first
sowing sadly drawn.

Stuck the dwarf-early-pease with sticks out of ye faggots.

†Feb: 12. From Farmer Kelsey 3 loads of Dung. p^d
           From F: Berriman 4 loads. p^d of my own one: 1. p^d
March 13. From Farmer Parsons p^d 5 loads.
       14. Farmer Berriman 5 loads p^d of my own pd seven.
           Farmer Kelsey 3 loads p^d
April 2.   Farmer Kelsey 3 loads. p^d
           Parsons . . 3 loads p^d of my own two. p^d
           Berriman . . 2 loads. p^d
June 1.   Keldy . . . 4 loads p^d of my own 3 p^d
       5. Berriman . . 5 loads. p^d

MAY   1. Pulled-away the Hedge round the fir-quincunx, & hoed the
               Ground clean.
           2. The Hanger out in full leaf; but much banged about by the
               Continual strong East-wind that has blown for many days. The
               buds, & blossoms of all trees much injured by the wind. The
               ground parch'd, & bound very hard. The cold air keeps the
               nightingales very silent. No vegetation seems to stir at present.
               Disbudded some of the vines: the buds are about an Inch long.
           3. Made second annual bed with 6 barrows of Grass; & weeds only;
               no dung.
               Planted-out the five hand-glasses with the great white-Dutch-
               Cucumbers; 4 plants in a hill. The plants are pretty much drawn.
               This evening the vehement east-wind seems to be abated; & the
               air is soft, & cloudy. Ground bound like a stone.
           4. Sowed a pint, four rows, of small dwarf white-kidney-beans in
               the lower field-garden.
               Earthed the Cantaleupes the third time: found all the plants in
               a very flourishing way, & the fibres extended to the very outsides
               of the hills. Cut-away the plants to one in some of the hills; & left
               two in some, stopping down the worst plant very short towards

---

†Notes inserted where one notebook ends and a new one is started for the
second part of the year.

the bottom of the runners, for experiment sake, to see what the small wood about the stems will do. Some of the plants offer for male bloom.

Saw the first Redstart, & Cherrysucker.

Sowed about two doz: of the large white-Dutch-Cucumber-seeds for ye latter handglasses: the first sowing got full tall, & big.

Delicate soft rain all the afternoon, & all night, which soaked the Ground well to the roots of all vegetables.

5.   Fine Growing weather.

Several of the Cantaleupes have male blossoms fully expanded.

7.   Disbudded all the vines according to Hit. Almost every shoot shows bloom. Housed 21 barrows of the last prepared Cantaleupe loam: by means of the late rains in [it] is in most delicate order, & crumbles quite to dust.

9.   Berriman sowed Baker's Hill with Barley, & after it 8 pounds of Clover, & two bushels of white-seed, or Rye Grass. The Ground cold, & cloddy, & pretty full of daisey-roots, & grass, & not in very fine order. Added since 8 p^{ds} more of Clover.

10.   Several Cantaleupe-plants shew fruit, & grow away at a great rate. Pricked-out the annuals into the second hot-bed. Fine showery, growing weather.

12.   Gave the Cantaleupe-hills a full barrow of loam each: the fourth time of earthing. Cut away the plants to one on a hill.

14.   One Cantaleupe-fruit in full bloom. Made three hills for large white Cucumbers in Turner's Garden.

15.   Sowed the second pint of french-beans, large white Dutch: soaked them in water over night.

18.   Sowed a Crop of white, green, & black Coss-lettuce.

All my Savoy-seed, & Boor-cole fails this Year: not one plant appears.

20.   Strong sun-shine for many days, & a sharp east-wind. cold white dews in the mornings. Our clay ground as hard as a stone. This burning Sun, as usual, makes the Cantaleupes not look quite right: most of the fruit, as soon as it appears, turns yellow. The single fruit, that is out of bloom, not likely to stand.

The Dwarf french-beans are come-up pretty well. The lettuce that stood the winter are finely loav'd.¶

This unkind weather stops the setting of ye Cucumbers.

21.   Earthed the Cantaleupes the last time within their boxes. Finding the Cantaleupes much exhausted, & dryed by the fierce heat of the Sun, & the dry air, I watered them all over, leaves & all, with one small pot of water. The leaves all hang-down, & have a dry, paper-like feel, & look woolly; & the fruit all turns yellow. I remember they had all just the same appearance at this time last Year, the sun-shine & east-wind being as vehement.

Planted 100 of late Cabbages.

26.   The burning, sunny weather continues. The Gardens suffer much by the drought.

29.   Frequent showers.

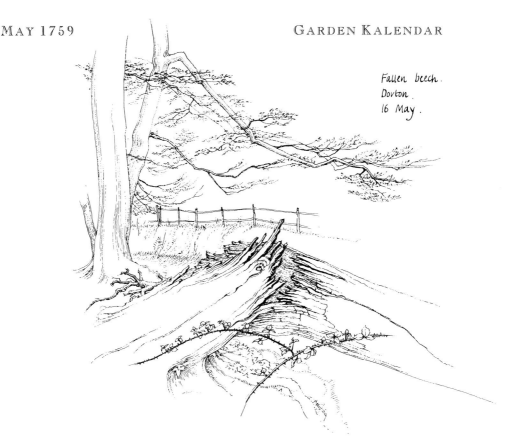

Fallen beech.
Dovton.
16 May.

The watering the Cantaleupes twice over yᵉ leaves seemed to
refresh them very much; but has occasioned one of Mʳ Hunter's
plants to grow a little mouldy at a Joint on one of the leaders near
the stem. So that water, tho' never so much wanted, is dangerous
near the stem.

The Armenian plants in general have small leaves, & vines: &
one in particular is so fine, & wire-drawn that one would imagine
it would never be able to carry any fruit to perfection. The rest
are healthy, & are disposed very regularly in their frames; & are
full of fruit. No fruit set yet.

Took off the Glasses from yᵉ early Cucumbers, & annuals to
give them yᵉ benefit of the showers.

28: 29.　　Housed four loads of peat in most excellent dry order. The
uncommon dryness occasions some waste by making the bats¶
crumble.

Gathered two scarlet strawberries.

The early beans have large pods: the early pease are well
blown.

30.　　The rain on the 29ᵗʰ very heavy for some Hours; so as to make
the Cart-way run. Raked all the rough-dug ground that was, 'till
moistened, like an heap of stones. Prick'd a plot of Celeri.

31.　　Sowed a pint more of large French-beans. The first sowings
strangely devoured by snails. Tull gathered a bowl-dish three
quarters full in one evening; & still the plants were almost

covered with them ye next. Cold winds, & frosty nights since the rain.

Hoed the strawberries that were planted last Autumn, & filled-up the vast cracks in their beds. At least half the Autumn-planted pine-strawberries are dead.

The scarlet will have some fruit; & so will the few plants of Collison's. The Nova Scotia will not bear this Year. Stringed the bearing pine-strawberries, which are full of bloom.

The Autumn-sown Capuchin, & Brown-Lettuce, now in high perfection. I have a very poor Crop of Coss-Lettuce this Spring.

JUNE	1.	Distant thunder, & fine showers all the evening, & part of the night.
MAY	31.	John tacked all the vines for the first time this Year according to
JUNE	1: 2.	Hitt. Those vines that were dressed in that method last Year, are now full of fruit: those that have been trained only this Year have little, or none.

Frequent good showers. The ground is now finely soaked.

Continued picking vast quantities of slugs from the french-beans, which are in a poor way.

3. Continual heavy showers all night, & all day. The Ground is now well soaked.

5. Lined-out the Cantaleupe-bed with twelve dung-carts of hot dung. The bed is now 12 feet broad, & 40 feet long. Continual showers all day: so that no loam could be laid on ye bed, but what was already housed in the earth-house.

The Fig-tree has plenty of fruit, which grows apace.

5. Such a violent Rain, & wind all the evening, & most part of the night that they broke-down, & displaced the pease, & beans, & most of the flowers; & tore the hedges, & trees, & beat down several of the shrubs.

6. Continual rain all day. The lining of the Cantaleupe-bed, which is not yet earthed, in danger of losing it's Heat by being so thoro'ly soaked.

8. Earthed the lining of the Cantaluepe-bed, & raised the frames to the top of the earth. The Waverley plants had filled the frames with their roots: the fibres of ye Armenian sort had not extended themselves so much.

Sowed a pint more of dwarf-kidney-beans in the room of those that were devoured by snails. Fine summer weather.

Turned-down the three forward basons of Cucumbers from out their Hand-glasses.

9. Gathered first beans, a large Mess.

10. Fine soft weather for some days; now a soaking rain.

11. Finished-off the borders in the new Garden, by cleansing, raising, & laying a good coat of fine peat-dust, finely sifted, in order to make them light, & dry.

Sowed the first plot of Endive; & a plot of Lettuce, green & white Coss.

Molehill in Dorton.
7 June.

12. In the Evening began a vast storm which continued all the night, & tore & destroyed the things in the Gardens worse than the former: it broke down vast boughs in the Hedges, & had like to have overturned the Limes in the Butcher's Yard. If the Annuals had been planted-out they must have been quite whipped to pieces. The hedges look bare, & unsightly by being lashed, & banged by the wind: & the Ground is strawed with leaves.

13. The middle Waverley-Cantaleupe has some decayed, rotten runners: Quae: if occasioned by those two waterings all over their leaves in that scorching weather in May.
     The leaves of the Armenian-Cantaleupes have a much blacker aspect than those of the Waverley.

14. Planted the empty basons in the field, & two borders in the New-Garden with annuals, French, & Afr: Marrygolds, Sunflowers, Nasturtiums, pendulous Amaranths, & China Asters.
     Hot growing weather: vast showers about.

15. Planted 150 savoys from Alton.

16: 18. Lined-out the Cantaleupe bed with loam very deep quite down to yᵉ Ground on each side: the fibres may now, if they please, extend themselves 16 feet. The plants look in a most thriving way, & are loaded with fruit; but they hold-off from setting strangely: no one set yet. Cut-off a great branch of one of the Waverley Cantaleupes, that was quite rotten.

19. Planted-out Crop of leeks; & some late Coss: Lettuce.
     Furious hot summer weather.

20. To be planted pint of french-beans: & an early row of Celeri to be trenched.
     All the former Crops of french-beans like to come to nothing.

23. Called-in upon Mᵣ Miller at Chelsea, ¶ & found he had 18 lights of Armenian-Melons in excellent order. There were about two brace, & half of fruit to a light, full-grown, & very rough, & black. He pushes his lights, it seems, quite down in dry weather: & says the defect of male bloom is owing to yᵉ seeds being of some age.

30. On my Return from Sunbury I found my Cantaleupes in very bad plight indeed: two of the Waverley plants were quite rotten, & corrupted at the stem; & one of the Armenians, the day after I

came home, withered away, tho' perfectly sound; & dyed as if eaten-off at the root: tho' upon search no grub could be found in the mould. And what is stranger, no one fruit was set upon any plant; tho' hundreds have dropp'd away. There certainly is a want of male bloom in the Armenians to a degree: but then the Waverley plants over abounded, & yet cast all their fruit.

I found a vast crop of pease, thro' the dripping season; & green pease soup every day. The first hand glass-cucumbers are in full bearing: I intend to save 4 more (the large white Dutch) for Seed. The small forward beans have an unusual Crop. The fourth & fifth crop of french-beans like to come to good.

JULY

2. Planted-out a vast bed of Holy-oaks.

6. Not one Cantaleupe set yet.

Planted-out about 50 Polyanths, raised this spring from Seed given me by Mr Hale.

7. Finished my Hay-rick in most excellent order. The weather has been so perfectly hot, & bright for these five days past that my Hay was all cut, & made in that time. The Crop was so great that Kelsey's people made 8 carryings of it: & the burden in the great mead was supposed to be considerably greater than ever was known. To my own stock I added two tons from Farmer Lassam, which in all make a considerable rick.

Finished cutting the hedges round Baker's Hill.

21. On my return from Dene on this day, I found I had but one Cantaleupe set, & that a fig-shaped one, not likely to come to good. The plants are in uncommon vigour, & grow unaccountably, & are full of fruit still; but strangely deficient in male-bloom. The void spaces in the frames are quite filled-out with the remaining plants.

Mr Cane's Cantaleupes were all burn-up, with a noble Crop on them, about ten days before the fruit would have been ripe. He had a fine Crop: but the intense heats scorch'd-off all the fibres thro' his light, dusty earth.

Tull planted-out Endives, & lettuce in my absence; & pronged-up the bulbous roots against Parsons's, planting annuals in their room. John trimmed & nailed the vines in a very handsome manner according to Hit. Those vines that have been managed in that manner for two Years, have a noble crop of fruit very forward. My Crops of beans, & pease are very extraordinary this Year. The annuals against the broad walk in the new-Garden are uncommonly large.

23. Gathered 36 Cucumbers. Earth'd-up the Chinks round the hand-glasses with melon-loam.

Unusual hot summer-weath for three weeks past. Wheat-harvest is begun in some places.

26. Pulled-up an other of the Armenian Cantaleupes, which was rotten at Stem. So now I have lost four plants out of nine.

The fruit begins to set now at a vast rate on the remaining

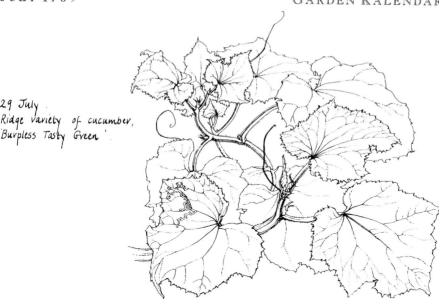

29 July
Ridge variety of cucumber,
Burpless Tasty Green

plants; as fast as ever they fell-off before.

    The hot vehement season continues: the ground is wonderfully burnt.

31.   Now a great rain after several weeks drought.

AUGUST   1.   On Examination I found above 20 brace of Cantaleupes set: about 10 brace on one of the Armenian plants; about 8 brace on the only remaining Waverly plant; about 3 brace on an other Armenian; 2 brace (one a full-grown fruit) on an other: & one Armenian is quite barren. The Waverley plant is infected with the rot that destroyed the rest, which I endeavour to stop by wiping, & dust. It is observable that those plants that bear so prodigiously are those which (their fellows being rotten) have the space of two or three lights to run in. Had the fruit set in this manner a month or six weeks ago (when it all dropped off) there had been a noble early Crop.

10.   The first-set Cantaleupe, tho' unpromising at first, now a fine, beautiful large fruit just like Miller's. The rest of later date come-on apace. Prodigious hot, sunny weather.

    Sowed half pound of spinage mixed with Capuchin, & Dutch-Lettuce, & white-turnep-Radishes. Trenched four rows more of Celeri: & planted-out 150 more Savoys.

    Tyed about 20 of the Endives.

    Sowed a little more Endive-seed.

14.   Lost the third, & last Waverley-Cantaleupe with a Crop of 4 brace of fruit on it. I have now lost five plants out of nine. The four Armenians now remaining have 10 brace of fruit likely to come to good. Pulled-off two brace & half of fruit, some of a considerable size.

    Hot dry weather still.

16.   Sowed a Crop of Coss-Lettuce, & Endive to stand the winter.

Trimm'd the side-shoots of the vines for the last time. The Clusters are unusually large, & forward.

Perfect Summer-weather, but cooler.

27. Cut a vast Quantity of White-Dutch-Cucumbers. One that was young & eatable weighed 2 pounds 5 ounces, & measured 12 inch: & half in length.

The Canker continues to spread among the Cantaleupes, & is likely to destroy plants full of beautiful fruit within a fortnight of being in perfection.

28. Planted on the bank several large white Lilly-roots, Crown-Imperials, & double white-rockets. Cut the first Endive.

SEPTEMBER 4. Planted some tree primeroses on the bank.

It has been very wet, blowing weather for several days past.

8. Tyed-up about two doz: of the best bunches of Grapes in Crape-bags.¶

11. Cut ye first Cantaleupe: it was finely emboss'd, & weighed 3 p^{ds} 11 ounc: but when it came to be cut-up it had hardly any flesh, & was rank, & filthy.

Tyed-up more Endive.

Uncommon sunny, sultry day.

15. Tyed-on 18 more Crape-bags on the best bunches of Grapes.

Fine dry weather with pretty cold dews.

29. All the Cantaleupes cut. Not one in perfection; tho' many were finely embossed, & looked wonderfully promising. The Canker, I suppose, had prevented their drawing any nourishment, & getting any thickness of flesh.

Fine dry weather for a long time past, & the roads perfectly good.

The small bunches of Grapes are very good: the large ones not yet ripe against the wall.

OCTOBER 1. Tyed-up last Crop of Endive.

The largest Cantaleupe was finely embossed, & tho' almost all rind, weigh'd 4 pounds 2 ounces.

3. Now a vast rain after many weeks fine Autumn weather.

5. Gathered the two first bunches of bag'd Grapes: they were a little mouldy; but the sound parts of the bunches were perfectly ripe, & sweet.

8. Now perfect summer weather again after one wet day.

The Grapes in the bags unusually fine; & both bunches, & single Grapes are as large again as usual. It is to be observed that as this new Culture swells the berries so much; they are apt in this Cluster-sort to press too hard on each other, & prevent ripening, & occasion mouldiness: therefore if the grapes were thinn'd out the beginning of the summer with the points of a pair of scissors, it would certainly prove an advantage.

10. Planted two rows of Crocuss along the borders under the dining-room windows: both borders, especially that that hath the vines in

it, were made very light, & mellow with an abundance of Sand, & blacksmith's cinders.

Weeded, & cut down the leaves of the strawberries; & mended-out those beds that failed with the pine sort.

Now very dry, & warm: but there are great tokens of rain.

11.   Now great rains, & wind.

Tunn'd three quarters of an Hogsh: of raisin-wine. The Quantity of raisins in the mash-vat were 1 hund: & half Smyrnas, & 3 Quarters of an hundred of Malagas. The Quantity of water put-up was 18 3 gallon-buckets; which made sufficient Quantity without any squeesing. The Colouring was 14 Quarts of Elder-syrop. The weather was so hot that it stood but eleven days to ferment in the vat. The elder-Juice was boiled-up with 14 pounds of sugar.

16.   Finished-off the bank in the new-Garden, & planted the front row of the additional part with pinks both red, & pheasant-eyed: laid it with turf some days agon.

On measuring the great oak in the meadow, which was measured in yᵉ spring, I found it to be encreased in girth about one inch.

18.   The mornings begin to be frosty, yet yᵉ Grapes continue in high perfection.

19.   Finished a broad brick-walk thro' yᵉ new wicket at the end of the dining-room; & carryed a narrow one up by the side of yᵉ pitching to the orchard-walk; rectifyed the broken pitching, & turned the gutter at the brew-house door, so as to get a 12 inch border four feet long for a white-muscadine-vine.

22.   Planted a row of Coss-lettuce touching the wall along the vine-border under the dining-room window to stand the winter. Planted a row of Holyoaks against the boards of the wood-house.

24.   Planted the irregular slip without the new wicket in the Garden with first two rows of Crocuss; a row of pinks; several sorts of roses; persian Jasmine, & yellow Dᵒ several sorts of Asters; French-Willows;¶ a curious sort of bloody wallflowers; Double Campanulas white, & blue; double daisies; & a row against the hedge of good rooted Laurustines. Planted the back row of the part of the bank newly lengthened-out with blue, & white Double Campanulas; & the border under the dining-room window with the bloody-Double-wallflowers. Planted a bason in the field with french-willows.

Planted many dosens more of Coss-lettuce against the buttery-wall, & down yᵉ wall against the Yard.

25.   Planted a large layer of the musk-rose from Mʳ Budd against the boards of the old barn.

Wet season after very dry weather.

26.   Trimm'd, & tack'd the bottoms of the vines according to Hit: the lower parts of those under the Dining-room window are deficient in wood, till more can be got from yᵉ stems. Began curving two

shoots in order to reduce two of the vines to regular shapes from the bottom by degrees.

NOVEMBER 5. Planted my Hyacinths, Narcissus's, Ranunculuss, Tulips, Crown Imperials, & Anemonies in the border against Parsons's. It had been trenched very deep with a good Quantity of rotten tan, & was in perfect dry order when the roots were put-in.

Planted a small thriving larch at the east corner of Baker's hill; two well-grown Provence-roses in the field-shrubbery; & two Monthly roses in the orchard walk; all from North-Warnboro'.

Fine dry sunny weather. Planted two rows of hardy lettuce under the filbert hedge against Parsons's.

6. Trimmed & tack'd the fig-tree, leaving a leading bough in the middle to fill the wall by degrees quite up to the eaves. This tree is full of young wood, & fills the wall well; & may be carry'd by a second stage according to Hit up to the tiles.

Planted a number of Goose-berries & Currans from Mr Johnson, good plants, in the orchard-walk, & among the rasps.

The Grapes lasted in good perfection 'till the beginning of Novemr those that were hung-up in the study¶ are very sweet, but shrivelled-up like raisins, notwithstanding a grape was stuck on the stem of each Cluster.

12. Plunged the seven pots of Pyram: Camp: in the border against Parsons's under ye Filbert-hedge. Planted a nursery-border of small bulbous-roots. Dug-up a decaying Cluster-pine, & parsley-elder in the shrubbery, & put a two-thorned-*Acacia*, & Judas-tree in their room. A most delicate summer-like day.

14. Transplanted the striped-*Epilobium* into a fresh bason. Planted about 20 fraxinellas, seedlings from Mr Budd, in a nursery. Planted several Laurels in the gaps of the Hedges round Baker's Hill.

The potatoes, raised from about 14 large ones cut in pieces, turned-out a fine Crop of about 3 Bushels: several single ones weigh'd about a pound. Put-by about 30 of the finest as a supply for a crop next year.

Planted some cuttings of parsley-elder, with some Cuttings of fine white Currans.

15. Planted in the new-garden two standard-Duke-Cherries;¶ an espalier-Orleans-plumb; an espalier-green-gage plumb; a duke-cherry against the north-west-wall of the brewhouse; & a standard muscle-plumb in the orchard. These trees came from Forster of North Warnboro', & seemed to be good in their kind; were planted the day they were taken out of the nursery, in basons, which being prepared before, were in excellent crumbling order.

16. Planted 3 pints, 7 rows of small early beans in the lower field-garden.

— 1760 —

MAY   17.   On my return this day (after six months absence at Lyndon, & London) I found my Garden in general in very good order, considering the long drouth this spring.

                         The Cucumbers in full bearing, but stunted in their vines. The Cantaleupe-melons in good condition, & just shewing fruit; & the Succados very stocky plants. The Asparagus-beds are got stronger & bore wonderfully this spring. All the kitchen-crops are in good plight: & the Coss, & hardy lettuce that stood the winter, very fine. The Bergamot-pear, & knobbed-russet grafts like to take.

            18.   Fierce storms of Hail, which batter'd the vine shoots¶ at the end of the Dining-room very much. They were very forward this sunny spring: the leaves were cut full of Holes, & several shoots were beaten quite off the trees. The persicaria-plants in the border under suffered much.

            28.   Dame Turner, & Girls weeded all the brick walls. Prick'd-out first Celeri, & prick'd-out, & planted a good many Savoys.

JUNE   4.   Furious hot weather for several days. The pease, & beans kept back for want of moisture. Some Cantaleupes in bloom. Covered all the inside of the boxes with wheat-straw to keep the sun from drying the mould; & to prevent much watering. Tull employed in cleansing the garden from weeds. The vine-shoots grow in a most extraordinary manner, & are full of fruit.

            5.   Planted some persicarias in the New-garden border.

                         Out of one vine-shoot, which was procur'd from the old stem of a vine last summer; & being exceeding strong was laid-in five feet long, arise as many shoots this spring as produce 14 bunches of Grapes.

                         Fine rain all night.

            6.   Planted-out all the persicarias; & about 2 doz: of the slips of the double bloody-wallflowers.

                         Moist, hot, growing weather.

            7.   Lined-out the melon-bed very strongly, more than three feet on each side, with eleven loads of dung, & a large Quantity of weeds.

                         Planted out a plot of late Cauliflowers.

            9.   Gather'd first strawberries, scarlet, & Nova Scotia.

                         Cut the crop of rye-grass, & clover in Baker's-hill: a good Crop.

            10.   Planted 22 basons in the field with annuals, french & Afr: Marrigolds, China-Asters, pendulous Amaranths, & sun-flowers.

            11.   The vines at the end of the dining-room in bloom; about three weeks sooner than usual: occasioned, I suppose, by the very sunny season.

            12.   Housed the Baker's-hill-hay in excellent order: there

were three decent loads.

14. John finished his second tacking & thinning the vines: those against the Yard shew prodigious strength; but are not yet blown.

Dry, settled weather.

Planted annuals in the home Garden.

15. Wood-strawberries¶ came-in in plenty.

16. Set Tull to earth the Cantaleupe-bed all over to the Ground very thick.

The Cantaleupes are full of fruit in bloom, & now shew a tolerable share of male bloom.

The vines begin to blow against the Yard. Stopp'd-down the shoots of the vine over the entry-door.

17. Sowed first endive-seed.

A fine rain after scorching weather.

Three vine-layers (last Year's shoots) have produced between them 39 bunches of Grapes.

19. It being dripping weather, planted & pricked-out plenty of Savoys, & Celeri; trench'd out one row of Celeri; & tyed-up several spring-sown Coss-lettuce. Those that stood the winter are are all gone to seed.

Cold frosty air.

The muscadine vine-cuttings in the gutter thrive well; & so do the cuttings of the same sort, & of the cluster-vine in the nursery.

The grafts of the Bergamot-pear, & knobbed-russet from Ringmer take well.

This cold, windy weather likely to injure the vine-bloom at the end of the Dining-room.

The Cantaleupe-bed earth'd all over down to the Ground in an unusual thick manner.

The Nova-Scotia-strawberry a good bearer, & ripe even before the scarlet.

20. Planted-out leeks, & Boorcole; & sowed a plot of turneps. Continual showers.

21. On looking over the Cantaleupes, found one fruit set, & more in a promising way. Some few bunches on the dining-room end have some Grapes set on them. Showers.

23. The Succado-melons (of which I have three basons in the space of two lights) have got several fruit in full bloom.

Vast rains from the East.

26. Great rains.

27. Sowed a small plot of Coss-lettuce.

28. Agreed with John Wells to purchase the upper part of Lassam's orchard.

Stopp'd part of the vines against the yard, which are in bloom.

JULY   1.   Finish'd stopping the vines.

                2.   Sowed second Crop of Endive, & more lettuce.

                3.   Sultry dry weather for three days: vast rains, & thunder in the night.

Planted-out two rows of seedling-polyanths all along the orchard-border.

New-planted two basons of the cold cucumbers: all the cumbers are in a strange way, have no vines; & are likely to come to little. The complaint is general.

                6.   Vast rains, & a flood.

                7.   Clear'd-out the melon-frames that were quite choak'd with vines: not above 4 or five Cantaleupes set: the biggest fruit about the size of a hen's egg: the Succades shew no disposition for setting yet. Rain still.

Finish'd cutting the tall hedges.

Some grapes as big as young pease: all the bunches in bloom, & yield a smell that may be distinguish'd at many Yards distance.

              14.   Cut both the meads; a decent Crop. The weather was so hot, & sunny that we carry'd most of the Hay the next day; & finish'd the rick in excellent order the third.

              18.   Planted-out endive, a large plot, in the field-garden.

              20.   The vehement sunny weather for these 8, or 9 days past has brought-on the annuals strangely; & forwarded the white Cucumber-plants sown in the middle of May so much that they seem likely now to come to good.

              21.   Trench'd-out a Crop of Celeri in Turner's Garden.

The first hand-glass white-Cucumbers all perish'd with the blight.

Melons make out lamely: one Cantaleupe full-grown; no Succade set.

Trimm'd the vines the third time. The grapes swell this hot weather.

The tree-primroses in full bloom; & are a shewey proper plant for large outlets.

Scented geraniums, in a window at the Wakes. July.

| AUGUST | 1. | Returning from Dene I found the Melons in a poor way: but two Cantaleupes full-grown, & those small; & only five or six more just set; & only one Succade set. |

The late-sown white-Cucumbers begin to bear a little; the first are quite wither'd away. An universal blight has this summer more or less affected all the vegetable world. The grapes to the Yard are very thinly set: those to the South-west are thick set, & very forward; but the Bunches are small.

Tull in my absence trench'd four rows of Celeri in Turner's Garden; & planted-out a Crop of Savoys. No rain for three weeks & three days 'till Aug: 1: & then showers.

4. Sowed a box of Mezereon-seed.¶

7. Planted-out a Crop of Coss-lettuce to come-in in Septemʳ
Continual showers; & the Corn begins to grow.

9. The Succade-melons now set apace.
The white cucumbers bear but poorly.

10. Vast rains.

11. Cantaleupe-melons set now; but are seemingly too late for ripening.
Sowed Coss, & Dutch lettuce to stand the winter. Sowed a quarter of a pound of spinage mixed with white turnep-radishes.
Put the bulbous roots in paper-bags, & hung them in the lumber-garret. They are vastly increased, especially the Hyacinths.

14. Trimm'd the side-shoots of the vines the fourth time: the fruit thin on the bunches.
Fine harvest-weather for several days past, with cold drying north winds.
The white-cucumber-plants, which produced one fair large fruit; now show nothing but spotted, sickly ones. The early bed bears pretty tolerably still.

18. Cut more than half the second Crop of Clover on Baker's hill, which by reason of yᵉ dripping weather could not be housed till yᵉ 23rd. There was one good load in pretty good order.

23. Some of the Clusters of Grapes against the end of the dining-room begin to change colour.

27. Cut Miller's first Armenian-Cantaleupe: by no means a curious fruit.
Brought three plants of curious Celeriac from Waltham: the leaves are jagged like curl'd parsley.

SEPTEMBER 1. Housed the remaining Clover in Baker's Hill; which, considering the showery season, was got in good order.

2. Found several large Cantaleupes in a neglected frame.
Tyed-up the first Endives, & late Coss-lettuce; & earth'd-up the early row of Celeri quite to the top.

8. Gathered the first bunch of Grapes from the end of the dining-room, which was quite ripe: those on the Yard-side are but just turning colour. My Grapes in general are but thinly set.

Vine in herb garden,
growing with Southernwood,
August

Plenty of figs in good ripe order.

Curious summer weather for many days.

11. Gather'd the first Mulberry that my tree ever produced: it was very sweet; & good, but small. There are some more on the tree.

12. Cut the first Succade-mellon; it was very weighty for it's size, which is always small. It proved very fleshy & high-flavoured, & seems a valuable sort.

Cloudless skies, strong sunshine, & strong East-winds for many days, which rise & fall with the Sun. Fruits ripen at a vast rate; & the roads are perfectly dry.

Tull & John are busy every day in grubbing, paring, & burning the new-purchased Garden; & harrowing-out the couch-grass. The weeds & turf have produced already many bushels of ashes; & will soon be burnt-up if this dry weather lasts.

The Persicarias are vastly large, & fine. All the annuals are come to a good size.

13. Tyed-up 20 more Endives.

Gather'd two bunches of Grapes, which were perfectly sweet & ripe. Very sunny weather still.

26. The Succado-melons now come apace.

Vast rains, thunder, & lightening for 8 to 10 days; & a likelihood of great floods.

Grapes in great plenty, & perfection.

29. Cut a brace of Succado melons.

Gather'd the Cadilliac pears, about half a bushel: three parts in four were blown-down.

Vast rains, & storms.

OCTOBER 1. Used the first Celeri.

2. Cut the last Succados, & a good-looking Cantaleupe. Continual rains; & frequent thunder still. The labourers work at the Haha when the weather permits.

14. Continual wet weather for a month: so that the fallows are full of water,¶ & no corn can be sown.

15. Transplanted six Geraniums into six penny-pots to stand the winter.

The new part of the Garden quite cleared from trees, & stools of trees.

Grapes in plenty, & perfection.

18. Turned-out seven pots of Pyram: Campanulas into a mellow, sandy Border.

22. Transplanted a White-Muscadine vine of Mr Budd's sort into the border under ye Dining-room window. John annointed it with Dr Hill's mummy,¶ & planted it a Cutting last March; & now it was a strong plant, & had a quantity of long fibres. In the summer it made a shoot of about four feet, & was now headed down to 4 or 5 buds.

No frosts yet.

24. Put the whites of 8 eggs, shells & all, with a little sand, to 3

quart:rs of an hogshead of raisin-wine, which would not draw fine. Put Quart of Brandy.

Grapes continue very good.

25. Received from M.rs Snooke a basket of swans-egg, Doyenne, White Buree, & Colmar-pears for a specimen: also some Crasans, & Spanish Boncrêtiens.

27. Took-up from the Laurustine-hedge about 40 layers: laid-down about as many more.

NOVEMBER 8. Began dressing the vines: found plenty of new wood in most places.

There have been a few smart frosts this autumn: but in general a continual run of wet weather for these six weeks past; & great floods.

10. Widened the grass-plot towards the wall-nut-tree.

The farmers have been greatly hindered in their wheat-season by the rains; & will hardly be able to sow all their fallows.

12. Removed 8 black-cluster, & 6 muscadine-vines (which were planted Cuttings last April) into the sandy bed at the end of the Asparagus. Most of them were well rooted, & had made good shoots. Set the Geranium-pots in y.e Garret-window.

15. Continued to curve the leading shoots of the two vines against the end of the Dining-room, which in one Year more will be at their full length, & may be reduced to a single stem.

The vines against the yard abound in Young wood of vast length, & will have fresh Horizontals every where, without bending back any shoots.

18. Planted-in between the rows of Crocuss round the dining-room 100 Scotch-Crocuss, & 50 double Snow-drops.

19. Planted the new bank with perennial sunflowers, rose-campions, tree-primeroses, & several sorts of Asters.

Planted a bed of tulips, Hyacinths, *Ranunculus*, Anemonies, in a plot well-mellowed with lime-rubbish. A tolerable dry season for four or five days, after a glut of rain for many weeks. Dug the walks at the top & bottom of the new garden in order to prepare y.m for leveling.

22. Dug-up the double white rockets under the back of the melon-screen, & planted them on the end of the bank next the dining-room: planted with them some double white Campanulas.

Planted 20 double daffodils near the other bulbs. Laid a shoot of the Moss-provence rose, binding it round very hard in two places with wire twisted very tight, in order to make it take root.

25. New-planted a bason of red-martagons: planted some Crown-Imperials, red Martagons & Jonquils on the bank: planted the ofset bulbs, & roots in a nursery bed.

Finished the vines.

DECEMBER 8. Sent 30 Coss-lettuces to M.r Etty's little wall'd Garden to winter.

16. Brewed half Hogsh: of milder strong-beer with only five bush: of

malt, & two p^{ds} & half of Hops: made at the same time half hogsh: & 12 gallons of small beer.

17. Trimm'd & tack'd the fig-tree, which is full of young wood; & laid a long tender shoot from the stool to the Corner of the House to supply that part of the tree with fresh wood.

Very mild growing weather yet for the time of Year.

19. Made half Hogsh: of raisin-wine with one Hund: of Smyrnas, & half Hund: of Malagas; & put to them 13 buckets of water, each bucket containing three Gallons.

31. The Year went-out, as it had continued ever since winter began, in a very mild way. There have been scarce more than two smart night's frost, & those early in Autumn: so that the Grass in pastures has kept springing the whole season; & the early, & hardy flowers, & plants are very forward. There has been a pretty deal of gentle rain; & now & then soft sunny days like April, which brought the flies, & other Insects out of their lurking holes.

— 1761 —

JANUARY 1. Transplanted a polyanth-Narcissus, many of whose Cups were in bloom, into a large pot to set within doors.

2. Finish'd a new wicker melon-screen, & lin'd it well with straw, & made a border about four feet broad under it, & dosed the earth well with sand, & some ashes, & dung; intending to make it a border for early Crops, & to plant some Espalier pears along it, & to run a narrow brick-walk by the side of it.

3. Brought-in two loads of hot dung for the seedling-Cucumber-bed; & many loads of stones for the Haha. The ground treads sadly for want of frost.

Sowed a long row of persicaria-seed under ye dining-room window. The wall-flowers begin to blow. Put some Cucumber-seeds in a pot by the parlour fire.

5. Made the seedling Cucumber-bed. Warm foggy weather, with a very high Barometer.

6. Tunn'd the wine: there did not run-out sufficient to fill the barrel by one bucket-full; which was squees'd out of the Chaff.

8. Earth'd the Cucumber bed with mellow, sanded mould. The bed in fine moderate order.

10. Sowed about 40 Cucumber-seeds. The bed promises well.

10. Put seven bottles of rasp: syrop to ye raisin-wine.

12. Tunn'd 8 gallons of good small raisin-wine in the vinegar barrel. What vinegar is bottled, is very fine, & good.

14. Plenty of Cucumbers up in the Hot-bed; & in the pot by the fire side.

Planted a row of Laurel-cuttings in the field-garden.

Hot-bed goes-on well: sunny weather for ye plants.

15. Sowed a Crop of radishes, lettuce, & Carrots on the sanded border under the melon-screen.

Transplanted some Cucumber-plants that came-up apace.

17. Smart frost; which enabled me to plough the new garden after waiting the whole winter.

Put more Cucumber-seeds into the bed.

19. The frost continues: carted into the new Garden 20 loads of marl¶ well dissolved; 7 loads of lime-Rubbish, & soot from the Malt-house; & a load & half of ashes. The ground began to thaw towards noon, & was much trodden, & kneaded before the Job was done. Put the rubbish & ashes on the two lower Quarters, & the marl on the four upper ones.

24. Long the mason finish'd the dry wall of the Haha in the new garden, which is built of blue rags,¶ so massy, that it is supposed to contain double the Quantity of stone usual in such walls. Several stones reach into the bank 20 inches. The wall was intended to be 4 feet & an half high: but the labourers in sinking the ditch on inclining ground mistook the level, especially about the angle: so that at that part to bring it to a level it is 5 feet 8 inch: high, & 4 feet 6 inch: at the ends: an excellent fence against the mead, & so well fast'ned into the clay bank, that it looks likely to stand a long while. The workmanship, exclusive of carting the stones, cost 1: 8: 10.

24. Cucumbers thrive well, & shew a rough leaf. Misty, still weather with an high Barometer. John finish'd Mr Etty's wall-trees in 4 Jobs.

26. Sowed about 14 Succado-melon-seeds to plant an early melon-frame, if they succeed.

Cucumbers look finely; & begin to shew a second rough leaf.

Sloped, & finish'd-off the ditch of the terrass; & levell'd most of the terrass.

Spread the marle, & rubbish on the new garden: there is a good Coat of each.

Smart frosts for three or four days.

29. Frost continues very smart. Finished cutting all the Alleys thro' the new Garden; & levelled all the terrass as far as it can be, 'till it settles. Cleared away the roots of trees in the meadow.

30. Frost smarter than ever. Wheeled the dung that was left after paying the farmers out of the melon-ground. Trench'd a well-dung'd plot above the earth-house for melon-loam; & turned some old melon-loam. The heat in the Cucumber-bed declining, order'd the bed to be lined with 15 barrows of very hot-dung.

Beautiful rimes for several mornings on ye Hanger. It froze within to night.

31. Carted in 10 loads of Hot-dung for the bearing Cucumber-bed.

Succado-melons begin to appear.

Dug-out all the under-ground dung in ye melon-Ground, & levell'd the Area.

FEBRUARY 2. The over-fierce lining scalded all the plants. Sowed more seeds.

3. Potted the Succado-plants that were not much damaged.

Very high barometer, & settled fine weather. Sowed more Succado seeds.

5. Made the bearing Cucumber-bed with 10 loads of good dung: it is, I think, too deep; being four feet odd inch: behind, & 3 feet odd inch: before. The bed is made full early, as the plants are but just peeping out of ye ground: but the dung being brought-in for the forward plants would not keep without making-up.

6. Planted seven rows, about ⅞ of a Gallon of Winsor-beans in one of the middle quarters of my new Garden. This is the first crop in my new purchase, which was in so wet a condition as only to be fit for beans.

7. Last sown Succados, & Cucumbers come up apace.

9: 10. Levelled the terrass, & new walks so far that they will want but very small amendments before they are turfed. Fierce March-like winds from the west for many days, that had quite dry'd the Ground.

12. The wind turning suddenly to the north, last night was the fiercest frost this winter. Dug one of the lower new Quarters, which came up pretty well. Snowed hard all the Afternoon, & rain'd at night.

16. Put the mould on the Cucumber-bed, which seems now to be pretty mild.

Continual showers.

The first Succados have a perfect rough leaf. The second sowing are potted, & look pretty well.

19. Planted-out the Cucumbers in their bearing beds, five plants in an Hill: each plant has a fair rough leaf. The bed seems very mild. Heavy showers.

23. Sowed a dung-cart, & an half of ashes in the great mead. There was a very strong wind while they were sowing, which seem'd to carry away a great deal into the Air.

Sowed more Succados for fear of accidents; & some small early Cucumber-seed.

24. Made a seedling-Celeri-bed with one barrow of dung, & covered it with an hand-glass.

25: 26. Clear'd the meadow of faggots, & wood; & levell'd the Ground, where the hedge was grubb'd.

MARCH 2. Sowed 12 Waverley-Cantaleupe-seeds in one of the bearing Cucumber-frames.

4. Carted into the melon-ground ten loads of hot dung for the Succado-frame.

The Cucumbers thrive surprizingly, & have three Joints each. Earth'd-up the hills a little to day. The bed maintains a fine gentle, genial heat. The Succado melons thrive; & the forwardest begin to shew a Joint.

Continual stormy weather from ye west with small rain.

7. The Cantaleupes come-up well; every seed.

9: 10. Long finish'd the brick-walk along by the melon-screen; & Tull sowed the border with radishes, lettuce, & Carrots. Long made a large stone-drein also at the bottom of the new-garden across the walk into Lassam's ditch: it is so placed that in great floods the waters from every alley must run with a swift descent towards it.

10.   Cucumber plants thrive wonderfully, & begin to throw-out wires. Some have five Joints, & are stopp'd-down for runners.

     Stopp'd some of the forward Succades in pots.

     Sowed five more Waverley Cantaleupe seeds to supply in Case of accident.

     Planted about 200 Cabbage-plants in part of one of the middle new-quarters.

     An other levelling Job at the terrass.

     Frequent showers.

11.   Made the Succado-melon-bed with ten loads of dung for one three light frame. The bed is very stout; full four feet deep behind, & near three before. The frame & bed are more than six feet high.

     Planted some double bloody-wallflowers, from last year's Cuttings, in the border of the melon-screen.

     Planted the 12 Cantaleupe-plants in six pots.

     Frequent showers.

13.   One of the plants that was stopp'd down shows a Cucumber at the foot of a runner.

     The sun in a few minutes scalded Part of a leaf that touch'd the Glass.

14.   Mowed the Grass-plot the first time: there was a vast deal of Grass, which lined the Cucumber-bed.

     †Planted the following fruit-trees sent me by Murdoch Middleton: on the north side of the first lower quarter of my new Garden one Crasan-Burgamot pear; on the South side one Swan-egg Dᵒ on the north side of the second lower Quarter one Virgoleuse-pear; on the south side one Doyenne: at the two middle ends of the same Quarters two Green-gage plums & in the border of the melon-ground one Colmar-pear. All these trees are espaliers, & in good Condition, except the Doyenne-pear, which has a miserable tap-root with hardly any fibres. Some of the pears shew a little tendency to canker. Put a large quantity of stones, & rubbish at the bottom of every bason, & planted as high as possible.*

     Sowed a Crop of Carrots, parsneps, Coss-lettuce, Onions, radishes, & spinage, in the first lower Quarter of the new Garden; which raked, & crumbled in pretty good order.

16: 17: 18.   Finished leveling the terrass, & new walks; & dug the new borders, & Quarters. Fine still settled weather, with a rising Barometer, & wind to the East & North.

     The stopp'd Cucumbers have side-shoots with three Joints.

---

*Proved bad, and are changed.

†This entry was crossed out by GW, and his note added.

The five Cantalupe-seeds all up.

18. Sowed a gallon of dwarf marrowfat pease in one of the middle Quarters: they made just 9 rows at four feet apart, & exactly fill'd the quarter. The mould was hardly mellow enough to drill them; & they were covered-in with difficulty.

19. Dug the border at the back of the melon-screen, & planted a row of Holy oaks at five feet apart.

20. Earth'd-down the succade-bed; & put the hills into each light. Raised the Cucumber-frames. The plants are very large, & have vast leaves.

21. Sowed six large basons in the field, with double upright lark-spurs.
The sun at a few minutes neglect scorches the Cucumber leaves.

23. Turned the Succades out into their bed, which seems very mild. The best plants are forward, & show runners. Planted besides one or two very stocky plants in each hill, which never have been potted.
Cleared the Cucumber-bed of all pots; raised the frames, stopp'd the plants, & earth'd the bed out to the frames.
Fine sunny weather.
Four pots of succades left.
The Cantaleupes are very strong in their pots, & show a rough leaf.
Prong'd & raked the Asparagus-beds.
Watered the Cucumbers over ye leaves the first time.

25. Finish'd turfing the terrass, & new walks, which took-up 8 loads, & an half of turf, being each twelve feet wide; beside the slope of the terrass. Hot, dry, sunny weather, which makes the turf stare, & chop.¶
First cucumber blowed before any male bloom.
Transplanted out forward lettuce from ye wall.
Dress'd Rasps.

28. The Succade-bed was beginning to burn it's mould a little: put some fresh mould round the bottom of the hills.

26. Cast 18 loads of dung for the Cantaleupe-bed.
Planted some Catchflies on the end of the bank next the house.
Planted four rows of fine large potatoes cut to pieces: each row three feet apart; & each piece one foot.

30. Grafted the tall peaked pear-tree in the orchard with Doyenne-Grafts; & the standard pear in the new Garden with Crasan, & Chaumontelle Grafts. The Cions¶ came from Ringmer; & the two latter sorts were canker'd & bad. Put an handful of salt in the loam. Hot sunshine with a drying east wind.
Cut vent-holes in the front of the succade-bed to prevent burning.

31. Planted some wild, & Garden Lathyruss in the bank at the back of the melon-screen between each two Holyoaks: they were two years old in the seedling-bed, & had long tap-roots between 2 &

3 feet long running into the carrion. The seed of the wild
Lathyrus was gathered from a plant observed by my Bro: Tom to
flourish most beautifully in the midst of a bush in the short
Lythe.

APRIL   1.   The Succade-bed continuing too hot, I ordered a pole to be thrust
quite thro' the bed under each hill, so that one might see thro':
One hill being more furious than the rest I had the plants (top of
hill & all) taken off in a shovel, & the hill new-made-up with
cold earth. The plants grow, & are not yet injured.

              1.   Grafted-in two cuttings of M: Middleton's espalier-Crasane,
instead of the Ringmer ones, which were canker'd, & bad: left
one Ringmer one.

                     Planted 6 basons of double larkspurs in the new-garden
borders.

              2.   Sowed in the seed-bed in the melon-ground Battersea Cabbage-
seed, Savoys, borecole, leeks, Holyoaks, stocks, carnations, &
sweet Williams. Bright sunshine, with an east-wind, & very high
barometer. The Ground is bound like a stone.

                     Hoed, pronged, & cleans'd all the home garden, & borders,
during this parching season.

              3.   Planted a Garden *Lathyrus* on the new bank between every two
asters, & p: sunflowers. Stopped-up the vent-holes in front of the
Succade-bed; left them open behind. Most of the plants look well.

                     Sowed a great Quantity of Cucumber-seeds for the
neighbours.

              4.   Sowed tree-prime-roses, beet, & some seeds of a red cowslip¶
in a pot.

                     Sunny, burning weather.

                     Dress'd artichokes: in that hot weather the beginning of
December they sprouted thro' their ridges, & continued growing
very much the winter thro'; & have now vast greens.

                     Hoed & cleansed the grubb'd ground in the meadow.

              6.   Made the Cantaleupe-bed for two three-light frames with 18
loads of dung. It is about 14 Inches wider behind than y^e
Succade-bed, & about three feet deep.

              7.   Turn'd-out a fine pot of Succades into a hill joining to a former.
The succades were in great danger of being burnt by the hot
weather's setting the bed in a rage again: but by cutting & boring
vents, & frequent opening the hills all seems now to be safe.
These plants have long runners that have been stopp'd again.

              8.   The Cantaleupe-bed is in a great fury, & comes very early to it's
heat. Frequent still fine showers after near a month's dry weather.

                     Cucumbers blow a great pace.

                     Made the annual bed with 7 barrows of dung for the biggest
one-light frame.

              9.   Sowed one of the upper quarters of the new garden with 3 quarts
of marrow-fat dwarf pease, which made eleven rows at 3 feet
apart, & just fill'd the ground. The ground, which had laid

Bakers Hill
from the Great Parlour
The Wares.

rough all the late dry scorching weather, being slack'd with the rain, raked, & fell to pieces in very good order; the marl seeming to do a great deal of good.

11.   Put a finishing hand to the new Garden by cutting the edges of the turf round the water-tables,¶ & terrass, & mending any patch of turf that was wanting.

Planted 24 cuttings of the fine bloody-wall-flower. Those planted the beginning of last June came to little.

Sowed the annual-bed with dwarfsunflowers, Marvel of Peru, Basoms, China Aster purple, & white, Fr: & Afr: marrigolds, Pendulous Amaranths, & *Convolvulus minor*. Sowed some China pinks, *Convol: minor*, & dwarf sunflowers in the cold Ground.

15.   Planted a row of Laurels of 25ˢ· pᵗ Hund: from the filberts against Parsons's down by the rod-hedge to the new part of the Garden; with a Laurustine between every two Laurels.

Fine gentle rain for 12 or 14 Hours.

Planted some laurels at the lower end of the new bank. The fine rains make the new turf take kindly to the ground, & close-up it's Joints.

17.   Planted half hundred more cabbage plants; & some forward coss lettuce from under the melon screen.

Sowed the part of the meadow where yᵉ hedge was grubb'd, & the Haha with rye-grass: some white-Clover in the Haha.

18.   Made a low circular mount round the great oak in the mead, & Turfed it.

Earthed-down the Cantaleupe-bed, & hill'd the lights: found the bed very hot still.

Sowed more China-asters on the end of the Cantaleupe-bed. Perfect summer.

16.   Measured my new-purchased piece of Garden, which contained forty two rods of Ground; & the old part fifty six: in all half an acre, & eighteen rods.

18.   Planted some cuttings of the black Cluster, & Muscadine Grapes.

20.   Made a frame, or cradle for annuals of rods, & pease-haulm about four feet wide, & eight feet long; & put into it about 16 barrows of dung, & grass-mowings.

†Dung borrowed 1760.

Jan 10.	Of Berriman pᵈ	2 loads
Feb: 8.	Of Berriman pᵈ	2 loads
	Of Kelsey pᵈ	2 loads
	Kelsey carried out for us 2.	
Feb: 15.	Of Parsons pᵈ	2 loads
March 16:	Of Parsons pᵈ	5 loads

†Notes inserted where one notebook ends and a new one is started.

	Of Berriman p^d	6 loads
	Of Kelsey p^d	7 loads
	Kelsey carried out for us 2.	
June 3.	Of Kelsey p^d	5 loads
	Of Berriman p^d	3 loads
	Kelsey carried out for us 3.	

Dung borrowed 1761.

Jan: 3	Of Kelsey dung p^d car p^d.	1 load
	He carried of our's 1 load. p^d	
31	Of Kelsey dung p^d car p^d.	6 loads
Feb 2.	Of Parsons p^d car: dung p^d.	4 loads
March 3.	Of Parsons p^d car: dung p^d.	5 loads
4.	Of Kelsey dung p^d: car: p^d	4 loads
	carried 1 of mine p^d	
March 26	Of Berriman p^d car:.	2 loads
	Of Parsons p^d car: dung p^d.	3 loads
	Of Kelsey dung p^d Car: p^d	10 loads
	carried out of mine 3. p^d	

APRIL	20.	Made a small hot-bed for the small one-light frame to raise white-cucumbers in. Set-up the urns.

	21.	Turn'd-out six pots of Cantaleupes in the six hills: there were two plants in every pot except one. The plants are strong, & stocky; but seem to be somewhat injured by staying so long in the pots. The bed now seems safe from burning, having been made sixteen days.
		   Sowed some white-Dutch . . . Cucumbers in the one-light frame.
		   Cut the first Cucumber, which might have been cut some days before. More fruit were lost than usual but now there are abundance set. The bees frequent the frames much.
		   Planted 12 cuttings more of the double wallflower.

	28.	Planted five rows of dwarf-white-french-beans pretty thin in one of the new Quarters: used just a pint of beans.
		   Finding some of the Cantaleupe-plants look a little amiss, I prick'd two seeds into each hill.
		   Cutting N.E. Winds for many days.
		   Cucumbers sett at a vast rate: there are now about three brace fit to cut.
		   Sowed more white-Dutch-Cucumbers in the one-light frame: & a few large dark-green.

MAY	12	Fine rain after a long dry fit. Sowed a small crop of Roman-Broccoli.

Cucumbers in vast abundance, & very large.

The Succades offer fine fruit.

14. Hot summer weather: the Succades swell & seem several of them to be set.

Began building my fruit-wall.

15. Disbudded the vines for the first time: great quantities of fruit especially at the end of the dining-room. The fig tree shows about 140 fruit.

Finish'd a forest-Chair on the bastion; & a plain seat under the great oak. Hot burning weather.

19. Vast rain with a very stormy wind, which hinders the masons in their wall-building; & damages the vines, shrubs, flowers, & trees of all sorts.

20. Made six holes for the large white Dutch Cucumbers, with one barrow of dung to each hole, & planted three plants under each hand-glass.

20. My Brother Tho:¶ & I went down with a spade to examine into the nature of those animals that make that chearful shrill cry all the summer months in many parts of the south of England. We found them to be of the Cricket-kind, with wings & ornamented Cases over them, like the House kind. But tho' they have long legs behind with large brawny thighs, like Grasshoppers, for leaping; it is remarkable that when they were dug-out of their holes they shewed no manner of activity, but crawled along in a very shiftless manner, so as easily to be taken. We found it difficult not to squeese them to death in breaking the Ground: & out of one so bruised I took a multitude of eggs, which were long, of a yellow Colour, & covered with a very tough skin.

It was easy to discover the male from the female; the former of which is of a black shining Colour, with a golden stripe across it's shoulders something like that of the Humble bee: the latter was more dusky, & distinguished by a long terebra at it's tail, which probably may be the instrument with which it may deposit it's eggs in Crannies, & safe receptacles. It is very likely that the males only make that shrilling noise; which they may do out of rivalry, & emulation during their breeding time; as is the Case with many animals. They are solitary Insects living singly in Holes by themselves; & will fight fiercely when they meet, as I found by some which I put into an hole in a dry wall, where I should be glad to have them encrease on account of their pleasing summer sound. For tho' they had express'd distress by being taken out of their knowledge; yet the first that had got possession of the chink seized an other with a vast pair of serrated fangs so as to make it cry-out. With these strong, tooth'd Malae (like the sheers of lobster's claws) they must terebrate their curious regular Holes; as they have no feet suited for digging like the mole-cricket. I could but wonder, that when taken in hand, they never offer'd to bite, tho' furnish'd with such formidable weapons. They are remarkably shy, & cautious, never stirring but a few inches from ye mouth of their holes, & retiring backward nimbly into them, & stopping short in their song by that time you come within several yards of y^{ir} caverns: from whence I conclude they may be a very desirable food to some animals, perhaps several kinds of birds. They cry all night as well as day during part of the month of May June, & July in fine weather; & may in the still part of the night be heard to a considerable distance; abounding most in sand-banks on the sides of heaths, especially in Surrey, & Sussex: but these that I caught were in a steep, rocky pasture-field facing to the afternoon sun.

21. Frequent showers, & a strong wind. Sowed a Crop of large white-French-beans.

22. There are about 12 brace of Succade-melons set; the largest of which are about the size of a pullet's egg: & two Cantaleupes, which seem to be secure.

27: 28: 29. Vast rains, with black, cold weather for many days.

JUNE

1. Went thro' with tacking the vines for the first time.
   Cold black weather still, with a northerly wind, very unkind for all vegetation.

3. Great rain

4. Planted-out 2 hand-glasses of the large green Cucumbers: & a large plot of Savoys, & late-raised Cabbages.

8. Cold black weather, which makes the Cucumbers pale, & ill-flavoured; & hurts the melons.
   Drew first Carrots under the melon-screen.
   The Rooks are perchers:¶ there are but two; & one of the old ones was some how destroyed as soon as they were hatched.

9. Sowed the first Crop of endive.

17. Great rain: rak'd-down, & planted the winding-border over-against the fruit-wall with tall annuals behind, & a row of China-asters before.
   Cut-off a large Succade fruit that was rotted at a joint just by the stem of the fruit. It had firm seeds in it, & would have soon been ripe.

19. Limed the vine-borders round the house. Black weather without a gleam of sunshine for many days. Prick'd-out more Celeri.
   Planted more Savoys.

21. Discovered a curious *Orchis* in the hollow shady part of Newton-lane, just beyond the Cross. It is the *Orchis alba bifolia minor, Calcari oblongo;* grew with a very long stem; & has been in flower some weeks. I brought away the flower, & mark'd the root, intending to transplant it into the Garden, when the leaves are wither'd.

22. Hot summer weather. Cut my Clover-hay.
   Cut the first Succado.
   Hot burning weather, which grew more & more vehement 'till the 25; & then a great deal of thunder, & lightning all night.

23. Cut a brace more Succades.

25. Cut an other Succade.

The annuals are sadly scorch'd by the heat. The Succades, considering the long shady season they grew-in, & the early season of ripening, are good, & well-flavoured.

Put-up two loads of clover-hay on the rick, & covered it well with straw.

26. The vines begin to blow very fast.

JULY 4. Rick'd-up the meadow-hay in good order.

6. Planted-out leeks, savoys, & two plots of endive.

Locally grown carrots,
Village shop, Selborne.
July.

10. Most of the Succades being cut, I ordered the plants to be watered in order to try for a second Crop. The finest Succades weigh'd about 20 ounces, & were very good.

There are two Cantaleupes only which are just near cutting: the rest are only now setting in great plenty.

Cut the first white-Cucumber.

Took-in the Cucumber-frames. The early Cucumbers are now full of fruit.

Saved seed from two fine Succades.

Perfect fine summer-weather.

The Succades have some second fruit in bloom.

12. Cut the first Cantaleupe: it was a fair, well-emboss'd fruit, & weigh'd one ounce short of two pounds; but was pale-flesh'd, & not in so fine perfection as the best Succades.

16. Cut the second Cantaleupe, a small one.

Trench'd three rows of Celeri.

Raised the melon-frames to give the roots a little room. There are plenty of Cantaleupes; & a good second Crop of Succades.

Large white Cucumbers in great plenty; & plenty still on the old forward bed. Stewed 20 for dinner.

The Succades have some second fruit as big as hens eggs.

25. Finish'd my fruit-wall, coping the two returns at the ends with stones of a sandy nature out of the old priory. The coping-bricks were full of flaws, & cracks, being made of earth not well-prepared, & instead of over-hanging the wall, came but just flush with it: however, by using six that were broken ended, we had just enough, & they may lie on the wall many Years.

Began delving the fruit border which was trod very hard.

Finish'd peat cart; the spits were in excellent order: housed four loads; & brought in all my wood: & two loads of sand; one for ye fruit-border, & one for the hot-bed earth.

Hot, ripening weather for a long time.

Inoculated five budds of the double Hawthorn on a common one: the budds were poor, coming from a sickly tree, & did not part well from their wood.

27.   Look'd-over the melons, that were run pretty wild. There are about ten brace of well-grown Cantaleupes; & not more than two brace of second Succades; their haulm being damaged by over dryness.

Sprinkled all the plants within, & watered the boxes round; as the mould is uncommonly dry, & burnt, & the weather very scorching.

Large white Cucumbers bear vastly.

30.   Dress'd the fruit border the second time with lime, & sand.

Trench'd the next year's melon-earth, & dress'd it with a good coat of lime.

The earth very dry, & parch'd.

Looking across the ha-ha towards Selborne Hanger. 5 August.

AUGUST   28.   On my return from Ringmer after three weeks & four days absence, I found Tull had cut nine brace of melons. The continual sunny weather had brought on the Cantaleupes before I expected them, & made them come almost all in a week. They were divided among our Neighbours, & were much commended.

I found the annuals very handsome & very strong; the Savoys strangely grown; & the Endives very large. Tull had planted out rows of Sweet-Williams, & Stocks in my absence.

The vines were grown very wild; & have no fruit yet turn'd in

Colour, notwithstanding the heat of the summer. The best Cantaleupes weigh'd about two pounds & an half.

29.   Cut a Cantaleupe, which prov'd a very fine one. Weigh'd the largest of the great white-seed-Cucumbers: it's weight was three pounds & 14 ounces; & it measured 14 inch: & an half in length.

Tull has dug the fruit-border twice, & levelled it: but there has not been rain enough yet to moisten the stubborn Clods, so as to make them fall well to pieces.

29.   Sowed a small Crop of Coss-lettuce for plants to stand the winter.

31.   Pruned the vines, that were much over-run with shoots, for the last time. The Grapes just begin to turn Colour.

Tyed up about 20 endives, which run very large this Year. All the buds of the double Hawthorn seem to be dead.

SEPTEMBER 2.   Cut two Cantaleupes, very fine fruit. The Cantaleupes run to a fair size, notwithstanding the bed is very little wider than the frames.

The Succades produced about 6 brace of good second-crop fruit, which ripen'd well, & are almost all cut.

4.   Cut a fine Cantaleupe; the last of any size or value. It prov'd a very curious one.

Mark'd the best, & most double annuals for seed.

5.   Dug the fruit border the fourth time after a great rain: it fell well to pieces, & seems to be well-mellow'd with sand & lime: 'till this rain it lay in great Clods as hard as stones, being so much trod by the masons, & harden'd by a hot, sunny Summer. It has three coats of good mould on it, & must be full two feet deep in good soil.

8.   Earth'd-up the Celeri for the first time. Cut the two last Succades: good siz'd fruit. Cut in the whole about 30 brace of melons of both sorts; many were very curi: fruit. It is to be observ'd that, as my frames are so wide, a crop of melons succeeds better when the bed is little broader than the boxes, than when the bed has been lin'd-out, & earth'd down to the Ground. Because when the bed has been made so extensive in my strong soil the more delicate sorts of melons have collected more moisture than was proper, & have been liable to mouldy & rotten bines: but now with a narrow bed there has been no decay in the plants, notwithstanding there have been frequent great showers the summer thro'.

9.   The grapes now turn a great pace.

12.   Hous'd the lights, & took the melon-frames to pieces. Hot sunshine with cold dews.

18.   Dug the fruit-border for the last time, & levell'd it for planting. It is in fine mellow order, & falls very fine, having been dug five times; & dress'd with three Coats of sand, two of lime, & one of morter rubbish. It now lies-up within four inches of the upper Joint of the stone part of the wall.

Sad wet black weather for a long time; & some very heavy rains. The Grapes come-on but poorly.

28. Planted Sweet-Williams, & pinks alternately on the new bank.
Earth'd up the Celeri the second time.
Fine settled weather after above a month's cold, wet season.
Some little Succades, secured under handglasses, still continue
to ripen.

28. Made 18 quarts of elder-juice, & put to it 36 pounds of 4½
sugar, which made 29 Quarts of Syrop. Mem: two gallons &
half of pick'd berries, moderately squeesed, produced about a
gallon of Juice.

OCTOBER 7. Planted-out in a bed to blow 60 Carnation-plants, & 80 stocks:
the best are to be removed into borders.

14. Now the Grapes are good, notwithstanding the vast continual
rains.
The drein that goes from the bottom of the new-garden under
the walk, & fruit-wall runs apace.

21. Dry, fine weather.
Planted 130 of Cabbages in the new Garden at two feet apart to
stand ye winter.

22. A very white-frost with thick ice.

24. The ground being very dry I planted my bulbs; a row of
Hyacinths above 60, & a few Tulips, & polyanth-Narcissuss on
the edge of the fruit border: a row of tulips, & polyanth-
Narcissuss, Cornflags, & Jonquils next Parsons's: & two rows of
Crocuss under the buttery-window. Planted a large bed of
Nursery-ofset-bulbs in a bed by themselves.
Planted-out against Parsons's, & under ye Buttery-window
several of my fine bloody-double-wallflowers. Just before I
finish'd came a vast rain.

NOVEMBER 2: Planted two standard-golden-pippens in the old orchard;¶ & 12
3. small crab-stocks in the nursery. Took-up & removed the things
in the nursery, & planted them in regular lines three feet apart.
Dug-up & planted 6 pear-suckers for stocks.
Sanded, dung'd & trench'd the next year's melon-earth a
second time; it was dress'd once with sand & lime, & falls now
very mellow.
Dry, soft, delicate weather. Grapes continue very good still.

5. Planted four rasp-plants from Chidbury-hill Wilts at the nearest
end of the rasp-border; & several slips of pyram: Campanulas in
a Nursery-bed.

7. Planted one Quart, three rows, of small early beans in a Quarter
of the new Garden.
A smart frost with Ice.
Dress'd the basons for the espalier-pears with mortar-rubbish:
& laid some rubbish at the bottom of every bason.

13. Planted a quart more of early beans.

DECEMBER 15.   Brewed half Hogsh: of moderate strong beer with 5 bush: of Rich: Knight's malt, & two p.^d & half of hops. What was brew'd in the same barrel last Decr was excellent.

17.   Made half hogsh: of raisin-wine with hundred of Smyrnas, & half hundred of Malagas; & put to them 13 buckets of water, each bucket containing 3 Gal:

22.   Wheel'd-in 20 wheel-barrows of hot dung to cast ready for a seedling-Cucumber-bed.

     Vast quantities of rain have fallen the autumn & winter thro': & as yet there have been but a very few days of hard frost.

23: 24.   Vast rains, & floods.

26.   Made an hot-bed for the biggest one-light frame with the 20 barrows of dung.

     Planted a Dutch-medlar, & a Service¶ in the old orchard; & a mountain-ash in one of the basons in the field.

     Vast rains.

30.   The bed not coming to it's heat from the vast wetness of the Dung, I order'd in a load from Kelsey's; which with 10 barrows of my own made a new one.

     By the negligence of Murdoch Middleton my wall-trees never came 'till the 26: they are in general good trees, & were planted (considering the wetness of the season) in good condition; & in the following order, beginning from the terrass: Breda Apricot; Sweet-water vine;¶ Roman Nectar:¶ Mr Snooke's black-cluster vine: Roman Nect: white Muscadine vine: Newington Nectar:¶ Mur: Middleton's Sweet-water vine: Nobless-peach; M.^r Sn: white Muscadine; Nobless peach: John Hale's 2 Passion flowers, one at each end of the wall.

30.   Planted two Cistus's in Mr Etty's dry garden; & a *Phlomis*, & an *Halimus* in my own. Planted some cuttings of the American black Poplar, & the Groundsel-tree in the Nursery.

— 1762 —

JANUARY   1.   Put about 20 Cucumber-seeds into the Hot-bed before it was come to it's heat: it has been made only two days.

4.   The bed comes to a bold heat. Exceeding wet weather; & the ground full of water. There has been no settled dry weather since the end of August.

5.   Tunn'd the Half Hogsh: of raisin wine: there were about 3 gallons too much without any squeezing. Coloured it with 17 pints of Elder Syrop. The wine tastes very sweet. Added two more pints.

5.   Cucumber-plants begin to appear: the bed is very warm.

11: 12.   A violent storm with vast rains, & floods.

14.   The bed, when covered much from the great rains, too hot still.

Obliged to keep the light tilted anights.¶ The plants a little damaged by the steam, & heat. Continue to sow more seeds.

14. Bottled out the barrel of vinegar, which was very fine, & extreamly keen; & put-in 8 gall: more of strong small-wine.

20. Cucumber-plants have a rough leaf. Shut the light down quite close to night for the first time. The mercury mounts very high.

26. Brought in ten loads of hot dung for the bearing Cucumber-bed. Bright sunny weather & dry pleasant frosts for many days. Trench'd my flower-bank, & some of the Kitchen-ground.

Lane on Selborne Common.
in the snow.
Early February.

FEBRUARY 1. Sowed 8 Succade-seeds.

The Cucumber-plants look finely.

Frequent rains with a very high Barometre; & the Country in an unusal wet condition. The cast dung heats furiously.

5. Cold, dry, March-like weather for a few days, with a very high barometer. The ground being a little dry for the first time since last August, I sowed a small Crop of Coss lettuce, Carrots, & radishes in the upper part of the melon-screen border, which was but in very poor cold Condition, notwithstanding the quantity of ashes, & sand that have been put on it. As to the lower part, the water appeared in the Clods while it was digging-up rough.

7. A strong N: W: wind all night, which occasioned much the fiercest frost that has been this year, with ice full an Inch thick. The paths are now dry, & white.

Lin'd the seedling Cucumber-bed (which begins to abate of it's heat) with seven barrows of dung. The plants look well, & show a joint.

Hill'd & earth'd-down the bearing-bed; & as it comes but feebly to it's heat, lin'd it round with pease-haulm. High barometer, & a strong freezing wind.

A good part of my new garden has been dug since these dry days: the marl has done great good in the Quarters, & makes them Crumble well. Dung'd the flower-bank well, & the opposite border. Covered the roots of the new-planted trees with straw.

10. A violent fierce frost.

11. Finding the fruiting-bed by great covering-up was much improved in heat, I planted the hills with seven or 8 of my best plants each.

The plants have a large rough leaf, & some of them a joint; but have stay'd full as long in the seed-bed as will do them any good. The new bed is at present warm enough; but the danger is whether such moderate heat will continue long enough to set the fruit well; & 'till the sun gets strong enough to make the fruit grow. There are many fine plants left in the seedling-bed.

12. Sowed 14 Succade-seeds in the fruiting-frames; those that were sown in the seed-bed included, which never vegetated.

Strange sudden alterations from fierce frosts to heavy rains, & so back again.

15. The bed seems to be come to a good heat. Succades begin to appear.

18. The bed advances in heat, & rather draws the plants. Potted the Succades.

Nasty, wet, blowing weather.

19. Sow'd 10 more Succade seeds.

Sow'd a box of Polyanth seed.

The sun, which quite forsakes the upper walk of the new garden about the end of Octob: begins now to shine full along it about half an hour before it sets. The Hepaticas, Crocuss, snowdrops & double daisies begin now to make a very agreeable appearance as the first promise of spring. Warm moist weather, which makes the grass spring sensibly.

A shoot of a white vine, which I lately short'nd, bleeds pretty much.

The ground has never this winter been once covered with snow.

20. Made an hot-bed in the rod-frame with 16 barrows of dung; &, after covering it pretty thick with mellow mould, sowed it with radishes.

Sowed two basons of Persicarias in the border against Parsons's.

21. A most violent N: E: wind all the evening & all the first part of the night, with a small, dry, drifting sort of snow, which drove thro' the tiles, & every cranny in a most extraordinary manner. The ground is but just covered except in drifted places. A very

hard frost in the morning. Many people froze to death.¶

24. Severe frost with heaps of drifted snow on the Ground. A high barometer.

The Cucumber bed steams very much; & it has been so very cold lately, that there has been very few opportunities of giving the plants sufficient air. The plants look the worse for their Confinement.

25. Finding the bed full hot, I pull'd-off the pease-haulm-lining at the back.

Sowed the Clover in Baker's Hill all over with two dung-carts of Ashes.

27. Sowed 8 basons of double upright-larkspurs along the border of the Garden-door walk, & in the border between the Cherry-trees.

Cold black weather: the snow has now laid a week in shady places.

The forward Cucumbers look very poorly.

MARCH 1. Fierce frosts a nights, & strong cutting winds a days with storms of snow.

Murdoch Middleton's pear-trees of last year proving canker'd, & distemper'd, he changed them; & I added some more sorts. They stand now as follows in the new Garden, beginning from the first quarters on the side next the wall, then going down the middle quarters; & then by the side of the terrass.
N: Side of the Quarters next the wall:
Chaumontelle, & Virgoleuse:¶
S: side of D? Crasane, & Doyenne:
The middle quarters:
St Germain, Brown Bury, Doyenne:
Up the side of the terrasse:
Autumn Burgamot, & Swann's egg.

There are also at the inner ends of the wall-quarters two Green-gage plums:

One Crasane-pear in the border of the walk facing the Garden-door: & one le Royal, & one Queen-Claudia plum in the melon-screen border.

2. Planted a plot in Turner's with five rows, three pints & half of early pease at four feet apart.

Very strong frost with thick ice: freezing air all day with flights of snow.

6. This is now the 14 day since the snow fell; & it lies in great Heaps still under the Hedges. There have been every day since cold cutting winds with a dark cloudy skie, & strong frosts every night.

The want of sun, & freezing air make the Cucumber-plants look very poorly, & quite stop their Growth.

Sowed a Gallon, 11 rows of dwarf marrowfats, which at 3 feet & half a part just fill'd a quarter.

Sowed two ounces of spinage.

The dug-ground is quite dusty.

10.   Pull'd-up the forward Cucumbers, which have never thrived since the fierce weather began; & planted some from yᵉ seedling-bed which are better.

Sowed a Celeri-bed with seed from London, & some seed of a jagged-leaved sort from Mʳ Missing.

Planted some Spanish-Chestnuts from Mʳ Roman, & some variegated Sycomore-keys from bro: Tom. Sowed a bed of Leeks. This is the 18ᵗʰ day of the frosty weather: very thick ice last night; & the snow still lies in cold shady places. A freezing wind.

Dung borrowed for 1762.

Of Kelsey	Dung pᵈ	Car pᵈ	. . . .	1 load.
Jan: 26: of Kelsey D: pᵈ Car pᵈ			. . . .	7 loads.
Car: 3 of my own.				
March 15.	Kelsey	Dung pᵈ	car: pᵈ	5 loads.
	Parsons	Dung pd	car pᵈ	5 loads.
April 8.	Kelsey	Dung pᵈ	Car: pᵈ	8 loads.
10.	Parsons	Dung pᵈ	Car: pᵈ	9 loads.

11.   This the 19 & last day of the fierce weather.

13.   Cut-down all the wall trees,¶ & all the espalier pears. The two peaches seem unsound at the pith; all the rest are healthy trees.

Widened the walk down Baker's-hill, & turfed it. Planted several sorts of Asters in the new garden.

Soft spring-like weather for the first time.

15.   Carryed-in ten loads of Hot dung for the Succade-bed.

26.   Sowed Holy-oaks, sunflowers, Cullumbines, China asters, & savoys.

27.   Planted four rows of Potatoes; pieces from fine large roots.

APRIL   6.   Sowed a bed of onions.

7.   Planted the succade-bed, that has been now made a fortnight, with some good potted plants, & some plants raised in the bed. The bed is full hot. Sowed the first Cantaleupes. Sowed three rows of broad-beans.

The forwardest Cucumber about as big as the top of one's finger. The plants now grow away. Fine summer weather.

Planted holy-oaks, asters, & peren: sunflowers up the garden-hedge in Baker's hill.

8.   Sowed five rows of marrow-fat pease.

9: 10.   Brought in 17 loads of hot dung for the Cantaleupe bed.

Sowed some white Broccoli-seed from Bp's Waltham.

The Succade-bed is very hot; but the plants by being tilted a nights, & shaded a days look very well, & have runners.

12.   Sowed the Cantaleupe-seeds, & some Succade.

16.   Sowed some common Cabbage-seed, & some Roman Broccoli.

<table>
<tr><td></td><td>Made one hand-glass-bed to raise the large white Cucumbers. Made the Annual-bed.
Potted the Cantaleupes.</td></tr>
</table>

17.	Sowed the annuals.
19.	Made the Cantaleupe-bed with 17 loads of dung: it is of a very proper thickness.
20.	Dress'd the Artichokes.
24.	Earth'd the Cantaleupe-bed, & hill'd it. Made six hand-glass beds, with one barrow of dung to each, for the large white Cucumbers, & planted them.
	The fruit-wall & espalier-trees are all alive, & begin to shoot.
26.	Cut the first Cucumber. There are plenty coming-on.
	Fine hot summer weather for these twelve days past, which has brought every thing on in a wonderful manner.
27.	Planted the Cantaleupe-bed, the two first Hills with Waverley plants, & the rest with plants from my own seed; all save the last Hill, which is planted with Succades to keep up a Succession. The plants are beautiful & thriving beyond Common; but the bed is very hot & wants watching.
	Very hot weather with the appearance of thunder.
27.	The first Succades fill the hills with their fibres, & have runners with several joints.
	The fruit-trees against the wall push apace. I disbudded them today. The vines also are all alive.

MAY	3. Sowed 6 rows of white Dwarf-french-beans. The seed looks but poorly.
	8. The Succades begin to shew fruit.
	Hot sunshine with very cold winds.
	11. The Succades have male bloom full blown.
	17. The Succades have now fruit in bloom.
	22. Some Succades seem to be set.
	Brought some Geraniums, & a *Sedum* from Bp's Waltham.
	Shady moist weather: prick'd-out plenty of Savoys, Celery, & Celeriac.
	25. Tack'd the vines, & disbudded them for yᵉ first time: the appearance of an abundance of fruit. Hot sunny weather for many days.

JUNE	4. Vehement hot dry weather for many days (a fortnight past) so that the fields & Gardens begin to suffer greatly. The early Cucumbers hardly bear at all tho' constantly water'd: & the melons swell very slowly.
	Turn'd-out the white Cucumbers from under the Glasses.
	8. This long hot sunny season has forced some of the vines into bloom. They did not blow last year 'till about the 26.
	Cut my Clover-hay.
	The forwardest Succades nearly full-grown: the Cantaleupes have abundance of fruit in full bloom, but

hardly any male bloom.

A long dry hot season: the Corn begins to suffer.

16. Cut first white Cucumbers from the hand-glasses. Hot burning weather still.

Began stopping-down the vines. They are all in full bloom.

The Cantaleupes begin to set.

17. This morning a valuable shower for an Hour & half that made the Cartway run.

Cantaleupes & Succades now set at a vast rate.

18. Sowed four rows of white-dwarf-french-beans: soak'd the seed in water.

Sowed a small plot of Endive.

26. Dry & hot weather yet.

Some bunches of Grapes, that used in general to be only just in full bloom, now so forward, that they are grown pretty well to the third part of their full size.

An abundance of Cantaleupes set: the vines are in good health, & some fruit are the size of a large apple. The Succades have but a scanty first crop, which is near cutting: but promise well for a second.

We transplant the annuals only a few at a time as they can be watered. They are stocky in their nursery bed.

The fruit-trees against the wall, by being sprinkled over the leaves two or three times a week during this burning season, have been kept in a constant growing state, & have not one curled leaf.

A fine shower on June 20.

28. A fine rain. Planted out some Savoys; & more annuals. The pine strawberries bear well.

30. Hot summer weather.

JULY   3. Cut first Succade.

5. Set-out for Tidworth.¶ During that week Tull cut 4 brace of Succades.

About the 10th Mr Cane began to cut his crop of Cantaleupes, which were extraordinary delicate, & of a good size.

On my return to Selborne the 24 I found 3 brace & an half of Succades cut, & ready to cut in the early box. The late hill of Succades are not come; & the Cantaleupes are small & not very rough; but the vines look healthy. People are in the midst of wheat-harvest, & have cut some oats. Not the least rain since wednesday seven night. The Country is burnt-up in a most deplorable manner, beyond what any middle-aged person remembers;¶ all the ponds & many wells are dry.

The grapes are uncommonly forward, & flourishing; & the vines have made vast shoots.

28. Cut the first Cantaleupe at six weeks from the setting: it was, I suppose, hurried by the vehement hot summer; but was not very curious.

29. Cut second Cantaleupe.

Windfalls in the orchard,
Baker's Hill
26 July

Cut the first Succade of the Hill in one of the Cantaleupe-boxes; which came not 'till after two Cantaleupes, tho' planted at the same time. There usually is a fortnight difference in their ripening.

31.   The Succades of the latter hill come apace. Those in the first box have been well watered; & shew a pretty good Crop.

Vehement hot weather still.

AUGUST   3.   Cut all the Succades of the farther hill, which came a great pace this very hot dry weather. Watered the hill well, to try for a second Crop. They were excellent.

4: 6.   Frequent showers with a strong wind that blew down many apples & pears. The first rain.

The rain improved Mr Etty's wallfruit visibly in a day or two. Cut a large delicate Cantaleupe.

7.   Planted-out Savoys; & sowed half p^d of spinage, & some radish-seed.

The ground is moistened in but a little way.

4.   Cut my field of oats.

10.   A fine rain. Sowed a plot of turnep-seed & trenched-out the first Celeri, four rows in Turner's Garden.

12.   A fine rain with some distant thunder.

The Grapes begin to turn Colour.

Planted in the new garden two trenches more of Celeri; & two of Mr Missing's parsley-leaved Celeriac. Mr Etty's Nectarines, & peaches begin to shew their fine ripening Colours.

13.   Frequent heavy thundershowers with hot growing weather.

14.   Hot moist weather. The Succades have plenty of new wood, & shew several brace of promising second-crop fruit.

The grass-walks have in ten days quite recovered their verdure, tho' they were so deplorably burnt.

Planted 12 stock-gilliflowers from M.ʳ Etty.

Eat a very curious Cantaleupe: it weigh'd two pounds, & an half, & was very dry, & thick in flesh.

16. Cut the last Cantaleupe. Many were very delicate, cracking both at Eye, & stem.

21. Planted three rows of Polyanths on the bank next the Alcove: & planted two plots of backward Savoys.

SEPTEMBER 8. The wasps (which are without number this dry hot summer) attack the grapes in a grievous manner. Hung-up 16 bottles with treacle, & beer, which make great havock among them. Bagged about fifty of the best bunches in Crape-bags. Some of the forwardest bunches are very eatable, tho' not curiously ripe. M.ʳ Snooke's grapes were eat naked to the stones a fortnight ago, when they were quite green.

There are about 3 brace of second-crop Succades, which will come in good time if the weather proves good.

Frequent showers since the 4.ᵗʰ of Aug: now a promise of dry weather. The fields abound with grass as if there had been no drought this summer.

18. Delicate Autumn weather for a fortnight. Began eating the grapes, which are good, but not curiously ripened yet.

By means of bottles & birdlime I have prevented innumerable swarms of wasps from doing the grapes any considerable damage. They are reduced now to a very moderate number; not more than appear in common Years. Gather'd some nonpareils & golden-rennets,¶ which are very fair & ready to be laid up, being a fortnight at least earlier than common.

Cut a decent second-crop-succade.

Walnuts & apples are innumerable this year; but there are no small-nuts.

20. Tyed-up a large parcel of endives: they are but small this year.

21. Cut a succade.

23: 24. Exceeding heavy rains with tempestuous winds, which blowed down an abundance of apples.

Gather'd-in the Cadillac-pears: near one third were blown-down.

Cut-up a very good-flavoured Succade.

OCTOBER 5. Trimm'd & tack'd the wall fruit-trees for the winter. They are all alive, & healthy. Planted-out some Coss-lettuce to stand the winter under the fruit-wall.

13. Grapes very curious. The wasps begin to be very troublesome, so that we caught 200 of a day. Eat two very good Succades within these few days. Dry weather, with white frosts.

15. Supply'd the row of Hyacinths on the fruit-border with several double blue, & a few very double flat-blowing flowers.

		Very dry seasonable weather.
16.		Dug-up the Crown-imperials on the bank, & took-out a large basket full of roots, & planted only two roots in each bason. Grapes very curious.
17.		First very great white frost.
23: 24: 25.		Vast floods. Vast damage in many parts.
26.		Plenty of Grapes, & very curious.
29.		A flight of snow for a few hours.

NOVEMBER	1.	Grapes very fine.
	3.	Gathered the last Grapes, which were above thirty curious bunches, from the vine over yᵉ Entry door.
		Planted four curious gooseberry-trees from Waltham, & two basons of ragwort¶ from Funtington.
	11.	Great snow.
		Planted some very small Coss-lettuce against the fruit-wall.
		Shut-up the Alcove with straw-doors for yᵉ winter; & took-in the urns.
	13.	Severe frost with very thick Ice.
		Eat the last Grapes.
	19.	The frost still continues very fierce. Bearing Ice for many days. Uncommon early frost.
		The fierce frost continued eleven nights.
	24.	Trimm'd & tack'd the vines, whose shoots are both smaller & shorter than usual: perhaps owing to the vast Crop, & very burning Year. However there is wood enough to fill the walls.
	29.	Planted the border by the necessary full of tulips, Polyanth-Narcissuss, Double daffodils, & Jonquils. Moved the two plum-trees from the melon-border to the rasp border: they had taken poor root.

DECEMBER	5.	Planted one hundred & a Quarter of stocky Cabbage-plants, to stand the winter. Made a strong rod-hedge against parsons's Yard.
	10.	Sowed three pints of small early beans. The ground was in fine order; there having been hardly any rain for a month past.
	18.	By the favour of the long dry weather I prevailed on Parsons to set-about cleansing the river course from Gracious-street to Webbs bridge, which was quite choak'd, & in great rains occasion'd a very troublesome flood. We threw out about 50 loads of mud, & have open'd so free a channel, that the road is quite dry, & the water will have an easy passage as fast as it comes to those parts.
		Finish'd a paved foot-path from the Butcher's shop to the Blacksmith's, above 70 Yards: it cost just one pound.
	27.	Very hard, still frost. Pleasant weather, & no rain for several weeks.
	31.	Extream severe frost with a cutting wind.

— 1763 —

DECEMBER 24: †Made a seedling-Cucum.ʳ bed with two dung-carts of hot dung,
1762 which was in fine order, & had never received any wet since it
was thrown-out.

JANUARY 1. Sowed about 20 seeds: the bed is in very fine order. Very fierce
frost indeed, which begins to reach things within doors. The
wall-flowers seem to be much damaged.
There has been no fall now, except a trifling shower, since the
11ᵗʰ of Novem.ʳ when there was a pretty deep snow. The ponds
begin to get low.

4. Extream hard frost still. The Cucum.ʳˢ begin to appear.

11. Fierce frost still, but not very windy. The sun has scarce
appeared for many days: so that the paths & roads have been hard
& dry all day long. The Thames, it seems, is so frozen, that fairs
have been kept on it; & the Ice has done great damage to the ships
below bridge.
Covered the bulbs with straw, & the artichokes, & some of the
most curious Asters: & put straw round the bloody wall-flowers.
Lined the Cucum.ʳ bed a little: the plants look pretty well.
This frost began on Xmass-day.

15. The frost more fierce than ever with vast rimes in the night, &
sunny days. No snow yet. I have covered the wall trees, & all
tender things with straw. The frost has been three weeks to day.

17. Carted-in & cast 10 loads of good hot dung for the bearing
cucumber-bed.
Most severe frost still. There has been no rain since Nov:
11th. The Country is all in a dust, & many people are obliged to
draw water for all their Cattle.

19. Vast rimes all day long for these two days without the least thaw.

20. To day is 10 weeks since there was rain.

21. Vast rimes still day & night.

22. To day the frost has been a month.

24. Made my bearing-cucumber-bed with ten loads of very good
dung.
The first-sowed cucumber-plants look very well for such a
severe season, & have a rough leaf, & an other opening. I keep
sowing more seeds every week. Very bright still weather.

25. I measured in a new-dug grave in Faringdon Church-yard, &
found the frost had enter'd the ground about 10 inches. Vast fog.

27. This day the dry weather has lasted eleven weeks.

28. The frost begins to slack.

29. Strong south-wind with rain & a mild thaw. The frost began this
day five weeks.

31. A thoro' thaw with strong wind, & a great rain.

---

†This 1762 entry was placed here, at the beginning of 1763.

FEBRUARY 5.   After ten days absence at Ringmer I found the Cucumber-plants in pretty good order; but the bearing-bed too hot to plant-in.

8.   Planted my Cucumber-plants in the bearing bed, which seems to be pretty mild. The plants are of different ages: the forwardest have a joint, & a broad rough leaf.
    Wet blowing weather for several days.

9.   Brewed half Hogsh: of strong-beer with 5 bush: of malt, & two p^{ds} & half of hops. Used only rain-water to try the difference. Added one bush: of malt, & made an hogsh: of table-beer.

12: 13.   Heavy snow for 14, or 16 hours.

14.   Deep snow notwithstanding the ground was so wet; & a pretty hard frost, & bright sunshine.
    The cucumber-plants grow, & look very well; & some of them have two joints.

15.   A second deep snow in the night, which goes-off to day with a swift thaw, & rain.

15.   Made half an Hogsh: of raisin-wine with one hund: of Malagas, & half an hund: of Smyrnas. One basket of ye Smyrnas were pretty much candyed: the rest were pretty good. Put to the raisins 12 buckets of water, each bucket containing 3 gallons.

19.   Frequent rain, & dark weather in general since the thaw.
    Sowed 12 Succade-seeds in the Cucumber-bed. Lined the bed round with hay to keep in the heat. The plants look very green, & thrive. The bed seems in fine gentle temper.

21.   Sowed two Jobbs of ashes of my own making; which with what few more I may make will manure the great meadow all over.

22.   Constant rains.

23.   The Succade-plants come-up well. The Cucumbers thrive.
    A very soft spring like day.

25.   Sowed 8 rows of marrow-fat pease: the first crop on account of the frost & rain. Planted a white muscadine-vine from Ringmer at the end of the Dining room: a moss-provence-rose from a layer in the border opposite the fruit-wall; & a monthly-rose in the same border. Mended the Laurustines against Parsons's.
    Sowed ten more Succade-seeds: eleven of the former sowing look well.
    Dry sunny weather for three days.

26.   Potted the first Succades, which are fine plants. The Cucumbers begin to fill the Hills with their fibres, & to want earthing.

26.   Sent a small flitch of bacon to be hung in Mr Etty's smoke loft; it lay in salt six weeks, but two of them were fierce frost.
    Lay'd several small twigs of the Moss-Provence-rose: the larger shoots do not root kindly.

MARCH   1.   Planted about three Quarts of broad beans in the room of the small ones which were all kill'd by the frost.
    Vast rains still. We are now entered into the 5th week of the wet weather.
    The last-sow'd Succades are coming-up.

2.   Great rains for several days past: to day stormy wind & thunder.

There are vast floods about the Country: & incredible damage is said to be done in the Island of Ely by the breaking of the banks. It has been a very wet season now for near five weeks.

The ground is so wet that nothing can be done in the Garden.

5.   Tunn'd the raisin-wine, which held-out exactly, leaving about a gallon for filling-up. Coloured it with twelve bottles of elder-syrop; & put to it one quart of brandy. I have usually put but a pint at the beginning.

5.   Made the Succade-bed with ten cart-loads of dung, brought-in the same day. The bed & frames are full seven feet high behind: somewhat the higher for it's being made by mistake full scanty for the frame.

Several of the best Cuc: plants are just ready to burst into male bloom. They & the melon-plants thrive well, & have been earth'd twice. Potted to day the second-sown Succades.

Fine, sunny weather for two days.

The Passion-flowers at the ends of the fruit-wall appear to be much injured by the great frost, tho' they were in appearance well covered with straw.

6.   Two of the Cucum: plants have male-bloom full-blown. Beautiful weather.

7.   Sowed a Crop of Carrots, radishes, Coss-lettuce, & parsneps altogether in part of one of the lower quarters of the New-garden. The ground is in good order.

Planted a standard Orleans-plum, & a standard Autumn-Bergamot-pear in the Orchard next Baker's Hill.

Beautiful weather.

Cucumbers blow male-bloom apace.

The Succade-bed begins to fume.

10.   Sowed a row of parsley.

Sowed an Ounce of Onion-seed in one of the new Quarters: the ground in excellent order. Fine sunny weather for a week.

12: 13   Furious N: E: winds with so very keen an air, that things froze within doors in not much less degree than they did in January.

14.   Fierce clear frost, but a still air.

Sowed carrots, radishes, & Coss-lettuce under the melon-screen.

The Cucumber-plants first began to discover some fruit on the 13.

15.   Fierce still frost, & strong sunshine.

These frosts cut-down the wallflowers & Polyanths in a sad manner just as they are coming into bloom.

The Succades are stopp'd down, & thrive vastly.

17.   Earth'd, & hill'd the Succades, the bed being very moderate in appearance.

Soft, spring-like weather.

Sowed a spot of Polyanth-seed on a border facing to the South: the seed was saved in 1761.

19.   Planted the Succade-bed with two pots of plants in each hill. Each pot contained two fine stocky plants, that have each two large rough leaves; & have been stopp'd down, & show for runners. The bed seems to be mild; & has been made a fortnight to day. Matted-down the bed¶ with three of my 9 new London-matts; & trigg'd the lights a little.¶

       A stormy west wind.

22.   Found several Cucumbers in bloom this morning. Wet windy weather.

24.   Sowed 18 Cantaleupe-seeds in the Succade-frame. They were saved from a fine fruit in 1756, & are very plump, & large; & are the same with those from which M⸢ Cane raised such fine Melons last year at Tidworth.

       Set several of the Cucumbers in bloom. The bed rather declines in heat.

       The Succades begin to grow, & extend their roots in their new hills.

       Some of the young Nectarines are in bloom; & one peach.

       The Hyacinths under the wall are blowing apace: some are blown.

25.   Gave the Cucumber-bed a strong lining of hot dung to set, & forward the fruit. The plants had extended their fibres quite without the frames.

       Planted 20 good Cauliflowers from Hartley in a well-dung'd spot, & covered them with hand-glasses, & pots.

       Transplanted into a good mellow plot of Ground those few Coss-lettuces under the fruit-wall that survived the severe winter.

26.   Planted five rows of Potatoes quite across one of the middle quarters of the new-garden in well-dunged deep mould. The pieces were cut from large firm roots that had been well-preserved from y⸢ frost. If the pieces had not been planted 15 inc: apart, they would not have held-out.

       Sowed a good large plot of Savoys; & a plot of leeks.

       Fierce frosts with very thick Ice.

28.   Sowed London-Celeri, & M⸢ Missing's Parsley-leaved Celeriac under an Hand-glass with two barrows of dung.

       Earth'd the Succades (which had pretty well run their hills) for the first time. The middle hill was hot; but there were no tokens of burning.

       The young Cucumbers begin to swell, & seem to be set.

29.   Earth'd the Cucumber-bed for the last time. One of the forwardest fruit is gone-off. Removed the Cantaleupe seeds, that did not come-up so soon as they should do, into a warmer part of the bed.

30.   Moss'd the Cucumb⸢ bed all over to see if that will promote the swelling of the fruit by keeping the bed moist & warm. It is a practice much in use among Gardeners.

APRIL   1.   Sowed in the borders round the Garden 21 little basons of double upright larkspurs; from an ounce of London seed.

Sowed a plot of stocks from seed of my own saving: they came first from Ringmer.

All my stocks were kill'd last winter.

Sowed 18 more Cantaleupe-seeds: the last now come-up pretty well.

The Succades extend their fibres a second time without their hills; & have runners four or five inches long. Delicate soft dry weather. The ground works well.

2. Sowed a bed of Sweet-Williams.

Earth'd Succades the second time.

Beautiful soft grey weather.

Sowed a few more Bentworth-Cantaleupes & a few Succades.

Put a bottle of brandy at the time of tunning to the raisin-wine; & now an other to prevent it's working too long.

4. Planted several sorts of curious Asters, & Golden-rods sent me by Mᵣ Gibson in the borders, & field-basons. Potted the first-sown Cantaleupes, ten good plants.

5. Cut the first Cucumber, a good fruit, to carry to London. The rest, several brace, are swelling-away; but are yet of no size.

The Hyacinths are blowing-out apace.

7.¶ Sowed second crop of marrow-fats.

8. Carted-in 17 loads of hot dung for the Cantaleupe-bed.

9. Made the Cantaleupe-bed.

11. Sowed a plot of white helebore-seed: & potted the Succades.

13. Made 1 hand-glass bed, & sowed it with white-cucumbers.

13. Cut 13 large well-grown Cucumbers, which were sent me to London by the coach when they were two shill: apiece in town.

16. Planted half hund: of Cabbage-plants.

18. Sowed more savoys.

21. Earthed the Cantaleupe, & annual beds.

22. At my return from London found the Cucumber-bed full of fine fruit; & the Succade-plants well-grown; but not yet in bloom. The Hyacinths are now in high beauty: there are many curious ones in the nursery that must be mark'd for transplanting.

25. Earth'd-up the Succades for the last time: the plants are very stout; but do not shew any bloom or fruit.

25. Sowed the annual-bed with Alton, & London-Balsoms, China-asters, African & French-Marrigolds, Pendulous-Amaranths, Marvel of Peru, & dwarf Sunfl:

26. Stak'd & tack'd the espalier-pears, & plums; & eased, & disbudded the fruit-wall trees. Dry cold weather.

27. Planted five hills with Cantaleupe-plants from Seed of my own: & in two hills where there were only two plants to a pot I put-in one more from Mᵣ Acton's seed. Planted the first Hill with Succades to keep-up a Succession. The bed has been made 18 days; but yet is hot, & must be tilted when covered; & well-watched in very hot sun-shine. Mᵣ Acton's plants (from his seed which I gave him first) are in the first and second hills.

| | The Cucumbers bear wonderfully, & large well-grown fruit. |
| 30. | There have been cut this month from four lights only above 40 well-grown Cucumbers. |

Sowed some of Gordon's Celeriac (much commended) between the Cantaleupe boxes. The Cantaleupe-hills by tilting a nights, & frequent waterings go-on very well.

Tyed those Hyacinths that are white with pink-eye with a piece of scarlet worsted as a mark to save ofsets from. Mark'd the blue Hyacinths with a blue piece of worsted tyed to the sticks that stand before them.

MAY   2.   Sowed six rows (about three fourths of a quart) of white dwarf french beans in Turner's Garden. The Ground is very mellow.

Extreme sharp wind with hail for these two days past.

Stopp'd-down the Cantaleupes, which are settled in their Hills, & seem past all danger of burning.

Layed-down several branches of the fine bloody wall-flowers. Many of the wallflowers were kill'd last winter: as the Artichokes seem all to be.

4.   Several smart claps of thunder which appeared extraordinary in the midst of such cold weather.

Very white frosts every night.

6.   Made a row of Handglass-beds, with one barrow of dung to each, for the white cucum.ᵖˢ

White frosts, & sunny days.

The succades begin to show fruit.

7.   Planted the Hand-glasses with white-Cucumber-plants.

Weeded the brick walls in the Garden.

The Cantaleupe-plants take well to their Hills, & begin to shew runners.

8.   A strange tempestuous day, with violent thunder, storms of hail, & gluts of rain. Very cold weather before, & since.

10.   Observing that some of the Cantaleupes were a little of a Yellowish hue, I examined the hills, & found that notwithstanding the cold black weather, & that the bed had been made a month, yet the mould began to be a little burnt. Upon which I gave them a good watering, & a second earthing, which will soon bring them right. The fibres were run thro' the hills; & most of them shew good runners.

One imperfect male blossom of the Succades is blown-out.

11.   Added a pint more of brandy, in all five pints, to the last raisin-wine, which still hisses pretty much.

13.   Lined & earth'd-out the Succade-bed, which seem'd to be declining in it's heat. Several male blossoms are open.

Hot summer. The grass grows apace in the meadows.

14.   The Succades have now a fruit in bloom.

The Cantaleupes, which seem'd a little injured by too much heat, by watering are pretty well restored to a good Colour.

15.   Planted about 40 late Cabbages in the new Garden.

The Fruit wall,
Early September.
The Wakes.

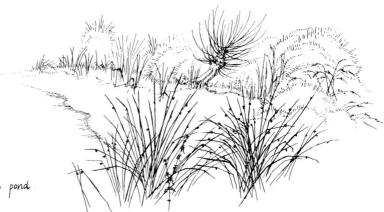

Newton Valence pond.
26 May.

Prick'd about 200 fine Savoy-plants from M͞r Etty's in the Garden near the tub.

25. The Succades blow pretty well; but no fruit is set yet.

One Cantaleupe has a male bloom, & a weak fruit blown: the rest are in good healthy order.

One of the Newington-Nectarines has three fruit that seem likely to stand.

The vines on the House shew well for fruit: the Muscadine-vine (which was planted a cutting April was three years) promises to have 31 bunches of Grapes.

Continual cold N: E: Winds.

26. Observing that the Succades were backward in setting, & went-off soon after blowing, I examined into the mould that lay on the lining, & found that it was so over-heated by a thick coat of mowed Grass as to be scalding hot, & quite unfit for vegetation. Took-off the grass, & trod-down the earth close to the bed, where it was sunk away, watered it very stoutly, & fill'd it up to the frames with good fresh earth.

27. Planted six rows of dwarf white french-beans in the new garden. The first crop are come-up pretty well.

Earthed the Cantaleupes quite out, & raised the frames.

Cold, black, dry weather: no rain for a fortnight.

28. Prick'd-out the first Celeri.

Added about half a pint more of brandy, in all five pints & an half, to the last-made-wine, which hisses still pretty much. Cold, bright weather.

JUNE 4. The weather has been dry, except one trifling shower, for these three weeks today. No Succades set yet.

The Cantaleupes thrive, & shew fruit.

Water'd the Succades well at their stems.

Sunny, dry weather: rain is much wanted.

5. The Succades now begin to set. The Cantaleupes have some fruit that promise for setting. The Succades this very dry Season wanted more water at their hills.

The fields & gardens begin to suffer by the long dry season.

        Cold, dry weather with an high Barometer.

6.   Tack'd-up the vine-shoots.

11.   It is exactly a month to day since there has been any rain except a trifling shower or two that did not half lay ye dust. The fields & Gardens begin to suffer; & there is but a poor prospect of a Crop of hay; & most people's old stock is quite spent. There have been great showers about for this week past; but we have had none of them yet.

        The Succades have now many brace set; & there are a brace or two of Cantaleupes secure. The Succades have lost a fortnight for want of more water this severe dry season. Widen'd-out the Cantal: Bed before & behind, & laid-on a good depth of earth.

        Heavy showers now about.

13.   Only a few showers that did not lay the dust.

14.   Hot burning weather again.

        Potted two curious Pyram: Camp: one has 23 stalks, the other 17. They were so large that no garden-pot would hold them; so were planted in large butter-pots with Holes bored in the bottom. Several large roots were broken-off in the removal; but possibly that loss may not affect the blowing.

15.   Vast rain at Alton; but only a small sprinkling here.

        The Cantaleupes set apace.

16.   Small showers that refresh the fields & Gardens a little.

        The Cantaleupes set all their first fruit, & promise for a good Crop. Some of the Succades are pretty well grown, but they are all on second & third wood.

        Planted-out the annuals, which are backward & weak.

        Sowed Endive & Coss-lettuce.

        The vines are beginning to blow.

        To day compleats the fifth week since there was any rain here except a few small showers lately, which never laid the dust. The grass-walks look rusty. There have been fine rains round the Country.

20.   Raised & earthed the melon-frames for the last time: the boxes are now even with the tops of the hills, & the beds are earth'd-down with a great depth of mould. The Cantaleupes continue to set well; & the single Hill of Succades: hardly any of the first fruit has been lost. But they have had a deal of water this burning season.

        Prick'd-out some of Gordon's Celeriac, & some Common Celeri in the shady end of the melon-border.

        Planted the bank in the new-garden, & part of the back of the melon-screen with annuals. China-asters run very scanty this Year. Some of the Succades seem to be full grown. Trod-down the mould on the melon-bed, & spread some loose earth over it.

25.   This is now the sixth week of the dry weather. A small shower this evening that has not laid the dust.

        Watered the Cantaleupes well, round the frames, & laid some short hay over the mould to keep it moist.

The Cabbages begin to look blue.

27. Gather'd the first marrow-fat pease.

The Corn begins to suffer by the long dry weather.

I continue to water the melon-beds often. The Grass-walks look exceeding rusty.

28. Cut the grass in the meadow, & slip.

29. Just as all the grass was spread-about came a great rain all day from the east: the only rain to do any good for six weeks, & three days.

30. Vast showers with Thunder & hail. Planted a plot of very forward Savoys; & a plot of later-sown ones.

The thunder-shower damaged the zigzag a good deal. The rain has thoro'ly soak'd the ground down to the roots.

JULY   4. Tyled the Succades¶ that are but a midling Crop. There is a second Crop coming on.

Took-off the frames from the early cucumbers, which bear still vastly.

Half the hay is housed on waggons in barns: the rest is in Cock.

Soft, showery, growing weather.

The Cantaleupes come on unequally; some scarce swell at all, & some are full-grown.

5. Rick'd the hay in very moderate order: the load that stood in Kelsey's barn was strangely damp, & heated: & was spread & dry'd over again.

6. Finish'd stopping-down, & tacking ye vines: they are in full bloom.

Planted a good plot of leeks in Turner's.

Showery, growing weather.

8. Put a quarter of a pound of hops to the strong-brewed in Feb: which promises to be good.

9. Showery weather still.

Putty'd the melon frames to keep-out the wet: housed the cucumber-frames. The plants that were in full bearing are much check'd by being exposed at once to the open air; but their fruit is not much wanted, now the hand-glass-hills are in full bearing.

14. Trenched-out four rows of stocky Celeri in one of the lower quarters of the new garden.

Showery weather.

†13. Mr Tho: Mulso, & Lady, & Mr Edw: Mulso & Miss Harriot Baker¶ came to visit me.

19. Finished planting-out 6 trenches of Celeri, & a second plot of Endive.

Cut the first Succade.

Very wet weather.

26. Succades come very fast. Cut some tollerable Cauliflowers.

---

†15? Probably an error in dating.

Moss rose, 'Louis Gimard'
the Wakes.
9 July.

Succades weigh 24 ounces, & are very dry. Continual showers, & a quantity of hay damaged.

    Planted two rows of Gordon's Celeliac [Celeriac].

27.   Divided out & planted round the new garden M:rs Snooke's fine double Pheasant-ey'd-pinks.¶

28.   Drank tea 20 of us at the Hermitage: the Miss Batties, & the Mulso family contributed much to our pleasure by their singing, & being dress'd as shepherds, & shepherdesses. It was a most elegant evening; & all parties appear'd highly satisfy'd. The Hermit appear'd to great advantage.¶

29.   A vast rain. The hay lies about in a miserable way.

30.   Cut the first Cantaleupe, which, considering the wet season, proved a good one.

AUGUST   1.   Wet weather still.

2.   Took-up my Hyacinths under the fruit-wall: they have many offsets, & seem not to be damaged with the wet season.

3.   Terrible rain, & my neighbour's hay in a deplorable way. The rainy season has lasted just five weeks to day.

    Cut a fine-looking Cantaleupe, & sent it by the Ladies (who left Selborne this day) to D:r Battie. Cut several Succades: they want Sun & dry weather.

4.   Vast rains still. The wet has lasted five weeks yesterday.

5.   Eat an extraordinary fine Cantaleupe notwithstanding the rains.

9: 10.   Two fine days: during which my Neighbours got in their Hay rather better than was expected.

11.   Sowed a crop of spinage. Dry weather for three days, but distant thunder.

15.   Sowed a plot of turneps. Dry weather for some days.

16.   Showers again. Cut some fine Cantaleupes. People are just entering on wheat-harvest.

22: 23.   Showery weather, & very little wheat housed: it begins to grow under the hedges. Finished cutting my Cantaleupes, & Succades. The Grapes are very backward & small, having seen nothing but black showery weather for these eight weeks.

25.   Mr Mulso's family left me.

26.   Now a long rain after two fine days. The wheat grows pretty much.

SEPTEMBER 4.   Now frequent showers after some fine days. There is a good deal of wheat still abroad.

7.   Now wet weather after some fine days. Much wheat abroad still.

10.   Tyed up endive. Showery, bad weather.

13.   Many days black wet weather.

    The Grapes begin to change Colour.

    Planted a row of stocks on the fruitwall border, & under the dining-room window.

18.   Black wet weather.

Dung borrowed in 1763

Kelsey p^d Car: Dung p^d. . . . . 1 load
Brought in of my own 1 load.
Jan: 17 Kelsey p^d Car Dung p^d. . . . . . . 5 loads
    . . . . . my own 3 loads.
Parsons Dung p^d . . . . 2 loads
Jan: 18. Pd: Kelsey his last five loads of dung by allowing him to take three loads from the dung-hill in the orchard.
March 5. Kelsey Car p^d Dung p^d . . . . . . 5 loads
    . . . . . my own 2 loads
Parsons Dung p^d . . . . 3 loads
Apr: 8. Kelsey Car pd Dung pd. . . . . 10 loads
    . . . . . my own 2 loads
Parsons Dung p^d . . . . 5 loads

The rainy season continued 12 weeks; since which there has been some delicate weather in the latter end of Septem^r & Octob^r that has made the grapes better than could be expected.

OCTOBER 18.   Planted an hundred of Cabbages to stand the winter.

24.   Dug up the potatoes which are large & fine. Trimm'd & tack'd the fruit wall trees: the wet summer had forced most of them into too much large willow-like wood, which will not blow so well next year as smaller. The vines against the wall have got well-ripen'd shoots, & promise for plenty of fruit next year. The garden abounds with good Celeri, & spinage, & a very fine sort of Savoys.

    Tolerable grapes in plenty. Hares or some vermin have gnawed almost all the fine Pheasant-eyed pinks,

       & the new-planted cabbages.
30.   Now rain, & stormy wind after just three weeks soft, still dry, summer like weather.

NOVEMBER 4: Vast rains, & floods.
    9. Very fine grapes still: there have been no frosts to any degree.
    16. Serene, beautiful weather for several days, with the Mercury within half a degree of settled fair. Planted my Hyacinths in two rows all along the border opposite the fruit-border: dug-in first some well-rotted dung. Put the blue & best pink-eyed intermixed in front. Planted my Tulips, *Narcissus*, & Jonquils in the border opposite the bank. Dug & cleared the banks, & dining-room-shrubbery this fine season.
18: 19: 20. Most severe frost indeed with thick bearing Ice, & a very cutting wind: a small snow. There has been a very mild season till now.

DECEMBER 19. Planted some hepaticas, fritillaries, & winter aconites from Ringmer, & some fine persian Jasmines, & cobnuts. Vast rains & floods of late.
    21. Brewed half Hogsh: of strong beer with 6 bush: of coal-dry'd malt, & 2 p^{ds} & an half of hops; the water all from the well. Continual wet weather.

— 1764 —

This year begins as the former concluded with continual heavy rains, & vast floods. There has indeed been little else but wet weather (a few short intervals excepted) ever since the 29th of June.

JANUARY 5. Made a seedling Cucumber-bed with dung that had been very much wash'd.
    9. Finding the bed come to a pretty good heat I sowed about 20 seeds.
    13. A most violent storm all night, that must have in all appearance done great damage: vast rains at the same time. The Cucumbers are come-up & look well. The wind blew-down the hot-bed screen.
    23. The second sowing of Cucumbers are come-up very well.
    28. Very stormy weather still, with great showers. The Crocuss begin to blow.
    31. Vast rains, & storms of wind. Prodigious inundations all over England, Holland & Germany. Lined the Cucumber-bed with many barrows of hot dung.

FEBRUARY 7. Brewed 45 Gallons of strong-beer with eight bushels of malt dryed with Welch-coal; & three pounds & three quarters of good hops. The strong-beer was closely covered down with sacks, while infusing in the mash-vat: & the yeast was beat into the beer several times, till it was put into the barrel. Made with the same malt Half an hogsh: of ale, & an Hogsh: of small. The strong-beer was made entirely with rain-water. Tunn'd the strong beer¶ the third day.

10. Made a bearing Cucumber-bed with between eight & nine loads of good hot dung for two two-light frames.

Vast rains, & high winds still.

Sowed the great mead all over with about 30 bushels of my own ashes; & the little mead with 12 bushels bought of Mr Etty.

13. Bottled-out half an Hogsh: of Mrs Atherley port-wine. It had not, I think, quite so good a smell & flavour as usuall; & seem'd always to shew a disposition to mantle in the glass.¶

17. Put the Hills of earth on the Cucumr Bed: the earth by means of the long wet season was not in curious order.

18. Planted the Cucumber-plants on their Hills. The plants are grown to two Joints, & are stopped down. The bed seems to be in good order.

20. It has been now pretty dry ever since the fifteenth day. There have not been so many dry days for some months. The weather glass is very high, & the wind N: E.

21. Sowed 10 Succade-seeds in the Cucr bed. A very white-frost & bright sunshine.

The snails after so mild a winter are very numerous, & get into the bed & eat the plants.

26. This is now the eleventh day of the dry weather: the roads are finely dry'd. A strong North E: wind, & a sinking Glass.

27. A considerable snow on the ground. A severe frost this evening.

The snails continue to annoy the Cucr bed; & have destroy'd all the plants in one hill, & damaged several others.

29. Very hard frost, & snow on the ground. The hot-bed goes-on but poorly: the plants don't grow, the snails damage them every night, & the succades don't come-up.

MARCH 1. Gave the hot-bed a good lining of hot dung. In general the plants don't grow; but one begins to shew a runner. Blowing black weather, & snow on the ground.

5. The frost has been so bad for a day or two past that the plants in the bed seemed in a very poor way, & the bed almost cold: but now the lining begins to take effect, & there is some warm sunshine that will set ym to growing again. The snails continue to gnaw the plants tho' we kill numbers.

Sowed 12 Succade-seeds. A mouse devoured the first; indeed the bed would not bring them up. The frost has been now a week last saturday. The rose-trees, Crocuss, Hyacinths, & polyanths are much pinch'd by the severe weather.

10. Very severe, black, cutting weather for a fortnight past, with several pretty large falls of snow, that do not lie long at a time. The hot bed succeeds very poorly.

12. Sowed five rows of marrowfat pease, the first crop; & some

radishes & Coss-lettuce under the fruit-wall: the border is very mellow.

Planted a row of laurels against Parsons's behind the filbert hedge.

There has been now no rain for these three weeks: the landsprings¶ are much abated.

15.   Gave the hot-bed a strong lining.

Planted six rows of broad beans.

Planted a row of Laurustines before the laurels against the street.

16.   Sunny, summer-like weather, & the ground in good dry order.

The Hot-bed comes into good Condition again, & the Cuc⸢ plants throw out runners. Mossed the bed round the hills. The second sowing of Succades come-up well at last: there are only four plants of the first sowing.

Dress'd the border next Parsons's, & new-planted the perennials; & planted a row of sweet Williams in the front. Dress'd the Rasp bed.

The Crocuss, that seem'd to be so much coddled with frost, now make a great shew again.

17.   Planted half hund: of Cabbage plants; the second planting.

18.   Very bright sunny weather with a vast white frost after several grey days. During this late dry weather the Garden has been cleaned & put in pretty neat order.

19.   Now rain after a fit of dry weather that would have lasted five weeks, had it held out till tomorrow. The long fit of wet that occasioned such floods & devastations all Europe over, lasted, with very few Intervals of dry between from June 29: 1763: to Feb: 15: 1764.

One of the Cuc⸢ plants has got a male-bloom full blown. The Cucum⸢ˢ now thrive, & the melons-plants come-up well.

Potted all the first-sown Succades, which were a little drawn, in three pots. The last-sown come-up very well. Soft, showery weather.

20.   Made the Succade-bed (the dung brought-in the same day) with eight loads of dung: it proves full stout enough, but is made rather too narrow & longer than needs be. Blowing March-weather. Mowed part of the grass-plot for the first time: there was a great swarth¶ of grass, that made a good lining for the Cuc⸢ bed, which now works well: Several plants have male-bloom.

22.   Planted five rows of potatoes in a mellow rich part of the garden with pieces from very large sound roots that had been very well-preserved. The ground had been well dunged, but no thatch was used. Sowed a deep, well-dug plot with a Crop of Carrots, Coss lettuce, & parsneps together. Planted a row of pine, & Nova Scotia strawberry-plants: the bed is run to ruin & must be destroy'd.

Raked-down the Asparagus-beds.

Planted some basons in the field with Sweet-Williams. The

garden is now mowed all round. Blowing cold weather with some showers in the evening.

The Cuc: bed heats well; & the plants keep throwing-out male-bloom.

Made a hill with one good barrow of dung for an handglass, & sowed it with Celeri-seed.

24. Earth'd the Cucumber-bed: the plants extend their fibres very fast.

Sowed four pots of fraxinella-seeds.¶

28. Sowed a Crop of Onions, & a plot of leeks. Planted Horse chestnuts in the nursery.

29. Earth'd the Succade-bed: & sowed some white Cucumbers.

APRIL 3. Lined the Cucumber bed again.

5. Planted-out the Succades. Two Cucumbers in bloom. Sowed sixteen Cantaleupe seeds, & 6 succade seeds.

7. Planted the second Crop of pease.

13. Potted the Cantaleupes: they are fine plants. The Succades come-up poorly. The Succades in the hills are fine stocky plants, & full of runners. There are two Cucumbers of some size; & more setting.

16. Sowed about 18 basons in the best garden with larkspurs, one ounce of seed.

17. Rain & snow

19. Suddain transitions from hard rains to fierce frost, & ice.

21. Cut a brace of Cucumbers, large fruit, the first this season.

Made the Cantaleupe-bed for six lights with sixteen loads of dung.

Many Cucumbers are now set, & coming on.

All the wall-trees had each a little bloom.

Planted about three doz: of wall-flower cuttings.

27. Made the annual bed, & sowed it with African & French-marrigolds, marvel of Peru, Iraquois-Gourds,¶ Pendulous Amaranths, Sowed Dwarf-sunflowers in the cold ground.

Sowed a crop of Savoys: & a little plot of burnet.¶

30. Earthed the Cantaleupe-bed, & made the hills for the plants.

MAY 2. Sowed four rows of white-dwarf-french-beans.

Planted-out the Cantaleupes in the Hills.

5. On my return from Oxōn I found the Succades in great vigour, with third wood of some length, that shewed the rudiments of bloom. The Succades take well to their Hills, & look very green. The Cucumbers are full of fruit.

Many of the blue, & white Hyacinths are very beautiful indeed.

Bright summer-like weather; & all things in a very growing Condition.

7. Earth'd-out the Succades.

Disbudded the wall-fruit trees, that were grown very rude. In all appearance they will have no fruit this Year.

Open'd, & painted the Alcove.

Cut the Laurustine-hedge in the Yard down to the Ground.

12.   One Succade-fruit is blown before any male bloom.

15.   Great showers for several days with a S: W: Wind that damages the flowers & trees. The Ground is well soak'd. The grass grows very fast, & the spring-corn comes-up well. Many of the double-stocks are very beautiful.

The Cantaleupes throw-out good runners.

17.   Hot weather: things grow very fast after such fine showers. Planted out 4 Iroquois-Gourds against the fruit-wall. The Cucumbers bear well.

Finished weeding the brick-walks.

The Succades are full of male-bloom, & begin to shew pretty good-looking fruit.

21.   Lined the Succade-bed with two loads of hot dung, one before, & one behind. The plants now throw-out plenty of promising fruit; some of it is in bloom. Tacked the vine-shoots against the wall for the first time. The vines round the House shew for fruit; but not in such Quantities as for some years past.

26.   The weather for some days very sultry: to day was thunder & rain; & in some places very heavy showers; but not at Selborne.

JUNE   2.   On my return from Fifield I found an abundance of Succades set; & some as large as Goose-eggs. The Cantaleupes (tho' the Haulm has not half-filled the boxes) are setting very fast. The very hot weather has drawn the stalks of the fruit pretty long.

4.   Earth'd-out the Cantaleupes & Succades to the full; & brought the mould in front quite down to the Ground: raised all the melon frames quite above the mould.

Planted 100 of Savoy-plants from Ludgershal in a nursery-bed; but was forced to water the ground very much before it would plant. The ground by means of the wet winter & later drying winds is as hard as a stone; so that there is no sowing or planting any quantity till rains come. On account of the hardness of the Ground the Lent-corn begins to want rain very much. The fine double stocks are still in full bloom.

Very cold, black, drying weather for these ten days past.

6.   Sowed a Crop of Endive: watered the Ground to make it rake.

Garden snails out on a wet afternoon,
Selborne Common.
6 June.

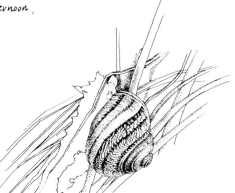

7.   Prick'd-out a plot of Celeri.

8: 9.   Now fine rains, after the Ground had been bound-up like so much stone for some time. Thinn'd-out, & tack'd the peaches, & nectarines in a very regular manner; so that the shoots will have the benefit of the sun & air to ripen them. There was not one fruit to be found. The trees are kept open in the middle, but make a very regular appearance on the sides.

12.   Sowed second crop, a pint of white dwarf-french-beans in five rows. The ground is still very hard, & dry; the late rains were not plentiful enough to make it work well. The first sowing of french-beans are tolerable.

Some few of the Burnet-plants have escaped the fly, & are got pretty large.

13.   Very hot summer weather.

15.   The vine against the fruit-wall from Mrs Snooke's black sort is now in bloom before any of my black Grapes against the House; which confirms me in my suspicions that her sort was earlier than mine.

Turn'd-out the white Cucumbers from under the Hand-glasses: they are full of fruit.

Hot weather; & the garden requires a deal of water.

Finish'd tacking the vines.

18.   Mowed the greatest part of the great mead: but was deterr'd from finishing the whole by a vast tempest of thunder & lightening that lay along to the N: W: N: & E: all the afternoon. It thundered loudly for hours together; but not one drop fell with us. The heat, being reflected from white thunder-clouds, was unusually severe. The weather cock stood all day plumb S: but the storm came-up from the N: W: There is a very fine crop of Grass in the meadow. This day has burnt & scalded things in the Gardens in a strange manner. Gave the Cantaleupes a good watering within the frames: but gave no water to the Succades, as many brace of them, at least ten, are full grown, & near ripening.

19.   The thunder-storm, which threat'ned so hard, sunk quite away in the night. A fine sunny day with a brisk wind at E:

20.   The same weather; & the hay makes at a vast rate. Carry'd four Jobbs to the rick.

21.   A Continuance of hot sunshine with brisk air. Carry'd four more Jobbs, all my hay in most curious order without one drop of rain. This is now the ninth day of hot sunshine: so that the ground is greatly burnt; & the grass walks look very rusty. Nothing can be done in the Garden, which is like an heap of stones. Laid pease-haulm, & straw round the outsides of the melon-beds to keep out the fierce heat. Water'd the Cantaleupes well round the extremities on the straw. They have several fruit about half grown; & several that never moved at all after setting: they now begin to throw-out fresh shoots, & fair fruit. The succades have had no water all this fierce sunny weather. The cucumber-frames are beat-out of bearing by the Heat. The hand-glass Cucumbers

are shaded all day, & yet are injured by the intense sunshine. There has been no weather to plant-out annuals: they are damaged by the hot season. The self-sown Larkspurs all turn out single: the basons of double seed never came-up.

22. Thunder in the morning; & a little shattering of rain, being the skirts of the storm: clear burning weather the rest of the day.

23: 24. Little soft showers: but heavy rains at Farington, & all round us. Such gluts of rain near Odiham as did great damage to the Corn & hay. Vast damage in London, & round Reading.

25. The grapes of M\ers Snooke's black-Cluster fairly set. The black Hambro', Sweet-water, & Muscadine but Just coming into bloom. My own black-Cluster on the House but just blowing. Prick'd-out more Celeri: the ground is very little moistened. Stopped-down the vines against the wall. Began planting-out the annuals: & tyled the Succades; which are a fine plentiful Crop.

26. Finished planting-out the annuals; & sowed a Crop of turneps mixed with Coss-lettuce. Frequent soft showers: but the Ground yet but little moistened.

28. A good lasting rain that moisten'd things well down to the roots. Rak'd-down the rough ground, & planted-out a large plot of Endives, & a plot of Savoys; & a plot of leeks. Potted-out two Pyramidal Campanulas, one with 14 stalks, & one with two.
     The Martagons make a vast figure.
     Cut the first white Cucumbers.
     Sowed a row of curled-parsley.
     The Grapes of M\rs Snooke's sort quite large: some of my own just set: the other sorts just coming into bloom.

29. Several showers. Planted more Savoys.

30. Planted half hundred of common cabbages. Cut the laurel-hedge against the necessary very neatly with a knife.

JULY   2. Hot, burning weather for two days. Cut the first Succade; but a small fruit. Housed my Cucumber-frame, & Glasses.

3. Cut the second Succade. Very hot weather.

4. Cut a brace more Succades. Stopped-down, & tacked all the vines against the House: they are now in full bloom, & smell very sweetly.
    Fine soft showers. Dug-up the tulip bed; & several Hyacinths from an old nursery.

5. Planted some stocks from M\r Budd's in a nursery bed. Stopped-down, & trimmed the Laurels against Parsons's Yard, & the street. The Cantaleupes run vastly to bine, but do not fruit well. Some few Cantaleupes in every light are almost full-grown, & look very black, & rough.

6. The first stout shower, that soaked the Ground well.

7. Cut a Succade that was crack'd very deeply at the eye. The Cantaleupes usually crack so; the Succades never before. Sunny weather. Cut two brace more, the most choice fruit of the whole Crop.

9. Cut all the crop of Succades, three brace & an half, tho' they were not crack'd at the tail, to carry them to Fifield. Hot sunny weather. Ordered the bed to be well-watered for a second Crop. Saved the seeds of a very delicate Succade, that grew close to the stem.

 The Succades proved good at Fyfield.

Martagon lily growing on BaRers Hill 16 July.

21. At my return from Fyfield I found the Cantaleupes greatly over-run with haulm, but no more fruit set. There will be a slender crop; not more than a brace to a light, & those but small. The Grapes on the fruit-wall are large (especially those on Mrs Snooke's black Cluster) & much forwarder than those on the walls of the house. The peaches, & Nectarine trees grow too much, & run into willow-like wood. Showery, hot weather for a fortnight past.

22. Cut the first Cantaleupe: it proved a very good one, tho' under-sized.

    Put some hops, & sand into the stronger-beer brewed in Decem^r to fine it down.

    The Iroquois-Gourds are very peculiar in their growth: they are short stocky plants without any runners. Some of them have variegated leaves. The Pyram: Camp: are drawn by standing in the brewhouse: put them in the Alcove. The White Cucumbers bear plentifully.

27. Trenched three good long rows of Celeri in Turner's Garden.

    The Ground is in good order. Showery weather. Planted a plot of Savoys from Hartley.

28. Cut two fine Cantaleupes, that crack at the eye; but they are undersized.

AUGUST 1. Cut a fine black Cantaleupe: it was crack'd at the eye. Sowed a large plot of Ground with prickly spinage, & Coss lettuce. Showery weather with a strong wind that damages the Garden. Cleaned the vines of their side shoots.

2. Planted three more rows of Celeri in Turner's garden: the six rows make a large stock. Black, windy, showery weather. The black Cantaleupe proved a curious one.

    Thinn'd the leeks in the seedling-bed, & left the largest to stand as part of a Crop. Dresh'd the bank, & borders. The Iroquois-Gourds shew pretty large fruit; but have no runners. The grapes on the fruit-wall are much larger & forwarder than those on the House. Saved a little Polyanth-seed. Trimmed the side-wood from the shoots of the wall-trees, & tacked them down close as they grow.

    There will be a small second Crop of Succades: 2 brace of small succades of the single hill are not yet come.

    Many people have just began Harvest.

7: 8. Two dismal wet days: vast quantities of water fell.

11. Tyed-up 25 endives; the first tying.

12: 13: 14. Showery, bad harvest-weather.

15. Put a pint of brandy to the Half hogsh: of raisin wine made Jan: 1763. In the spring it was got fine, & in good order: but now it is in a great ferment. I have beat-up the bung, & left it open.

    Very wet weather still.

17. A pretty fine day with a brisk drying wind. Many people were

housing wheat all day, which went-in in better condition that could be expected.

18.   Vast heavy drowning rains. The white Cucumbers were in full bearing; but are damaged by the rains, & long cold black weather. The annuals are injured by the wet. The Grapes on the House are small, & backward; those of the wall are much before them. The first-sown french-beans bear vastly: the latter don't come-on.

24.   No rain since the 18: & this is the fourth most beautiful harvest-day that ever was seen; during which the farmers in these parts have quite finish'd their wheat-harvest. Those that had the most patience will have by much the best corn.

Planted two ofsets of a fine sort of *Lychnidea*, given me by Mr Gibson, in my flower border; & a sucker of a fine purple lilac in the nursery.

Planted half a doz: of my fine bloody wallflowers on the fruit-border: they are fine plants.

Cut a Cantaleupe-melon, that is much crack'd at the eye. Figs are large & good.

The grapes on Mrs Snooke's black-cluster vine just begin to turn: those on the house are small, & backward.

The vine Murdoch Middleton sent for Warner's black Hambro', seems, as it approached towards ripening, to be some ordinary sort of white Grape.¶ The barometer is very high.

25.   Beautiful weather still: but the Glass falls. The Cantaleupe, tho' it had but little smell, was very fine.

Put a bottle more of brandy to the raisin-wine, which works much.

Made and housed the second cutting of the shrubbery, & orchard in fine order, without a drop of rain. Housed two of the melon-frames, & put a few fruit under the hand-glasses.

Tyed-up the second Crop of Endive: they are very large.

26.   Cut a brace of every [?very] fine-flavoured Cantaleupes, the last of the season: they were not large. Housed the last frame. The wasps were got to be very troublesome at the melon-bed, gnawing great holes in ye fruit. Set bottles of treacle, & beer.

27.   Very hot, summer-like weather: the glass after sinking a day or two, is now going up again. Mrs Snooke's black Clusters change Colour apace; & the white sorts begin to grow transparent. The wood of the vines ripens apace. The wood of the peaches, & Nectarines ripens well, & begins to shew it's blowing budds surrounded with three leaves.

There are two brace of pretty good Succades under the hand-glasses.

29.   Sowed some more Coss-lettuce: those among the spinage, as well as the spinage, come-up but poorly. The grapes against the yard

just begin to turn. A soft rain after ten hot, dry days.

31.   Very hot sunny weather. Cut the first-tyed endives, they are delicately blanched.

     The barometer is now very high.

SEPTEMBER 1.   Got a stone-mason to fix the stone with my name & the date of the wall in the middle of the fruit-wall. When the mason came to chizzel a hole for the stone he found the wall perfectly sound, dry, & hard.

3.   Returned the raisin-wine (which had been drawn into a tun-tub two days) into the barrel again, & put in one more pint of brandy: there is left behind near three Gallons of grout.

     Hot sunny weather still. The wine frets a little still.

7.   Tyed-up more endive: the third tying: the endives are very large, & fine. Earthed-up two rows of Celeri for the first time.

     Beautiful weather still: it has now lasted three weeks. Harvest is finished in general; except some vetches, & barley that are not yet ripe.

     The Grapes on the fruit-wall ripen very fast.

     During this sunny weather fresh Cantaleupes, & succades set very fast since the frames have been taken away.

12.   Now a great rain after three weeks, & three days delicate weather.

16.   Cold, windy weather still. The annuals are much damaged.

18.   Gathered the sweet-water grapes on the fruit-wall which are ripe; & some of Mrs Snooke's black-cluster-grapes, which are very eatable but not highly flavoured.

     In the night between the 16: & 17: my melons & Cucumbers were pulled all to pieces; & the horse-block, three handglasses, & many other things were destroy'd by persons unknown.¶

22.   Fine settled weather: the Grapes are now good, but not delicate. The wasps are not very numerous; but have damaged some bunches.

24.   A very white frost, & Ice in some places. Gather'd a plate of Grapes from the wall of ye House next the yard; these are the first that have been perfectly fine.

25.   A second very white frost. Beautiful sunny still weather with a very high barometer. The annuals are much cut-down. Took-in three of the Iroquois Gourds, which are very peculiar fruit: those from the variegated plants are of a yellowish Cast; those from the green-leaved of a dark-green Colour.

     The succades that were taken-in before they were ripe, & hung to the beam over the Kitchen-fire, have ripen'd well; & proved of a good Colour & flavour; but are some what moist & flabby. Dug the border of the fruit-wall, & took-away all the gourds, & annuals. Tyed-up more endives: they are vastly large; but some what damaged by the frost. There have been a few good mulberries; but they ripen too late. Earthed-up all the rows of Celeri; & two rows for the second time. The Mich: Daiseys covered with butter-flies, & other gaudy insects make a very gallant appearance in the sunshine. We have continued to catch the wasps, & hornets, which are not very numerous, with birdlime. the late Cabbages, & savoys are in great perfection: the french-beans are quite cut-down, & destroy'd. The potatoes are good, but not very large.

30.   A very sharp March-like wind from the N: many days with frosts & Ice. The ground is very dry; & the Clays have a fine season for wheat. Wind & rain, & a low glass.

OCTOBER   1.   Now a brisk wind, & sunshine. Planted-out several double-bloody-wallflowers under the fruit-wall, & melon-screen. Planted several ofsets from the potted Campanulas. Sent a basket of Grapes, & Cadillac pears to Lady Stuart.

6.   Gather'd-in a moderate quantity of all the keeping apples: they are well-coloured, but small, being vastly thick on the trees.

The Grapes are now delicate, both white & red. Fine, serene, summer-like weather: except now & then a small shower: the dry season has lasted seven weeks to day.

7.   Beautiful clear weather.

20.   Fine soft weather intermixed with some gentle showers. This delicate weather makes most curious Grapes. The farmers put their wheat into the ground in fine order.

23.   Dry sunny weather with an high barometer. Earth'd-up the Celeri for the last time: made use of some, which was well-balanced, & well-grown.

24.   Bright, cold weather. Grapes in the greatest perfection.

26.   Planted 100 of Cabbages to stand the winter. Planted my Coss-lettuces, some very large some very small, against the fruit-wall to stand the winter. The farmers carried-out their dung from the melon-bed in a fine dry season. The weather very dry & cold. Gather'd 6 medlars, the first fruit that ever the tree produced.¶

28.   Very bright, cold, sharp weather with considerable Ice. Gather'd-in a considerable part of the grapes, which are very curious. The dry fit has lasted ten weeks to day.

NOVEMBER 1.   Planted-out some stocks from Mr Budds & a few from Ringmer. Dry still weather; but thick Ice in the morning. The ground is dry like summer. The ponds, & wells are exceeding low: many wells are quite dry.

5: 6.   Put the tulips, taken-up in Summer, into the ground; & made a nursery of the best offsets. Dug-up the Polyanth-Narcissuss, & Daffodils, that had stood two years, & transplanted them; they were greatly encreased. Mrs Snooke's tulips are planted in the border where the two Cherry-trees stand. My own filled-out the Border towards the alcove, & made a bed near the tub for water. Planted a row of Jonquils on the fruit-border near the Haha.

The rain that has fallen yet is very trifling, only just enough to make the ground slippery. To day, the 6th a stormy wind, &

sinking glass.

6. Now a very heavy rain with a violent stormy wind.

7. Gather'd-in a large basket of Grapes, the last of the season: they are in fine order.

8. A very great rain: so that the dry season might be said to last just eleven weeks from the 19 of August.

8. Bottled half an hogsh: of elder-raisin wine, made in Feb: 1763: it took a second fermentation last spring; but is now very good except a little smatch of the brandy which I put-in to stop the working.

6: 8: 10. A great deal of rain.

14. Trimm'd & tack'd all the trees against the fruit-wall. The peaches, & nectarines all promise to produce bloom: some have made shoots too gross & willow-like. Dug & laid down the border in curious order. Tack'd the vines some perpendicularly, some horisontaly. A smart frost in the morning.

22. Eat my last Grapes.

23. Planted a Golden-pippin, & a Queen-Claud-plum,¶ both standards, in the orchard: & a Portugal-Laurel in the shrubbery. The golden pippins planted in the orchard two or three years ago are both much annoy'd with the Canker, tho' they were planted on Hillocks to avoid the wet.

Dung borrowed in 1764

Feb: 8	Of Kelsey Dung p^d Car: p^d.	5 loads
	Of Parsons Dung p^d Car: p^d.	2 D^o
March 1	Of Kelsey (no Car: to pay for this)	1 load
19	Of Kelsey Dung p^d Car: p^d.	5 loads
20	Of Parsons Dung p^d car: p^d	3 loads
Apr. 11	Of Parsons Dung p^d car: p^d	3 loads
	Of Kelsey Dung p^d car p^d.	4 loads
	car: out two of my own car. p^d	
	Of Berriman Dung p^d Waggon-loads	2 car. pd.
19	Of Kelsey Dung pd: car p^d.	3 loads
May 21	Of Kelsey Dung pd: car p^d.	1 load
	car: of my own one. car p^d	

— 1765 —

JANUARY   4. Made half an Hogsh: of raisin-wine with one Hund: of Malagas, & half an hund: of Smyrnas: one of the half hund: of Malagas was very indifferent, the rest were fine.

Put to the raisins eleven buckets of water containing three Gallons each. The Smyrnas cost 32s: p^r Hund: the Malagas 30s.

From the eve of last Xmass-day to the eve of New-year's day was a very dry, severe frost: it went-off with a very mild thaw.

5. Received a ten gallon barrel of mountain-wine from my Bro: Thomas.

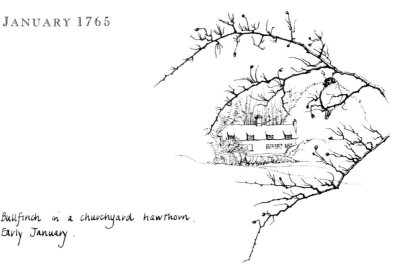

Bullfinch in a churchyard hawthorn,
Early January.

12.   Great rains, & strong winds for several Days.

8.   Made an hot-bed for the one-light Cucumber seedling frame.

14.   The Cucum.ʳˢ come-up well; but the bed is full hot. Moist, foggy weather.

19.   Tunn'd the half Hogsh: of wine: it ran the barrel full, all save about one Gallon that was squeezed. Put to it the 14 bottles of elder-syrop for colouring. Put-up on the raisins four buckets of water to make vinegar, & raisin-wine. Put one pint of brandy to the wine.

22.   Wet mild weather since newsyear's [new year's] day. The snow-drops are in bloom; & the Crocuss swelling.

24.   Press'd-out the second run of raisin-wine, four buckets of water having been put-up after the first wine was drawn-off. Fill'd the vinegar-barrel about three parts full: & there remained about 8 gallons for present drinking.

30.   A high barometer, & N: E: wind, with some dry days: but frequent fogs, & some sunshine.

        The first sown Cucum.ʳˢ have now a rough leaf. There is now a good Quantity in the earth-house of mold for the bearing: cucum.ʳ bed, consisting of some old melon-mould, some from the bottom of the faggot-stack, & some earth cast-up by the moles on the Common; all well turned & blended together. The Hepaticas are well-blown: & some Crocuss are blown-out.

31.   Sowed my own ashes, which were sufficient for what used to be called the great mead. Bought ten bushels of M.ʳ Etty, which sowed the slip.

FEBRUARY 1.   Sowed a box with Polyanth-seed from Bp's Waltham said to be good. Dry but dark weather.

4.   Carry'd into the melon-ground 8 loads of hot dung for the bearing Cucum.ʳ bed.

        A very severe frost all day with a great rime. The ground was so very hard that the carting all day made not the least Impression. There has been some frost for several days.

        Empty'd the dung hole.

7.   Very hard frost still, with great white dews. Things begin to freeze within. The sun shines hot & strong all day. The glass fell much some days agon; but rises again. It is most probable snow fell farther north: here was a little scattering one morning. The sun now, just before setting, shines plumb into the Dining-room-Chimney.

9.   A very swift thaw.

10.   Rain all day: this second frost lasted just a week.

12.   Made the bearing Cucum.ᵗ bed for two two-light frames of yᵉ 8 loads of dung. The dung has never shewed any great Heat. The bed is of a good thickness, & is well made. The Cucum.ʳˢ have one broad rough leaf; & shew a second.

13.   Sent-down a large portmanteau full of all sorts of perennials to my Brother Harry at Fifield. Gave the flower-bank a large dressing of rotten dung. Dug-up the bank at the end of the barn, to prepare it for planting.

16.   Hard black frosts for many mornings. To day frequent flights of snow. The Cucum.ʳˢ have a joint, & two rough leaves. The bearing-bed begins to heat well.

17.   A very severe frost with a scattering of snow. There has never yet been snow enough at one time to cover the Ground.

18.   A very severe frost. Laid the Hills of earth on the Cucum.ᵗ bed. The bed seems in fine temper. It froze hard all day in the shade. Stopped down the Cucum.ᵗ plants.

19.   A very severe frost; & the ground as hard as Iron: strong sunshine, & a freezing air all day. Turned-out the Cucum.ʳˢ into their Hills: they were well-rooted in their pots.

20.   A most severe frost, which came in a doors, & froze under my bed. Strong clear sunshine. The ice that was broken Yesterday, could not be broke to day without great violence. It is difficult to cover the Hot-beds enough.

     Cut-down two beechen-stocks at Lawn-acre for boards, & planks. They yielded 593 feet of sawn stuff; out of which there were three planks for a manger; the rest were all boards. The stock out of which the planks were cut proved faulty: so that they were not so good as could be wished. Plunged the planks Yesterday in James Knight's pond.

     Hung an Ham of my own making in a paper-bag in the Chimney.

     Destroyed 24 bullfinches, which lay very hard on the Cherry-trees, & plum-trees, & had done a great deal of Mischief.

21.   Hard frost & bright sunshine; but nothing near so severe as it was. The wind from full E: is turned full W:

22.   Sowed about a doz: Succade seeds. A thaw with a very sharp wind at S: E: the ground is still very hard under the surface, & the Ice very thick on the waters.

23.   The mercury, which was very low yesterday, now rises again very fast; & the frost seems likely to go-off without any fall at all. The ground would dig well, if the frost was out.

26.   The Succades are come-up extraordinarily well every seed. The frost went-off on the 24th with some rain. The Cucum.^{rs} seem to be settled in their hills, & begin to shew runners.

27.   Potted the succades in four pots. A good deal of rain & wet melting snow.

28.   A great snow with a fierce driving wind from the West, which forced it into every cranny & opening; so that the peat & mould in the houses were covered. It lies in very unequal depths on the Ground, being drifted by the strong wind: but would have been about ten inches in general had the air been still. The ever-greens were so loaded that they were weigh'd down to the Ground. The wind was so strong, & the snow so searching, that the Hotbeds were not uncovered above two Hours all day. The sun broke out in the evening: but ye Horizon looked very threatening, being of a very livid Colour, & promising more fall. The Mercury fell very low indeed in the night; & was quite concave at the top when I went to bed.

MARCH   1.   A pretty smart frost in the night; but a swift thaw all day with some rain. The snow lies very thick still; so deep that I could not get-out on Horse-back at the Northfield-land end. The Glass very low still. The Cucum.^{rs} look well, & the bed is not injured by the bad weather. Sowed twelve more Succade-seeds: those in the pots look well.

3.   A frost in the morning, & strong sunshine all day. The snow is still very deep, & melts only by the Heat of the sun. Newton-lane has been quite stopp'd-up, and impassable. The Glass keeps rising, but is still very low. The lane towards Rood is not passable.

3.   Exceedingly bright sunshine; a frost in the morning, & a rising Glass. I found on going to Faringdon that the snow had been much deeper than I was aware. Newton-lane below the Cross was barely passable. People more than 50 years old hardly remember such a snow.

4.   A smart frost, & very strong sunshine all day. The bees work very briskly on the Crocuss amidst the banks of snow. The snow melts only where the sun shines. The blackbirds begin to whistle.

5.   A great rain from the E: which melted the snow at vast rate.

6.   Great rains, & a flood at Gracious street.

7.   The snow is all gone, except under some Hedges, &c. Removed some of the Cucum.^r plants, & put in some from the pots, which have a better Countenance. The bed has been a little too hot.

8.   Brewed half an Hogsh: of beer with six bushels of Richd Knight's malt, & two pounds & three quarters of good Hops of the second year. When Hops were new 2 p^{ds} & ½ used to be sufficient. Made an half hogsh: of ale & ½ hogsh: of small of the same brewing. The water for the strong was all rain & snow water; which stood some days in tubs to mellow, & soften.

     Put about a Quarter of a pound of Hops, & an handful of sand into the 45 Gall: barrel of strong beer brewed Feb. 1764 to fine it down for use.

8.   Cast 8 loads of hot-dung for the Succade-bed. Put a second pint of Brandy to the new-made wine: it is very quiet for it's age.

10.   A vast rain & flood. The snow lies very thick still in some ditches, & hollow places.

11.   Tunn'd the strong-beer, having stirred-in the Yeast two or three times a day while it stood in the tun-tub.

     Hung the flitch of bacon in Mr Etty's Chimney.

14.   Great storms of Hail, rain, & snow, with several loud Claps of thunder. The farmers are much behind in their season.

18.   Vast rains; & nothing done in the Garden.

     The Cucum^rs have got male-bloom.

     Sowed 12 more Succade seeds: those sowed last die in the pots: the first sowing thrives, & has a rough leaf. Turn'd the Succade-dung in the Yard: it was very hot.

19.   Farmer Parsons brought 60 bush: of tan from Alton for the Cantaleupe-bed. Vast hail storms with some thunder.

21: 22.   Continual heavy showers. The floods are much out. Cucum^rs thrive.

23.   The Cucum^rs are full of male bloom. No fruit shows yet.

24: 25.   Vast showers. Gave the Cucum^r bed a lining in front for the first time. Moss'd the bed.

     The Apricot tree has two blossoms blown-out; which seem to be the only promising ones it is likely to have. Some Peach-blossoms are just ready to open.

26.   Made the succade-bed with the 8 loads of Dung which had been brought-in ever since the eighth of this month, & turn'd once. As it seem'd to make but a shallow, weak bed, I laid about twenty bushels of tan on it.

     A very great rain. The Country is in a sad, wet Condition.

27.   One of the Cuc^r plants shews a fruit. A vast storm from the west, which blow'd one of the melon-lights quite off the frame against the espalier-plum-tree, but without breaking any panes. The Cuc^r lights were in danger of being blown-off, & were secured by heavy slabs.

28.   Mowed the grass plot the first time. A great rain. The succades decay in their leaves thro' the dampness & shadiness of the weather.

29.   I planted five fann'd Elmes to screen Will: Carpenter's necessary House; & five large Laurels in a curve to screen my own, which I propose to move to the Corner next Parsons's Yard: & three elms in the corner of Parson's Yard to conceal my own from the street. Continual rains still.

30.   Put a little mould in the Succade-bed, & sowed sixteen Cantaleupe-seeds in it. The bed is yet full hot to lay-on the hills of earth. Raked-down the asparagus-beds, & sowed five rows of pease; the first crop of any kind put into the Ground this year. A stormy wind all day, & frequent showers.

31. & first of April. Stormy Winds, & great rains.

APRIL 2. Earthed the Succade bed, & put-on the Hills. The mould in a cold, clammy Condition. Planted three Dutch-Honey-suckles in the new-Garden. Sowed 16 basons of double-upright-larks-spurs. A very wet afternoon. A vast rain at night.

4. Planted three pots of Succades in their Hills: those that were forward were so damaged in their leaves by the long continuance of bad weather, that the second sowing were preferable, which shew only seedling leaves. Sowed more Cantaleupe seeds in the Succade-bed: the first-sown are just coming-up. Sowed more Succade-seeds. Lined the back of the Cucum.ʳ bed with one load of Dung. Planted seven rows of Rasps in one of the upper quarters of the new Garden; three of white, & four of red. Planted five rows of beans; the first planting.

Made a Celeri-bed for an Hand-glass with two barrows of dung.

The Peaches & Nectarines begin to blow-out.

Frequent showers still: & the Ground sadly wet.

Berriman brought 20 bushels of tan; in all 80.

The Cantaleupe-dung brought-in is 12 loads.

Set some boards a nights against the fruit trees in bloom.

Sowed some spots of persicarias; & a drill of parsley.

6. The Cucm.ᵗ is blown-out to day. A vast rain last night, & great wind to day. A very great flood at Gracious-street. The springs are vastly high; & the Lavants broke-out at Chawton.

Turn'd the Cantaleupe-dung.

7. Tempestuous winds, with vast rains, hail, & thunder.

8: 9. Stormy wind, & showers. The farmers are vastly backward in their season. Very little lent-corn sown. Frequent Claps of thunder, & a very cold air.

12. The first fine spring-like day, & no wet the whole day long. Potted the Cantaleupes. Sowed a Crop of Carrots, parneps, Coss-lettuce, radishes, onions, leeks, & savoys; & sowed one long row of finochia in a drill with a little rotten dung mixed with the mould. The ground worked as well as could be expected. The Mercury is shot up very tall; but the skie threatens again for wet. Lined the Cucumber-bed with some grass-mowings: fruit blows every day. The Nightingales begin to sing. The Hyacinths begin to blow.

Planted five rows of potatoes in Turner's Garden, & put old-thatch in four of the trenches, & peat-dust in one for experiment sake. Exchanged roots with M.ʳ Etty, as his ground is so different: his sort came originally from me.

13. Made the Cantaleupe-bed for two frames in the new Garden with 12 loads of dung that had been brought-in just a fortnight, & cast once, & 60 bushels of tan on the top of it. It is a stout bed; & the tan lies at least six Inches thick. There have been three pretty fine days together, without any wind, & with very little rain. Some

peaches & Nect: blow finely: some have little bloom.

   Farmer Knight is to follow, & plow Baker's Hill in an Husband-like manner, this summer, & to sow it with wheat at Mich: & to allow me the straw of the Crop for the use of the Ground. The year following he is to sow it with oats, & allow me the straw: & I am to sow a Crop of S.^t foin along with his Corn.¶

17.   Layed-down about 100 Laurustines; & grafted 6 crab-stocks with Cuttings from ye Lunning tree. Made a new bed for aromatic Herbs. Little rain for a week past; but shady mild weather.

18.   Bright, spring weather. Cut the first Cucum.^r a small one: there are many swelling away.

19.   Laid-on the Hills on the Cantaleupe-bed. The earth is all prepared in the earth-house; because the mould will not work at all in the new Garden. Now heavy showers after several fine days.

23.   No Sun at all for several days; but black weather & frequent showers. It rains from all Quarters of the Compass. To day several Claps of thunder. The Ground is in a wet Condition. Something bites-off the Cuc.^r bloom, & gnaws the fruit. The grass grows very fast.

24.   Turn'd-out the Cantaleupes into their Hills: they are fine plants, & well-rooted. The Succades succeed but poorly.

   A soft, spring-like day, & some sunshine.

   Caught the mouse that eat the Cucum.^{rs}

25.   A very heavy rain.

26.   Extraordinary foggs, & moist air without any Sun.

27.   Cucum.^{rs} come every day. Hot growing weather.

29.   Made an annual bed, & sowed it with China-asters, Fr: Marrigolds, Dwarf-sunflowers, Chrysanthemums, & pendulous Amaranths. Sowed some large white Cucum.^{rs} for the Hand-glasses. There have been two beautiful summer-like days together.

   There are 99 considerable trees in Sparrow's hanger; 94 beeches, 3 ashes, & two oaks: there are also three large oaks in the pasture-field adjoining.

MAY   3.   Sowed a second Crop of Pease in the ground where the turneps stood; sowed four rows of dwarf white french-beans. Harsh, cold winds from the N: E: with an high barometer.

6.   Cut-down an Head of the Burnet, & gave it the Mare. The Heads are very large, & just offering for Bloom. Very fine dry weather.

7.   Planted half Hund: of Cabbage-plants for a succession. Planted some slips of the double wall-flower. The melon-plants grow but poorly. Very dry weather; & the ground very much bound. The fleas eat the Savoys.

   Cut some Heads of Burnet, & gave it the Horses, intending to observe how long it will be before they spring again. Each root has a vast head.

8.   Made four Hills for hand-glass Cucum.^{rs} with two barrows of

dung to each Hill. Very sultry weather; & showers about.

13.   Hot burning weather: the ground is bound very hard. There has been hardly any rain for 18 days. The peaches & Nect: by being sprinkled with water now & then this dry time, swell away. One Nect: tho' treated with the same care with the rest, is quite overrun with blistered leaves & shoots; & must, in all appearance, be taken away.

The Succades in one Hill have long runners that have been stopped down. The Cantaleupes seem not to take well to their Hills.

All the tulips seem to have run from their original beauty.

14.   Rack'd-off half an hogsh: of raisin-elder made last January, which was not quite free from fretting. Let it stand one night in the Kiver,¶ & returned it into the same barrel well wash'd, with half a pint of brandy. The wine is strong, & sweet enough at present. There came out about a Gallon of Groat; so that the barrel is not full.

No rain yet, but a sinking Glass.

The melons grow now.

Stopp'd-down some of the most vigorous of the peach, & Nect: shoots, which seem to threaten to run to Willow-like wood. There is some fruit on each tree. All the trees save one look healthy. The vines promise a great deal of bloom.

15.   A very moderate rain, that just moistened things.

18.   Burning sunshine with a strong drying E: wind. I have sprinkled the peach, & Nect: trees twice a week during this drying weather. Most things want watering. The melons, which have been earthed & watered frequently, grow away. There has been rain but once for these three weeks.

21.   No rain yet; but strong sunshine, & a very drying East wind. The Ground is much parch'd on the surface. The Succades begin to shew the rudiments of bloom.

24.   Very harsh winds with some flights of Hail. No rain now, save one little shower, for a month past. The ground bound like Iron.

Earth'd-out the melons to the full in their frames.

Put 10 field-crickets in the bank of the terrass:¶ made the Holes with a spit.

26.   Several small showers from the N.

27.   Now dry weather again with a very high Glass. The Succades begin to blow, & to shew some fruit.

The Country is in great want of rain.

JUNE   1.   No rain yet; but drying scorching weather. The corn, & Gardens suffer greatly. I do not remember my Garden to be so totally overcome with heat & dryness so soon in the Year. The walks are burnt up past mowing.

2.   Thunder was heard at distance.

3.   Drying winds, & fierce sunshine.

The Succades have fruit blown.

4.   No rain yet: scorching sunny weather. A sinking glass, & some tokens of showers.

6.   Thunder in the evening, & very black clouds to the E: & S: E: a fine rain at Petersfield, but not one drop here.

7.   Lined the succade-bed: as the dung was very stale & dry we intermixed some layers of new-mown grass, & some weeds. The horses have been all so long at Grass that there will be no getting any fresh Dung.

8.   The Succade-fruit begins to set. We water the melon-beds a good deal this scorching weather.

        The drought has continued six weeks from the 6th & is now entered on the seventh week. The succade-lining heats furiously.

10.   The weather continuing very burning, we water the melons largely. The Succades set apace, & the bines are of a good strength: the Cantaleupe-vines run rather weakly.

11.   Earthed-out the Succades to their full depth, & extent; raised the frame, & found the roots were got-out very strong. Planted the basons in the field with annuals which are weak & drawn: there was no planting but by dint of great waterings: & no making melon-earth by the same expedient. The stones & bricks are so extreamly dry, that the mason, who is facing my stable, is obliged to dip them all in water. The grass in the walks breaks & crumbles under peoples feet as they tread.

        The lining of the succade-bed is very hot, & throws a good heat into the bed.

12.   I set about five brace of promising Cantaleupes in the first frame: there are a few Succades about as big as pidgeons eggs.

        Finish'd tacking the vines, which have an unusual quantity of budds for bloom. Some shattering showers; & some large ones about.

13.   Sowed four long rows, one pint of dwarf white kindney-beans; & prick'd out a large plot of Celeri. The ground was well-watered before any thing could be done. Planted annuals in the borders of the Garden. Several very soft showers many times in the day; but not moisture enough to lay the dust, or make the eaves drop.

14.   Soft showers for four Hours this morning, & showers again in the evening. So that Yesterday the dry weather might be said to last exactly 8 weeks, beginning the day after St Mark.

        Turn'd-out the white cucumbers from under ye Hand-glasses: they are very strong, & shew fruit.

15.   Sowed a Crop of Endive; two rows of fenochia, & some vast white kindney-beans from Lima. Hot, sunny weather.

17.   Trimm'-out the Succades, which were grown very rude & wild: the fruit keeps setting here & there, but not very fast. The bed is very warm, & has been pretty frequently water'd. The Cantaleupes seem to be setting; the bines are still but weak. Some little shattering showers, which refresh the leaves of things: but the ground is still as hard as ever.

        Mrs Snooke's black-cluster Grape is beginning to blow before any of the other Vines, even the white-sweet-water.

19. Hot dry weather with an high Glass. Cut my Grass: four mowers cut the great mead, yᵉ slip, & the shrubbery by dinner-time. Some of the Succades are almost grown, some setting, & some plants have no fruit swelling yet. Watered the outsides of the Succade-bed this very dry weather. Tack'd & thinn'd the Peach, & Nect: trees: there is but little fruit. Some of the trees run to too vigorous wood. The ground is strangely dry'd, & burnt. My Crop of Grass is very well for so burning an Year.

21. Rick'd-up my Hay without one drop of rain; tho' the Clouds, a sinking Glass, & an hollow wind threatned very hard: there were five jobbs. Water'd the Crops very much.

22. A N: Wind, a rising Glass, & all tokens of rain over for the present. Water'd the Cantaleupes: there are a good many fruit set in yᵉ first frame; but a poor promise in the second. Water'd the things again.

24. Gave the Cantaleupe-bed a good lining with two waggon loads of dung, & some layers of Grass from the orchard to set it in a ferment. The Cantaleupes now shew a good many likely fruit. Very hot dry weather & no rain yet. We are obliged to water very much to keep things alive. The melons have had an unusal share of Water.

28. A little rain; which was a noble watering at Fyfield for 12 hours.

JULY 5. A little rain.

6. On my return from Fyfield I found a large Crop of Cantaleupes set; & some above half grown: & a good many Succades coming-on: the forwardest are full grown. The bed is well lined out, & very warm; & the fibres are running very strong without the frames.

There have been fine rains round Andover & Salisbury: the verdure on the Downs is very delicate, & the sheep ponds are full of water. But when I came on this Side Alresford I found all the ponds without one drop of water; & the turf & Corn burnt-up in a very deplorable manner; & every thing perishing in the Gardens. The peaches, & Nectarines keep casting their fruit. Cherries are now very fine.

The downs between Alresford & Andover are full of Burnet:¶ so full in many places that it is almost the only herb that covers the Ground: & is eaten down very close by sheep, who are fond of it.

The Case is the same between Andover & Sarum where in many places the Ground is covered with Burnet now in seed: a Child might in those places gather a considerable Quantity in a day. It is worth observation that this herb seems to abound most in the poorest, & shallowest chalkey soil. On Selborne Common (a rich strong piece of Ground) it has not been yet discovered.

Near Waller's Ash I rode thro a piece of Ground of about 400 acres, which had been lately pared by a breast plough for burning: here the burnet was coming-up very thick on the bare ground, tho' the crown of the root must have been cut off of course along with the turf: this shews that it is a plant tenacious of life, since it spring from the severed root like plantain.

P^d Will Dewey for 8 Doz: of young sparrows.¶

The drought has lasted 10 weeks last thursday.

The peaches, & Nect: have cast most of their fruit.

8. A gentle rain most part of the day: & in the evening a great shower for about half an Hour that moistened things well. The cartway ran with water, which is more than it has done before since the 25th of April. This rain did not reach Faringdon or Empshot; so that it was of small extent.

9. Planted-out a bed of leeks; & sowed a little spot with Batavian-Endive; & a quarter with turneps.

10. Finished stopping-down, & tacking the vines. The Grapes on Mrs Snooke's tree as big as small pease. Harsh drying winds. The garden quarters not moistened enough to plant. Dug-up the Hyacinth-roots, which seem very moist considering the very dry time.

12. Tiled 8 of the forwardest Succades. Hot dry weather, with cold dews at Night. My Cherries are now in high perfection. Large showers about yesterday; but a few drops only fell here. Some of the Cantaleupes swell very fast. It appears by the trial sticks that the bed has now as good a ground heat as most beds when made only five or six weeks; this must be owing to the lasting heat of tan. The Swallows & martins are bringing-out their young. Young partridges that were flyers seen.

12 July.
Salad burnet in the herb garden
the Wakes.

13. Farmer Knight, having plowed Baker's Hill twice before, stirr'd it across to day.¶ The weeds are all kill'd, & the soil is baked as hard as a stone; & is as rough as the sea in an hard Gale: the Clods stand an end as high as one's knees.

14. Saw Pheasants that were flyers.

16. A good rain for about three Hours. A great rain at Haslemere, where I was then. Several fern-owls or Goat-suckers¶ flying about in the evening at Black-down House.

18. Cut the first Succade-melon, a very delicate one; & deeply crack'd at the Eye: it had not one drop of moisture in it. Dry hot weather ever since the rain.

Nettle-leaved bellflowers,
Wool Lane,
14 July

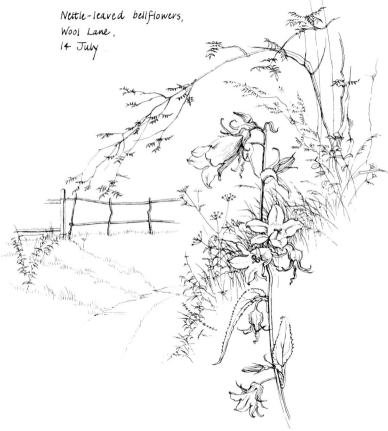

19. Rains about, but none here. Hot ripening weather. The dry fit has lasted 12 weeks yesterday. The wheat turns colour very fast. Added some earth to the melon-bed, where the lining was crack'd away from the main bed.

20. Gather'd a good quantity of Burnet-seed from my plants. This plant sheds its seed as soon as ripe; & therefore whenever it becomes a field plant, it must be cut as soon as it shews any tendency to ripeness.

The melon-bed has still a moderate Heat.

Some shoots of the Laurustine are blowing, others budded for bloom.

21.   The Glow-worms no longer shine on the Common: In June they were very frequent. I once saw them twinkle in the South hams of Devon as late as the middle of Septemʳ

The Redbreast just essays to sing.

Dry dark weather with an high glass. The garden dry'd-up as hard as a stone: the Crops come to nothing; & no opportunity of planting out the Autumn, & winter Crops. Cherries still very fine.

The haulm of the Cantaleupes (notwithstanding the continual drought) shews some disposition for rotting: in many parts it splits longitudinally, & heals up again. There will be a very fine Crop of Succades.

23.   Cut the second Succade, a small one. The field-crickets cry yet faintly. Hot dry weather still. No rain coming we were forced to put-out more Annuals in the dusty border; to shade 'em well, & to give them a vast quantity of water. The garden looks quite destitute of crops: no turneps will come up; no Celeri can be trench'd, nor endives, nor Savoys planted-out. The ponds in most parishes are quite dry'd-up.

24.   Succades come apace.

25.   Some people have hack'd pease. Two most sultry days. Succades come by Heaps. The wells in the street begin to fail. Turn'd all the large Cantaleupes.

This day the dry weather has lasted just 13 weeks.

Some of the Succades crack very deeply at the eye: those are always delicate.

26.   Gathered a good basket of french beans; the first of the season. Put some tall sticks to the Lima-beans. Gave the Garden a good watering.

27.   Housed my billet in curious order.¶

Abraham Low has got above 50 bunches of grapes on a vine of my Sort, which is but three years growth from a cutting.

Many samples of new wheat were shown this day at Alton market: the Corn was said to be very fine.

28.   The Martins begin to assemble round the weather-cock; & the Swallows on the wallnut-trees.

Dry hot weather still, with a N: wind.

The Goldfinch, Yellow-hammer, & sky-lark are the only birds that continue to sing. The red-breast is just beginning. The field-crickets in the Lythe cry no longer.

29.   Eat a most curious Succade: & saved it's seed.

The beetles begin to hum about at the Close of day.

Trench'd one row of Celeri to try if it can be saved.

31.   Berriman began to reap in yᵉ Ewel-close. The best of the Succades being cut, I gave the bed a good watering within & without: water'd the Cantaleupe-bed on the outside. Sultry weather. Wind S: for two days.

AUGUST 1. This day the drought has lasted 14 weeks. Sultry, cloudless weather. Planted-out four rows of loaf cabbadges, & two of Savoys between the Rasps in the midst of this burning weather, as there is no prospect of rain. The well sinks apace: we have watered-away 26 well-buckets in a day. No Endives can be planted-out yet. No rain at all since the 16 of July.

3. A plentiful rain for five hours & an half with a great deal of thunder & lightening. It soaked things thoro'ly to the roots, & fill'd many ponds.

4. Cut the first & the largest Cantaleupe, it weighed three pounds. The Succades keep coming. The swifts have disappeared for several days. Newton-pond was just got empty; & yet there was a pretty good share of water in the pond on the Common.

   The Cantaleupe-bed by the trial stick shews still a considerable Heat: it is owing no doubt to the tan.

   Laurustines cast their old leaves.

5. Did a great stroke of Gardening after the rain: sowed a quarter with turnep seed, & planted it with savoys, the rows wide apart. Planted-out five more rows of Celeri; in all six long rows: & planted a plot of endives. The endives seem to be planted too late to come to any size; & the Celeri & savoys probably will not be large. The ground falls to pieces, & works as well as can be expected.

   Gather'd the only & first Apricot the tree ever bore: it was a fair fruit, but not the sort sent for; being an Orange & not a Breda. Scarce any of Murdoch Middleton's trees turn-out the sorts sent for.

7. Dripping warm weather since the thunder-storm.

8. The first Cantaleupe, growing on a faulty stem, was not curious. Very showery weather.

   Cut the second Cantaleupe: is [it] is crack'd at the eye. Great showers with distant thunder.

   Mʳ Yalden saw a single swift. Glow-worms appear'd again pretty frequent; but more in the Hedges, & bushes than in June, when they were out on yᵉ turf.

9. Melons keep coming. Saw two swallows feeding five young ones that had just left their nest: they usually bring them out the beginning of July.

Dung borrowed in 1765

Feb: 4	Of Kelsey Dung pdᵈ.	5 loads
Dᵒ	Of Parsons Dung pᵈ Car pᵈ.	3 loads
March 8	Of Parsons Dung Pᵈ Car pᵈ.	5 loads
Dᵒ	Of Kelsey Dung pᵈ car pᵈ	3 loads
March 29	Of Kelsey Dung pᵈ car pᵈ	3 loads
	Of Parsons Dung pd Car: pᵈ.	5 loads
	Of Berriman Dung pd Cʳ pᵈ	4 loads
April 4	Of Kelsey Dung pᵈ car pᵈ	1 load
June 24	Of Kelsey Dung pᵈ car pᵈ waggon	2 loads

A CALENDER OF FLORA, & THE GARDEN ¶ FROM AUGUST 9th 1765

†The distinction between yᵉ *Scirpi*, & the *Junci*.

Scirpus, a bull-rush: this kind of plant bears stamineous flowers, & naked seeds gathered into a squamose Head; each scale holding a flatish triangular seed: the stalk is without any knots, round, & has a spongy pith.

Juncus, a rush, differs from yᵉ bull-rush in having an hexapetalous Calyx, & as many stamina as yᵉ Calix has leaves; & many seeds contained in a seed-vessel.

AUGUST   9.   Planted a double row of Polyanths all along the great bank in the garden: they are all very small, being much stunted by the dry weather. Planted also some slips of the double Pheasant-ey'd pinks, which have very near blowed themselves to death.
Some hard rain, & distant thunder.

10.   A beautiful dry day. Many people are housing their wheat. The dripping week past has done a world of service.
Planted a large plot with savoys, & sowed it with turnep seed. The last-sown turneps come-up by hundreds.
Cut a large Cantaleupe that was crack'd neither at eye nor tail.

11.   Cut an other not crack'd.

12.   Vast showers: very little wheat carry'd. The rains have restored a fine verdure, to the grass-walks that seemed to be burnt to death for many weeks.

14.   Great showers. The Cantaleupes come very fast, but do not crack well in general. Ten showery days restore a verdure.
Sent a brace & an half of Cantaleupes & a Succade-melon to Bro: Benjⁿ at London. Some small Cantaleupes, that were not at all crack'd are delicate. A very rising Glass. Penny royal, baum, sage, mint, thyme, rue, marjoram, & lavender in high bloom.
Baker's hill is harrowed-down after these great rains: it was no easy matter to subdue the clods at all. Some of the old elders round the garden are almost leafless. Wallnuts are this Year innumerable. The white-apples¶ are fit to make pies. Grapes, peaches, nectares very backward.
The Ground is now well-soaked.
The yellow-hammer continues to sing.
Wheat grows in the gripes.
Tremella abounds now on the walks;¶ & the lichens encrease in size. The french-beans are still lousy in some degree.

14.   Sowed a Quarter of a pound of prickly-seeded spinage, & some Coss-lettuce to stand the winter. The ground was in good order, & fell well to pieces. A cold north wind.
Planted several slips of red pinks round yᵉ borders, & some

---

†Entry at the beginning of a fresh notebook.

stocks, & bloody wall-flowers. The burnet-seed, where it shatters on the Ground, comes-up very thick.

The catkins for next year are formed on the Hasels.

16. A cold N: E: wind, & rising glass. Much wheat has been housed to day. Some Cantaleupes, & Succades crack well at yᵉ eye.

The stone-curlues clamour.¶ The mornings, & evenings are chilly. Plums & figgs are very backward.

The large *Aster* with yellow thrums, supposed to be Virgil's Amello, begins to flower. Trimm'd the vines of second wood for yᵉ last time: the grapes are very backward.

The Yellow-hammer continues to sing.

The uncommon *Aster* with a black thrum blowing.

The variegated *Epilobium* in bloom.

17. Very cold weather for the season, with a N: Wind. People house their wheat very briskly.

A very high barometer.

Melons continue in plenty.

The flea eats-up the Young turneps at a vast rate. The weather so cold & dry, that nothing grows well in the Garden.

19. Cut all the Cantaleupes: they are not in general so well-grown, & so thick-flesh'd as in former Years, owing perhaps to the burning summer, which all the while was attended with N: drying winds not at all kindly to any kind of fruit, or Crops in the Garden.

The bed maintains still a sensible heat.

20. Most beautiful harvest-weather for several days: the wheat will soon be all housed: that that was not carry'd in too hastily will be in curious order.

The wren whistles. A nest of young water-wagtails is just come forth. Tack'd the wall-trees: their tops are shrivell'd, & their fruit advances but poorly.

21. Took-in all the melon-frames in very dry order. The bed has still some sensible heat in it. Very dry sultry weather with a falling glass. The night-moths, & earwigs, I find, feed on the flowers by night, as the bees & butterflies do by day: this I found by going-out with a candle.

22. Upon digging into the melon-bed down to the tan after the frames were taken away, I found that the tan maintained an heat equal to what is usual in a mild bed at first planting. From whence I concluded that the heat was too powerful this sunny scorching summer for the fruit by forcing them into ripeness before they are full-fleshed: in common Summers, when there is a good deal of shady wet weather no doubt the use of tan is of excellent service for Cantaleupes, as I have experienced.

Put some little melons remaining, under hand-glasses. Hot sun-shine breaking-out of a thick fog which lasted 'till eleven o' the Clock. A vast uncommon dew.

Wild-ragwort, scabiouss, hawkweed, knap-weed, burdock, Yarrow, rest-harrow, &c: in flower.

Put a Quartʳ of a pound of hops to the strong-beer brewed in

March, which was work'd fresh this Summer.

24. Wheat is housed in general; all the latter part of the Crop in most curious order. Barley & oats are beginning to be cut.

Haws begin to turn red: elder-berries from red to black. Most sultry ripening weather for many days. Some few of my black grapes just begin to turn; & some of the sweet-water begin to grow a little clear.

Wasps increase very fast. Orleans-plums ripen.

Coveys of partriges are very large. Martens are grown very numerous at Selborne: they are much encreased within these few Years. Vast crops of hops in some Gardens.

25: 26. Most severe Heat, with a falling Glass, & probably rain at a distance. People are beginning to pick Hops. Black Grapes begin to turn on the wall. Several Martens have now second broods: qua: if these late hatchings are not rather in favour of hiding than migration.¶

27. Gathered my first figs. No rain now for 16 days. My only Nectarine, & two only peaches begin to tend towards ripeness. Mich: daiseys begin to blow.

Earth-nuts,¶ & blue Devil's bit in bloom. *Althaea frutex* in high bloom: Ladies bed-straw just out.

Yellow-hammer seems to have done singing.

House-martins over the fields, Selborne. 25 August.

28. Still, hot, gloomy days. Rain begins to be much wanted by the farmer, & Gardener.

30. A moderate shower with a brisk Gale. The melons left under hand-glasses keep coming. Full moon.

Yellow toad-flax (*linaria*) great purple snap-dragon, (*Antirrhinum*) (found in a lane at Empshot, & supposed to be thrown-out from some Garden) Eye-bright, betony; small spear-worth, (*Ranunculus flammeus*) vervain-leaved mallow, the common-reed, many sorts of *Epilobium*; Scabious, purple, & deep blue; wild basil, now in bloom. Wild Basil is a pretty flower, & a common weed.

Swallows feed flying, & water-wagtails running round Horses

in a meadow. The gentle motions of the Horse stir-up a succession of flies from the grass.

The water-wagtail seems to be the smallest english bird that walks with one leg at a time: the rest of that size and under all hop two legs together.

The Alders have form'd their young catkins against next spring.

The Grapes change pretty fast.

SEPTEMBER 5.
Brisk winds, & showers for several days. The apples are pretty much blown-down in some places; & the hops received some Injury. The winds beat-down many of my figs, & baking pears. Since my melon-frames have been taken-in, & before the rains fell to moisten ye mould on the bed, there grew up at once a very singular appearance of the fungus kind that seemed rather to be poured over the ground¶ than to vegetate: it was soft & pappy, & about the consistence of thick milk, & of a very ill savour. Where I wounded it with a stick it sent out a sort of bloody Ichor; & soon hardened into a dark substance; & is now turn'd into a fine Impalpable dust like that of the *Lupi Crepitus*. I have had them on beds before the frames have been taken-off; when they have crept in part up the side of the frame. To the best of my remembrace they have never appeared on any beds that have not been covered with tan. On consulting Ray's *methodus* I find no traces of any such kind of fungus.

On the Lythe I found a few days since in full bloom the *Dentaria aphyllos*, *seu Anblatum*; a peculiar plant, of the same class with the *Orobanche*. Hill says it begins flowering in May. This was ladies traces.¶

7.
Fine ripening weather. Grass, & garden-plants grow apace. Howed & thinned my two plots of turneps. Earwigs eat the Nect: by night, but not the peaches.

9.
Beautiful Autumnal weather: most of the Corn housed. Gathered my only Nect: it was not ripe; but the earwigs had gnawed it so that it could not come to any thing. Gathered my first peach: it's flesh was thick, tender, white, & juicy; & parted from the stone. It was a good fruit; but not so high-flavoured as some I have met-with.

Gather'd some of my forward white grapes: they were very agreeable tho' not quite ripe: the black Grapes in general are backward.

On the steep chalky end of Whetham-hill I discovered a large plant, of the deadly Nightshade (*belladona*) full of ripe fruit: & on the bogs of Beans-pond in Wullmere forest the same day that peculiar plant the sun-dew (*rorella*)¶ in plenty. There are it seems on the same bog plenty of cranberry-plants: but I could not venture on the moss to look after them. Cranberries, (*vitis Idaea*). I thought I discovered a small *Parnassia* but was not sure. Found also southern wood (*abrotanum*) in a lane; & dyer's weed

(*luteola*) very vigorous, & full of seed in a farm yard at
Faringdon.

Owls hiss round the Church¶ in a fierce threatning manner: I
suppose they are old ones that have Young. There are young
martens still in some nests. About five days ago S: Sim: Stuart's
game-keeper kill'd an wood-cock in the moors. Not true.

11.   Gathered my second & last peach: it was from a different tree
from yᵉ first, but seems to be the same sort.

13.   Bagg'd-up between 40, & 50 bunches of black grapes in Crape.
Ty'd-up all the best endives for blanching: they are but small.

Procured several Cranberry-plants from bean's pond with
berries on them.

15.   Fine Autumn weather for many days.

16.   Gathered some good white Grapes. Took-in the Hand-glasses, &
cut the two last melons; not ripe.

17: 18.   Went down to Ringmer. The second day there was a moderate
rain for eight Hours, during which I lay-by at Brighthelmstone.

In a lane towards the sea near a village call'd Whiting not far
from yᵉ above-named town, I discovered a shrub of the rose kind,
that had heps of jet-black Colour, & very beautiful small
pinnated leaves. As the leaves resembled those of Burnet, quae: if
this was not the Burnet-rose,¶ which I think is said to grow wild.
As it was quite out of bloom I had not yᵉ satisfaction of seeing the
flower.

I saw a flower afterwards, & it was white & single.

On the poorer parts of yᵉ Sussex downs I saw the smaller Burnet
in plenty; but it had shed it's seeds. I find the rich pasture-
grounds at Ringmer very bare of Grass: they seem to have
suffered by the drought this summer as much as in any parts of
the Country.

Ladies-bedstraw frequently in flower on the downs; & a thistle
with an echinated head, & little down to yᵉ seeds.

20.   Discovered plenty of the prickly rest-harrow (*Anonis*) & dier's
broom, both in bloom, & pod, in the pasture-fields at Ringmer.

Mʳˢ Snooke's grapes are very good; especially the black. Her
crop of apples fail. Blue Scabiuss in plenty still. The rooks
frequent yᵉ nest-trees great part of yᵉ day. I saw a few wheatears
(birds) on the Sussex down as I came along. Vast quantities are
caught by the shepherds in the season; (about yᵉ beginning of
Harvest) & yet no numbers are ever seen together, they not being
gregarious.

Showers, & some brisk winds. Hawkweeds all yᵉ Country
over from the highest downs to the lowest pasture-field. Wasps
seem at present to be very much check'd: they have gnaw'd the
Grapes pretty much.

This very dry summer has damaged Mʳˢ Snooke's buildings by
occasioning such vast chops in the clay-soil, that they loosen the
walls, & make settlements. Since I came there were cracks in the

ground deeper than the length of a walking-stick.

24. Made a visit to Mr John Woods at his new mill. On the downs near Bpstone I found the downs covered with Burnet: & in one place, where the Ground had been devonshired¶ the beginning of the summer, the ground was cloath'd-over with Burnet & *filipendula*, whose crowns had been severed with the turf. Found French-mercury (*mercurialis*) the smallest sort of Cudweed; & saw abundance of sea-plants on ye shore which I had not time to examine.

26: 27: 28. Returned from Ringmer. Fine dry soft weather; & the roads quite dusty. Very little rain has fallen yet: the deep pasture-Grounds round Ringmer are bare of Grass, & in great want of water. Many ponds on ye road are quite dry.

Saw plenty of the whorttle-berry plants on Rogate heath.

I found my grapes in general very backward, notwithstanding the dry sunny weather. The wasps seem to have done very little damage; they seem to be quite gone.

30. Made 10 quarts of elder-juice; to which when I had put 10 p^{ds} of sugar, & boiled them up together, there came 13 bottles of syrop.

Ivy in full flower. Scabius, some mulleins, throat-worts, bugloss, hawkweeds, wild basil, marjoram, eye-bright, mallows, knapweeds, &c: still in bloom.

Found the Woodruffe (*asperula*) in plenty in my beechen Hanger. The beeches begin to be ringed with Yellow.

A great rain.

The men are weeding the garden, which is very much over-run with groundsel.

OCTOBER 1. A very cold, blustering day. Began fires. Began gathering the white apples,¶ & golden pippins. Earthed-up the Celeri, some rows to ye top. Used ye first Endive: it is too small to blanch well. Planted a row of Burnet-plants brought from ye Sussex-downs. The caterpillars have been pick'd off the savoys several times: those that have not used that precaution have lost every plant.

The Cucumbers, & kidney-beans are cut-down with the Cold. The ashes, & maples in some places look yellow.

The wood-lark sings, & the wood-pidgeon coos in ye Hanger. John took his bees.

3. Vast showers with frequent claps of thunder. Discovered the Enchanter's nightshade (*Circaea*) it grows in great plenty in the hollow lanes.

4. Gather'd in my baking-pears, about three bushels.

The woodruffe, when a little dryed, has a most fragrant smell.

5. Examined the wild black Hellebore (*Helleboraster niger flore albo*) an uncommon plant in general, but very common in Selborne-wood.¶ Vast heavy showers, with a tempestuous wind.

6. Vast showers: the Ground is well-drench'd.

8. Planted a row of coss-lettuce along against ye fruit-wall to stand the winter.

Gather'd some very good grapes, both black & white, from the fruit-wall: but there are an abundance on the House, that seem as if they never could be ripe.

10.   Discovered the small creeping tormentil (*tormentilla*) the gromwell (*lithospermum*) & the small Centaury (*centaurium minus.*)

The wren sings. Martens are plenty flying abut under the shelter of the Hanger.

8.   A great light seen, & a vast explosion from ye S: about a quarter past nine in the evening: the Cause unknown. It shook peoples houses very much. It seems to be meteorous.

10.   Discovered common fumitory. Ray classes it under his anomalous plants.

11.   Discovered the Common-figwort (*scrophularia*) in bloom, & in pod; & the Common dog's mercury (*cynocrambe*).

12.   Discovered in Mrs Etty's garden the silvery Alpine Crane's-bill (*Geranium argenteum Alpinum*), & the red Valerian (*Valeriana floribus rubris caudatis*)

Snakes are still abroad, & wood ants creeping about. A great rain again last night.

The black Hellebores are budded for bloom on the Hill. The small creeping tormentil pretty frequent on Selborne common.

15.   Set-out for Oxon. Saw ye first field-fare, martens still flying about. Saw none of the swallow-kind afterwards.

Farmer Knight sowed Baker's hill with wheat.

16.   Discovered on the banks of the Thames as I walked from Streatly to Wallingford –

The water hoar-hound (*marrubium aquaticum*)
the yellow willow-herb, or loose-strife (*lysimachia*)
the purple spiked D^o (*lysimachia purpurea*) & the Comfrey (*symphytum magum*) in bloom, being one of the *Herbae asperifolia*: water figwort (*scrop: aquat:*)

I also saw in Oxford dry specimens of the less stitchwort (*Caryophyllus holosteus arvensis glaber flore minore*) & the Cross wort (*cruciata*)

I saw at the Physic garden Madder (*rubia tinctorum*) the Cymbalaria (*linaria*) *hereraceo folio glabro*: the stinking Gladwin (*Iris sylvestris*) stinking hoar-hound (*marrubium nigrum*) white hoarhound (*marrubium album*) a large sort of Burnet: moth mullein (*blattaria*) Bugle (*bugula*) Water-scorpion-Grass (*myosotis scorpioides palustris*) the hawkweed called *Hieracium echioides capitulis cardui benedicti*; al: *lang de beuf.*

21.   Weather uncommonly mild: grass & garden-plants grow very fast.

26.   Returned from Oxon to Selborn. A very white frost in the morning. I have seen no Swallows since the 15th. Planted in my Garden nine large plants of small burnet, which I gathered in a Chalkey lane on my Journey.

John planted in my absence a plot of cabbages to stand y^e

winter. The garden-burnet still continues very vigorous; & the Celeri is grown very gross.

28. A very smart frost that made the ground crisp, & has stripp'd the mulberry-tree & some ashes.

The Hanger looks very much faded; & the leaves begin to fall. In general the new-sown wheat comes-up well.

Plants still in bloom¶ are the wild-basil, white behn, common mallow, several Hawkweeds, bugloss, the hoarhounds, Hedge-nettles, dead-nettles, dandelion, wild succory, Ivy, furze, blue-bottles, thistle, sow-thistle, mullein, fumitory, Yarrow, wild Marjoram, (*origanum*) tufted Basil (*clinopodium*) small Centaury, honeysuckle, wild; *Arbutus*, Bramble, clover, charlock, throatworts, crane's-bill, Scabious, Knap-weed, Mother of thyme, wild red Campion, butter-cups, stinking Mayweed, the common daisey, the great daisey, ragwort, broad-leaved allheal, fluellins.

29. Discovered in the lane leading to the North-field base-hoar-hound with a white blossom, but just going out of bloom (*stachys*) common Self-heal out of bloom (*prunella*) Nettle-leaved throat-wort or Canterbury-bells (*Trachelium*) Cluster-flower'd, or little throat-wort (*Campanula pratensis flore conglomerato*) Dwarf spurge (*tithymalus pumilus angustifolius*) creeping mouse-ear (*pilosella repens*) Crow's foot Crane's bill (*Geranium batrachoides*)

30. Discovered in my Ewel-close a wheat-stubble, Sharp-pointed fluellin just coming into bloom (*Linaria, Elatine dicta, folio acuminato*) & round-leaved female fluellin (*Linaria, Dᵒ dicta, folio subrotundo*) in plenty: also Mouse-ear scorpion-grass (*Myosotis scorpioides hirsuta*): & broad-leaved little All-heal (*Sideritis humilis lato obtuso folio*)

The skie, & wood-lark sing in fine weather: rooks frequent their nest-trees. The ground is now full wet for a wheat-season. The wren sings.

31. Discovered the Ivy-leaved Sowthistle, or wild lettuce (*Lactuca sylvestris Murorum flore luteo*) in a most shady part of the hollow lane under the cove of the rock as you first enter the lane in great plenty, on the right hand before you come to the nine-acre-lane: there was also male fern (*filix mas*) & hart's tongue (*Phyllitis*) discovered also common nipplewort (*Lampsana*) it is distinguished from Hawkweeds by having no down to it's seeds.

NOVEMBER 2. Gromel, figwort, & viper's bugloss, & mouse-ear-scorpion-Grass still in bloom. I suspected I saw the leaves of the *parnassia*, on a bog. Examined the viper's bugloss, (*echium vulgare*) & the small wild bugloss (*buglossum sylvestre minus*) the wild tanzy (*tanacetum*) great water horsetail (*equisetum palustre majus*) Sun spurge (*tithymalus helioscopius*) wood-spurge (*Tithymalus characias Amygdaloides*) common Sᵗ John-wort (*Hypericum vulgare*) dwarf-hawkweed with sinuated very narrow leaves (*Hierachium parvum inarenosis nascens, seminum pappis densicus radiatis*) Knawell,

Clown's allheal (*Sideritis foetida*) small procumbent S! John wort (*Hypericum procumbens minus*) Herb Gerard, Gout-weed, or ashweed (*angelica sylvestris minor seu erratica*)

4.   Racked-off my half Hodsh: of raisin-wine, which began to ferment again: there was a great deal of sediment at bottom.

5.   A Considerable snow for many Hours: but it melted pretty much as it fell. Gathered-in a great quantity of Grapes, which are still very good.

6.   A hard frost, & ice. Gathered-in all the grapes, about a bushel, the weather threatning for more frost. Spread the best bunches on a sheet in the dining room.

12.   Replaced the rasp-plants that dyed in the summer. The leaves of ye Butcher's limes but just begin to fall. The leaves in general hold-on well this year, thro' the mildness of the season.

17.   I planted the border by the wallnut-tree in ye best Garden with two rows of my fine white, & blue Hyacinths: the blue are altogether at the end next the House. The border was well-dunged; & planted in good dry order. I planted also a good large spot with smaller roots, & offsets to make a nursery. The blue at the end next the House.

Dark still weather for many days, with some small rain sometimes, & a very high barometer. The water is much sunk away in the roads, & lakes.

18.   Discovered the common polypody (*polypodium vulgare*) in the hollow lane; & the stinking flag-flower, called Gladdon or Gladwin (*Iris foetida*, *Xyris dicta*) in the hollow lane between Norton-yard, & French-meer just without the gate: it was thrown, in all probability, out of the garden which was formerly just on the other side of the Hedge. In general it is esteemed a bad blower; but this parcel of plants has produced many flowers this summer; & have several pods, which open in three parts, & turn-out y^ir scarlet berries much in the manner of the male piony. There is but one seed in each berry.

Discovered the common Spurrey (*alsine spergula dicta major*) in pod, & bloom in a ploughed field: most exactly described by Ray.

22.   A very fierce frost for two nights: it froze within the second.

Discovered little field-madder (*rubeola arvensis repens caerulea*) & the small-flowered pansy (*viola bicolor arvensis*) in a wheat-stubble in great abundance.

The potatoes turned-out well beyond expectation after such a burning summer: those planted on peat dust were superior to those on old thatch.

25.¶   Discovered the Ivy-leaved speedwell, or small Henbit (*veronica flosculis singularibus*, *hederulae folio*, *Morsus Gallinae minor dicta*) plenty in every garden & field.

Discovered on a bank at Faringdon *Filex elegans*, *Adianto nigro accedens*, *segmentis rotundioribus*; a beautiful fern about six inches high: Pilewort, or ye less Celandine (*Chelidonium minus*) in it's first leaves; it blows in March, & April: The greater Celandine in it's first leaves (*Chelidonium majus vulgare*) & chervil in it's first leaves (*Cicutaria vulgaris; sive Myrrhis sylvestris seminibus lavibus*) called also wild Cicely, & cow-weed.

DECEMBER 6. Finish'd tacking, & trimming my fruit-wall trees: the peaches, & Nect: lie well to the wall, but seem not to be well-ripened in their wood this Year. The vines, (which were contracted to make room for ye Peach: & nectarines) have large well-ripened shoots.

12. Found in a stubble in bloom, & pod the oval-leaved *Turritis* (*Turritis foliis ovatis*)

The flowers now in bloom are Yarrow, *Turritis*, spurrey, butter-cups, *viola bicolor*, dandelion, dead nettle, hedge D^o

Put a finishing hand to my new stable by making my saddle cup-board, shelves, etc.

Discovered in shrub:wood Rough spleen-wort (*lonchitis asperae*) it is known from polypody by the tapering leaves reaching down to ye bottom of ye stem.

14. An hard frost.

31. A severe frost with an harsh E: wind, & cloudy skie: the Ground does not thaw in the middle of the day. Dug-up melon-earth, & turn'd it up to the frost. Put some mellow earth in ye border under the melon-skreen.

— 1766 —

JANUARY 1. The last Year concluded, & this began with a very dry, still frost.
Wheeled into the melon-ground a parcel of my own dung that had never taken any wet; there having been no rain worth mentioning for many weeks.

4. Made the seedling cucumber-bed.

10. Sowed about 30 cucum^r seeds.

13. The bed heats well, & the plants begin to appear.

Severe, still frost yet. The ground has never thawed at all in the middle of the day, since this weather began; but is covered with dust. There have been several small flights of snow; but never enough quite to cover the ground: & yet several red-breasts, & some red-wings have been found frozen to death. It froze within very much to night.

17. The same still, dry weather continues, with a dark sky, & high barometer. The snow is quite gone; & the ground all dust. To day the frost has lasted just three weeks. The cucum^rs come-up well: sowed more.

18. Somewhat of a thaw.

19. A thaw still with an high barometer & a fog: the first Cucum^rs are potted, the second sown are come-up well.

21. A dry thaw with a N: wind, & high barometer. There has been no rain now for seven or eight weeks. The ponds are very low, & the wells sinking. The wind has been remarkably still since it has

been so dry.

25. A gentle thaw still, with vast fogs, but no rain. The ground that was so dusty, is now very dirty without any fall. The soil is strangely puffed-up, & lightened.

Sowed a box of M.ʳ Gibson's polyanth-seed: & five rows of marrow-fat-pease in a very mellow, well-dunged quarter.

Some of the Cucum.ʳ plants keep dying for want of sun, being rotted by the reek of the bed.

28. The same still, dark, dry weather with the glass higher than ever.

29. A vast white dew; & fog in the day. The barometer is higher than ever. The Cucum.ʳˢ hang their leaves, & want Sun.

30. Sowed half the border under the melon-skreen with lettuce, & radishes. All the stiff soil is taken-out of that border, & laid-up to the frost to make melon-earth; & mould that has been in the frames is laid in it's place. Very fierce frost, & partial fogs.

FEBRUARY 1. A thaw: rain & wind with a sinking glass. The first rain for many weeks.

3. Severe frost returns.

8. Severe frost.

10: 11. Rain, soft weather, & a thoro' thaw.

13: 14: 15. Continued Rains from the East which occasioned vast floods in some places. This fall was in several parts of the Kingdom a very great snow; & in others a rain which froze as it fell, loading the trees with ice to such a degree, that many parks, & forests were miserably defaced, & mangled. A strong E: wind contributed much to this damage.

18. Made a fruiting-bed for Cucum.ʳˢ with 8 loads of dung.

19. Planted six rows of Winsor-beans.

25. Planted the Cucum.ʳ bed with plants that have two joints, are stopp'd down, stocky, & well-coloured.

Mild, grey weather, with a tall barometer. Land is in excellent mellow, dry order: people are sowing pease in the fields.

MARCH 1. Dry weather still with a sinking glass. Brewed half an Hogsh: of strong-beer with 6 Bushels of Rich: Knight's malt, & two pounds & three quarters of good Hops. The water was from the well.

Sent a large flitch of bacon to be dryed to M.ʳ Etty's chimney: it lay seven weeks & three days in salt on account of the frost, during which it did not seem to take salt.

The sun broke-out after many shady days.

2. A white frost, & very wet afternoon.

3. Sun-shine morning, the first for a long time.

Put some fresh Cucum.ʳ plants into some of y.ᵉ Hills: the first-removed were coddled in their own steam for Want of Sun.

Sowed the first Succades.

6. The succades appear: the bed is full hot this mild weather.

7. Potted the succades: sowed more.

Finished a low rod-hedge between y.ᵉ garden, & the orchard.

Soft delicate weather.

Planted some wood-straw-berries along at ye back of ye new hedge.

8. Transplanted some burnet, self-sown last summer: sowed carrots, coss lettuce, radishes in ye border under the melon-skreen.

Brought-in 10 loads of dung for the succade-bed; & one load to line the Cuc^r seed-bed.

Cucum^rs begin to shew runners.

10. Planted one Chaumontelle-espalier-pear at the S: W: side of the second middle quarter; & one Crasan-burgamot-pear opposite across the alley; & one D^o near the standard nonpareil tree. These trees are from Armstrong at N: Warnboro; & are to supply the place of those that failed.

Planted two more fan-elms at the back of the necessary-house.

Hot, sunny weather. The cucum^r bed is full warm.

12. Sowed five rows of pease in the orchard; the first crop begins to appear.

No rain for ten days. Sunny, hot days, with an E: wind, & frosty nights.

Made half an hogsh: of raisin-wine with one hund: of Malagas, & half an Hund: of Smyrnas. Put to the raisins ten buckets & an half of water. The raisins were new, & fine: the former cost 24s: the latter 17s.

13. Racked-off my last-made wine the third time. It is very good; but will not be quite fine, as it moves a little still. Took-away about two quarts of very thick Grout.

Planted some stinking gladwins in the garden, a sweet bryar, and a black hellebore from ye wood. Raked-down my asparagus-beds: the mould every where falls in a dust.

14. Turned the melon-dung, which is very hot.

15. Earth'd, & moss'd the seed-cucumber bed, which has the forwardest plants.

Hot sun-shine, & cold E: wind.

17. Pegg'd-down the Cucum^rs which were grown up to the Glasses.

The Succades are very fine, & have two rough leaves.

Hot sunshine with frosts. There has been now no rains for fifteen days.

18. Turn'd the melon-dung a second time. It is very hot. Black, windy weather, with some small flights of snow.

20. Thick Ice.

Made a Celeri-bed for an hand-glass.

Sheltered the wall-trees (which are too much blown) with boards, & doors.

22. Sowed Celeri.

Some rain after 19 very dry days.

Sowed rows of parsley.

23. Snow with thick ice, & a severe North-wind.

24. More snow, & fierce frost.

Covered the fruit-trees against the wall with boards, & mats during these frosty nights.

    Made the succade-bed with ten loads of dung that had been twice turn'd, & had heated much. It is a very stout bed, & seems in good order. The fruit-trees against the wall are much blown-out, & in danger from this severe weather.

25.	Snow in the night, & Ice.
26.	Rain in the morning from the S: 'till twelve; then the wind turned N: & there came a violent snow for six hours, which lies very deep on the ground; & is but a bad sight so late in the Year. The wall-trees have been boarded, & matted all day; & the hot-beds have scarce been opened at all.
27.	A very heavy snow all day; which by night lay a vast thickness on the Ground; in many places three feet. All the shrubs were weighed flat to ye earth. The hot-bed was never uncovered all day; but the plants lived in darkness. The boards & mats were kept before ye wall-trees.
28.	The snow melted in part with a strong sunshine: but it is still as deep as an horse's belly in many places.
	The Cuc^r plants look very well to day.
29.	Warm air, & a swift thaw: yet ye snow is very deep in some places: all along ye N: field it is deeper than an Horse's belly.
	Stopp'd-down the Succades: they are fine plants.
30.	Snow goes away with a gentle rain.

APRIL	1: 2.	Great rain.
		Female bloom of a Cucumber blows-out.
	3.	Black moist weather: the Hot-beds want sun.
	4.	Put the hills in the succade-bed: the earth is rather too moist, not being housed before ye snow. The dung has been brought-in ever since the eight of March: the bed seems now to be mild.
	5.	Turned-out the Succades into the Hills: the plants are stout, & well-rooted; but look rather pale for want of sunshine.
		Sowed some Romagnia melon-seeds from Mr Humphry; & some Cantaleupe-seeds.
	5.	Tunn'd the raisin-wine after I had let it settle a day & a night: I kept back a great quantity of grout. There was a gallon or two over for filling-up. Coloured it with 15 bottles of elder-syrop.
	7.	Mowed the grass-plot for the first time.
	9.	Planted five rows of large fine potatoes, with a layer of peat-dust in every trench. Sowed a crop of Carrots, parsneps, coss-lettuce, & onions; a plot of leeks; double-stocks, dwarf-Sunflowers, & savoys.
		Sowed twelve basons more of Selborne-saved larkspurs.
		The ground in curious, mellow order.
	10.	The last-sown melons are coming-up.
		Dry, March-like weather.
		The succades push-out runners.
	12.	Potted the Cantaleupes, & Romagnias.
		Cucum^{rs} throw out fruit very fast.

	Beautiful weather.
19.	Cut the first Cucumber.
	Small showers.
22.	Cut the second cucumber.
	Soft showers.
	Cucumbers show a great succession of fruit.
26.	The succades have runners with three joints, are stopped, & shew third wood.
	Cut three Cucumbers. Cucumbers grow very fast.
	Soft, showery, growing weather.
26.	Finished moving my barn, which I set at the upper end of the orchard. It began to move on thursday the 17, & went with great ease by the assistance of about 8 men for that little way that it went in a straight line: but in general it moved in a curve, & was turned once quite round, & half way round again. When it came to the pitch of the Hill it required 20 hands; & particularly when it wanted to be shoved into it's place side ways, parallel with Collins's hedge. Near one day of the time was taken-up in making new sills,¶ one of which was broken in two by skrewing it round sideways. No accident happened to the workmen, or labourers; & no part of the frame-work was broken or dislocated, so as to do any material damage.
	The Workmen were three days in pulling down yᵉ skillings,¶ & blocking & removing obstructions, previous to the removal. The barn is 40 feet long.
28.	Made some holes for the hand-glasses, fill'd them with the mowings of the walks, & sowed some large white Cucumbers.
	Summer-like growing weather.
	Cut 4 large Cucumbers.
	Put the sticks to the pease. Weeded & thinn'd the lettuce.
29.	Sowed a plot of lucern-seed to transplant. Earth'd the succade-bed pretty near to the full; & moss'd it all over.
	Most beautiful, shady, growing weather.

MAY	5.	Made the second melon-bed with eight loads of hot dung, & some grass-mowings. The dung is full hot still. There will be dung this year only for two frames.
		The succade plants show fruit, & grow, & look well.
		Black wet weather of late.
	6.	Sowed seven rows, one pint, of dwarf-white-kidney-beans: the Ground has been dug three times this spring, & is very mellow.
	8.	Made an annual-bed with grass mowings, & sowed it with African, & French Marigolds, pendulous amaranths, & China Asters.
		Sowed some snap-dragon seeds, & some dwarf-sun-flowers.
		Planted five short rows of globe-artichokes, sent me by Mʳ Fort of Salisbury.
		Black, showery, growing weather for many days.
	12.	Turned-out two pots of Romagnia-melons, & one of Cantaleupes

into the new bed. Bored holes in yᵉ bed, which is still full hot.

Succades shew male, & female bloom.

Thunder, & heavy cold showers.

The wheat, & barley turns somewhat yellow.

13.   Vast heavy showers, with Hail, & frosts at night.

14.   Covered the mould all over under the succades with whole wheaten straw: beat down the earth first.

Moss'd the hills of the new bed: the bed is very hot, & requires Care.

18.   Began mowing grass for yᵉ Horses.

Hot, summer-weather.

20.   Black, wet weather with a fierce N: wind, that tears-off the leaves from the trees.

27.   Thinn'd-out, & tack'd the peaches, & Nect: & laid some of the gross wood of last Year bare of their willow-like shoots, in order to make room for more moderate wood. The Nect: that was blistered last year, is blistered again: & the first Nect: from the house is curled, & lousy, & wants good shoots. Yet in the whole there will be fruit on each tree which grows well: the apricot abounds with fruit.

The succades abound in strong healthy haulm, & begin to shew promising bloom.

The last bed begins to be more moderate: the plants are just not burnt, & have not very weak runners, which are stopped-down.

28.   Succades begin to set.

Planted 50 cabbages.

Prick'd-out a plot of Celeri.

Black, cold, showery weather.

31.   Lined the succade-bed; but did not put any mould on the lining.

JUNE   2.   The succades keep blowing with good fruit. The frame is crouded with vigorous vines: but the plants want some sunny weather.

Earthed the second frame the second time. The mould is somewhat burnt under the Hills: but the plants look pretty well, & send-out second wood.

3.   Prick'd-out more Celeri. Black wet weather.

4.   Very wet night, & morning.

Thinn'd-out the succade-vines, which quite choak the frame, & begin to rot for want of air & sun. Plenty of melons are sett, & setting.

Every thing is strangely wet: & grass & corn begin to lodge.

5.   Mended-out the rows of french-beans, which are come-up very poorly.

7.   Succades as big as pidgeon's eggs.

Earth'd-out the second melon-bed, where there is pretty good Haulm.

Sowed a few Indian-turnep-seeds, given me by Sʳ Simeon Stuart.

Pricked-out a large Quantity of Savoys.

Hot, summer weather.

10. Fine weather.

Plenty of Succades, which are as large as a goose-egg.

13. Sowed six rows, a second Crop of dwarf-white-french-beans. The first Crop is in a poor Condition.

Earth'd-out the lining of the Succade-melon-bed, & raised the frame. Thinn'd-out the haulm, which is full of fruit.

13. Set several Cantaleupe, & Romagnia melons.

The succades are half grown. The frame now raised stands too high.

Very windy weather.

16. Sowed a crop of curled, & Batavia Endive, & a crop of Coss lettuce; & planted-out a bed of Leeks.

21. A week of most uncommon weather; nothing but wet, & cold winds. Planted-out annuals.

23. Summer-like weather. The Succade-bed has plenty of fruit well grown: the Cantaleupes & Romagnas have fruit set; but the Haulm, & stems of the fruit are too much drawn.

The shoots of the peache, & Nect: are very curled, & lousy.

24: 25. Cut my Hay, a good Crop.

26. A vast rain all night.

27. Showers.

28. Showers.

Lined the Romagna-bed with hot dung. Some of the Romagnas are large fruit: the Cantaleupes are only just setting.

The hay in a poor Condition.

18. Received an Hogsh: of port from Southtōn between M͞r Yalden, & myself.

29. A very wet day.

JULY 1. The hay toss'd about a little.

2. Vast rains from the N:

5. Ricked my hay on the 12ᵗʰ day from cutting: it was as well as could be expected, but has but little smell. The Crop was great.

6. A storm of thunder, & lightening.

Cut a brace of melons. They come very quick from the time of setting; but are not curious this wet shady summer.

8. Cutt a brace of melons.

11. More melons.

Vast showers.

15. Melons come in heaps.

19. Planted-out a plot of curled endive, & a plot of savoys: put sticks to the large french beans.

Finished cutting the hedges.

Sultry weather, & showers.

22. Planted-out more curled endive, & some Batavian Endive; & planted-out some rows of German turneps.

26. Planted more rows of German turneps.

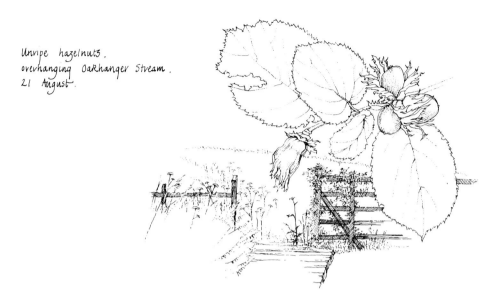

Unripe hazelnuts,
overhanging Oakhanger Stream.
21 August.

Shady showery weather still. All the succades come; but none good.

AUGUST	4.	Bottled-off the hogsh: of port between M! Yalden, & myself.
	5.	Hot, summer weather, with an high glass.
	6.	Trimmed, & tack'd the fruit trees.

    Romagna melons are come; but not good.

    8.   Sowed three ounces of prickly-seeded-spinage; & some Coss-lettuce: planted-out more savoys. Severe heat, & fine ripening weather.

    15.   Trenched three rows more of Celeri in Turner's Garden.

SEPTEMBER

    13.   Found the rows of Celeri backward, & not thriving.

    The Crop of spinage fails.

    Peaches & Nect: begin to ripen well: they are both large, & fair.

    Grapes do but just begin to turn.

    13.   Tyed-up endives both curled, & Batavian. They are curled well, & well-grown.

    One crop of Savoys was well nigh destroyed by ye dry weather.

    All the Nect: trees this Year produce fine fair fruit; but the first tree is distempered, & shrivelled.

    The Apricot-tree produced a decent crop of fine fair fruit.

    There are filberts, & nuts without end.

    Potatoes are large, & good.

    Peaches, & nectarines were fine in Septem! being brought-on by the delicate autumnal weather.

OCTOBER	4.	Black grapes are very good.

    The first great rain with much distant thunder, & lightening.

    5.   Planted-out two long rows of polyanths from the seed-box: the seed came from M! Gibson's. Planted-out some

Mowing the grass.
Selborne.
August.

stock-july-flowers.

The endives by the heat of the weather run much to seed.

25.   Planted 100 of Cabbages to stand the winter. Planted Coss-lettuces to stand the winter against the fruit wall.

Grapes, black-cluster, are very delicate. Autumnal rains come on.

NOVEMBER 10:   Trimmed the vines against the House. Those at the end of the
11.   dining-room are weakly towards the top.
13.   Dug-up all the potatoes, a good crop, & large bulbs.

The Celeri arrives at no Growth, & is cropp'd by the Hogs.

17.   Planted a new Nectarine-tree against the fruit-wall, which the Nursery-man, Armstrong, calls a   Violet.¶

Planted a standard golden-pippin in the orchard.

— 1767 —

1.   Hard frost begins to set in.
10.   Intense frost.
11.   Very deep snow.
14.   Very hard rain on the snow for many hours.
17: 18.   Most severe frost, & the Country covered with ice.
19.   Made an hot-bed.
21: 22.   Regular thaw.

FEBRUARY   6.   Cucumᵗ plants shew a rough leaf.
14.   A very wet season.

House-pidgeons begin to lay.

Cast dung in the farm yards.

25.   Made half an Hogsh: of raisin wine with one hund: of Malagas, & half an hund: of Smyrnas. The former cost 25s pr Hund: & the latter the same. Put to the raisins ten buckets, & an half of water.

Vast rains still, with wind & lightening.

MARCH   4.   Great rains.
5.   Sowed some Succade seeds. Stopped-down the Cucumᵗ plants that have got several joints.

A fine spring day.

10.   Sowed a crop of pease, the first. Sowed a small crop of Carrots, lettuce, & radishes.

Began planting the bank by the stable.

12.   Made the Cucumber-bed with 8 loads of dung. Some plants in the seed-bed show male-bloom. Beautiful sunny weather.

17.   Turned-out the Cucumber-plants into the Hills of the bearing-bed; they are fine plants, but full tall. The bed is hot & requires care. The plants for fruiting in the seedling-bed have good side shoots, & shew the rudiments of fruit.

Made a Celeri-bed with an Hand-glass.

Coletit among beeches
at foot of Selborne Hanger
Late January.

18.	Sowed Cantaleupe-seeds.
23.	Tunned the raisin-wine which filled the half hogsh: there was about one gallon over. The wine, after drawn from y^e raisins, stood two days in a tub to settle, by which means a large quantity of grout was kept back. Put to the wine ten bottles & one pint of elder syrop.

Mem: the syrop by being made with only one pound of sugar to a bottle of juice, fermented, & broke one bottle, & blowed-out some corks. Put one p^d of sugar to the wine to make amends for the bottle of syrop which was lost. The wine is very sweet now.

25.	Brewed an half Hogsh: of strong-beer with six bushels of Rich: Knight's malt, & three pounds of hops: well water.
28.	Cucumber-fruit blows out.

    Planted some strong cuttings of my sweet-water grape against the fruit-wall, & against the wall of the House near the fig-tree, & brew-house door.

30.	Many Cucumber-fruit blown. Lined-out the seedling-bed for the last time.
31.	Swallow appears.

APRIL	2.	Put three Gallons of wine, half of which was of the strongest sort, into ye vinegar barrel.
	3.	Rain, gentle & warm constantly for four whole days to this time. Grass grows wonderfully. Earth'd-out ye seedling-cucum^r bed: fruit swells.
	4.	*Motacilla trochilus* Lin: *Regulus non cristatus* Raii:¶ & *Parus ater* Lin: & Raii, Angl: colemouse,¶ sing.
	6.	Saw more than twenty swallows & bank-martins at Mrs Cole's at Liss over the Canals.
	10.	The nightingale, *motacilla luscinia*, sings.

    The black-cap, *motacilla atricapilla*, sings.
    The red-start, *motacilla Phoenicurus* appears.
    Raised, & earth'd-out the large Cucum^r bed to the full, & mossed it.

11.	Cut a very large Cucumber.
12.	Cut five large ones, & sent them to London.
13.	Miller's thumb, *Cottus gobio*, spawns.

14. Planted three rows of potatoes in a mellow quarter near the fruit-wall.

15. Made the melon-bed, for two frames only, with 16 loads of hot dung, which had been cast, & turned over twice. The bed is stout, & consists of short, solid dung.

   Put a good layer of cold dung at the top to keep down the steam.

   Cold dry weather; & the fruit-trees are matted every night.

   Sowed carrots, parsneps, radishes, onions, leeks, lettuces, savoys, German turneps.

16. Sowed Baker's Hill (which is about an acre & an half of ground, walks, & melon-ground excluded) with seven bushels of Saint-foin along with a crop of barley of dame Knight's. The field was winter-fallowed, & has had two plowings besides: but by reason of the wet spring is sown in a very rough Condition. It has been hand-pick'd of the weeds by women, & is got clean; & is to be rolled, & harrowed again.

   Made an hand-glass bed for large white Dutch-Cucumbers.

   Cold winds, & sleet.

   The brambling, *fringilla montifringilla*, appears. The cock is a fine gay bird.

17. Some snow, with Ice & a fierce cutting wind.

18. Went to London.

JUNE 12. Returned to Selborne.

   Cold black weather; & the fruit of all kinds cut-off in general.

16. Lined the melon-bed with four loads of dung: the succades are full of haulm, & the fruit beginning to blow: the Cantaleupes look poor, & distempered.

18. Succades begin to set.

   Sowed a plot of endive.

9[19?]. Planted-out annuals on a showery day.

29: 30. Cut my hay, a good Crop.

JULY 2. Ricked five jobbs in excellent order: one jobb in large cock catched in the rain.

3. Pricked out savoys, & German turneps. Some Succades are large: Cantaleupes begin to blow.

   Alauda minima locustae voce, the titlark¶ that sings like a Grass-hopper seems to have finished his song.

   The *stoparola* builds in the vine.

   Spipola prima Aldrov: the white throat, sings. The titlark sings.

   Great showers about.

   Planted-out Cucumbers for pickling.

5. Rain & a tempestuous wind that damaged the garden much, & blowed down a green-gage plum-tree.

7. Housed the last load of Hay.

8: 9. Strong winds, & heavy showers unfavourable to the wheat.

11. Vast showers still. Slip'd & planted out pinks, & wall-flowers.
    The titlark sings still.
    Young swallows appear.
    The *Stoparola* brings out it's Young.
18. Vines begin to blow.
20. *Ananas* are in cutting at Hartley.¶
    Trenched-out some Celeri.
    Planted-out some endive.
    Hot, summer-like weather.
    The titlark sings still.
    The Nect: trees put-out some young shoots, & look better; the
peach-trees shrivel-up, & get worse, & worse.
29: 30. Vast rains, & wind.

AUGUST   1. The first crop of Succades were all cut: they are not good for want
of sun, & dry weather.
    Parus ater, the cole-mouse, sings.
10. Hot, dry weather for some time.

SEPTEMBER
11. Much wheat abroad, & some standing. Second crop of Succades
good. Cantaleupes good, but small.
    Regulus non cristatus chirps.
    Peaches begin to ripen.
    Peach, & Nect: trees a little recovered from y^{ir} distempered
condition.
17. Discovered the yellow centory,¶ *Centaurium luteum perfoliatum* of
Ray, in plenty up the sides of the steep cart-way in the Kings field
beyond Tull's. This is a very vague plant for ascertaining
according to the sexual system. Linn: makes it a gentian, & places
it among the pentandrias: but it has commonly seven stamina.
Hodson [Hudson] makes a new Genus of it (*Blackstonia*)
unknown to Linn: placing it as an 8 *andria digynia*. It is best
known by it's boat-like, very perfoliated leaves.
    Moist black weather, which much retards harvest.
19. Sultry weather, with a very high barometer. Peaches are good, &
Nectarines delicate, & large. Black grapes begin to turn colour.
Wheat in general is housed, & housing.
    The black-cap, red-start, & white throat still appear.
    Cantaleupes small with me, but good. Succades good.
24. Tyed-up many large endives.
    Sweet Autumnal weather.
    Ear-wigs, when small, fly about with ease: but, when full-
grown do not attempt to rise; as if their wings were not then
adequate to their weight. This is a mistake; there are two species.¶
    Melons over.
18. *Musca meridiana* of Linn: & Scopoli appears.

OCTOBER   5. Great hail-storms, & cold weather.
    Martins appear still.

Very few wasps.

Missle-thrushes come to the Yew-trees.

Endives are very fine.

8.　Celeri is blanched.

Gathered my apple, & pear-crop, which consisted literally of one Golden-pippin, & one Cadillac.

Dung borrowed in 1766

Feb: 7.	Of Kelsey dung p^d car: p^d	4 loads.
	Car: of my own 1 load car p^d	
Feb: 7.	Of Parsons Dung p^d Cr p^{d}4 loads.	
March 8.	Of Parsons Dung p^d Cr p^d	5 loads.
	Of Kelsey dung p^d car p^d	4 loads.
	Car: of my own 2 loads.	
April 17.	Of Parsons Dung p^d C^r p^d	4 loads.
18	Of Kelsey dung p^d car: p^d	1 load.
26	Of J: Hale Dung p^d p^d.	3 loads.

Dung borrowed in 1767

March 6.	Of Parsons dung p^d C^r p^d	3 loads.
	Of J. Hale little cart car: pd: dung p^d ...	3 loads.
	Of Kelsey car: pd: dung p^d	2 loads.
April 2.	Of Parsons dung p^d C^r p^d	4 loads.
2.	Of Kelsey car: p^d dung p^d	4 loads.
3.	Of Berriman car: p^d at three times.....	4 loads.
3.	Of J: Hale a little cart car: pd: dung p^d .	4 loads.
June 15.	Of J: Hale D^o car pd: dung p^d	2 loads.
	Of F. Parsons dung p^d C^r p^d	2 loads.

OCTOBER　20.　Being on a visit at the house of my good friend Mr John Mulso Rector of Witney, I rode out on purpose to look after the base horehound,¶ the *Stachys Fuchsii* of Ray, which, that Gent: says, grows near Witney park: I found but one plant under the wall: but farther on near the turnpike that leads to Burford, in an hedge opposite to Minster Lovel, it grows most plentifully.

It was still blowing, & abounded with seed; a good parcel of which I brought away with me to sow in the dry banks round the village of Selborne. It is not known to grow in any Country save that of Oxōn, & Lincoln.

29.　Saw four or five swallows flying round & settling on the County-hospital at Oxōn.

NOVEMBER　4.　Bees & flies still continue to gather food from ye blossoms of Ivy.

5.　Gathered the first grapes; they are very sweet, & delicate; tho' the buches [bunches], & berries are smaller than usual. There is not one fifth part of the usual crop.

12.   Continual wet, & high winds. People are much hindred in their wheat-season.

12.   Bro: Benj.ⁿ saw a Marten flying in Fleetstreet.

16.   Vast rains.

18.   The first considerable frost.

23.   Put the Hyacinths in rows in part of a Quarter near the fruit wall. Many of the roots were decayed; & the rest would have been better, had not the rains prevented their being put-out for several weeks.

     Earthed-up all the Celeri. Some of it begins to pipe.¶

     Grey still weather with an high Glass.

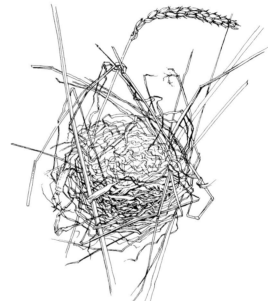

Harvestmouse nest drawn at the Wakes Museum , found locally .

DECEMBER 1.   Dug-up the potatoes, a good Crop.

4.   A very hard frost with a little snow.

     Car: away the melon-bed.

     Sent two field-mice, a species very common in these parts (tho' unknown to the zoologists) to Thomas Pennant Esq of Downing in Flintshire.¶ They resemble much in colour yᵉ *Mus domesticus medius* of Ray; but are smaller than the *Mus domesticus vula: seu minor* of the same great Naturalist. They never enter houses; are carryed into ricks, & barns with yᵉ sheaves, abound in harvest; & build their nests, composed of the blades of corn, up from the ground among the standing wheat; & sometimes in thistles. They breed as many as eight Young at one time.

6.   Planted one golden-rennet,¶ & six curious sorts of Goose-berries from Armstrong.

10. The nuthatch, *sitta sive picus cinereus*, chirps. It runs about on trees, & hangs with it's back downard like the titmouse. It builds in hollow trees, stopping-up great part of the hole with clay, so as to leave barely room to go in & out. There have been several nests in an hole in the yew-tree in Selborne church-yard. Some of the clay remains still at the top of the Crevice.

15. Planted one Roman Nectarine, & one melting peach from Armstrong.

16. Mild, pleasant weather. Daiseys, Herb Robert, ragwort, hepaticas, primroses, in bloom. Crocuss, & snow-drops spring.

22. Strong frost after a long dry fit without any.

24. Strong, bearing Ice, & a severe N: E: wind. Covered the Celeri, & put straw to the roots of the new planted trees.

26: 28. Frequent flights of snow, & severe frost within doors.

30. Severe frost, & still sunny fine days. It freezes even in the Kitchen.

31. It froze under people's beds. Great rimes, & beautiful sunny days.

MARCH 6. 1771.
Brewed half an hogshead of strong beer with 6 bushels of Rich: Knight's malt, & 3 p^{ds} & half of Berriman's hops. Kept it in the tun-tub, & laded in the yeast til the 8th

Severe frost at the [blot] All rain-water save one bucket.¶

†GARDEN CALENDAR FOR 1766, & 1767

FEBRUARY 8: 1769.
Brewed half an hogsh: of strong beer, with six bushels of Rich: Knight's malt, & three p^{ds} & an half of John Berriman's hops.
The water was about three parts rain-water.

FEBRUARY 27: 1769.
Mashed an hundred of Malaga raisins in order to make twenty gallons of wine. The raisins were good & cost 23s per hund: Put 6 buckets & two thirds of a bucket of water.

MARCH 21.
Tunned the raisin-wine, & added to it ten bottles of elder syrop.

MARCH 2: 1770.
Brewed half an hogsh: of strong beer with six bush: of Rich: Knight's malt, & 3 p^{ds} & an half of Berriman's hops. Mem: put one bush: of brown malt to the second mashing.

MARCH 12: 1770.
Mashed an hundred of Malaga raisins in order to make twenty

---

†These notes were originally entered under this title at the beginning of the Calendar for 1766. Perhaps these were the only spare pages in a full notebook.

gallons of wine. The raisins were good, & cost 23s. p^r hund: Put 6 buckets & ¾ of water to the raisins.

APRIL	6.	Tunned the wine & put to it eleven bottles of elder syrop. There was barely liquor enough to fill the barrel.
FEBRUARY 16: 1768.		Made then 20 gallons of raisin-wine in a new barrel with one hund: of Malaga-raisins. The raisins were good, & cost 25s p^r. hund: Put 6 buckets, & two thirds of water.
MARCH	8.	Tunned the raisin-wine, & put to it 10 bottles of elder syrop. It just held out.
MARCH	9.	Brewed half an Hogsh: of strong beer with six bushels of Richd Knight's Malt, & three pounds of Turner's hops. Well-water. The beer work'd well.
MAY	19.	Rack'd-off the elder-wine, which worked too much: took from it two quarts of grout, & put to it one pint of brandy. It is sweet, & well flavoured.
SEPTEMBER	12.	Bottled-off the elder-wine made Feb: 16: it was fine, & well flavoured. The cask ran seven doz: of bottles: some bottles were very large.
	22.	Bottled-off the Hogsh: of port: it was very bright: my share ran 11 doz: & 10 bottles.
	23.	Made 12 bottles of elder-syrop: put to it 10 pounds of coarse sugar.

Dung borrowed in 1768

March 5th	Of Kelsey dung p^d car: p^d	4 loads.
	Of Parsons car p^d dung p^d	2 loads.
7.	Of Hale dung paid car p^d.	2 loads.
25.	Of Hale dung paid car p^d.	4 loads.
	Of Kelsey dung paid car p^d	8 loads.
	Of Parsons car p$^{d.}$ dung p^d.	4 loads.
Ap: 19:	Of Parsons car p^d dung p^d	2 loads.
June 10.	Of Parsons car p^d dung p^d	1 load.

Dung borrowed in 1769

March 6.	Of Hale dung p^d car p^d.	4 loads.
	Of Benham car p^d dung p^d	3 loads.
Apr: 13th	Of Hale dung p^d car p^d.	4 loads.
	Of Benham car p^d dung p^d	4 loads.
May 12.	Of Benham car p^d dung p^d	1 load.
June 12.	Of Benham car p^d dung p^d	2 loads.

Feb: 22.	Of Hale car pd: dung p^d	. . . . .5 loads.
23.	Of Benham car: p^d dung p^d	. . . . .3 loads.
Dung p^d	Of Benham car: p^d	. . . . .6 loads.
	Of Hale car p^d dung p^d	. . . . .5 loads.
June 8.	Of Hale dung p^d car: p^d	. . . . .4 loads.

Aug: 2. Master Hale brought me in one load of Hay p^d.

JUNE 1: 1770. Racked-off the raisin-wine made in March, & put to it one pint of brandy. Took out a gallon of grout.

March 8.	Of Hale dung p^d car p^d	. . . . .5 loads.
11.	Of Benham Car p^d	. . . . .3 loads.
April 1.	Of Hale one load dung p^d car p^d	. . . . . . .1 load.

NOVEMBER 29: 1771 Brewed half an hogshead of strong beer with 6 bush: of Richd Knight's malt, & 3 p^ds & an half of Berriman's hops for the year 1770. The water was all from ye well, but it was drawn some days before, & stood in the open air.

MARCH 24: 1772. Brewed half an hogshead of strong beer with 6 bush: of Rich: Knight's malt, & near 4 pounds of Berriman's hops of the year 1770. All rain water. Put one bush: of brown malt to the second mashing. The beer works well.

MARCH 5: 1773. Brewed half an hogshead of strong beer with 6 bushels of Rich: Knight's malt & three pounds & an half of Berriman's hops. All rain water. Put one bush: of brown malt to the second mashing. Beer works well.

NOVEMBER 1: 1773. Brewed half an hogshead of strong beer with six bushels of Rich: Knight's malt & three pounds & an half of Berriman's new hops. All rain water. Put one bushel of brown malt to the second mashing.

Early September.
Ripe elderberries.
Selborne churchyard.

Hops outside the brewhouse,
The Wakes late August.

FLORA
SELBORNIENSIS:

with some co-incidences of the coming, & departures of
birds of passage, & insects; & the appearing of Reptiles:
for the Year 1766.

The plants are according to Mʳ Ray's method; & the birds
according to Mʳ Willughby's ornithology: the Insects according
to Ray's *Hist: Insect:*
& the Reptiles according to Ray's *Synopsis Animalium
Quadrupedum.*

THE CALENDAR OF FLORA 1766

JANUARY	1.	The Year begins with a remarkable dry frost.
	13.	Severe still frost yet; the roads very dusty.
	25.	A gentle thaw.

The bat (*Vespertilis*) appears.
Hepaticas in bloom all the frost.
Wall-flower (*Leucoium*) in bloom.
Laurustine blows.

FEBRUARY 1. Thaw. Wind & rain: none for many weeks. The great titmouse
(*Parus Major*) begins his spring note.
Moles work much.
Rooks assemble on their nest-trees. 3ʳᵈ Severe frost.

13: 14: 15. Continued rains that occasioned vast floods in some parts: in some
parts the fall was a very deep snow: in others a freezing rain
which broke & defaced multitudes of trees.

22. On my return from London I found the snow-drop, & winter
aconite in bloom; & the Crocus blowing; the Hazel, *corylus
sylvestris*, blowing, with vast numbers of their male catkins
opening which give the hedges a yellowish tinge: the primrose,
primula veris¶, is also blowing.
   The thrush, *turdus simpliciter dictus*, the chaffinch, *fringilla*, &
the skie-lark, *Alauda vulgaris*, sing: the titmouse, *parus major*,
makes his spring note. Soft grey weather, & the ground in fine
order.

MARCH 1. Soft, grey weather with a sinking glass. Groundsel, *senecio*, in bloom.

3. The wry-neck, *Jynx*, pipes: alias *Torquilla*. This was only the black-headed titmouse, *parus major*. The Elder, *Sambucus*; honeysuckle, *caprifolium*, begins to shoot.
    Crown-imperials, hyacinths, tulips, Narcissuss, Jonquils begin to peep: polyanths begin to blow.
    Wood laurel, *laureola*, buds for bloom.
    Great black Hellebore, bear's foot or setter-wort,¶ *Helleboraster maximas, seu consiligo enneaphyllon Plinii*, in flower in Selborne-wood.
    The flies in the dining-room begin to come forth out of the lurking-holes.
    The long-tailed titmouse, *parus caudatus*, chirps.
    Lady-cows, *scarabaei subrotundi*, & earwigs appear, *forficulae*.

4. In flower *veronica flosculis singularibus, cauliculis adhaerentibus*, speedwell-chickweed.¶

5. In flower common chickweed, *alsine vulgaris, seu morsus gallinae*.
    Bees, *apes domesticae*, are busy in the flowers, crocuss.
    Sunny spring weather. Some ants, *formicae*, appear. The missel-bird or shrite, *turdus viscivorus major*, (in Hants the storm-cock) sings.
    The gooseberry-tree, *grossularia*, shoots.
    White hellebore, *helleborus albus*, begins to shoot. The fungus *membranaceus, seu coriaceus, acetabuli modo concavus, colore intus coccineo* is now common on rotten sticks under every hedge; & is one of the earliest funguss. A *peziza*.
    Columbines, *aquilegiae*, emerging.
    Spiders creep forth.
    Foreign asters begin to shoot.
    The bay-tree, *laurus*, budding for bloom.

6. Red dead-nettle, *lamium vulgare rubrum*, flowers: *folio subrotundo*.
    The wren, *passer troglodytes, regulus*, sings.
    The moth, *tinera vestivora*, appears.
    The partridge, *perdix cinerea*, pairs.
    The yew-tree, *taxus*, buds for bloom.
    The buds of the apricot, *malus armeniaca*, swell.
    The buds of the peach, *malus persica*, swell.
    The yellow-hammer, *emberiza*, sings: *scil: flava*.
    Common avens, *Caryophyllata vulgaris*, has leaves very large.
    Cuckow-pint, *Arum*, emerges: called also wake-Robin.
    Wild Cicely, or cow-weed, *Cicutaria vulgaris*, much advanced in growth.
    Herb Gerard, gout-weed, or ash-weed, *angelica sylvestris minor, s: erratica*, peeps-out.
    Less hemlock or fool's parsley, *cicutaria tenuifolia*,

much grown.

White dead-nettle, *lamium vulgare album*, much grown.

Cleavers, or goose-grass, *Aparine vulgaris*, growing from the beginning of the year.

7. The wood-lark, *Alauda arborea*, sings.

The rook, *cornix frugilega*, begins to build.

The jack-daw, *monedula*, comes to churches, & steeples.

Sallow, *salix*, flowers.

The mullein, *verbascum*, grown to a great tuft.

8. Saw yᵉ first butterfly, *papilio sulphureus*, a brimstone-coloured one: some people saw several of these, & several that were coloured with black spots; these are, I believe, *papiliones Urticae*.

Spiders, *lupi nigri*, begin to dart their webs.

A beautiful summer day.

Blackbird, *merula vulgaris*, sings.

9. Hedge-sparrow, *curruca*, sings.

Vipers come forth.

Dogs-mercury, *cynocrambe*, buds for bloom.

Very hot sun shine, & a steady barometer.

Woodstrawberry, *fragaria*, blows.

The ring dove, or queest, *palambus torquatus*, cooes.

Field cricket, *gryllus sylvestris*,¶ appears at yᵉ mouth of its hole, which it has rounded-out very elegantly. Those that I saw had only rudiments of wings: from whence I should suppose that yᵉ old ones of last year do not survive yᵉ winter.

10. The daisey, *bellis*, blows.

Teasel, *dipsacus*, emerges.

Pear tree, *pyrus*, buds for bloom.

Wormwood, *absinthium*, peeps out.

11. Dandelion, *dens leonis*, blown.

Sycomore, *acer majus*, budding.

12. Furze, *Genista spinosa vulgaris*, in bloom.

Laurel, *laurocerasus*, budding for bloom.

Dog's mercury, *cynocrambe*, blowing, the male bloom only.

Birch, *betula*, budding.

Wood-laurel, *laureoa*, in bloom.

Humble-bee comes forth, *Bombylius*.

Periwinkle,¶ *vinca pervinca minor*, in bloom in Shrub-wood: this is a scarce plant.

Jack in the hedge, *alliaria*, springing all the winter.

Ragweed, *Jacobaea*, shooting.

Hounds-tongue, *cynoglossum*, springing.

Malva sylvestris, the common mallow, grows.

Ground-ivy, *calamintha humilior folio rotundiore*, creeps about all the winter.

Wood-ruffe, *asperula*, appears, or rather has not disappeared the winter thro'.

Mezereon blows.¶

Crocuss make a most gallant show.

13.   Ivy-leaved speedwell, or small henbit, *veronica flosculis singularibus hederulae folio*, in bloom.

Common mint, *mentha vulgaris*, sprouts.

Pilewort, *chelidonium minus*, blowing; less celandine. This & other things are forced before their time by the hot sun shine.

Wood-sorrell, *oxys*, grown up.

Frog, *rana*, croaks, & spawns.

Toad, *bufo*, appears.

The air is full of gnats.

14.   Marsh-marigold, *populago*, budds for bloom.

Blue & white violet, *viola martia purpurea* & *alba*, blows.

Meadow-sweet, *ulmaria*, sprouts.

Very white frost.

15.   Feverfew, *matricaria*, springs.

Strawberry-tree, *Arbutus*, shews the rudiments of fruit.

White dead-nettle, *lamium album*, blows.

Ladies-bedstraw, *Gallium*, shoots.

Cucumber, *Cucumis*, shews rudiments of male bloom & fruit.

Apricot, *malus armeniaca*, blowing.

Peach, *malus persica*, blowing.

Larch, *larix*, budding.

17.   Apricot, *malus armeniaca*, blows.

Peach, & Nect: *malus persica*, blows.

Curran, *ribes*, shows rudiments of bloom.

Asp, or aspin, *populus tremula*, shews full blown catkins.

Gelderrose, *opulus*, budds.

Laburnum budds.

Lilac budds.

Rose, *Rosa*, leafes.

Weeping willow, *salix Babylonica*,¶ budds.

Cherry-tree, *Cerasus*, budds.

Coltsfoot, *Tussilago*, in bloom.

Burdock, *lappa*, sprouting out of the ground.

Discovered, as I suspect, the tuberous moschatel, *ranunculus nemorum Moschatella dictus*, in it's radical leaves. This was sanicle.¶

Discovered the earth-nut or pig nut, *bulbocastanum*, in its first leaves.

19.   Cucum: *Cucumis*, flowers.

Wych-elm, *Ulmus folio latissimo scabro*, budds for bloom.

Soap-wort, *saponaria*, sprouts.
Larch, *larix*, budds for bloom.
Sloe-tree, *prunus sylvestris*, budds for bloom.
Piony, sprouts.
Butcher's broom, *ruscus*, budds.
Horse-ants, *Hippomyrmeces*, or great wood-ants appear.
Vernal equinox. Ice.
Single garden-hyacinths blow.
Daffodils,¶ *Narcissus sylvestris pallidus calyce luteo*, blows.

21.   Common elm, *Ulmus vulgatissima folio lato scabro*, blows.

23.   Snow, & thick Ice.

24.   More snow, & a freezing wind.
        The bloom of the wall fruit in danger.

25.   More snow, & Ice.

26.   A very deep snow!

27.   A second day's snow; which lies very deep on the Ground!

28.   Snow melts very fast in the sunshine.
        Crown Imperial, *Corona Imperialis*, buds for bloom.
        Catkins of the hazel, *corylus*, fall.
        A small grass-hopper, *locusta*, appears in the cucumᵣ frame,
hatched no doubt in the mould of the bed.
        The female bloom of the Cucumᵣ towards blowing.

29.   The more-hen, or water-hen, *Gallinula chloropus major*, chatters;
& sports in the water.
        Common shepherd's purse, *bursa pastoris*, blows.

31.   Wood anemony, *anemone nemorum alba*, blows.
        Snow pretty well gone.
        Wood-spurge, *tithymalus characias Amygdaloides*, continues
green all thro' the winter.

APRIL   2.   Female blossom of the Cucumᵣ blows-out.
        Great rains; & the snow gone.

4.   Bees gather on the Sallow-bloom, & Laurustines.
        Fritillaria budds for bloom.
        Agrimony, *agrimonia*, emerges.
        Cow-parsnep, *sphondylium*, shoots.
        Peach, & Nect: leafes.
        Goose-berry leafes; *Grossularia*.
        Curran, *Ribes*, leafes.
        Fraxinella shoots; white Dittany.

Pease-everlasting, *lathyrus sativus flore purpureo*, springs.
Solomon's seal, *polygonatum*, sprouts.
Honey suckle, *caprifolium*, makes shoots.
Double daffodils blow.
Black snails appear.
Polyanthus *narcissus* budds for bloom.
Hyacinths, double garden, push-out long flower-stems.
M.ʳˢ Snooke informs me that her tortoise, *testudo terrestris*, in
the Garden came-forth from under the ground on yᵉ 17 of
March, it being a very sunny season. On common Years it did
not use to appear 'till the beginning of April, O: S:¶

6.   White dead-nettle, *lamium album*, blows.
     Coloured shelled-snails appear, & engender.
     Cherry tree against a wall flowers.
     Plum against Dᵒ blows.
     Rook, *cornix frugilega*, sits.
     Hop, *lupulus*, sprouts.
     Holly, *agrifolium*, budds for bloom.
     Turkey lays.

7.   Hollow-rooted fumitory, *fumaria bulbosa*, blows in gardens.
     The animalcula in frog-spawn grow in length.
     Common whitlow-grass, *paronychia*, blows.
     Pansy, *viola bicolor arvensis*, blows.
     Lamb's lettuce, *valerianella*, shoots.

8.   Pagil, or cowslip, *paralysis vulgaris praetensis flore flavo simplici
     odorato*, blows.

9.   Wood-sorrel, *oxys alba*, blossoms.
     Greater bistort, or snake-weed, *bistorta major*, sprouts out of yᵉ
     ground.
     Sheep's sorrel, *lapathum acetosum repens lanceolatum*, appears in
     leaf.
     Ramson, *allium sylvestre latifolium*, budds for bloom.
     Wild tansey, or silver weed, *pentaphylloides argentina dicta*,
     emerges.
     Misletoe, *viscum*, blows.

11. Asparagus, sprouts.
     Curran, *ribes*, blows.
     Tuberous moscatel, *moschatella*, blows.
     Golden saxifrage, *saxifraga aurea*, blossoms.
     Medlar, *mespilus*, budds.
     Pezizas appear still.
     Several Ichneumon-flies appear.
     Rosebay willow-herb, *Lysimachia speciosa*, *quibusdam Onagra
     dicta*, emerges.

Filex aculeata mas, prickly male-fern.

12.   Early tulip, *tulipa praecox*, blows.
        Marsh-marrigold, *populago*, blooms.
        White-thorn, or haw-thorn, *oxyacantha*, leafes.
        Black-thorn, or sloe-tree, *prunus sylvestris*, flowers.
        A bee-like hairy fly with a sharp head, & long proboscis
appears. *Musca bombyliiformis*, &c: *Hist: Ins:* p: 273.

14.   Swallow, *hirundo domestica*, returns.
        The martin or martlet, *hirundo agrestis*, was seen by
neighbours on the 2nd? *Pulmonaria*, bugloss-cowlips, blooms.
This uncommon plant was found in the lane that leads from the
hollow-lane to Norton-yard.
        Crown-imperial, *corona imperialis*, blossoms.
        Common Ladies-smock, or cuckow-flower, *cardamine, seu
nasturtium pratense majus*, blows.
        The wryneck, *Jynx, al: torquilla*, pipes.
        Jack by the hedge, *hesperis allium redolens*, budds for bloom.
        Sun-spurge *tithymalus helioscopius*, blows.
        Ground-ivy, gill-goby-ground, *calamintha humilior folio
rotundiore*, blossoms.
        Shepherd's needle, or Venus's comb, *scandix semine rostrato*,
blows.
        Lamb's lettuce, *valerianella*, budds for bloom.
        Winter-cress, or rocket, *eruca lutea, seu barbarea*, budds for
bloom.
        Hen-bane, *hyoscyamus*, emerges.
        Dog's violet, *viola martia inodora*, blows.
        Young rooks in their nests.

15.   The vine, *vitis*, budds.
        Polyanth-Narcissus blows.
        Young figs appear.

17.   Nightingale, *luscinia*, returns, & sings.
        Bloody wall-flowers blow.
        Privet-leaved lilac, or persian Jasmine,¶ *Syringa ligustri folio*,
buds for bloom.
        Raspberry, *Rubus idaeus spinosus*, leafes.

19.   Wood pease,¶ or heath-pease, *Orobus sylvaticus foliis oblongis
glabris*, blossoms.
        the titlark, *alauda pratorum*, sings.

20.   Jack-by-the Hegde [hedge], or sauce alone, *Hesperis allium
redolens*, blows.
        †Branched whitlow-grass, *patonythia ramosa hirsuta*, blows. A

---

†Crossed out.

mistake.¶
    Dyer's-weed, *luteola*, comes into leaf.
    The Cuckow, *cuculus*, returns, & sings.
    White bryony, *bryonia alba*, shoots.
    Greater stichwort, *caryophyllus holosteus arvensis glaber flore majore*, blossoms.
    Privet, *ligustrum*, in full leaf.
    Round-podded, lunar violet, vul: Honesty, *lunaria siliculis subrotundis*, blows.

21.   Young Ravens,¶ *corvi*, are fledge.
    Young Geese.
    The berries of Ivy, *Hedera*, ripen: it flowers in October; & is the last flower the bees, & flies feed-on.
    Pile-wort, *Chelidonium minus*, every where in high bloom.
    Quince-tree, *malus cydonia*, leafes.
    Dwarf-elder, or Dane-weed, or wall-wort, *sambucus humilis, seu ebulus*, emerges.

22.   Garden-strawberry, *fragaria*, buds for bloom.
    Black-beetle appears on evenings.
    Wild black-cherry-tree *cerasus sylvestris fructu nigro*, begins to blow. The Cypress, *cupressus*, blows.

23.   White-throat, an *spipola prima Aldrovandi*? appears.
    Young apricots.
    Garden standard-Cherry blows.
    Fritillaria blows.
    Bear's foot, or wild black Hellebore, *helleborus niger hortensis flore viridi*, flowers in the stony lane towards Alton: this is a different species from that on the hill; has a much greener flower, & greener leaves. The other has whitish flowers, & blackish leaves.
    Harts-tongue, *phyllitis*; & Male-fern *filix mas*, sprout: the old leaves are not yet decayed.

24.   *Ros solis*, sun dew, emerges.
    Ivy-leaved water-crowfoot, *Ranunculus aquatilis hederaceus*, blows.
    Water crowfoot with various leaves, *ranunculus aquatilis folio rotundo*, & *capillaceo*, blows.
    Less spear-wort, *Ranunculus flameus minor*, shoots.
    wood-spurge *tithymalus characias Amygdaloides*, blows.
    The lapwing, or bastard plover, *capella, sive vanellus*, is paired, & flies round with a querulous note.
    The wild duck *boschas major*, sits.
    The sand-martin, *Hirundo riparia*, al: shore-bird, appears.
    The snipe, or snite, *Gallinago minor*, poises in the air, & whistles: this it does only in breeding time.
    The sand-piper, *tringa minor*, in a flock on the banks of

oakhanger ponds.

24.   The swift, *Hirundo apus*, returns.
    The beech, *fagus*, begins to leafe.

25.   *anblatum Cordi, s: aphyllon*, blows.
    Half a doz: of these curious, strange plants spring up in a cluster under a hedge in M.͏ͬ Yalden's orchard.
    The common blue Hyacinth, or hare's bells, *Hyacinthus Anglicus, oblongo flore caeruleo*, begins to blow.
    Barley, *hordeum*, springs finely.
    Distant thunder, & fine showers.
    Myrtle leaved sumach, *coriaria*, buds for bloom.
    Scarlet-strawberry buds for bloom.
    Cuckow-pint, *arum*, shews it's spatha.

27.   Gold-finch, *carduelis*, sings.
    Green-finch, *chloris*, chirps.
    Rue-whitlow-grass, *saxifraga verna annua humilior, s: sedum tridactilides tectorum*, blows.
    Germander-speedwell, *veronica chamaedryfolia*, begins to blow.
    Common-fern, or brakes, *filix foemina*, sprouts.
    Yellow dead-nettle, *lamium luteum*, blows.
    Flesh-fly, *musca carnaria*, appears.
    The chafer, or tree-beetle appears.
    Pear-tree, *pyrus*, blooms.
    Plum-tree, *prunus*, blows.

28.   Lamb's lettuce, *valerianella*, blows.
    Woodruffe, *asperula*, flowers.
    Cuckow-pint, *arum*, blows.
    The uplands glow with pile-worts, & dandelions; the wet meadows¶ with marsh marrigolds.
    Colt's-foot, *tussilago*, shedding it's down.
    Vine, *vitis*, leafes.
    Young peaches, & Nectarines appear: the trees make long shoots.
    Garden-strawberry scarlet blows.

29.   Ribwort-plantain, *plantago quinquenervia*, blows.
    Greater celandine, *papaver corniculatum luteum, chelidonia dictum*, flowers.
    Mountain-ladies-bedstraw, *mollugo montana*, buds for bloom.
    Tower-mustard oval-leaved, or *turritis, brassica spuria caule magis folioso hirsutior*, blows in dry clover-fields.
    Laurustines in high bloom, & beauty still.
    Birch, *betula*, in catkin.
    Yellow toad's-flax, *linaria lutea vulgaris*, grown-up.

Sheep's-sorrel, *lapathum acetosum repens lanceolatum*, in flower.

Male fool's-stones, *orchis morio mas foliis maculatis*, blossoms.

The elm, *Ulmus*, leafes.

Orpine, *telephium*, shoots into stalks: it abounds in the sandy fields near the forest.

Star of Bethlehem common, *Ornithogalum vulgare*, blows in a garden.

Herb-Robert, *Geranium Robertianum*, blows.

Early-flowering water-cress, with smaller leaves, *Nasturtium aquaticum foliis minoribus praecocius*, flowers in wet ditches.

Bugle, *bugula vulgaris*, flowers.

Mouse-ear scorpion grass, *myosotis scorpöides*, blows.

Female wasps appear.

Tadpoles are hatched.

MAY   1.   The Redstart, *ruticilla*, appears.

The hanger much in leaf.

Soft, showery, growing weather for many days past. All plants grow very fast.

         2.   Herb-Paris,¶ true-love, or one-berry, *Herba Paris*, in berry in a coppice in Far: Lassam's great.

Worthies without number: in Comb wood.

Common twayblade, *bifolium majus, seu ophris major*, spindles for bloom.

Marsh red rattle, or louse-wort, *pedicularis palustris rubra*: & *alba*, blows.

Small wild, or marsh-valerian, *valeriana sylvestris, seu palustris* blows.

Great-marsh, or water-horsetail, *equisetum majus*, blows; but has no leaves.

Corn-horse-tail, *equisetum segetale*, blows; but has only the rudiments of leaves appearing.

Sycomore, *acer majus*, leafes.

Lime, or linden tree, *tilia*, leafes.

Balm of Gilead fir, *abies taxi folio, odora*, blows.

Spruce fir, *abies tenuiori folio, fructa deorsum inflexo*, blows.

Weymouth pine, or new England white pine, blows.

Scotch pine, *pinus sylvestris foliis brevibus glaucis*, shoots.

Great rain.

Wood anemony, *flore rubro*.¶

The dogsviolet, blue hyacinths, common ladysmocks, & primroses cover the banks.

Sweet violets disappear.

         3.   Cock-pheasant, *Phasianus*, crows.

Turnep, *rapa sativa*, blows.

Vervain-mallow, *alcea*, comes into leaf.

English Mercury, or all-good, *Bonus Henricus*, blowing.

5. Red-flowered, wild campion, *lychnis sylvestris flore rubello*, flowers.
> Creeping tormentil, *tormentilla reptans*, blows.
> Milk-wort, *polygala*, begins to blow.
> Wild-Cicely, or cow-weed, *myrrhis sylvestris*, blows.
> Tulip, *tulipa*, blows.

7. Dove's foot crane's bill, *Geranium columbinum*, blows on Mr Yalden's tank.
> Little smooth-speedwell, or paul's betony, *veronica pratensis*, *serpyllifolia*, blows.

8. Charlock, *rapistrum arvorum*, blossoms.
> Winter-cress, *eruca lutea, seu barbarea*, flowers.
> Young Goose berries.
> Young Currans.
> Lilac blows.
> Sycomore, *acer majus*, blows.
> Crown-Imperials, & Fritillaria out of bloom.
> Cock redstart sits on ye top of the high wallnut-trees, & sings a very mean song, consisting of two or three notes.
> The martin, *Hirundo agrestis*, frequents the nests built in former summers. One nest serves these birds for many Years.
> Apple-tree, *malus*, blossoms.

9. Garden-cabbage, *brassica*, blows.
> Laurel, *lauro cerasus*, shoots, & flowers.
> Vine, *vitis vinifera*, shews the rudiments of bloom.

10. Sanicle, *sanicula sive diapensia*, begins to blow.
> Little field-madder, *rubeola arvensis repens caerulea*, blows.
> Young grass hoppers appear, but are very small.
> Melon, *melo*, shews both male, & female bloom.
> Rosemary, *rosmarinus*, blows.
> Bulbose-crowfoot or butter-cups, *ranunculus rectus foliis pallidioribus hirsutus*, flowers.

11. The Goat-sucker, fern-owl, or churn-owl, *Caprimulgus*, returns.

12. Lily of ye valley, or May-lily, *lilium convallium*, blows.
> Maple, *acer minus*, flowers.
> Scorpion-sena, *colutea scorpioides*, blossoms.

13. Laburnum begins to blow.
> Ash, *fraxinus*, flowers.
> Oak, *quercus*, shews rudiments of bloom.
> Wallnut-tree, *nux juglans*, begins to leafe.
> Mulberry, *morus*, buds.

Wych-elm, *ulmus folio latissimo scabro*, perfects it's seeds.

14.   Upright meadow-crowfoot, *ranunculus pratensis erectus acris*,
       blows.
           Great, & small bind-weed, *Convolvulus major*, & *minor*,
       shoots-up.

15.   Bush-vetch, *vicia sepium perennis*, blows.
           Bloody, double wall-flower blows.
           Stock-gilly-flower blooms.
           Swann's egg pears are set.
           Narcissus blows.

Herb Paris growing under
coppiced hazels.
Coombe Wood
18 May.

16.   The Robin-red-breast, or Ruddock, *Rubecula sive Erithacus*,
       sings much.
           The fly-catcher, *stoparola, an Moucherolle Bellonii?* appears.
           German-Knot grass, or Knawel, *Knawel Germanorum*, blows.
           Pileworts, *chelidonium minus*, out of bloom.
           Lady-smocks, *cardamine vulg:* out of Dᵒ
           New-sown lucern, *Medica*, in it's seed-leaves.
           Persian Jasmine blows.
           Garden-bean, *Faba*; &
           Garden-pea, *pisum*, blow.
           Tree-juniper, *Juniperus*, blows.
           Chafers fly about, but not in any numbers *Scarabaeus arboreus
       vulg: major*.

16.   Field-cricket, *gryllus sylvestris*, sings.
           Mole-cricket, *gryllo-talpa*, makes it's jarring noise.
           Buck-bean, *menyanthes*, blows in Bean's pond in the water.

Cran-berry, moss-berry, or moor-berry, *oxycoccos, seu vitis Idaea palustris*, makes red shoots, but has yet no bloom.

Sun-dew, *ros solis*, is now covered with clammy moisture, but has no flowers.

Great hound's-tongue, *cynoglossum*, begins to blow.

Small wild bugloss, *buglossa sylvestris minor*, in flower.

Field-crane's bill¶ without scent, *geranium Cicuta folio inodorum*, out of bloom.

The less spear-wort, *Ranunculus flammeus minor*, blows.

Wild tansey or silver-weed, *argentina*, begins to blow.

Orchis morio foemina, female fools-stones, blows.

Great hen-bit, *lamium folio caulem ambiente*, flowers.

Quince-tree, *cydonia*, in blossom.

Apple-trees in high beauty.

Bay, *laurus*, blows.

Holly, *agrifolium*,¶ blows.

Marsh marigolds growing up through golden saxifrage,
Dorton – in a marshy clearing among trees.
17 May.

17.   Fern-owl, or goatsucker, *Caprimulgus*, makes it's chattering
        noise.
            Adder's-tongue, *ophioglossum*, shews it's spike.

19.   Bees, *apes melliferae*, swarm.
            Honeysuckle, *caprifolium*, blows.
            Common purple-trefoil, *trifolium pratense purpureum*, blows.
            Hop-trefoil, *trifolium pratense luteum*, flowers.
            Hawthorn, *mespilus sylvestris spinosa*, begins to blow.
            Rye, *secale*, shoots into ear.
            Pansy, *viola tricolor major*, blooms.
            Blue flower-de luce, *Iris hortensis vulgaris*, flowers.
            Caraway, *carum*, blows.
            Solomon's seal, *polygonatum vulg:* blows.
            Broad-leaved pond-weed, *potamogiton latifolium*, emerges, &
        floats on the water.
            Great water-plaintain, *plantago aquatica*, shoots.
            Young rooks are perchers.
            Thrift, statice, flowers.
            Great water-horse-tail, *equisetum palustre majus*, blows.

20.   Spinage, *spinachia*, blows.
            Burnet little, *sanguisorba minor*, blows.
            Burnet, such as is lately become a farmer's grass, *sanguisorba
        major*, blows.
            Potatoe, *solanum tuberosâ radice*, emerges.
            Berberry, *berberis dumetorum*, blows.
            Some rooks have flown, & forsake their nests.

21.   The downy seeds of the common white willow, *salix maxima alba
        arborescens*, shed, & drive before yᵉ wind.
            Pursley-piert, *percepier Anglorum*, in flower.
            White saxifrage, *saxifraga rotundifolia alba*, blows.
            Golden lungwort, *Hieracium murorum folio pilosissimo* begins
        to blow.
            Gromill, *lithospermum*, blows.
            Chickweed-speedwell,¶ *veronica flosculis singularibus cauliculis
        adhae rentibus*, going out of bloom.

22.   The dragon-flie, *libella*, appears.
            Brook-lime, *becabunga*, blows.
            Creeping mouse-ear, *pilosella repens*, blows.
            Dwarf cistus, or little sun-flower, *Helianthemum vulgare*,
        flowers.
            Field-crow-foot with a very small flower, *Ranunculus hirsutus
        annuus flore minimo*, going out of bloom.

23.   The green scarab, commonly called the rose-fly, appears: *Scarab:
        major colore viridi serici instar.*

Garden-Columbines, *aquilegia*, flower.
Field-crickets, *Grylli sylvestres*, sing most merrily.

24. Male & female piony, *paeonia*, blow.
The turtle-dove, *turtur*, cooes.
The hasel, *corylus*, shews the rudiments of nuts.
The beech, *fagus*, is out of bloom, & shews the rudiments of fruit.
The marsh-marigold, *populago*, is in pod.
Twyblade, *ophris*, blows.

25. Medlar, *mespilus*, blows.
Hounds-tongue, *cynoglossum*, blows.
Common fumitory, *fumaria*, blows.
Avens, *caryophyllata*, blows.
Horse-chestnut, *hippocastanum*, flowers.
Cinnamon-rose, *rosa odore Cinn:* blows.
Gelder-rose, *Opulus*, flowers.
Alaternus flowers.
Rocket, or dames-violet, *Hesperis*, blooms.
Backward apples in full bloom still.
Wallnut, *nux juglans*, casting it's male-bloom.

27. Discovered the rudiments of a wasp's nest: it had ten Cells compleat, three of which were each furnished with a single egg. Killed the breeding wasp that belonged to it, which was very large.
Great daisey, or ox-eye, *leucanthemum vulg:* blows.

28. Quicken-tree, or mountain-ash, *Sorbus sylvestris foliis domesticae similis*, blows.
Quaking-grass, cow quakes, *Gramen tremulum*, blows.
Dandelion seeds every where.

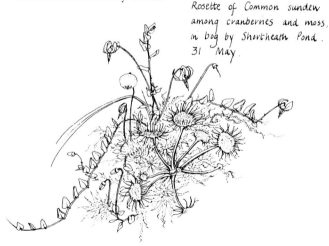

Rosette of Common sundew among cranberries and moss, in bog by Shortheath Pond. 31 May.

30.   Sea-colewort, *crambe maritima brassicae folio* blows.
      Garden-thyme, *thymum vulg*: flowers.
      Yellow pimpernel of ye woods, *anagallis lutea nemorum*, blows.
      Knobby-rooted figwort, *scrophularia*, blows.
      The pliant mealy, or wayfaring tree, *viburnum*, going out of
bloom.
      White-beam-tree, *mespilus alni folio subtus incano, Aria
Theophrasti dicta*, begins to blow.
      Ramson, *allium sylvestre latifolium*, blows.
      Wild chervil, *cherefolium sylvestre*, blows.
      Wild cicely, or cow-weed, *cicutaria vulg*: begins to go into
seed.
      Greater bird'sfoot trefoil, *Lotus pentaphyllos, flore majore luteo
splendente*, flowers.

JUNE   1.   Yellow goat's beard, go to bed at noon, *tragopogon luteum*, begins
      to blow.
      White briony, *brionia alba*, blows.
      Woody nightshade, or bitter-sweet, *Solanum lignosum, seu
dulcamara*, flowers.

          2.   The wild bees with long antennae bore holes for nests in the
      field-walks.
      Yellow rattle or cock's-comb, *pedicularis seu crista Galli lutea*,
      blows.
      Cow-parsnep, *Sphondylium*, in flower.
      Wild white campion, *Lychnis sylvestris flore albo*, flowers.

          3.   Mulberry-tree, *morus*, leafes.
      Lovage, *levisticum*, buds for bloom.
      Pyramidal *sedum* blows.
      Creeping crowfoot, or butter-cups, *ranunculus pratensis repens*,
flowers.
      Hawkweed with bitten roots, or yellow Devil's bit, *Hieracium
minus praemorsâ radice*, in flower.

          5.   Austrian-Rose, *Rosa sylvestris Austriaca, flore phoenicio*, blows.
      Fraxinella flowers.

          6.   Red corn-poppy, *papaver erraticum rubrum campestre*, in bloom.
      Greater smooth-leaved willow-herb, or loose-strife,
Lysimachia siliquosa glabra major, blows.
      Dove's-foot Crane's-bill with jagged leaves, *Geranium folio
tenniter diviso*, flowers.
      Cleavers, or goose grass, *Aparine*, blows.
      Enchanter's night-shade, *Circaea*, grown-up.
      Horse-radish, *raphanus rusticanus*, blows.
      Henbane, *Hyoscyamus*, flowers.
      Clover-grass, *trifolium purpureum majus sativum*, begins to
blow.

7.   Dwarf-yellow-Jasmine, *Jasminum humile luteum*, flowers.
        Mock orange, *Syringa*, in blossom.
        Field-pease begin to blow.
        Mountain-Ladies-bedstraw, *Mollugo montana Gallio albo*
    similis, in bloom.

9.   Herb Gerard, gout-weed, or ash-weed, *Angelica sylvestris*
    erratica, blows.
        Bistort, or snake-weed, *bistorta*, flowers.
        S.t foin begins to blow, *Onobrychis*.
        Hedge-mustard, *eruca hirsuta, siliquâ cauli appressâ, Erysimum*
    dicta, blowing.
        Earth-nut, or pignut, *bulbocastanum*, blows.
        Tutsan, or park-leaves, *Hypericum maximum Androsaemum*
    vulg: dictum, coming into bloom.
        Common Elder, *sambucus*, blows.
        Purple fox-glove, *digitalis purpurea*, flowers.
        The birch-tree, *betula*, shews it's cones.

10.   Yellow succory, or rough hawkweed, *Hieracium asperum, majore*
    flore, in agrorum limitibus, flowers.
        Virginian spiderwort, *Ephemeron*, in flower.

11.   Viper's bugloss, *echium vulgare*, blows.
        Hairy impatient Ladysmock, *Cardamine impatiens hirsutior*, in
    seed: the seed vessels split, & curl-up on the least touch.
        Meadow pinks, wild Williams or Cuckow flower, *Lychnis*
    plumaria sylvestris simplex, blows.
        Yellow water flower-de-luce, *Iris palustris pallida*, in blossom.
        Water-elder,¶ *Opulus Ruellii*, flowers.
        S.t Peter's wort, *Hypericum ascyron dictum, caule quadrangulo*,
    shews the rudiments of bloom.
        Mithridate-mustard, or bastard-cress, *Thlaspi vulgatius*, in
    seed.
        Treacle-mustard, or penny cress, *Thlaspi Dioscoridis*, going
    out of bloom.
        Male speedwell, or fluellin, *veronica mas supina*, &
    vulgatissima, blows. *Tota est hirsuta, folio rotundiore*. This is
    supposed to possess the greatest virtues of any speedwell.
        Dier's weed, or wood-waxen, *Genistella tinctoria*, begins to
    flower.

12.   Tare everlasting, common yellow bastard-vetchling, *Lathyrus*
    luteus sylvestris dumetorum, blows.
        Garden Chervil, *cerefolium sativum*, blows.
        Scorzonera angustifolia subcaerulea, flowers.
        Salsafie, *tragopogon purpureum*, in bloom.
        Bush-vetch, *vicia sepium perennis*, in pod.
        Rasp-berry-bush, *Rubus Idaeus spinosus*, blows.

Alpine Geranium blows.
Garden-pink flowers.
Garden red valerian, *Valeriana floribus rubris caudatis*, in bloom.

13. Provence-rose blows.
   Sweet Williams flower.
   Kidney-vetch, or Ladies finger, *vulneraria rustica*, in bloom.
   Butterfly-orchis, *orchis alba bifolia minor calcari oblongo*, in flower.
   Romagna melon blows.
   Cantaleupe melon, *melo cortice tuberosus*, blows.
   Briony black, *Tamnus*, blows.
   Garden-parsnep, *pastinaca sativa*, in flower.
   Spurrey, *alsine spergula dicta major*, buds for bloom.

14. Sage, *salvia*, flowers.
   Strawberries begin to redden.
   Cherries begin to change colour.
   Narrow-leaved, branched, clammy Catch-fly, *Lychnis angustifolia, viscosa, ramosa, sive muscipila vulg*: flowers.
   Female handed-orchis, or female Satyrion Royal. *Orchis palmata speciosiore thryso, folio maculato*, in Bloom.
   Field-Scabious, *Scabiosa major*, blows.
   Upright tormentil, *tormentilla erecta*, flowers.
   Bladder-campion, or white corn-campion, *Lychnis sylvestris, benalbum vulgo*, blows.
   Long-rooted Hawkweed, *Hieracium longius radicatum*, begins to flower.
   Great bur-reed, *sparganium ramosum*, flowers.
   Great vernal Cyperus-grass, *gramen Cyperöides cum paniculis nigris*, blows.
   The glow-worm appears.
   Wheat ears begin to peep.

15. Small wild mallow, or dwarf mallow, *Malva sylvestris folio rotundo*, blows.
   The wild briar, dog's rose, or hep-tree, *rosa sylvestris inodora, seu canina*, blooms.
   Thistles begin to blow.
   The bramble, or black-berry bush, *Rubus fructa nigro*, blows.
   Great purple monk's-hood, *Aconitum purpureum maximum*, blowing.
   Mulberry tree, *Morus*, blows.
   Myrtle-leaved sumach, *coriaria*, blows.
   Jerusalem-sage, *Phlomis*, in flower.
   Shrubby cinque-foil, *potentilla*, blows.

FYFIELD.

16. S^t foin is cutting every where.

Great wild Valerian, *valeriana sylvestris major*, blowing.

Common English wild Clary, *Hormium sylvestre lavendulae flore*, blows in vast plenty.

Nep, or cat-mint, *Nepeta major*, not yet blown.

Burnet-leaved rose, *rosa spinosissima*, blows.

17. Cross-wort, or mugweed, *Cruciata hirsuta, sive Gallium latifolium*, flowers.

Yellow toad's flax, *linaria lutea*, blows.

Great knapweed, or matfellon, *Jacea major*, blows.

Water scorpion-grass, *myosotis scorpioides palustris*, blossoms.

Long-leaved water speed-well, or brook-lime, *veronica aquatica longifolia*.

Privet, or prim, *ligustrum*, blows.

Buck-thorn or common purging thorn, *Rhamnus catharticus*, blows.

Water-cress, *Nasturtium aquaticum vulgare*, blows.

Spindle-tree, or prick-wood, *Euonymus*, blows.

Greek valerian, *polemonium vulg:* in flower.

Hoary perennial ragwort with groundsel leaves, *Jacobaea senecionis folio incano perennis*, blows.

Windy, black, showery weather for many days.

The missle-thrush, *turdus viscivorus*, sings.

Cuckow sings in ashen-Coppice.

Male pimpernel, *Anagallis flore phoeniceo*, blows.

Common mallow, *malva vulg: folio sinuato*, blows.

Yellow ashphodel-lilly, *Hemerocallis scapo ramoso, corollis monopetalis*, blossoms.

Alpine bastard-lilly, called Savoy spider-wort, *Hemerocallis scapo simplici, corollis hexapetalis campanulutis*, going out of bloom.

20. Deadly nightshade, or dwale, *Belladonna, seu Solanum lethale*, begins to flower. It is in great plenty in the trenches round Ludgershall castle.

Base rocket¶ blows in the borders of the cornfields.

Yellow cow-wheat, *melampyrum sylvaticum flore luteo, sive satureia lutea sylvestris* in flower, & pod: in great plenty in the woods.

Blue bottles, *Cyanus*, blow.

Female cornel, dog-berry-tree, gatter-tree, or prickwood, in flower; *Cornus faemina*.

Venice-sumach, or *Coccygria, Rhus foliis simplicibus obovatis*, buds for bloom.

21. Drop-wort, *Filipendula*; blows on y^e downs.

Foxgloves in Dorton.

Hollow Lane to Alton
27 June

Thorow-wax, *Bupleurum perfoliatum rotundifolium annuum*, not yet shewing for bloom.

Wild Columbine, *Aquilegia flore simplici*, blows in Lanes.

SELBORNE.

22.   Yellow stone-crop, or prickmadam, blows, *sedum minus haematöides*.

Water-cresses, *Sisymbrium Cardamine, seu nasturtium aquaticum*, blows.

Self-heal, *Prunella*, begins to flower.

25.   Rosebay willow-herb, *Lysimachia speciosa quibusdam onagra dicta, siliquosa*, flowers.

Hedge-nettle, *Galeopsis legitima Dioscoridis*, blows.

Great white mullein, high taper, or Cow's lungwort, *verbascum mas latifolium luteum*, blows.

Red garden-pinks flower.

London-pride, *Geum folio subrotundo majiori, pistillo floris rubro*, blows.

Common nettle, *Urtica racemifera major perennis*, blows.

Moss-Provence rose blows.

Narrow-leafed bulbous Iris flowers, *Xiphion*.

Garden-Larkspur, *Delphinium*, blows.

The horned beetle, called by the French Cerf volant, appears: *scarab: max: platycerus, taurus nonnullis*.

Crow-foot Geranium, *Geranium Batrachoides flore caeruleo*, in bloom. The blossom is very large, & shewy.

26.   White Ladies-bedstraw, *molluginis vulgatioris varietas minor*, blows.

27.   Agrimony, *agrimonia*, flowers.

Wheat, *triticum*, blows.

Meadow-sweet, *Ulmaria*, blows.

28.   Ivy-leaved sowthistle, or wild lettuce, *lactuca sylvestris murorum flore luteo*, flowers.

Nipple-wort, *lampsana*, begins to blow.

Devil in a bush, *nigella*, flowers.

Great purple snapdragon, *Antirrhinum purpureum majus*, blows on walls, &c.

Garden & wood strawberries are ripe.

A showery season, & hay damaged.

Common Yarrow, or milfoil, *millefolium vul:* blows.

JULY   1.   Dock, *lapathum vulg:* blows.

The Rudiments of acorns appear.

Dwarf elder, or Dane-weed, *Sambucus humilis, seu Ebulus*,

buds for bloom.

Great showers.

The least toad's flax, *linaria Antirrhinum dicta*, going out of flower.

Martagon, *lilium floribus reflexis*, blows.

Cantaleupe-melons are setting.

Perennial Sun flower, *Helianthus radice perenni* begins to blow.

The Portugal laurel, *padus foliis semper verentibus ovatis*, Lin: flowers in a beautiful manner.

Common Cinquefoil, or five-leaved Grass, *pentaphyllum vulgatiss^m* blows.

Stinkhorns, or stinking morel, fungus *phalloides*, appear in the Lythe, & smell abominably. Lin: for a certain reason, calls it *phallus impudicus*. It is not common.

Hares-foot, or hares-foot trefoil, *trifolium arvense humile spicatum, seu lagopus*, blows.

2.   Meadow-saxifrage, *Seseli pratense nostras*, flowers.

Caught, & ascertain'd the *Regulus non cristatus*:¶ it is a very small bird, but bigger than the golden-crowned wren; pretty common, & very mischievous among pease, & cherries. I suspect it is a bird of passage, as I have never seen it in winter.

5.   Enchanter's night-shade, *Circaea lutetiana*, blows.

Stinking May weed, *Chamaemelum foetidum* blows.

S: John's wort, *Hypericum vulg*: flowers.

Water-betony, or more truly water-figwort, *scrophularia aquatica major*, blows.

Smallage, *Apium palustre*, flowers in the wet ditches of the meadows.

Greater bird's foot trefoil, *loti corniculatae major species folio hirsuto*, blows.

6.   Frogs migrate in great numbers from James Knight's ponds: the lanes are full of them.

Barley in ear.

A storm of thunder, & lightening.

Broad-leaved tree-primrose, *Onagra*, blows.

Melons begin to come.

Smooth succory-Hawkweed, *Hieracium luteum glabrum*, blows.

7.   The vine, *vitis vinifera*, blows.

Eye-bright cow-wheat, *Euphrasia pratensis rubra*, blows.

Hypopitys lutea (discovered by Thomas Mulso Esq on the zigzag)¶ in bloom. There were three or four plants together. It is allowed by all writers to be uncommon. In the stalk it is a perfect *Orobanche*; but the bloom is so different that it is not class'd with them either by Ray, or in the sexual system. It is said always to

grow in beechen-woods. Common in the hanger near the
Woddens.

8.   Purple, late-flowering *orchis, orchis purpurea spicâ congestâ
pyramidali*, flowers.
      The lime-tree, *tilia*, is blowing.
      Tufted-vetch, *Cracca multiflora*, blows.
      Mignonette,¶ or small sweet-scented *reseda, reseda Oegyptiaca
minor floribus fragrantissimis*, blows.

9.   Little throat-wort, or Canterbury-bells, *Campanula pratensis flore
conglomerato*, blows.
      Small bind-weed, *Convolvulus minor*, blows.
      Yellow Ladies-bedstraw, *Gallium verum*, blows.
      Vervain, *verbena vulg*: blows.
      Wild Carrot, or bird's nest, *Daucus vulg*: flowers.
      Stinking horehound, *ballote*, blows.
      Broad-leaved pond-weed, *potamogiton rotundifolium*, flowers.
      Pease-everlasting, *Lathyrus latifolius*, of the Garden, blows.
      Common ragwort, *Jacobaea vulg*: blowing.
      Borage, *borrago hortensis*, blows.
      Wild wold, yellow-weed, or dyer's-weed, *luteola*, blows.
      Wild-parsnep, *pastinaca sylvestris latifolia*, blows, & is going
into seed.
      Garden-rue, *ruta hort*: blows.

14.   Dwarf-elder, or Dane-wort, *Sambucus humilis, sive Ebulus*,
blowing.
      Scarlet *lychnis* flowers.
      White garden-lilly blows.
      Golden-rod, *virga aurea*, flowers.
      Hemlock, *Cicuta*, blows.
      Wild Lathyrus, or everlasting-pease, *Lathyri Majoris* species
flore rubense, blowing.
      Wild Marjoram, *Origanum vulg*: blowing.
      Small purple Centory, *Centaurium minus*, begins to blow.
      Oats in ear.
      Knot-grass, *polygonum mas vulg*: blows.

15.   Musk thistle, *Carduus nutans*; ⎫
    Spear-thistle, *Carduus †lance[ol]atus*; ⎭
      Wild perennial blue flax the larger, *linum sylvestre caeruleum
perenne erectius*, blows.
      Rasps ripe.
      The Redstart, *ruticilla*, still sings.

16.   Hairy sheep's scabious, or rather Rampions with scabious Heads,

---

†Letters crossed out.

rapunculus scabiosae capitulo caeruleo, blows.

Motherwort, *Cardiaca*, blows.

Sun-dew with round, & with long leaves, *Ros solis folio rotundo*, & *folio oblongo*, budding for bloom.

Less round-leaved bell-flower, *Campanula rotundifolia*, flowers.

Vervain-mallow, *alcea vulg*: blows.

Corn-marigold, *Chrysanthemum segetum*, blows.

Cross-leaved Heath, *Erica brabantica folio coridis hirsuto quaterno*, flowers.

Dwarf Carline-thistle, *Carlina acaulis*, blows.

Branched bar-reed, *sparganium ramosum*, blowing.

Young partriges are flyers:

St George Wheeler's tutsan flowers.

Feverfew, *matricaria*, blows.

Potatoes, *solanum tuberosum*, in flower.

18.   *Asparagus* blows.

Wood-betony, *betonica*, flowers.

Creeping water-parsnep, *Sium umbellatum repens*, blows.

Water-ragwort, *Jacobaea latifolia palustris*, blows.

19.   *Phaseolus*, kidney-bean, blows.

21.   Black whorts, whortle-berries, *vitis Idaea angulosa*, in ripe fruit.

Young pheasants are flyers.

Common Dragon, *Dracontium vulg*: going out of bloom.

Lavender, *lavendula vulg*: blows.

The lime, *tilia*, in high bloom.

Hyssop, *Hyssopus vulg*: blows.

22.   Cockle, *Lychnis segetum major*, blows.

Perennial arsmart, *Persicaria salicis folio perennis*, *potamogiton angustifolium dicta*, blows.

Corn-crow foot, *Ranunculus arvorum echinatus*, in seed.

Hedge-parsley, *Caucalis minor flosculis rubentibus*, blows.

Restharrow, or cammock, *anonis non spinosa purpurea*, blows.

Small flowered, hairy willow herb, *Lysimachia siliquosa hirsuta parvo flore*, blows.

Wild Basil, *acinos multis*, blows.

Great wild basil, *Clinopodium origano simile*, blows.

Less stitch wort, *Caryophyllus holosteus arvensis glaber*, *flore minore*, flowers.

Corn-spurge, *tithymalus segetum longifolius*, blows.

Petty spurge, *tithymalus parvus annuus*, *foliis subrotundis non crenatis*, in flower.

Great throat-wort, or Canterbury bells, *Campanula vulgatior foliis Urticae*, *vel major* & *asperior*, blows.

Cocks head, *onobrychis*, flowers.

Male fern, *filix mas*, full of seeds.

Harts tongue, *Phillitis*, forming it's seeds.

Purple-spiked loose-strife, or willow-herb, *salicaria vulg:
purpurea foliis oblongis*, blows. At Whorwell.

Rest-harrow, or cammock, *Anonis spinosa flore purpureo*,
flowers.

Eye-bright, *Euphrasia*, blows.

Elecampane, *Helenium*, flowers.

25.   Great wild Climber, or traveller's Joy, *Clematis latifolia seu
atragene quibusdam*, blows.

Young swallows appear.

Young redstarts in plenty. Redstarts are a very common bird
both in the fields & gardens.

Young martins appear.

26.   Burdock, or clot-burr, *lappa major, seu arctium Dioscoridis*,
blows.

Garden, or common nightshade, *solanum vulg.* blows.

Hop, *lupulus mas*, & *foemina*, begins to blow.

Kidney-beans begin to pod.

Shady, black, showery weather the summer thro', & much hay
spoiled; & many loads carried away by floods near great rivers.

Sneeze-wort, *ptarmica*, blows.

Upright S.t John's wort, *Hypericum pulchrum*, blows.

28.   Fern-owl, or Goatsucker, *caprimulgus*, appears still.

Fine tare with smooth pods, *Cracca minor siliquis singularibus,
flosculis caerulescentibus*, blows, & pods.   Continual wet weather.

Black bind-weed, *fegopyrum scandens sylvestre* in seed.

AUGUST   1.   Wood sage, *scorodonia, s: salvia agrestis*, blows.

White water lilly, *Nymphaea alba*, blows in Wych hanger
pond.

Arrow-head *sagitta*, blows in D.o

Buckwheat, *fegopyrum*, flowers.

Pease are hacking.

Purple spiked loose-strife, or willow-herb, *salicaria vulg:
purpurea foliis oblongis*, blows on the stream at Hedley.

2.   Common water-hoar-hound, *lycopus palustris glaber*, blows.

Clown's alheal, *sideritis anglica strumosâ radice*.

Cat mint, *nepeta vulg:* not blown.

Comfrey, *symphytum magnum*, flowers.

Trifid water hemp-agrimony, *verbesina, sive cannabina aquatica
flore minus pulchro, elatior* & *majus frequens*, buds for bloom.

Great-flowered willow herb, or codlings, & cream, *lysimachia
siliquosa hirsuta flore magno*, blows.

Common bastard-hellebore, *helleborine*

latifolia montana, blows.

    Woolly-headed thistle, *Carduus tomentosus, corona fratrum dictus*, flowers.

    White Jasmine blows.

    Pale arsmart, *persicaria mitis major foliis pallidioribus*, blows.

4.   Narrow-leaved willow herb, *lysimachia siliquosa glabra media sive minor*, going out of bloom.

    Marsh mallow, *althaea vulg*: blows.

    Water-rocket, *eruca aquatica*, goes into pod.

    Corn-parsley, or hone-wort, *seum arvense sive segetum*, begins to blow.

    Great bind-weed, *Convolvulus major albus*, flowers.

5.   The swift, *Hirundo apus*, seems to be gone.

    The stone-curlew, *charadrius oedicnemus*, clamours late in the evening.

    Hot summer weather with an high glass, after months of black wet days.

6.   The martins, *hirundines agrestes*, begin to congregate on the brask of the may-pole.

    Dews large, & white.

    Gold finch, *carduelis*, sings still.

    Green finch, *Chloris*, chirps.

    French, & African marrigolds blow.

    Winged ants, the male ants, begin to appear.

7.   Broad-leaved spurge, *tithymalus platiphyllos* goes into pod. It is a tall, handsome plant.

    Lychnidea, *Phlox foliis lineari-lanceolatis, caule elatior, floribus in longam spicam densè spicatis*, begins to flower.

    Wheat is beginning to be cut: in many fields it seems to be much blighted.

    White maudlin blows.

    Yellow-hammer, *emberiza flava*, sings still.

    Winged ants forsake their nests.

    Laurustines bud for bloom.

9.   Wild teasel, *dipsacus sylv*: blows.

    Thoro' hot weather.

    Sharp-pointed fluellin, *linaria elatine dicta folio acuminato*, blows, & seeds.

    Nep, or cat mint, *nepeta major vulg*: blows.

    Common tansy, *tanacetum*, blows.

    Wormwood, *absinthium vulg*: flowers.

    Sweet-scented camomile, *chamaemelum odoratissimum repens*, blows.

    Middle flea bane, *conyza media*, flowers.

12. Wild Angelica, *Angelica sylvestris*, blows, & seeds.
    Plowman's spikenard, *Baccharis Monspeliensium*, begins to blow.
    Hare'sfoot trefoil, *trifolium arvense humile spicatum*, going out of bloom.
    Mugwort, *Artemisia vulg*: blows.
    Fern-owl, *caprimulgus*, still appears.
    Mulberry-tree, curran, hazel, white poplar, wall-nut, begin to cast some of their leaves.
    Barometer very high, & rising.
    Hooded willow-herb, *Cassida palustris vulg flore caeruleo*, blows.

13. Pyramidal Campanula begins to blow.
    The wheat that is not touched with the blight is not yet cut.
    Sope-wort, *lychnis, saponaria dicta*, blows.

14. Fern-owl, *caprimulgus*, chatters.
    Small wild teasel, *dipsacus minor, seu virga pastoris*, going out of bloom.
    Wheat harvest begins to be general.

16. Corn-mint, *mentha, sive calamintha aquat*: blows.
    Mugwort, *artemisia*, blows.

18. Laurustines flower.
    Apricots ripen.
    Potatoes are large.
    Yellow-hammer sings still.
    Swallows, *Hirundines domesticae*, assemble on the wall-nut trees.
    Orpine, or live-long, *anacampseros, vulgo faba crassa*, blows.
    The aster, supposed to be Virgil's amello, begins to flower.
    Fennel, *foeniculum vulg*: blows.

19. Ivy, *Hedera*, buds for bloom.
    Redstart, *ruticilla*, still appears.

21. Delicate harvest-weather still.
    Nectarines, & peaches begin to turn.
    Fern owl appears still.
    Cran-berries, moss-berries, or moor-berries, *oxycoccus, seu vaccinia palustria*, are ripe.

23. Less field-scabious, *scabiosa minor, sive columbaria*, Ger: Em: 719: blows.

23 August.
Caught miller's thumb under footbridge.
Oakhanger Stream.
Lifesize.

JOURNEY TO RINGMER.

26: 27: 28. Common reed, *arundo vallatoria*, blows.
Field Calamint, *Calamintha odore pulegii*, blows.
White horehound, *marrubium album*, going out of bloom.
Great cat's tail, *typha palustris major*, in seed.
Meadow-saffron, *colchicum commune*, blows.
Wild succory, *cichoreum sylvestre*, blows.
Burnet rose, *rosa spinosissima*, abounds near the Coast.
Marsh sampire, jointed Glasswort, or saltwort, *Salicornia geniculata annua*, buds for bloom.
Star-thistle, *Carduus stellatus*, going out of bloom.

29. Blue Devil's bit, *scabiosa radice succisâ*, blows.
Yellow willow-herb, or loose strife, *lysimachia lutea*, flowers.
Strawberry-trefoil, *trifolium fragiferum* in seed.
Autumnal Gentian, or fell-wort, *Gentianella pratensis flore lanuginoso*, blows.
White water-lilly, *nymphaea alba*, blows still.
Arrow-head, *sagitta*, seeds.
Great bur-reed, *sparganum ramosum*, seeds.
Money-wort, or herb two-pence, *nummularia major lutea*, going out of bloom.
Upright water-parsnep, *sium erectum foliis serratis*, blows.
Dodder, *Cuscuta major*, in bloom, & in seed.

31. Some few wasps begin to appear.
Grass-hoppers fly.
Round-leaved fluellin, *linaria Elatine dicta folio subrotundo*, blows. This herb, made into a tea, is much recommended in spitting of blood by an experienced Apothecary at Lewes; especially if the patient is not of an hot consititution.

SEPTEMBER 1. Common Calamint, *Calamintha vulg*: going out of bloom.
Common melilot, *melilotus vulg*: going out of bloom.
Ox's tongue, or lang de boeuf, *Hierachium echioides capitulis Cardui benedicti*, blows.

Cricket resting on Hedge parsley.
Coneycroft Bottom.
3 September.

5.   Rooks frequent their nest-trees.
        Uninterrupted fine harvest-weather still.
        Glow-worms still appear.

6.   Black grapes begin to turn.
        French-mercury, *mercurialis annua glabra vulg:* begins to blow.
        Welted thistle, *Carduus spinosissimus capitulis minoribus*, goes out of bloom.
        Wild Carline-thistle, *Carlina sylvestris quibusdam atractilis*, withers.
        Common cudweed, *Gnaphalium minus, sive herba impia*, withers.

6.   Flies begin to assemble in windows.
        Broad-leaved myrtle blows.

8.   Wet weather returns.
        Bladder-nut tree, *staphylodendron*, in seed.
        Dead, or spotted arsmart, *persicaria maculosa*, blows.

8.   Hemp-agrimony, or Dutch-agrimony, *Eupatorium cannabinum*, going out of bloom.
        Small burnet-saxifrage, *pimpinella saxifraga minor, foliis sanguisorbae*, blows, & seeds.

9.   Horn-beam, *ostrya ulmo similis, fructu in umbilicis foliaceis*, in fruit.
        Arbor vitae in fruit in the Broil.
        Peaches, & Nectarines are in good perfection.
        White Ladies bedstraw, *Molluginis vulgatioris varietas minor*, seeds.
        Hop-trefoil, *trifolium pratense luteum capitulo lupuli*, seeds.
        The least water-hemp-agrimony, *verbesina minima*, blows.
This plant was not known by Mr Ray; but is inserted in his *Synopsis* by Dillenius.

12.   Sea star-wort, *aster maritimus caeruleus, tripolium dictus*, blows, at Bramber within reach of the tides.

13.   Yellow Devil's bit, *Hieracium minus praemorsâ radice*, blows on every down, & pasture-field.
        The Redstart, *ruticilla*, still appears.
        The fly-catcher, the flat-headed bird that builds on ye plates of houses, still appears; *Stoparola: vide Raii synop: avium* p: 77.

SELBORNE

15.   Hops, *lupulus mas*, & *foemina*, are gathering-in.

Black-berries are black, red, & green on the same bramble.
Bramble, *rubus vulg*: blows also.
The seeds of the Arum turn red.

18. Water-mint, *mentha aquatica, sive sisymbrium*, blooms.
Perennial arsmart, *persicaria salicis folio perennis, potamogiton angustifolium dicta*, flowers.
Hedge-parsley, *Caucalis minor flore rubente* in seed.
Hedge-sparrow, *currucca*, in the mornings makes it's winter chirping.
Vast flocks of swallow, & martins congregate on the wall-nut trees.
Most beautiful weather.
Young broods of Swallows appear. Are not these late hatchings more in favour of hiding than migration?

19. Fool's parsley, *Cicutaria tenuifolia*, blows, & seeds.
Ivy, *Hedera*, blows.
Chaffinch, *fringilla*, chirps.

20. Common goose foot, or sowbane, *blitum pes anserinus dictum*, blows.
Wood-pidgeon cooes.
Peaches, & Nectarines are in good perfection.
Green blite, *chenopodium foliis integris racemosum*, blows, & seeds.

21. Wild bees, & flies gather together in vast swarms on the Ivy-bloom.
Sultry weather.
No wasps this Year: but the peaches, & nectarines are devoured by the garden-bees, *apes melliferae*, which come in swarms.
Many Martin's nests have broods of young still.
China-aster blows.
The tops of the beeches, *fagi*, are tinged with Yellow.
Stinking-morel, fungus *phalloides*, smells still.

29. Some martins are still in their nest unfledged.
Least snap-dragon, or calf's snout, *antirrhinum angustifolium sylvestre*, blows.
Tutsan or park-leaves, *Hypericum maximum Androsaemum vulgare dictum*, in berry.

OCTOBER 1. Small corn-parsley, *Caucalis segetum minor, anthrisco hispido similis*, blows, & seeds.

4. The first great rain.
My late garden-asters, & golden-rods begin to flower.

1. The wood-cock, *scolopax*, returns.

5. Swallows, & martins gone.
    Rooks steal the wallnuts from yᵉ trees.
    Spider's webs appear.

10. The Guernsey-lilly, *Amarillis spathâ multiflorâ, corollis aequalibus patentissimis revolutis, genitalibus longissimis*, blows.
    Spurrey, *spergula*, flowers.

12. White frost, & Ice.

13. Apples, & pears are gathering.
    Woodlark sings.
    Provence, & monthly roses blow.
    The hedge-sparrow, *currucca*, pipes in the morning.

14. Strawberry-tree, *Arbutus*, blows.
    White frost, & Ice.
    The buck, *dama*, grunts, & goes to rut.

17. Barometer is very high at 30 inch: & 4 10ᵗʰˢ
    Black cluster-grapes are delicate.
    Common snake, *natrix torquata*, still appears.
    The blind-worm, or slow-worm, *Caecilia*, is seen.
    Catkins of the alder, *alnus*, are formed:
    The cones are full of seed.
    Musca apiformis, tota fusca, caudâ obtusâ, ex culâ caudatâ in latrinis degente orta, still is seen. This fly frequents sinks, & jakes, where it lays it's eggs. In the autumn it feeds on the flowers of late annuals, & perennials; & in particular on the blossoms of Ivy. Ray *hist: Insect:* 272.
    Musca bipennis major, diversicolor, cauda setis nigris obsitâ appears, & engenders. This fly is entirely a garden or field-fly, never entring into houses: it appears to feed on mellow fruit. Mʳ Ray seems not to have been aware that it smells strongly of musk: it might therefore not improperly be call'd *musca moschata*. 271. This seems to be an autumn fly altogether.

20. Common wild service-tree, or Sorb, *Mespilus apii folio sylvestris non spinosa, seu Sorbus torminalis*, in fruit; but it is hard, & austere still.

21. Wheat springs out of the Ground.

22. The fieldfare, *turdus pilaris*, returns.
    The glow-worm, *cicindela*, appears, & shines faintly.

23. Mulberry-tree is naked.

Rooks carry off the acorns from the Oaks.
The Scotch pine casts it's leaves of last Year.
Wall-nut-tree is naked.

24.   Plants naturally in bloom still:
Laurustine, Ivy, *arbutus*, great & less throat-wort, round-
leaved *Campanula*, burnet-saxifrage, Hawkweeds several,
round-leaved, & sharp-pointed, fluellin, blue Devil's bit,
knapweed, wild-thyme, herb Robert, groundsel, hop-trefoil,
soap-wort, yarrow, creeping tormentil, dwarf-cistus, chamomile,
great basil, mallow, red pimpernel, small stitchwort, viper's
bugloss, milkwort, dandelion, wild marjoram, white horehound,
creeping mouse-ear, plowman's spikenard, cat mint, many
foreign perennial asters, spotted arsmart, ragwort, marsh thistle,
shepherd's purse, pansies, sweet-scented *reseda*.
Plants continued in bloom by accidents, such as a shady
situation, the bite of Cattle, &c:
Mullein, wild angelica, daucus, spear-leaved thistle, musk D?
sow-thistle, corn-marrigold, spurrey, red & white clover, crow
foot several sorts, stinking may-weed, hedge-nettle, charlock,
small field-madder, woody night-shade, thorney apple, white
dead-nettle, baum, corn-poppy, yellow Ladies-bedstraw, betony,
meadow-saxifrage, violet common, mouse-ear scorpion-grass,
water D? wild bugloss, borage, white campion, common daisey.

28.   The Red-wing, swine-pipe, or wind-thrush, *turdus iliacus*,
appears.

NOVEMBER 4.   Most delicate seed-time. Wheat comes-up well.
The fruiting-Ananas are ranged in their beds to stand the
winter: fires begin to be lighted in the stoves.

6.   The dragon-fly, *libella*, appears still. Ice.
The musk-fly, & many field-flies bask in the sun on ye trunks
of trees.
Bee-flies feed on the blossoms of perennials.
Barometer up at 30 inch: & 4 10^ths

7.   Snow, & great showers.

10.   *Lychnidea* blows still.

13.   The wren, *passer troglodytes*, whistles.
The Hanger begins to be naked.
Finished dressing the vines.
Heavy showers which make the springs rise.

14.   The wood-lark, *Alauda sylves*: & the skie-lark, *Alauda vulg*: sing.
Flies appear still in numbers.
The Ground is now thoro'ly soaked.

16. The ripe berries of the yew-tree fall.

17: 18. Tempestuous winds.

19. The bat, *vespertilio*, appears.

The common dor, or clock, *scarabaeus magnus niger vulgatissimus*, is seen flying.

Fishes in the Rivulets at Selborne are the Bull's head, or Miller's thumb, *Gobius fluviatilis capitatus*; the trout, *Trutta fluviatilis*; the eel, *Anguilla*, the lampern, *lampoetra parva*, & *fluviatilis, pisciculus aculeatus*, stickleback.

DECEMBER 8. Delicate weather; the air is full of gnats, & the ground covered with spider's-webs: the flesh-fly, *musca curnaria*, appears in numbers. The song-thrush, *turdus simpliciter dictus*, sings.

AUGUST 11: †Brother Thomas & I discovered in the bogs of Bean's pond
1767. Marsh S! Peter's wort with hoary leaves, *Ascyron supinum villosum palustre*.

Purple marsh-Cinquefoil, *pentaphylloides palustre rubrum*.

Water dropwort, *Oenanthe aquatica*.

Yellow willow-herb, or loose-strife, *Lysimachia lut:*

Less, hooded-loose-strife, *cassida palustris minima*.

Marsh-goose-grass, *Aparine palustris minor*.

In the beechen woods of Sussex, *Hypopitys lutea* in plenty.

Trufles, *tubera*, large & in plenty were taken by the trufle-hunters dogs, Aug: 19. at Fyfield in a field of my Bro^r Henry's, among the roots of a Grove of beeches.

Two or three pounds are taken in that Grove every fortnight, from that time 'till the spring.

Water-hemp-agrimony with a divided leaf, *verbesina seu cannabina aquat: floreminus pulchro*, at the priory.

Water-hemp-agrimony with an undivided leaf, *verbesina pulchriore flore luteo*.

---

†An entry added in the following year.

NATURALIST'S
JOURNAL

Notes on the text

The original pages of the *Naturalist's Journal* were laid out in nine columns with printed headings. The first six columns of the original journals deal with data: place, date, barometric pressures, temperatures, rainfall, wind and other weather notes. These always relate to Selborne, someone else keeping the records while Gilbert was away.

While these notes are integral to the journals and most interesting when studied in the light of the miscellaneous observations which make up the main text, in themselves numerical and single-word records are by no means light reading. They have therefore been grouped together on the left-hand side of the page where, without interrupting the enjoyment of reading the main text, they may be consulted or ignored at the reader's wish.

Gradually, over the years, everything (except the weather data) comes to be written as 'observations', spreading more or less over the remaining space on the page, irrespective of columns. Sometimes, especially in the later years, notes have been continued over the top or bottom of a page or on to an inserted sheet. Some of these over-runs (which are printed in a different typeface) are dated, and their positioning usually indicates the date within the week to which they relate. Where the positioning is not clear the additional material has been placed with that of the adjacent day.

The way the columnar information has been interpreted in print is as follows:

Date and location – the month, year and place head each page and do not appear again unless there is a change. Each individual entry is dated.

Barometric pressures and any movements are next recorded. The end of this column is indicated by a semi-colon.

Temperatures in degrees Fahrenheit are shown next. The end of this column is again indicated by a semi-colon.

Wind direction and any changes are shown, as in the
manuscript, by initial letters: SE, SW and so on.

Weather conditions and their changes throughout the day are
listed next.

Trees, plants in flower, fungi and mosses follow, preceded by a
symbol   . Again the original column divisions are
shown by a semi-colon, and the entry ends in a full stop.

Birds and insects encountered on that date appear on a fresh
line and come last.

Gilbert White's comments and notes are reproduced in the
right-hand column just as he wrote them.

---

†*Omnia bene describere, quae in hoc mundo a Deo facta,
aut Naturae creatae viribus elaborata fuerunt, opus est
non unius hominis, nec unius aevi. Hinc Faunae & Florae
utilissimae; hinc Monographi praestantissimi.*
Joan: Ant: Scopoli annus 2^{dus} historico-naturalis.

Ineus est illis vigor, & caelestis origo Seminibus ... Virg:

*Ego apis Matinae
More modoq
Grata carpentis thyma per laborem
Plurimum circa nemus, uvidiq
Tiburis ripas*   ... Hor:

The Insects are named according to Linn:
The plants according to ye sexual system:
The birds according to Ray.

JANUARY   — 1768 —

Friday 1.   SELBORNE *Clay*
29½; 27; NE.
Severe frost, heavy
snow.

Saturday 2.
29, 3/10½; 27; SE,
E.

---

†These inscriptions appeared on the title pages of some of GW's original
journals. See *Notes* page 494 for a translation.

Severe, great snow.

Sunday 3.
29½, 3/10; 20, 19;
E.

Horses are still falling with their general disorder.¶ It freezes under peoples beds.

Monday 4.
29½, 3/10; 18; E.
Sn: falls, 9 inch:
deep.

The birds must suffer greatly as there are no Haws. Meat freezes so hard it can't be spitted.
Several of the thrush-kind are frozen to death.

Tuesday 5.
29½, 4/10; 20; E.
Frost intense,
bright.

Wednesday 6.
29½, 2/10¼; 18;
E.
Severe, bright.

Colds & coughs are general.
Provisions freeze within.

Thursday 7.
29½, 3/4/10; 17½;
N, SW.
Severe, dull, heavy.

Laurels begin to suffer. Laurustines suffer.

Friday 8.
29½, ½/10; 21½;
NE.
Fog, snow falls fm
the trees.

Moles work. Cocks crow. Crows crie. My provisions are kept in the Cellar. Birds pull the moss from the trees.

Saturday 9.
29, 4/10; 30; E.
Snow, thaw.

Lambs begin to fall.
Nothing frozen in my cellar.
Titmice pull straws from the eaves.¶

Sunday 10.
Rising, 29/10;
32½; NE.
Fog, snow & thaw.

Celeri remains good. It was covered with pease-haulm.

Monday 11.
Rises, 29 4/10; 33;
NW.
Snow on the
ground.

Tuesday 12.
Rises, 29½, 2/10   A cock-pheasant appeared at the dunghill at the end of my stable;

½; 33, 34; SE.
Icicles, frost.

Wednesday 13.
29½, 1/10; 35, 39;
E, SE.
Fog, thaw, swift
thaw.

Laurustines appear as if scorched in the fire. Portugal-laurel, red
American Juniper untouched.
Nuthatch, *sitta*, chatters.
Garden-plants were well preserved under the snow:

Thursday 14.
29½; 42½; S.
Sn: gone without
rain.
Gnats, & small flies;
Lepismae.

Friday 15.
29, 4/10; 44, 46;
SE.
Small rain.
✿ *Hepatica,*
Polyanthus, Bellis
perennis.

Turneps in general little damaged.

Saturday 16.
29½, 1/10; 42. W.
Sunshine, frost.
✿ *Leontodon*
taraxacum.

Wheat, being secured by the snow, looks finely.

Sunday 17.
Rises; 38, 37; NE.
Rime, frost, &
thaw.
✿ *Lonicera*
periclymenum.

Wren, *passer troglodytes*, & Red-breast, *rubecula*, sing.

Monday 18.
Falls; 36; E, S.
Fog, & rain.

Made an Hot bed for Cucumbers.

Tuesday 19.
Rises, falls; 38; W.
Frost, sunshine,
rain.

Wednesday 20.
Falls, rises; 40½,
40; N.

Cold rain.

Thursday 21.
Rises; 38; NW.
Sunshine.
🌱 *Lamium rubrum.*

Ananas budding for bloom: First crop of kidney-beans gather'd in the Hothouse at Hartley.

Friday 22.
Falls much; 38; S.
Rainy day.

House-sparrows chirp.
Sowed Cucumber-seeds.

Saturday 23.
35; SW.
White frost, & Ice.
Peziza acetabulum.

Lightning in the evening.

Sunday 24.
36; SW.
Frost & Ice, great rain.

Monday 25.
40; SW.

Strong wind.

Tuesday 26.
44; SW.
Great rain in the night.

Cucumbers appear.
Tempestuous wind.

Wednesday 27.
41; SE.
Great rain, & wind.

Thursday 28.
43; SE.
Mild weather.

Sowed more cucumber-seeds. *Fringillago*, great titmouse, begins some of his spring-notes.

Friday 29.
45; SE.
Rain.

Pricked out the cucumbers.

Saturday 30.
45; S.
Soft weather.

Sunday 31.
W, NE.

Hedge-sparrow, *curruca*, sings.

FEBRUARY 1768

Monday 1

LONDON
Jack-daw, *monedula*. chatters on churches.

Tuesday 2.

Went to London.

Wednesday 3.

Thursday 4.

Friday 5.

Saturday 6.

Sunday 7.

Monday 8.

Blackbird, thrushes and starlings,
Selborne churchyard in the snow.
February.

Tuesday 9.
Vast rains with wind.

Wednesday 10.
Do.
❀ *Corylus avellana.*

Thursday 11.
Vast rains with wind.
❀ *Helleborus hyemalis.*

OXFORD
Went to Oxford from London.

Friday 12.

Saturday 13.
48. Spring weather.
❀ *Galanthus nivalis.*

SELBORNE *clay*
Song thrush, *turdus simpliciter dictus*, sings.
Returned to Selborne.

Sunday 14.
48; SE.
❀ *Helleborus foetidus.*

Chaffinch, *fringilla*, sings. Fieldfare, *turdus pilaris*, still appears.

Monday 15.
48; SE.
Soft weather.
❀ *Crocus sativus.*¶

Earthworms engender.
Cucumber-plants shew two rough leaves.
Forward turneps rot.

Tuesday 16.
W.
Rain, soft weather.

Evergreens appear more damaged than at first was imagin'd; especially those in sunny aspects. Bees gather on ye winter-aconite.

Wednesday 17.
45; E.
Rain.

Chaffinch, *fringilla*, sings.

Thursday 18.
42; E.

House-pigeons begin to build.

Friday 19.
39; NE.

Arbutus but little damaged by the frost.¶ *Ilex* much hurt. Hollies, pinched by the frost, cast their leaves. Laurustines killed to the

Saturday 20.
39; W, S.
Rain.

ground.

Sunday 21.
51; S.
Vast rain.
Pulex irritans.

The Rook, *Cornix frugilega*, assembles on the nest-trees. Wood-lark, *alauda arborea*, sings.

Monday 22.
51; SW, S.
Great rain.

Tuesday 23.
50; S.
Great rain.
Oniscus asellus.

Prodigious floods in Yorkshire, which have swept away all the bridges.

Wednesday 24.
48; S.
Sunshine, rain, sunshine.
❀ *Tussilago farfara.*
Limax agrestis.

Cucumbᵗ plants thrive, & shew their claspers.

Thursday 25.
Rises; 46½.
Rain, bright night.

The missel-thrush, *turdus viscivorus major* (called in Hants, & Sussex the storm-cock) sings.

Friday 26.
42;
❀ *Taxus baccata.*

The male-yewtree sheds it's farina in clouds.
The catkins of the Hasel open.

Saturday 27.
45.

The yellow-hammer, *emberiza flava*, sings.

Sunday 28.
45; SW.

Wet continues still: has lasted three weeks this day. Pinched-off the tops of the cucumber-plants, which have several joints.

Monday 29.
47½; SW.

MARCH 1768

Tuesday 1.
48; SW.   The Colemouse, *parus ater*, & the long-tailed titmouse, *parus*
Moist, &   *caudatus*, chirp.
cloudy.

Wednesday 2.
45; N, E.   Rooks begin to build.

Thursday 3.
30, 2/4; 41; NE.   March-weather.
Sunshine, sleet.
✿ *Daphne*
mezereum.

Friday 4.
37; NE.   Crocus's in high bloom; & bees gathering on them.
Fierce frost.

Saturday 5.
37; NE.   Cucum.ˢ shew side-shoots.
No frost.   Female yewtree shews rudiments of fruit.

Sunday 6.
35; NE.   Rooks build.
Severe wind.

Monday 7.
33½; NE.   The Ground, & paths drie very fast. Wheat is fed-down by
Black frost.   sheep.

Tuesday 8.
39; NE.   Beans are planted in yᵉ fields; pease sown.
Severe wind.   Cut-down the newplanted nectarines.
✿ *Ficaria verna.*

Wednesday 9.
39; NW.
Cold winds.

Thursday 10.
37½; NE.   Made the four-light Cucum.ʳ bed with 8 cart-loads of dung.
Dry wind.
✿ *Veronica agrestis.*

[230]

Friday 11.
39; NE.
Cold dry air.
❀ *Cucumis sativus.*

Cucum.ᵗ blows in male-bloom.

Saturday 12.
39; NW.
❀ *Veronica*
hederifolia.

Sunday 13.
41½; W.
Blowing with hail.
❀ *Viola odorata.*

Viper appears.
Cucumber shows rudiments of fruit.

Monday 14.
45; W.
Showers, wind.

Turned-out pots of cucum.ʳˢ into the great bed.

Tuesday 15.
Rises; 45; W.
Showers, & wind.

Sowed Cantaleupe, & succade melon-seeds.
Sowed Cucumber seeds.

Wednesday 16.
Rises; 46; SW.
Small showers.
Scolopendra
forficata.

Planted rosetrees.

Thursday 17.
48; SW.
Soft weather.
❀ *Ribes grossularia.*

The ring-dove, *palumbus torquatus*, cooes.
Sowed larkspurs.

Friday 18.
30, ¼–⅛; 47; W,
N.
Sunshine.

Beautiful weather.
Oats are sown.

Saturday 19.
40; S, SW.
Ice, sunshine.
❀ *Ribes rubrum;*
Fumaria bulbosa.

Sowed Celeri.

Sunday 20.
Sinks; 45; W.
Strong wind.
❀ *Sambucus nigra;*

House pigeons sit.
Sowed carrots, parsneps, onions, leeks.
Planted potatoes.

🌢 *Prunus armeniaca.*   Sowed radishes.

Monday 21.
40; NW.   Cucumbers show several fruit.
Keen air, flakes of
snow.

Tuesday 22.
30¼; 38; N.
Keen air, frost.

Wednesday 23.
32; NE.   Cucumber shows female bloom.
Thick ice, wh: frost.
🌢 *Amygdalus persica.*

Thursday 24.
36; NE.   Blue mist, & the smell (as the Country people say) of London
Thick ice, wh: frost.   smoke.

Friday 25.
44; E.   Apricot is covered with boards.
Frost.   Lucern is 6 inches & ¾ high; burnet 5 inches & ½.
🌢 *Narcissus pseudo-*
narcissus.

Saturday 26.
45; E, SE.   Ground is all dust.
No frost.   Sowed various sorts of seeds from the physic-garden at Oxford.¶
🌢 *Fragaria sterilis.*

Sunday 27.
43½; E.   Ducks are hatched.
Sunshine.
Various flies.

Monday 28.
45; SW, W.   Stone-curlew, *Oedicnemus*, clamours.
Soft air.   Toads crawl forth.
Rana bufo.

Tuesday 29.
Rising; 45; NE.   Cock-pheasant crows.
Fog, s:shine.   Blue stinking mist.

Wednesday 30.
44; NE.   Canes foeminae catuliunt¶.
Raw fog.   Lined-out the small cucumber-bed.
🌢 *Oxalis acetosella.*

Coluber natrix.

Thursday 31.
42; NE.
Black weather.
❦ *Rosa canina;*
Caltha palustris.

APRIL 1768

Friday 1.
41; NE.
Strong wind,
s:shine.
❦ *Daphne laureola,*
Cheiranthus cheiri.

Saturday 2.
Sinks; 44; NE.
Frost, s:shine.
❦ *Salices.*
Papilio rhamni,*
Papilio urticae,
Bombylius medius.

Sunday 3.
Sinks; 45; SE.
Frost, sunshine.
❦ *Tulipa Gesneriana*
praecox,¶ *Buxus.*
Regulus non
cristatus.

Monday 4.
Sinks; 45; SE.
Wh: dew, soft air.
❦ *Glechoma*
hederacea, Ulmus
campestris.
Lacerta vulgaris,
Vespertilio murinus.¶

Tuesday 5.
46; E, SE.
Frost, s:shine.
❦ *Ulmus glabra,*
Ribes grossularia,
Ribes rubrum.
Luscinia!

Cucumber-fruit swells. Rooks sit. This day the dry weather has lasted a month.

*The *Papilio praecox sulphurea* of Ray. *Musca bombyliiformis dense pilosa nigra, abdomine obtuso, ad latera rufo. Longissimum spiculum quoddam, ceu linguam exore protendit.*¶
Ray's *Hist: Insect:* p: 273.

Hops are planting.
Ananas bloom.
Willow-wren appears.

Mice breed.
The Hen-rook sits, the cock feeds her.

Gold-finch, *carduelis*, whistles.
Cucum.ᵗˢ shew fruit in every light.
Tadpoles swell in the frogspawn.

Wednesday 6.
48. E, NE.
Cloudy, a few
drops.
☙ *Anemone*
nemorosa,
Hyacinthus muscari.
Bombinatrices; Rana
temporaria.

Thursday 7.
Rises; 45; E.   *Cottus gobio* spawns.
Strong wind,   Turkey lays.
cloudy.   This day the dry weather has lasted five weeks.
☙ *Primula veris,*
Adoxa
moschatellina.

Friday 8.
Rises; 42; E.   Grass-lamb.
Sharp wind,
s:shine.
☙ *Bromelia, Ananas*
fruits, *Fritillaria*
Imperialis.
Ruticilla, Musca
tenax.

Saturday 9.
41; E.   The titlark, *Alauda pratorum*¶, first sings. It is a delicate songster;
Sharp wind, ice,   flying from tree to tree, & spreading out it's wings it chants in it's
s:shine.   descent. It also sings on trees, & on the ground walking in
☙ *Viola canina,*   pasture fields.
Cardamine pratensis,
Chrysosplenium
oppositifolium,
Mercurialis perennis.
Atricapilla.

Sunday 10.
44; SE.   Ponds are drying up.
Cold wind.   Young Geese.

Monday 11.
Good shower.   Made the melon-bed with 18 loads of dung.

Tuesday 12.
S.   Thrushes sit.
Showers.

Wednesday 13.
Rises; 48; SE.
Soft air.
Hirundo domestica!!!

Showers about.
Black-cap sings.

Thursday 14.
Rises; 52; W, SW.
Wind, showers,
hail.
✿ *Pinus larix.*
White-throat,
Formica rufa.

Showers about.
Cut a brace of cucumbers.
Put the hills of earth on the melon-bed.
Thunder.

Friday 15.
Rises; 50; W, NW,
SW.
Summer weather.
✿ *Pedicularis
sylvatica.*
Musca carnaria.

Black-bird, *merula vulg*: sings. Willow-wren sings. Second
willow-wren chirps.¶

Saturday 16.
Sinks: 51; S.
Shower, soft
weather.
✿ *Pulmonaria
officinalis.*
*Coccinella
bipunctata, Hirundo
agrestis, Alauda
locustae voce!*

Showers about.
Barley is sowing.
Whitethroat sings.
Oats springs.

Saturday 17.
Rises; 53; SW.
Showers, showers.
*Alauda locustae voce
stridet.*

Rooks have young.
Young ravens fledged.
Fork-tailed kite lays three eggs.¶
Redstart sings for the first time.

Monday 18.
54; W.
Stormy, showers.
✿ *Prunus cerasus,
Prunus domestica.*
Formica herculeana.

Wheat looks finely.
Apricots begin to set.
Nuthatch, *sitta*, makes it jarring, clattering noise in the woods.

Tuesday 19.
53; W, SW.
Soaking rain, strong
wind.

The cartway runs with water.
The ground is well moistened.
The wind damages the buds of the trees.

🌱 *Prunus spinosa,*
Hyacinthus
nonscriptus.
Hirundo riparia.

Wednesday 20.
50; SW.   Turn'd-out the Cantaleupe, & succade melons into their hills.
Strong wind,   Bed is hot.
showers.   St foin 8 inches high.¶
🌱 *Narciussus*   Lined out the Cucumber-bed.
jonquilla, Hyacinthus
orientalis.

Thursday 21.
Sinks; SW.   Cut two brace of large Cucumbers.
Strong wind,   *Musca tenax* copulates.
showers.   Asparagus sprout.
🌱 *Pyrus sativa,*
Lamium album.
Cuculus.

Friday 22.
W.   Cut a brace of cucumbers.
Strong winds,   Green finch chirps.
showers.   Vines sprout.
Formica nigra.

Saturday 23.
Sinks; 51; SW.   *Arbutus,* & Cypresses now appear to be much damaged by the
Sunshine, shower.   severe winter.
🌱 *Orchis maculata;*
Fragaria vesca.

Sunday 24.
52; W.
Heavy showers.
🌱 *Prunus avium.*

Monday 25.
52; W.   Cut two brace of Cucumbers.
Showers.   Grass, & corn grow very fast.
🌱 *Prunus armeniaca;*
Fraxinus excelsior.

Tuesday 26.
46; W.   Melon-plants have shoots with several joints, & are stopped-
Wind, showers,   down.
hail.
🌱 *Amygdalus persica.*

Wednesday 27.
Rises; 47; W, NW.
Showers.
֍ *Sorbus aucuparia,*
Mespilus German:

Vast black, & rock-like clouds.
Trouts in season.

Thursday 28.
Falls; 47; N, S, SE.
Sun, great rain.
֍ *Fagus sylvatica.*
Jynx.

Cucumbers promise a vast crop.

Friday 29.
50; S, N.
Frequent showers.

Grass-hopper-lark chirps at eight o' the Clock in the evening.
Most growing weather.

Saturday 30.
48; N.
Vast rain.
Regulus non cristatus
cantat voce stridula
locustae. *

The grasshopper-lark chirps concealed at the bottoms of Hedges.
*This is the largest of the three willow wrens: it haunts the tops of
tall trees, making a shivering noise.

MAY 1768

Sunday 1.
49; N.
Great showers.
֍ *Ajuga reptans.*

The Country in a very wet condition.
Wheat begins to look a little wan.

Monday 2.

Melon-plants are over-steamed.
Cut Lucern for my Horses for the first time.

Tuesday 3.
֍ *Pyrus malus.*
Hirundo, Apus.

LONDON
Came to London.

Wednesday 4.
Cimex lectularius.

Herrings.
Mackerel.

Thursday 5.

Green gooseberries.
Thunderstorm in Hants.

Friday 6.
Hot.
Vespa vulgaris.

Apricots.

Saturday 7.
Sultry.

Sunday 8.
Hot.   Sturgeon.

Monday 9.
Sultry.

Tuesday 10.
                      Eleven brace of Cucumbers from Selborne.
Wednesday 11.

Green pease.
Mushrooms.

Thursday 12.

Pine-apples.

Friday 13.
Cold air.   Cauliflowers.

Saturday 14.
Cold.   SELBORNE
⚘ *Galeopsis*   Returned to Selborne.
galeobdolon,   Melon-fruit in bloom.
Chelidonium majus.   A brace of sand-pipers (*tringa minor*) at James Knight's ponds.
Stoparola.

Sunday 15.
49; NE.
Cold air.
⚘ *Quercus robur,*
Fagus sylvatica.

Monday 16.
50; NE.
Hot sun.
⚘ *Acer*
pseudoplatanus, Acer
campestre.

Tuesday 17.
56; W, SW.
Wh: frost.
⚘ *Berberis vulg:,*
Viburnum lantana.
Gryllus campestris
cantat.

Wednesday 18.
50.   Young wood-larks come forth.

Hail.
🌢 *Juglans regia*;
Coronilla emerus,
Cytisus laburnum.
Caprimulgus!

Young wood-larks come forth.
My appletrees are but poorly blown.

Thursday 19.
50; W.
Cold air.

Rudiments of wasps nests are found.
No chaffers, or tree-beetles appear yet.
The wasp's nest contained eleven eggs in eleven cells.

Friday 20.

Saturday 21.
SE.
Soft air.
🌢 *Tormentilla*
reptans.

Lanius minor ruffus, red-backed butcher-bird,¶ shot near the
village. It's gizzard was full of the legs & parts of beetles.

Sunday 22.
High; 59; S, E,
NE.
Summer weather.
🌢 *Asperula odorata*,
Aesculis hippo-cast:.
Scarabaeus
melolontha.

One chaffer.

Monday 23.
61; NE.
Hot sun, & wind.
🌢 *Crataegus*
oxyacantha, *Sorbus*
aucuparia.
Gryllus gryllotalpa.

Some appletrees are blown out within a week past.

Tuesday 24.
63; NE.
Summer.
🌢 *Crataegus Aria*,
Polygala vulg:.
Libellulae, *Apis*
longicornis.

Flesh-flies are very troublesome.

Wednesday 25.
High; 61; NE.
Summer.
🌢 *Cistus*
helianthemum,
Paeonia officinal:

Thursday 26.
65; NE.
Cool air.
❀ *Viburnum opulus*,
Mespilus German:.
Cantharis noctiluca.¶

Friday 27.
Sinks; 58; NE, SE.   Melons blow very fast.
Clouds, chilly.
❀ *Morus nigra*;
Crataegus torminalis,
Sanicula
Europaea.

Saturday 28.
Sinks; 58; SE.   Melons begin to swell. *Ananas* blow at Hartley. Grasses blow.
Cloudy.
❀ *Geum urbanum*,
Orchis morio,
Hedysarum
onobrychis.
Musca meridiana.

Sunday 29.
Low; 59; S.   The female viper has a string of eggs within her as large as those
Rain all day.   of a blackbird; but no rudiments of the Young are yet formed
❀ *Lychnis flos-cuculi*,   within the egg. The viper is
Stellaria holostea,   ᾽έσω μὲν ᾠοτόκα, ᾽έζω δε ζωοτόκα.   ¶
Poterium sanguisorba,
Aconitum
uncinatum.

Monday 30.
56.   Young turkeys.
Heavy clouds.   Melons swell both Succade, & Cantaleupe.
❀ *Rubus Idaeus*,
Hesperis matronalis,
Ranunculus repens,
bulbosus, acris,
Geranium
Robert:

Tuesday 31.
55; SE.   Cant: melon-haulm cracks a little.
Sun.   No chaffers appear.
❀ *Scrophularia*   Cucumbers bear well again.
nodosa, Crambe
maritima,

Lithospermum offic:

JUNE 1768

Wednesday 1.
Rises; 57; NW.
Fine weather.
♔ *Euphorbia
amygdaloides*, *Allium
ursinum*, *Myositis
scorpoides*, *Lychnis
flos cuculi*.

Grasshoppers begin to appear.
Strawberries (scarlet) begin to turn.
Young redbreasts appear.
Cucumbers come in heaps.

Tuesday 2.
Rises; 60; N.
Sun. Brisk air.
♔ *Iris pseudacorus*,
Secale cereale,
*Cynoglossum
officinale*.

Melons swell apace.
Grass is very backward.

Wednesday 3.
61; NE.
Cloudless.
♔ *Ranunculus
flammula*, *Lotus
corniculata*.
Phryganea nigra,
Ephemera vulgata.

Alis caeruleo-atris, antennis corpore duplo longioribus.¶
*The reed-sparrow, *passer torquatus in arundinetis nidificans*, sings
at Liss near M:ʳˢ Cole's ponds. It sings night & day while
breeding, & has a fine variety of notes
*As it appears since, this was the *passer arundinaceus minor* of Ray:
a thin-billed bird, & probably a bird of summer passage.

Saturday 4.
61; NE.
Sun, & wind.
♔ *Anthyllis
vulneraria*.
The angler's
mayfly.

Snipes play over the moors, piping, & humming. They always
hum as they are descending.¶ Is not their hum ventriloquos like
that of the turkey? Some suspect it is made by the wings.

Sunday 5.
Sinks; 61; E.
Cloudless.
♔ *Philadelphus
coronarius*.
Libellula virgo.

Corpore caeruleo nitido, alis erectis viridi-caerulescentibus.¶
Succade-melons shew their ribs.

Monday 6.
Sinks; 61½; SE.
♔ *Rosa cinnamomea*,
Sambucus nigra.

Distant thunder.

Tuesday 7.
Sinks; 65½; SE.
❦ *Dianthus*
caryophyllus.

Thunder all round at a distance.

Wednesday 8.
Sinks; 63; S.
Great rain.
❦ *Dianthus barbatus*,
Tamus communis.

Showers all night.

Thursday 9.
Sinks; 61; S, W.
Showers.
❦ *Cucubalus behen*,
Bryonia alba.

Wheat begins to be in ear.
Strawberries, wood & garden begin to ripen.

Friday 10.
SW.
❦ *Digitalis*
purpurea, Stachys
sylvatica.

Lined-out the melon-bed.
The nightingale, having young, leaves-off singing, & makes a
plaintive, & a jarring noise.

Saturday 11.
Sinks; 61; S.
Strong wind,
showers.
❦ *Solanum*
dulcamara.

This wind damaged the hops, pease, &c, &c.

Sunday 12.
Rises; 60; SW.
Cloudy.
❦ *Phallus impudicus*,
Epilobium
angustifolium,
Gladiolus communis.

Glow-worms abound.
Phallus stinks in the hedges.

Monday 13.
60; SW; E.
Rain all day.
❦ *Symphytum offic:*

Young titmice.

Tuesday 14.
58; W.
Rain all night &
day.

Young *reguli non cristati*.
Wheat lodges.
Grass grows.

Wednesday 15.
Rises; 55; NW.
Strong wind.
❀ *Tremella nostoc*;
Rosa alba.

Cantaleupes swell.

Tuesday 16.
55; SW.
Showers.
❀ *Rhamnus
catharticus*.
Cicada spumaria.

Earthed-out the lining of the melon-bed, & raised the frames.
Snails engender.

Friday 17.
58; SE.
Shower.
❀ *Lycoperdon
bovista*; *Triticum
hybernum*!

Wheat that was lodged rises again.

Toad hidden among long grass
at foot of gravestone.
Selborne churchyard.
17 June.

Saturday 18.
60; SW.
Shower, hot sun.
❀ *Verbascum
thapsus, Rosa Gallica
& centifolia*.

Sunday 19.
Sinks; 59; NW, S.
Great shower, sun.
❀ *Iris Xiphium,
Echium vulgare*.
Scarabaeus cervus.

Distant thunder.
Young sprarrows.
Melons grow: the lining is very warm.

Monday 20.
57; SW, W.
Showers, wind,
showers.
❀ *Borago offic:,
Euonymus
Europaeus*.

Heavy showers on the blowing wheat.

Tuesday 21.
Rises; 55; NW.
Cool air.
❀ *Cornus sanguinea*,
Scabiosa arvensis.

Young white-throats.
White-throat sings.

Wednesday 22.
Rises; 57; W.
Soft air.
❀ *Convolvulus*
arven:, *Epilobium*
montanum.

Cut my St foin.

Thursday 23.
Rises; 59; SE.
Soft air.
❀ *Heracleum*
sphondylium, *Bunium*
bulbocastanum.

Frogs begin to migrate.
Young nightingales.

Friday 24.
61; E.
Summer weather.
❀ *Verbena offic:*,
Papaver rhoeas;
Prunella vulg:,
Agrimonia
Eupatoria.
Tabanus bovinus.

Wheat blows finely.
Titlark sings.
Blackcap sings.

Saturday 25.
63; E, S.
Great rain.
❀ *Centaurea*
scabiosa, *Lilium*
martagon,
Phlomis fruticosa,
Prunus lusitanica.

Goatsucker jars.
St Foin in cock.
Rain all day.

Sunday 26.
61; SE.
Vast rains in the
night, blowing &
cloudy.
❀ *Agaricus*
campestris; *Malva*
sylvestris, &
rotundifolia,
Hypericum

The wind beats-off the blossoms of the wheat.

perforatum.

Monday 27.
61; SE.
Soft rain.
✿ *Hyoscyamus niger,*
Tragopogon
pratense, Atropa
belladonna.

Rain all day.

Tuesday 28.
Rises; 61; W.
Strong wind, little
shower.
✿ *Centaurea jacea,*
Spiraea ulmaria,
Genista tinctoria,
Vitis vinifera!
Thymus serpillum.

Showers about.
Dryed & cocked my S! foin.

Wednesday 29.
61; SW.
Drying day.
✿ *Galium verum,*
Galium palustre,
Lapsana communis,
Carduus acanthoides
& *crispus.*

Ricked my S! foin in good order.
The ears of wheat in general are very long. Wheat blows still.

Thursday 30.
SW.
Fine day.
✿ *Achillea ptarmica,*
Malva moschata,
Anagallis arvensis,
Lysimachia
nemorum.
Scarabaeus
solstitialis.

JULY 1768

Friday 1.
64; E.
Hot day.
✿ *Serratula arvensis,*
Adonis annua,
Ranunculus
arvensis.

Great storm of thunder & lightning; rain & some hail. Tiled the succades.

Saturday 2.
64.
Hot weather.
❀ *Prenanthes
muralis, Matricaria
parthenium,
Euphrasia odontites,
Bupleurum
rotundifolium,
Agrostemma githaco.*

FYFIELD *Hasel loam on chalk*
Wood-strawberries in plenty.
Cherries begin to ripen.

Sunday 3.
63; SW.
Cloudy, shower.
❀ *Sedum acre,
Ligustrum vulgare,
Antirrhimum
linaria.*

Monday 4.
65.
❀ *Linum perenne,
Orobanche major.
Coturnix.*

First young swallows.
Cut the first succade-melon.
Grass-hopper-lark sings day & night.

Tuesday 5.
29½, ½/10; 65;
SW.
Cloudy, misty rain.
❀ *Reseda Lutea,
Carduus nutans,
Centaurea
cyanus.*

Turneps begin to be hoed.
Black showery windy weather.

Wednesday 6.
65; SW.
Black weather.
❀ *Verbasum nigrum,
Typha latifolia,
Lithrum salicaria.*

No sun for several days.

Thursday 7.
29; 62; SW.
Blowing, showers.
❀ *Valeriana officin:,
Melissa nepeta,
Sherardia arvensis,
Salvia pratensis,
Ballota nigra.*

Bad time for corn. No cucumbers under hand glasses will set.

Friday 8.
29½; 63; SW.
Sun, showers.
❀ *Betonica officin:,*
Campanula
rotundifolia, Daucus
carota,
Chenopodium Bonus
Henricus.

Saturday 9.
Sinks; 64; SW.
Showers.
❀ *Nepeta cataria,*
Melampyrum
sylvaticum,
Valantia cruciata,
Spiraea
filipendula.

The capsule of The twayblade bursts at a touch, & scatters the dust-like seeds on all sides.

Sunday 10.
Sinks; 64; W, NW.
Summer weather.
❀ *Vicia cracca, Vicia*
sylvatica.

Monday 11.
62, SW.
Great shower.
❀ *Campanula*
glomerata, Jacione
montana.

Cut my great meadow.

Tuesday 12.
63; SW.
Misting rain.
❀ *Carduus*
lanceolatus, &
acaulos, Pastinaca
sylvestris.

Carduus eriophorus corona fratrum, or woolly-headed thistle, not blown.

Wednesday 13.
Sinks; 64½
Showers.
❀ *Lycoperdon tuber,*
Conium maculatum,
Cauculis Anthriscus,
Lysimachia
nummularia.

Truffles begun to be taken for yᵉ first time in my Brother Henry White's grove; & will continue to be found in great abundance every fortnight till about Lady Day.

Thursday 14.
Sinks; 64; SW.
Small rain, thunder.
❀ *Stellaria*
graminea, Aethusa
cynapium.

Thomas brings down Succade-melons from Selborne; & says he has cut four brace. They are very fine. Grass-hopper-lark sings still.

Friday 15.
Rises; 66; SW.
Thunder & vast
showers.
❀ *Angelica sylvestris,*
Senecio
Jacobaea.

Saturday 16.
64.
Vast showers,
thunder.
❀ *Hieracium*
murorum, Centaurea
calcitrapa, Oenothera
biennis.

SELBORNE
Grass-hopper-lark sings at Bradley.

Sunday 17.
Showers.
❀ *Galega offic:,*
Stachys palustris,
Epilobium ramosum,
Tilia Europaea.

Succade-melons come in heaps.

Monday 18.
58; E, W.
Great rain.
❀ *Blackstonia*
perfoliata, Lathyrus
Aphaca, Circaea
lutetiana,
Eupatorium
cannabinum.

The country is drenched with wet, & quantities of hay are spoiled.

Tuesday 19.
60; SW.
Great showers,
thunder.
❀ *Campanula*
latifolia, Euphrasia
officin:

Young swallows are able to take flies for themselves.

Wednesday 20.
Rises; 58; NW.
Dry day.
   Cuscuta Europaea,
Gentiana centaureum,
Tropaeolum majus,
Sium nodiflorum.

Ricked ye great mead.
Vast *aurora borealis.*
The white owl has young. It brings a mouse to its nest about
every five minutes, beginning at sunset.

Thursday 21.
59; NW, SW.
Fine day.
  ✧ *Spergula arvensis,*
Trifolium arvense,
Polygonum
fagopyrum.

Hay in tollerable order.
Cut my little mead.

Friday 22.
62; W, SW.
Summer's day.
   Sparganium
erectum, Hypericum
elodes, Drosera
rotundifolia,
Comarum palustre.

Saturday 23.
64, 69, 67; SE.
Summer.
  ✧ *Scutellaria*
galericulata,
Monotropa
hypopithys, Humulus
lupulus, Oenanthe
fistulosa,
Marrubium vulg:

Martins begin to congregate on the maypole.¶
Ricked my little mead, & finish'd my Hay-making.

Sunday 24.
66; SE.
Sultry.
  ✧ *Seseli caruifolia,*
Alisma plantago.
Hippobosca equina.¶

Thunder about.

Monday 25.
68, 74; NE, E.
Sultry.
  ✧ *Alopecurus*
myosuroides.

Rain in the night.
Thunder about.
Cut the first cantaleupe-melon.

Tuesday 26.
Rises; 66, 69; SE, S.
Summer weather.
♣ *Dipsacus sylvestris*, *Origanum vulgare*.

Cut more cantaleupes.
Threat'ning clouds at a distance; but most delicate ripening weather.

Wednesday 27.
Rises; 65, 68; E, S, SE.
Ripening weather.

The wheat turns yellow.

Thursday 28.
67; E.
Fine day.
♣ *Dipsacus pilosus*, *Teucrium scorodonia*.

Gathered frenchbeans.

Friday 29.
Thunder & great rain.
♣ *Hypericum humifusum*.

Vast storms about.
Field crickets are silent.

Saturday 30.
Warm day.
♣ *Anthemis nobilis*, *Scabiosa columbaria*.

Small showers.

Sunday 31.
64; SW.
Showers.
♣ *Phlox maculata*, *Helianthus multiflorus*.

Young partridges fly.
Distant thunder.

AUGUST 1768

Monday 1.
63; W.
Shower.

Rock-like clouds.
Oats, & pease are cutting.

Tuesday 2.
65; S, E, W, E.
Thunder showers.
♣ *Inula dysenterica*.

Vast showers.
Cantaleupes come apace.
Young martins flie.

Wednesday 3.
63.
Small showers.
꽃 *Sonchus arvensis.*
Oestrus bovis. *

*The whame, or burrel-fly of Derham,¶ lays its nits or eggs on the legs & sides of Horses at Grass. See *physicotheology.*

Thursday 4.
63; NW.
Heavy rain.
꽃 *Pieris*
Hieracioides.

Thunder at a distance.
The thermometer which stood at 63 in the dining room sunk only to 62 in the wine vault.

Friday 5.
Rises; 65; NW.
Summer day.
꽃 *Campanula*
trachelium.
Hirundo Apus seen
no more!

Harvest-bugs.
Apricots ripe.

Saturday 6.
66; W.
Heavy shower.
꽃 *Serapias latifolia.*

Wheat-harvest begins.
Goatsucker chatters.

Sunday 7.
Rises; 62; W.
Dry day.
꽃 *Carlina vulgaris,*
Hypericum Constan-
tinopolitanum.

Cold dew.
Mulberry begins to cast some leaves.
Tops of beeches in the hanger begin to look pale.

Monday 8.
Rises; 60; NW.
Grey day.
꽃 *Arctium lappa,*
Artemisia absinthium
vulgaris.

The lime casts some of its bracteal leaves.

Tuesday 9.
61½; NW.
Fine weather.
꽃 *Clematis vitalba.*

Some wheat in shock.
A white mist creeps over the meadows.

Wednesday 10.
62½; N.
Fine day.
꽃 *Centaurea*
solstitialis.

Young pheasants are flyers.
White butter flies gather in flocks on the mud of puddles.

Thursday 11.
66; N, E, W.   Wheat-harvest is pretty general.
Thunder all round   The male & female flying-ants leaving their nests, fill the air. See
but no rain here.   Gould on ants.

Friday 12.
64; N.   Great storms at a distance.
Thunder round,
fine day.

Saturday 13.
64; E.   Sweet harvest weather.
Summer day.   *Heleborus viridis* begins to wither.
                                Brisk gale of wind.

Sunday 14.
Sinks; 65½; NE,   Strong wind.
E.
Dark clouds, &
rain.
⚘ *Thalictrum*
flavum, Eryngium
maritimum.

Monday 15.
Sinks; 65; E.   Young broods of goldfinches appear.
Fog, showers.
⚘ *Campanula*
hybrida, Carthumus
tinctorius.

Tuesday 16.
Sinks; 64; E.   Wheat begins to be housed.
Fog, fine afternoon.
⚘ *Verbascum*
phoeniceum.

Wednesday 17.
Sinks; 66; E, SE.
Showers, distant
thunder.
⚘ *Scabiosa succisa.*

Thursday 18.
64½; S, W.   Martins continue to hatch new broods.
Vast rain, wind.   Flies begin to abound in the windows.
⚘ *Conyza squarrosa,*
Leontodon
autumnale.

Friday 19.
Rises; 62; W.
Dry day.
❀ *Aster Chinensis.*

White wheat begins to grow.
Plums ripe.

Saturday 20.
64; S.
Showers.

Smallest *regulus non cristatus* chirps.
Yellow-hammer sings.

Sunday 21.
Sinks; 63; SW.
Showers.

Monday 22.
Sinks; 61; S.
Showers.
❀ *Aster Amellus.*

Young gold-finches come forth.

Stinkhorn in Selborne High Wood.
Late August.

Tuesday 23.
Sinks; 60½; SW.
Drowning showers.
  Impatiens balsamina.

The wheat in a very bad condition.

Wednesday 24.
Rises; 60; W.
Showers, fine.
❀ *Carduus marianus.*

Much wheat bound up in the afternoon.
Gold-finch sings. Oats are cutting.

Thursday 25.
Rises; 58½; W.
Very small shower.
❀ *Saponaria officinalis.*

Cucumber-plants begin to decline.
Tyed-up endive.
Large showers about.

Friday 26.
58; W.
Black clouds.
❀ Mich: daisey.

White dew.
Peaches ripen. Barley begins to be cut.
Much wheat housed.

Saturday 27.
Rises; 60; NE, E.
Beautiful weather.

Much wheat housed. Blue mist.
Yellow-hammers have Young still, which they feed with *tipulae.*

Sunday 28.
Sinks; 57½; NE.
Dark sky.

Cold wind.
One or two wasps.

Monday 29.
Rises; 57; NE.   Cold air.
Rain, dark sky.   Wheat continues to be ricked, & housed.
🌱 Asters blow.

Tuesday 30.
57½; NE. Dark   The goat-sucker still appears.
sky.
🌱 *Hybiscus syriacus*.

Wednesday 31.
Sinks; 60; W.   Grapes begin to turn colour.
Shower.   Nectarines ripe.
                                   Stoparola brings out it's Young.

SEPTEMBER 1768

Thursday 1
Sinks; 60; E.   Transplanted some plants of the *Helleborus viridis*¶ from the
Rain, vast rain.   Honey-lane near Norton to the shrubbery in the orchard.

Friday 2.
Rises; 58½; N.   Smallest *Regulus non cristatus* chirps.
Great rain,   Owls have young still in the nest.
s:shine.

Saturday 3.
Falls, falls; 56; S.   Much wheat still abroad.
Rain, s:shine.   Hop-picking becomes general: there is a vast crop.
🌱 *Gentiana*
amarella.

Sunday 4.
Falls, falls; 55; N,
S.
S:shine, rain.

Monday 5.
Rises; 55; W.   Corn is housed.
Strong wind, dry
day, shower.

Tuesday 6.
Rises; 55½; W.   Corn is housed.
Strong wind, very   Glow-worms still appear.
small shower.   Small *regulus non cristatus* chirps.
Ortygometra, land-
rail.

Wednesday 7.
Rises; 56; W, N,
NE.
Hot sun, distant
showers, few drops.

First blanched endive.
Some wheat standing still.
A few wasps. *Jynx* still appears.

Thursday 8.
Sinks; 56½; NE,
E. Vast rain.

Martins still in their nest.
Wheat still abroad.
Thunder.

Friday 9.
55; NE, W.
S:shine, great rain.

Thunder.

Saturday 10.
Rises; 54; S, E.
S:shine, rain.

Hedge-hogs bore holes in the grass-walks to come at the plantain
roots, which they eat upwards.

Sunday 11.
Sinks; 57; E, S.
Vast rain.

Wheat still abroad; some standing.

Monday 12.
Sinks; 58; S, E, N.
Drowning rains.

Sheep die frequently on the common tho' so wholesome a spot.
Ravens flock on the hanger.

Tuesday 13.
Rises; 56; N.
Rain, strong wind.

Nectarines rot on ye trees.
Ravens are continually playing by pairs in the air.

Wednesday 14.
Rises; 52; N.
S:shine, grey
weather.

Gather'd first grapes, black cluster.

Thursday 15.
Sinks; 53½; SW.
Rain all day.

Black warty water-efts with fin tails & yellow bellies are drawn
up in the well-bucket.

Friday 16.
Sinks; 55½; W.
Vast rain in the
night, showers.

Strong wind.
Bank-martins still appear.

Saturday 17.
Sinks; 53½; NE.
Vast rains.

Wheat still abroad.
The fields are drenched with rains, & almost all the spring corn is
abroad.
Sheep die.

Rooks feed in the stubble,
Looking towards Newton Valence
from the Hawkley Road.
2 September.

Sunday 18.
Sinks, rises; 54;
SW.
Vast rains.

Thunder.
Young martins in their nest.

Monday 18.
Rises; 53; SW.
Sun, showers, vast
rain.

First blanched Celeri.
Wheat still abroad: oats & barley much grown.

Tuesday 20.
Sinks; 54; S, E.
Sun, grey sky, great
rain.

A few wasps which spoil ye grapes.

Wednesday 21.
Rises, rises; 55; W.
Sun, small rain.

Nectarines all water.
Great rain at night.

Thursday 22.
Sinks; 55; E.
Vast rain, drowning
rains.

Hops are still picking, but turned very brown by the rains.

Friday 23.
Rises; 53½; E, S.
Fog, sun, small
rain, bright night.

The whame or burrel-fly, *Oestrus bovis*, still lays it's nits on the horses sides.¶

Saturday 24.
Rises; 55; E.
Fog, showers, fog.

Much wheat still out, & spoiled.
Much barley & oats spoiled.
Young martins still in their nest.

Sunday 25.
Rises high; 55; E,
SW.
Fog, small rain,
fine.
Merula torquata¶
femina, & mas.

A few of these rare birds, (rock-ouzels) appeared just this time twelve months, in orchards about yewtrees. I have not been able yet to procure a cock.

Monday 26.
High; 57; S.
Cloudy, dry.

I saw a small Ichneumon-fly laying it's eggs on, or in the *aurelia* of a *papilio*.

Tuesday 27.
High; 56; E.
S:shine, fine.
Merula torquata mas.

People are now housing corn after 27 days interruption.

Wednesday 28.
High; 56; E.
Cloudless.
🌣 *Hedera helix*.

These ring-ouzels are seen again in the spring in their return to the north.

Thursday 29.
Sinks; 56; E.
Fog, sun,
sultry.

Swallows cluster on the bushes in the burnet.
Redstart.

Friday 30.
Rises; E.
Fog, brown
weather.

Stares flock at Chilgrove.
Oedicnemus does not flock yet.

OCTOBER 1768

Saturday 1.
Sinks, high; NE.
Grey, pleasant.

Harvest pretty well finished this evening.
Some wheat out at Harting.
Roads are much dryed.

Sunday 2.
Sinks; 55; NE.
Fog, fine day.

Swallows still.
Glow-worms shine.

Monday 3.
Sinks; 54½; NE.
Fine day, thunder
clouds.

Corn is housing.
Green wheat at Faringdon.

Tuesday 4.
Very low; 60; SE.
Showers, vast
showers.

Grapes are good.
The ash, & mulberry cast their leaves.

Wednesday 5.
Rises; 58; S.
Great showers.

Swallows.
Rooks carry off the nuts from ye wallnut-trees.

Thursday 6.
58; S, W.
Drowning showers,
wind.
🌣 Asters, Golden
rods.

Loud thunder.

Friday 7.
58; SW.
Showers.

Swallows, & martins.
Some corn still out.

Saturday 8.
59½; S, W, S.   Martins in plenty.
Warm air,
showers.

Sunday 9.
Rises; 56; SW, S.   Thunder-like clouds.
Dry.   Showers at a distance.

Monday 10.
56; E.   Few martins.
Shower, vast   Swallows.
shower.   Barley still out.

Tuesday 11.
Rises; 52; NW.   Gathered-in apples, & pears.
Sweet day.   Grapes are good.

Wednesday 12.
N.   Lapwings begin to congregate in the uplands.
Fine day.   Fields of barley abroad.

Thursday 13.   OXFORD
N.   Swallows, & martins at Streatley.
Fine day, rain.

Friday 14.
Dark day.   Meadows flooded.

Saturday 15.
Fine.

Sunday 16
NW.   Swallow.
Rain, s:shine.
Gallinago minor.

Monday 17.
E.
Fine day.

Tuesday 18.
SE, S.
Cloudy, rain.

Wednesday 19.
W.   Herrings.
Fog, s:shine.

Thursday 20.
E, SE.
Fog, s:shine.

Friday 21.
S.   Swallow.
Rain, sunshine.

Saturday 22.   SELBORNE
Sinks; 50; SE.   Returned to Selbourne.
Fog, great rain.
Scolopax.

Sunday 23.
Rises; 50; W, SE.   Fallows in a sad wet, weedy condition: scarce any wheat sown.
Cloudy, sun,
clouds.
Cornix cinerea
frugilega.

Monday 24.
Sinks; 50; SE.
Great rain.

Tuesday 25.
Rises; 48½; W.
Dry day.
⚘ Asters, & golden
rods.

Wednesday 26.
45; W, S, SE.
Sun, great rain.

Thursday 27.
Rises; 46; S, W.   Vast rock-like clouds.
Sun.
Turdus Iliacus.

Friday 28.
Rises: 45; W, NW.   Some wheat is now sowing.
Soft grey weather.

Saturday 29.
Sinks; 47; E.   Grapes are very good, but decay apace.
Much rain.

Sunday 30.
Sinks; 46; NE, SW.   Fallows gutted with water, & full of weeds.

Fine grey day, rain.   Wells rise very fast.

Monday 31.
Sinks; 45; NW, W.   Gathered-in all my grapes: they are very good.
Drying day, rain.   Some fields of barley still abroad.

NOVEMBER 1768

Tuesday 1.
47; NW.   Bucks grunt.
Drying wind, small
rain.

Wednesday 2.
Rises; 45; W, S, E.
Fine, wet evening.

Thursday 3.
Sinks; 47; W.   Bat appears.
Drying day.   Hedge-hogs cease to dig the walks.

Friday 4.
Sinks; 47; W.
Rain, dry, rain.
Turdus pilaris.

Saturday 5.
Rises; 43; NW.   Glass rises violently.
Dry wind, fine,   Planted a plot of cabbages to stand the winter.
small shower.   Wheat is sown.

Sunday 6.
30¼; 40; NW, S.
Ice, fog, fine
day.

Monday 7.
Sinks. 44. W, S.
Soft, fine day.

Tuesday 8.
Rises; 45; W.
Fine day.

Wednesday 9.
Sinks; 47; NW, W,   Fallows begin to work well.
S.   Wood-cocks in the high wood.
Sweet day.

Thursday 10.
Sinks; 46; W.
Rain, five aftern:
🌱 Late aster, &
golden-rod.

Friday 11.
Sinks; 45; E.
Rain.

Saturday 12.
Rises; 45; E, N.
Cold wind, dark &
dry.

Sunday 13.
Rises; 40; N, NE.
Frost, fine day,
sharp wind.

The Ground dries much.
Wheat continues to be sown.
Elms are still in full leaf.

Monday 14.
Sinks; 41; E.
Dark, misty rain,
hard rain.

Bat appears still.

Tuesday 15.
Rises; 45; W.
Fine day.

Lightening very early in the morning.

Wednesday 16.
Sinks; 47; S.
Dry, windy, gr:
rain.

Thursday 17.
Sinks; 48; NW.
Dull & hazy, rain.

Friday 18.
Rises much; 45; W,
NW.
Fine day.

Saturday 19.
Rises, high; 43; S.
Bright sun.

Many sorts of flies still appear, the *musca carnaria*, *meridiana*,
tenax, &c.

Sunday 20.
High; 46½; W.

Ground in a very wet condition.

Great rain in y^e
night. Fine day, wh:
frost

Rock-like clouds appear.

Monday 21.
Sunk 6 deg.; 43;
SW, W.
Vast rain all day, &
wind.

Tuesday 22.
Sunk to 28 1/10;
40; SW.
S:shine, great rain.

The barometer unusually low considering there is little wind.
Rock-like clouds.

This astonishing fall of the glass was remarked all the kingdom
over: we had no wind, & not much rain; only vast swagging rock-
like clouds appear'd at a distance.

Wednesday 23.
Rises, rises; 39; W,
S.
Fine day, vast rain.

The ground in a sad drowned condition.
The low fallows can never be sowed. Some snow. Thunder.

Thursday 24.
Rises, rises; 37; W.
Frost, bright day,
windy.

Vast rock-like clouds round the horizon.

Friday 25.
Rises; 38; W.
Ice, s:shine, cold
wind.

Saturday 26.
Rises; 38; W.
Ice, fine day.

Soft afternoon. Many gnats appear. A martin seen: it was very
brisk, & lively.

Sunday 27.
Sinks; 39; SE.
Great rain, fog, vast
rain.

Stormy wind in the night.

Monday 28.
48; S.
Rain, rain.

Tuesday 29.
Sinks; 51; S, W.
Great rain, rain.

Strong wind.

Wednesday 30.
Sinks, sinks; 50; 49;
W, SE.
Soft day, great rain.
☿ *Hepatica* blows.

Crysanthemums still in bloom.
Crocuss, Jonquils, winter aconite, snow-drops peep out of
Ground.

DECEMBER 1768

Thursday 1.
Rises, sinks; 45;
SW.

Vast floods. Vast rain & stormy wind all night.

Friday 2.
Sinks; 43; S, W.
Vast showers, wind,
fine night.

Thunder & hail.
Incredible quantities of rain have fallen this week.

Saturday 3.
Rises; 41½; W, S.
White frost, sweet
day.

Sunday 4.
Rises; 40½; SW, S.
Frost, fine day.

Monday 5.
44; S, SW.
Misty rain.

Tuesday 6.
Rises; SW.
Fog, small rain.

Wednesday 7.
High; 47; NW, N.
Grey, still weather.

Lavants¶ rise very fast at Farindon & Chawton.

Thursday 8.
Sinks; 42; E.
Fog, fine soft day.
Oenas sive vinago.

Stockdoves, or wood-pigeons appear in great flocks: they are
winter-birds of passage, never breeding in these parts.

Friday 9.
Sinks, rises; 38; E.
Streaky skies,
fine.

Wells run over at the bottom of the village.

Saturday 10.
High, stands still;
38; E.
Sharp wind, bright
day.

Paths get firm, & dry.
Rooks frequent their nest-trees.
People sow wheat again briskly.

Sunday 11.
Rises; 34½, 33; E.
Hard frost, sun
sharp.

The first great frost: the ground carries horse & man.
Wheat comes up well.

Monday 12.
Stands high; 30; E.
Very hard frost.

Moles work.
The ground was very white in the morning.
Ice bears.

Tuesday 13.
Sunk; 30½; E.
Hazy, sleet, thaw,
frost.

Wood-pigeons appear in flocks.
Ground very hard.

Wednesday 14.
Sinks; 32; E.
Snow, snow.

Milk freezes within.
Some snow all day.

Thursday 15.
Sinks; 27; E.
Hard frost, gloomy,
thaw.

Still but very sharp air.
Immundi meminere sues jactare maniplos.¶
The thermometer which was at 27 in the dining room, rose to
44½ in the wine-vault.

Friday 16.
Sinks; 32½; E, SE.
Gentle thaw, snow
gone.
✣ *Peziza*
acetabulum.

Hedge-hog appears.

Saturday 17.
Rises; 41½; NE, S.
Fog & rain.

Warm fog.

Sunday 18.
Rises, rises; 41½;
S, W.
Fair, great rain &
hail.

Fair evening.
Bat appears.

Monday 19.
Rises, sinks; 41½;
S, SW, S.

Wren sings briskly.
Smoke beats down.

Soft day.

Tuesday 20.
Sinks, rises; 47½;
S, SW, W.
Mild day, bright
evening.

Rain & wind all night.
Toad appears crawling.

Wednesday 21.
Risen; 44; SW, S.
Mild day.

Rooks feed earnestly in yᵉ stubbles.
Red-breast sings.

Thursday 22.
Sinks, rises; 44½;
SE, S.
Soft pleasant
day.

French-beans are planted in the hot-house at Hartley. Pines are
still cutting.¶

Friday 23.
Stands; 45½; SE.
Still: grey.

Wheat is sown.

Saturday 24.
Rises much; 45; S.
Still: fine.

Gnats appear much, & some flies. A dry, mild season.

Sunday 25.
Rising; 45; SW.
Soft day.

Wheat comes up well.
Lavants seem to abate.

Monday 26.
Sinks; 47¾; SW.
Fog, small rain,
wind.

Nuthatch, *sitta*, chatters.

Tuesday 27.
Rises much; 47; W,
SW, S.
Sweet day.

Weather more like April than the end of Decemᵣ
Hedge-sparrow sings.

Wednesday 28.
Sinks; 44½; SW.
Misty rain, soft air.

Grass, & corn grow.
Thrush sings.

Thursday 29.
Sinks, rises; 44½;
W.
Gr: rain early, fine
day.

Friday 30.
Sinks; 41½; S, SW.
Rain & wind.

Saturday 31.
Sinks; 45; S, SW.   Soft air. The ground very wet.
Rain, & wind.

A wet season began about the 9th of June, which lasted thro' haymaking, harvest, & seed time, & did infinite mischief to the country.

It appears from my Brother Barker's instrument, with which he measures the quantity of rain, that more water fell in the county of Rutland in the year 1768 from Jan: the 1 to Dec: 31 than in any other Calendar year for 30 years past; viz: 30 in: 9/10. Yet he has known more rain fall within 12 months for from Feb: 1 1763 to Jan: 31 1764 there fell 32 in: 1/8.
   A mean year's rain in Rutland is about 20 in: ³/₄.

JANUARY   — 1769 —

Sunday 1.   SELBORNE
29, 4/10½;¶ 43; S,   Nuthatch chatters. It chatters as it flies.
S.
Wind, showers,
sun.

Monday 2.
Dᵒ; 40; W.   Many flies appeared. Gnats abound.
W: frost, sun, fine
day.

Tuesday 3.
29½, 1/10½; 42;
N.
Frost, cloudy, small
rain.

Wednesday 4.
29½, 3/10; 42; N.
Cold, dry day.

Thursday 5.
29½, 2/10; 42; N.
Cold, small rain.

Friday 6.
29½, 3/10; 42; N.   Hen-chaffinches flock.
Grey day.

Saturday 7.
29½, 3/10; 38; N.
Grey day.

The ground is much dryed: people plow comfortably. Wheat comes up well.

Sunday 8.
†?0; 35; NE, SW, W.
Hard frost, thaw.
🌣 *Ulex Europ:*

Monday 9.
29½, 1/10; 40; SW.
Fog, rain at night.

Tuesday 10.
29 4/10; NW, N
Bright sun, rain in the night.

FYFIELD
The bunting, *emberiza alba*, appears in great flocks about Bradley.
Linnets congregate in vast flocks, & make a kind of singing as they sit on trees.
Rooks resort to their nest-trees.
Hepaticas, winter-aconite, wall-flowers, daiseys, polyanths, black hellebores blow.
Wheat looks well on ye downs.

Wednesday 11.
29 2/10; 46; SW.
Sun & clouds.

Thursday 12.
29 1/10; 46; SW.
Great showers.

Lavants, or landsprings, rise again.
Stocks blow.

Friday 13.
29½; 43; SW.
Grey, showers, star light.

Striped crocus, snow-drop, white lamium, creeping crowsfoot, trumpet-honeysuckle blow.

Saturday 14.
29½ 2/5; 42; SE.
Wh: frost.

Sunday 15.
29½; 43; SE.
Foul stormy day.

Mezereon, groundsel blow.

Monday 16.
29½; 43; SW.
Wh: frost, showers, sun, moonshine.

---

†First figure obliterated.

Tuesday 17.
29½ 3/10; 43; SE.   Wood-lark whistles.
Cold air.   Hogs carry straw.

Wednesday 18.
29½; 43; SE.   The sheep on the downs are very ragged, & their coats much
Cold dry wind.   torn: the shepherds say they tear their fleeces with their own
                           mouths, & horns: & that they are always in that way in mild wet
                           winters, being teized & tickled with a kind of lice.

Tuesday 19.
29 4/10; 44; E
Cold wind, sun.

Friday 20.
29 4/10; 40; NE.
Hard frost, cutting
wind.

Saturday 21.
29 4/10; 38; NE.   Thermom.ͭ down at 24 abroad.
Hard frost, sun.   . . . . . at 20.

Sunday 22.
29½; 22; NE, SE.   Ice in the roads bears horse & man.
Wh: frost, sun,   Vast halo round the moon.
ground very hard,   The landsprings in part of N: Tidworth street not fordable: they
strong frost.   run like a vast river.

Monday 23.
29 4/10; 38 abroad;   Brisk wind.
SE.
Hard frost, sun.

Tuesday 24.
29 4/10, 29 2/10;   Gnats appear.
42 abroad, 44; SE.
Grey morning,
great rain.

Wednesday 25.
29 4/10; 48; SE.   Bunting sings. A snipe appears on the high downs among the
Soft day.   wheat.
                           Royston crow. Skylark sings.

Thursday 26.
29½; 48, 52   Lambs fall.
abroad; SE.
Soft air, rain,
gr: rain.

Friday 27.
29 4/10; 42; SE.
Hot gleams, much
rain.

Saturday 28.
29 4/10; 43½; SE.
Wet day.

SELBORNE
Primrose blows.
Snails appear.

Sunday 29.
29 4/10; 39; W,
NW.
Cloudy, cold wind.

Thrush sings.

Monday 30.
29½ 2/10; 32;
NW.
Severe frost, cutting
wind.

Make the seedling cucumber bed.

Tuesday 31.
29½ 2/10; 28;
NW.
Hard frost, still, &
bright.

Sowed the meadows with ashes.

FEBRUARY 1769

Wednesday 1.
29½ 2/10; 28½;
SE, S.
Dark & still, misty
rain.

Things freeze in the pantry.

Thursday 2.
29 3/10; 40; S, SW,
W.
Driving rain, sun.

Hedge-sparrow sings.
Very sudden thaw.

Friday 3.
29 3/10; 40, 42; W.
Rain, sun.

The great titmouse, *Fringillago*, begins to sing.

Saturday 4.
29 1/10; 41; SW.
Small rain, sun.

Soft air.

Sunday 4.[5]¶
29 1/10; 41; NW,

Hedge-sparrows sing vehemently.

NW.
Fog, rain, sun,
grey.

Monday 5.[6]
29 3/10; 39½; N,   Paths get dry.
NW, W, S.
Fine day.
❦ *Corylus avellana.*

Tuesday 6.[7]
29 1/10; 38; W.   Great rain in the night with thunder & lightening. Cucumber-
Strong wind, sun.   bed heats at last: sowed some Cuc.ʳ seeds.

Wednesday
7.[8]
28½, 4/10; 37; W.   *Helleborus viridis*, planted in my orchard from the stony-lane,
Frost, cutting wind.   begins to spring. It rises from the earth with it's flower-buds
                         formed: & differs from *Helleborus foetidus* that it dies down to the
Thursday 8.[9]   ground in the autumn, while that maintains a large handsome
29 4/10; 36; N.   plant all the winter.
Frost, sun, dark.

Friday 9.[10]
29½; 35½; N.
Cold, dry, dark.

Saturday
10.[11]
29 4/10; 35; N,   Snow all day; but it melts as it falls.
NW.
Snow.

Sunday 12.
29½; 32; N, NE.   Icicles.
Snow, fog, sleet.   Snow on the hills.

Monday 13.
29½ 2/10; 34; NE,
NW.
Frost, dry.

Tuesday 14.
29½ 1/10; 36; SE.
Fine, & still.

Wednesday 15.   *Sheep with lambs*
29½ 4/10; 36; SE.   Chaffinch sings.   *Galley Hill*
Frost, wh: dew.   Yellow-hammer sings.   *February .*

[272]

Thursday 16.
29½ 2/10; 39; SE;
SW.
Rain, fog.

Rooks resort to their nest trees:
Daws to churches.

Friday 17.
29½ 4/10; 41½;
NW, N.
Dark, shower.

Pease are sown in the fields.
Landsprings abate.

Saturday 18.
29½ 4/10; 39½;
NW, W.
Spring weather.

The missel-bird, *turdus viscivorus major* (called by the country
people the storm-cock) sings. Some flies appear in the windows.
Gnats abound.

Sunday 19.
29½ 4/10; 43½;
W, NW.
Dark, sun.

Soft air.

Monday 20.
30; 43; N, NE.
Sweet day.
⚘ *Tussilago farfara*.

Bees gather on the Crocuss.

Tuesday 21.
29½ 4/10; 47; W,
SW.
Dark, small
showers, sun.

Wednesday 22.
29 4/10; 46; W.
Rain, sun, wind.

Thursday 23.
29 4/10, 29 1/10;
38; W.
Frost, wind,
rain.

The blackbird, *merula vulg*: sings.

Friday 24.
29 3/10; 35; NW.
Hard frost.

Frost all day in the shade.

Saturday 25.
29 2/10½; 35½; S,
W.
Snow, rain, sun.

Sunday 26.
29 1/10; 41½; W.
Showers, sun,
rainbow.
Pulex irritans.

Vast rain in the night.
Vast *aurora borealis.*¶

Monday 27.
29½; 41; S, SW.
Rain.

Ring dove, *palumbus torquatus*, cooes.
Bat appears.

Tuesday 28.
29 4/10; 47; SW.
Stormy & rain.

Raven sits.

MARCH 1769

Wednesday 1.
29½ 3/10; 41; SW,
SW.
Sun, small shower.
✿ *Veronica
hederifolia.*

Sheep rot in a most terrible manner in the low grounds.

Thursday 2.
29½ 1/10; 44½;
SW.
Wind, vast shower,
sun, showers, snow,
hail.

Wheat on the clays looks sadly poor & thin.
Stormy wind by fits.

Friday 3.
30, ½/¹/₁₀; 41½;
W, SW.
Strong wind,
clouds.
✿ *Thlaspi bursa
pastoris.*

Blue titmouse or nun, *parus caeruleus*, sings.
Young house-pigeons fledge.

Saturday 4.
29½, 4/10; 45½;
W, SW.
Spring day.
✿ *Ficaria verna.*
Papilio rhamni,
Podura fimetaria,
Aranea scenica
saliens, Araneus niger
Raji.

Young chickens.
Crocuss make a gallant shew.

Sunday 5.
29½, 3/10; 47;
NW.
Falling mist, sweet
day.
❦ *Helleborus
viridus.
Scolopendra
forficata.*

Paths begin to dry.
Men show wheat round Odiham.
Goose lays.
Duck lays.

Monday 6.
29½, 3/10; 42;
NW.
Wh: frost, dry, still
day.
Musca stercoraria.

The cock swan at two year's old "Between his white wings
mantling proudly rows."¶

Tuesday 7.
29½, 2/10; 40; W,
E.
Wh: frost, fog, dry
& cold.

Green woodpecker begins to laugh.
Last night I heard that short quick note of birds flying in the
dark: if this should be the voice of the *Oedicnemus*, as is supposed,
then that bird, which is not seen in the dead of winter, is
returned.

Wednesday 8.
29½, 4/10; 40;
NE.
Wh: frost, sharp
air.
❦ *Cucumis sativus:*
male bloom.

Blood worms appear in the water: they are gnats in one state.

Thursday 9.
29½, 4/10; 36½;
NE, E.
Wh: frost, fine day.

Cock-turkey struts, & makes love.
Beans are planted & pease sown in the fields.

Friday 10.
29½; 37½; E.
Dark & cold.

Oats are sown.
Crows build: rooks build.
Ews & lambs are turned in to the wheat to eat it down. ¶

Saturday 11.
29; 35; E, W, S.
Melting snow, sun.

Made the bearing cucumber-bed for four lights with seven loads
of dung. The bed was much wetted in making by the snow.

Sunday 12.
28½, 4/10; 38½;
W, S.
Sun, showers.

Great rain in the night.
Golden-crowned wren, *regulus cristatus*, sings. His voice is as
minute as his body.

Monday 13.
28½, 2/10; 42;
SW, S.
Frequent showers.
✣ *Sambucus nigra*.

Vast rain, with wind.

Tuesday 14.
28½, 2/10; 44;
SW.
Wind & showers.

Water-wagtail chirps.

Wednesday 15.
29½, 3/10; 43.
Sun, wind & black
clouds.
✣ *Veronica agrestis*.

Made cucumber-bed over again, & added many barrows of fresh
dung: it was so drenched with snow & rain that it would not heat.

Thursday 16.
29½, 3/10; 42;
NW.
Sun, wind, clouds,
hail.
✣ *Cucumis sativus*:
fem: bloom.
Rana temporaria.

Great hail storm.

Friday 17.
30, 2/10; 40; W.
Sun, wind, clouds.
✣ *Viola odorata*.

Black-bird sits.
Raven sits.

Saturday 18.
30 1/10, 30 2/10;
43; NW.
Sun, cold wind.

Planted-out the cucum.ʳˢ in the two-light frames: the plants are
stout, but pretty long. Several fruit have bloom in the first bed.
Paths dry very fast.

Sunday 19.
30 2/10, 30; 42;
NW, W, SW.
Sun, shower.
✣ *Fragaria sterilis*,
Ulmus campestris.
Rana bufo.

Turkey lays.

Monday 20.
29½, 4/10; 45; W,
NW.
Cloudy, small rain.
✣ *Salices*.

Young cucumber swells. The great bed heats well.
Sowed some succade-melons.

Tuesday 21.
30 1/10; 47; NE.
Clouds, sun.

Goose sits, while the gander with vast assiduity keeps guard, & takes the fiercest sow by the ear & leads her away crying.

Wednesday 22.
30 1/10; 40½; E,
SE, S.
Hard frost, sweet
day.
❀ *Prunus armeniaca.*

Oats are sowing in general.
Greenfinch sings.

Thursday 23.
30 2/10; 42; NE.
Fine day.
❀ *Amygdalus persica.*
Regulus non cristatus
*minimus.**
Coluber Berus.

*This bird appears the first of any of the summer-birds of passage, the *jynx*, or wryneck sometimes excepted. It has only two harsh shrill notes.

Friday 24.
30 3/10; 42; NE.
Sun, grey day.
❀ *Narcissus pseudo-*
narcissus.

Fine season for the husbandman.

Saturday 25.
30 3/10; 45; N.
Dark day.
❀ *Daphne laureola.*
Bombinatrices.

Frogs croak: spawn abounds.

Sunday 26.
30, 1/10; 44½; N.
Showers, fine &
cold.
❀ *Taxus baccata.*
Lacertae.

Apricot is beautifully studded with bloom.

Monday 27.
30, 1/10; 42; NE,
E.
Fine day, dry air.
❀ *Chrysosplenium*
oppositifolium.

Tuesday 28.
30; 41½; E.
Dry air.
Papilio urticae.

OXFORDSHIRE
Cut the first cucumber, a large, fair fruit.
Oedicnemus appears & whistles.

Wednesday 29.
NE.
Sharp dry day.

Ground much dryed: roads very dusty.

Thursday 30.
NE.
Fierce harsh wind.
🌢 *Caltha palustris.*

Friday 31.
NE.
Small flights of
snow.

WITNEY

APRIL 1769

Saturday 1.
NE.
Heavy snow.

Snow went off without frost.

Sunday 2.
NE.
Cold air.

Snow gone.

Monday 3.
Clouds, flakes of
snow.

Tuesday 4.
NE.
Dry air.
🌢 *Lamium album.*

OXFORD

Wednesday 5.
E.
Sun, dry air.
🌢 *Anemone pulsatilla*
budds.*
Coluber natrix.

*This plant, the pasque flower, which is just emerging, &
budding for bloom, abounds on the sheep-down just above
Streatley in Berks.

Thursday 6.
NE.
*Bombylius medius.***

**Musca bombyliiformis dense pilosa nigra, abdomine obtuso ad
latera rufo. Longissimum spiculum quoddam seu linguam exore
protendit.¶*
Raii *Hist: Insect*: P: 273.
Snow on the Chilterns of Bucks.

Friday 7.
Dark sky.

Young geese.

❀ *Mercurialis*
perennis.

Redwings remain still.
Green-plover appears.

Saturday 8.
29; 42½; NE.
Cold air, rain.
❀ *Amenone*
nemorosa.

SELBORNE
Ground very dry & dusty.

Sunday 9.
29 2/10, 28½ 4/10;
41; W, S, E.
Warm, sunny, rain.
Atricapilla.

The black-cap is usually the second bird of passage that appears.
Some snow under the hedges.

Monday 10.
29; 47; S, SW, W.
Showers, warm air,
rain.
Formicae.

Black-bird whistles.
Turkey sits.

Tuesday 11.
28 4/10; 51½; S.
Strong wind, &
rain.
Hirundo domestica!

Vast rain, & stormy wind.

Wednesday 12.
29 4/10; 48½; W,
SW.
Brisk wind, fine
day.
❀ *Primula veris.*
Musca tenax;
Hirundo riparia.

Tortoise comes out of the ground.

Thursday 13.
29 3/10; 52; S, E.
Cloudy, showers.
❀ *Adoxa*
moschatellina.
Regulus non-cristatus
*medius,**
Merula torquata.

*This second-sized willow-wren has a plaintive but pleasing note,
widely different from that of the first, which is harsh & sharp.
The ring-ouzels appear again on Noar hill in their return to the
northward: they make but a few days stay in their spring visit; but
rest with us near a fortnight as they go to the Southward at
Michaelmass.¶

Friday 14.
29 1/10; 52; SE.
Wind & rain, sun,
wind.

An hen which I opened had very small rudiments of eggs within
her; which shew that they are late breeders. In her crop was
nothing very distinguishable; but some what that seemed like
blades of vegitables nearly digested. In the autumn (thrush like)

❀ *Ribes grossularia.*
Spipola prima, yᵉ
whitethroat.

they feed on haws, yew berries, &c. A bird that I dressed was well-tasted, & juicy, & in high condition for plumpness. These birds from the observations of three springs, & two autumns are, most punctual in their visits, & exhibit a new migration unnoticed by any of the writers. They were supposed never to be seen in any of the southern counties. Do they migrate from the N: of England, or from the N: of Europe thro' this island?

Saturday 15.
29½ 1/10; 47; W.
Stormy wind, rain,
sun.
❀ *Glechoma
hederacea.*
Luscinia!

Cut a brace of fine cucumbers. Made the melon-bed for one 3 light frame with 8 loads of dung.

Sunday 16.
29½ 1/10; 47½; E,
SE.
Heavy showers,
sun.
Hirundo agrestis.

The titlark, *alauda pratorum*, begins to sing. It is a delicate songster: flying from tree to tree & spreading-out it's wings it chants in its descent. It also sings sitting on a bough. Vast rain in the night.

Monday 17.
29½ 1/10; 48; E,
N, NW, E.
Sun, hot, heavy
shower.
*Cuculus,
Ruticilla.*

Tuesday 18.
29½ 3/10; 47½;
W.
Soft air.
❀ *Viola canina,
Prunus spinosa.
Alauda locustae
voce.*

Oedicnemus sings late at night.
Cut two brace of cucumbers.

Wednesday 19.
29½ 3/10; 54; S,
W.
Wh: frost, sweet
day.
❀ *Oxalis acetosella.
Regulus non cristatus
voce stridula
locustae.*

*This is the largest of the three willow-wrens: it haunts the tops of tall trees making a shivering noise, & shaking it's wings. Its colours are more vivid than those of the other two species.

Thursday 20.
29½ 1/10; 51½;
W.
Wh: frost, sweet
day.
☙ *Cardamine*
pratensis.

Wheat thrives.
Black-cap has a most sweet, & mellow note.
The redstarts frequent orchards & gardens: the whitethroats are
scattered all over the fields far from neighbourhoods. Their notes
are mean & much a like; short & without any variety. The
whitethroat is a most common bird.

Friday 21.
30; 54; E, S.
Summer weather.
☙ *Orchis mascula*.
Hirundo apus!!!

Saturday 22.
29½ 2/10; 53; SE,
W.
Sweet day.
☙ *Stellaria holostea*.

Young thrushes.
The large species of bats appears.¶
Nightingales abound.

Sunday 23.
29½ 3/10; 54; W,
N, N.
Clouds, sweet day.
☙ *Erysimum*
alliaria.

Monday 24.
29½ 4/10; 54; W,
S. Wh: frost,
sweet day.

Tuesday 25.
E, E.
Dry wind, sun.
☙ *Hyacinthus non*
scriptus.

LONDON

Wednesday 26.
NE, NE.
Sun & dry air.
☙ *Pyrus communis*.

Herrings lately abound, & are the usual forerunners of mackrels.

Thursday 27.
E.
Sun, dry.
☙ *Cochlearia*
officin:, *Symphytum*
officin:

Dutch plaise abound.
Turbots.

Friday 28.
30; NE.
Summer, hot & dry.
♁ *Galeopsis Galeobdolon.*

Some mackrels.

Saturday 29.
30; E.
Summer.
♁ *Valeriana locusta.*

Young brown owl in a cage.

Sunday 30.
E.
Dry, sun.
Jynx.¶

Fresh ling.
Hallibut.

MAY 1769

Monday 1.
E.
Dry, sun, dusty.

Received from Selborne 12 brace of fair cucumbers.

Tuesday 2.
E.
Sun, wind, dust.

Cabbages begin to turn in.
Prawns plenty.

Wednesday 3.
NE.
Sun, dust.

Mackrels cryed in the streets.
Asparagus fallen to 4s p^r hundred.
Apricots, small green.

Thursday 4.
W, NW.
Sun, hot air.
♁ *Pyrus malus.*

Crayfish in high season.
Smelts in season.

Friday 5.
NW.
Sun, summer like.

Saturday 6.
NE.
Cloudy.
Hirundo apus.

Sunday 7.
N.
Cold air.
♁ *Menyanthes*

trifolia.
Caprimulgus!

Monday 8.
N.
Shower, cloudy.
❦ *Crataegus*
oxyacantha.
Gryllotalpa.

Green gooseberries.
Lapwing's eggs at the poulterers.

Tuesday 9.
NW.
Clouds, sun.

Green geese are driven along the streets in great droves.

Wednesday 10.
W.
Clouds.

Thursday 11.
NW.
Rain all day.

Friday 12.
N.
Cloudy.
❦ *Hottonia palustris.*

Young rabbits.

Saturday 13.
NE.
Sm: rain, strong
wind.
❦ *Cucumis melo.*
*Stoparola.**

SELBORNE
*This little bird seems to be the last summer bird of passage that appears.

A *salicaria*¶ that seems to be a nondescript was sent up to town to me from Selborne: it has some what the air of a Grasshopper-lark, but is a size less, & had a tawney rump. The person that shot it (if he does not mistake) says it sung very like a reed-sparrow, & continued singing in the night. It's tail-feathers were sharp-pointed like the Gr:h:lark: & I am inclined to think it is one of that species hinted at by M̲r̲ Derham: see Ray's letters p: 108.
   This proved on farther examination to be the *passer arundinaceus minor* of Ray, which he (tho' perhaps improperly) classes among his *picis affines.* Linn: more properly (I think) ranges it among his *Motacillae.* I much suspect that the singing attributed to the *passer torquatus* belongs all to this bird, & that the former does not sing at all. I should think that the *passer arund:* is a summer bird of passage.

Sunday 13[14]¶
29½ 1/10; NE.
Fierce wind.

Glass sinks.

Monday 14.[15]
29½ 2/10; N.   One shower only for a full month.
Sharp wind.

Tuesday
15.[16]
29½ 2/10; N.   The ground dryed-up in a very extraordinary manner.
Sun, cool air.   Much barley lying in the dust without vegetating.
Gryllus campestris.

Wednesday
16.[17]
29½ 1/10; 51; NE.   Apple-trees well blown.
White frost, rain.   Grass very short.

Thursday
17.[18]
29½ 1/10; 52; E.
Small rain.

Friday 18.[19]
29½ 2/10; 52; NE.   The ground well-moistened.
Steady rain.   Apple-trees continue in high bloom, & are well blown.
☙ *Bromelia ananas.*

Saturday
19.[20]
29½ 1/10; 49½; E,
SE.
Soaking rain.

Sunday 21.
29½ 1½/10; 54;   *This fly smells strongly of musk. White owls have young.
SE.
Soft growing
weather.
*Musca meridiana,**
Libellula.

Monday 22.
29½ 1/10; 58½;   Flesh-flies buz about the rooms.
SE.   Melon-fruit begins to blow.
Air, hot sun.

Tuesday 23.
29½ 1/10; 67; S,   Thunder at a distance.
SW; W.   Mole-cricket churs.
Sultry.   Not one chaffer appears yet.
Hippobosca equina.

Wednesday 24.
29½ 2/10; 67; W.
Hot air.

Thunder & rain in the night.
Fat sheep are shorn.
Young missle thrushes.

Thursday 25.
29½ 3/10; 61½;
SW.
Brisk wind.

Friday 26.
29½ 3/10; 58; SW.
Soft brisk air.

Fern-owl chatters in yᵉ hanger.
Grass grows.

Saturday 27.
29½; 59; S.
Shower, vast rain.

Hail at Newton. Rain in the night.
Winter-apples still in bloom.

If the bough of a vine is cut late in the spring just before the shoots push out, it will bleed miserably; but after the leaf is out any part may be taken off without the least inconvenience. So oaks may be barked while the leaf is budding; but as soon as they are expanded the bark will no longer part from the wood: because the sap, that lubricates the bark & makes it part, is evaporated off thro' the leaves.

Sunday 28.
29 3/10; 56; SW.
Brisk air, clouds.

No chaffers appear at all.

Monday 29.
29 4/10; 56; W, S,
W.
Showers, hail, vast
clouds.

Began to tack the vines; much shew for bloom.
Melons begin to set.
Thunder at a distance.

Tuesday 30.
29 4/10; 55; SE, E.
Sun, clouds, rain.
Apis longicornis.

Wednesday 31.
29 3/10; 57; W.
Showers.

JUNE 1769

Thursday 1.
29 4/10; 56½; S.
Rain, brisk wind.

Friday 2.
29½ 3/10; 55; W.
Fine day.
Scarabaeus auratus.

Showers about.

Saturday 3.
29½ 3/10; 58; S,
W.
Great showers,
fine.

Saw the planet Venus enter the disk of the sun. Just as the sun was setting the spot was very visible to the naked eye.
Nightingale sings; wood-owl hoots; fern-owl chatters.

Sunday 4.
29½ 3/10; 57½;
W, S, SE.
Sun, dark
clouds.

Bees swarm.
Turtle-dove cooes.

Monday 5.
29½ 2/10; 57; E.
Dark sky, rain.

Saint-foin blows.

Tuesday 6.
29½ 4/10; 55; N.
Rain & wind.

Wednesday 7.
30; 54; N, SE.
Sweet day.

Thursday 8.
29½ 4/10; 56; S,
W.
Soft air, sprinkling.
✿ *Geranium
pratense, Arenaria
trinervia.*

Friday 9.
29½ 3/10; 59; SW.
Cool, & windy.

Saturday 10.
29½ 1/10; 59; SW.
Winds, showers.

Young hedge-hogs.
Wood strawberries.

Sunday 11.
29½ 2/10; 59; W.
Windy, hard
showers.

Great species of bat appears; it flies very high. The fern-owl begins chattering just at three quarters after 8 o' the clock at night.

Monday 12.
29½ 4/10; 54; W.
Windy, fine
evening.

Tuesday 13.
29½ 4/10; 56; W.
Soft day, clouds.

Wednesday 14.
29½ 2/10; 56; W.   Wheat in ear.
Soft air, shower,
showers.

Thursday 15.
29½; 57; E, N.   The bank-martin brings out its young: they were so helpless that
Showers, showers.   we took one as it sate on a rail. Young swallows appear.

Friday 16.
29½ 1/10; 57; W,   The less reed-sparrow, *passer arundinaceus minor*, Raii, sings
S, W.   sweetly, imitating the notes of several birds: it haunts near
White frost, clouds,   waters, & sings all night long.
rain.   Cold weather: nothing grows well.
                       S! foin wants to be cut.
Saturday 17.   A distinct lunar rain-bow.
29 3/10; 58. W.
Rain, hail, vast rain.

Sunday 18.
29½; 57; W, NW,   Vast rain. Young swallows.
N.
Cold & wet.

Monday 19.
30; 57; NW.   The air is so chilly that kidney-beans, & tender annuals do not
Sun, cold air,   thrive at all.
shower.

Tuesday 20.
29½ 4/10; 56;   Melons swell, the bed being lined.
NW, SW, W.   Cuckow sings.
Sun, cold air,
clouds.

Wednesday 21.
29½; 57½; SW,   Quite a winter's day.
W.
Vast rain, cold
wind.

Thursday 22.
29½ 1/10; 56½;
W, S.
Sun, grey, rain.
❦ *Carduus*
nutans.

Swallows begin to feed their young flying.

Friday 23.
29½ 2/10; 60; S,
SE.
Grey, sprinkling.
❦ *Carduus crispus*.

Thistles begin to blow.
Young wheatears, birds so called.

Saturday 24.
29½; 60; SW.
Rain, sun.

NEWTON

Sunday 25.
29½; NW.
Rain, fine.

Cuckow sings.

Monday 26.
30.
Dark clouds.

Kidney beans, & young Cucumbers hardly survive.
No cucumbers for some weeks.

Tuesday 27.
29½ 4/10; W, SW.
Fine, rain &
wind.
❦ *Vitis vinifera*.

Began to cut my S! foin: it is very large, & almost out of bloom.
Vines begin to blow.
Stormy, wintry, wet night.

Wednesday 28.
29½ 3/10; N.
Sun, cloudy.
❦ *Carduus*
lanceolatus.

Cold air.

Thursday 29.
Rises; N.
Sun, small
showers,
cold air.
❦ *Carduus*
acanthoides.

Hedge sparrow sings.
Cold evening.

Friday 30.
30; N.
Shady.

JULY 1769

Saturday 1.
30; W, SW.
Summer day.

Fine haymaking: hay carting.

Young hedge hogs are frequently found, four or five in a litter. At five or six days old their spines (which are then white) grow stiff enough to wound any body's hands. They, I see, are born blind, like puppies, have small external ears; & can in part draw their skins down over their faces: but are not able to contract themselves into a ball, as they do for defence when well-grown.

Sunday 2.
30; W, NE.
Beautiful hot
weather.

Hops are very lousy.
Wheat blows well.
Ricked my S! foin in curious order: there were five small loads with out a drop of rain.

Monday 3.
30; 67; SE, S.
Sweet day, grey
skie.
❦ *Orchis conopsea.*

Tuesday 4.
30 1/10; 66; SE.
Sweet sunny day.

Vast dew.
Hay makes very fast.

Wednesday 5.
30 1/10; 70; NE.
Fine, gale, glorious
sun.
❦ *Carduus acaulos.*

Great dew.
Grasshopper-lark chirps.

Thursday 6.
30; 73; NE, E.
Brisk air, clouds,
fine even:.

Finished my hay-rick consisting of about seven tons without one drop of rain.

Friday 7.
29½ 4/10; 66; SE,
SW.
Strong gale, still
even:.

Distant thunder.
Distant lightning.

Saturday 8.
Sinks, sinks; SW,
W.
Strong gale, clouds.

Distant showers.

Sunday 9.
30, rises; 64; NE,
N.
Dark morn, sweet
even.

Monday 10.   WHITCHURCH
N.
Fine, brisk
air.

Tuesday 11.   OXFORD
☙ *Butomus*   The stint, *sinclus* Aldro: appears about the banks of the Thames.
umbellatus.   At Oxford it is called the summer snipe.

Wednesday 12.
Sprinkling showers.
☙ *Nymphaea lutea*
alba.

Thursday 13.
Sultry.   Vast flocks of young wagtails on the banks of the charwel.¶

Friday 14.   WHITCHURCH
Fine.

Saturday 15.   NEWTON
Sprinkling.

Sunday 16.
Sinks, sinks; 68; S.   Great showers in sight to the E & NE.
Sultry, thunder,   The ground is very much burnt up, no rain having fallen, very
small shower.   small showers excepted, since June 27.

Monday 17.
66; S.
Small shower.

Tuesday 18.
W.   Moor buzzard, *milvus aeruginosus,*¶ has young.
Dark clouds, fine.   It builds in low shrubs on wild heaths.
                Five young.

Wednesday 19.
Rises; NW.   Young pheasants fly.
Shower.   Partridges fly.

Thursday 20.
Fine day.

Friday 21.
Shower.

Saturday 22.
Showers about.

Sunday 23.
NW.
Dark skie, fine.

Monday 24.
30; N.
Vast fog, fine.

Cucumbers bear well again: they never bore one fruit for more than a month.

Tuesday 25.
30; N.
Sweet day.

The dry weather has lasted a month, some small showers excepted. The ground is very much scorched.

Wednesday 26.
30, ½ 1/10; N.
Fine day.

Thursday 27.
29½ 2/10; 62; SW,
NW.
Strong wind,
driving rain.

SELBORNE
Some grapes are got pretty large.
Finished cutting the tall hedges.

Friday 28.
29½ 1/10; 63; W.
Strong winds,
showers.

The showers do not at all moisten the ground, which remains as hard as iron.

Saturday 29.
29½, 29½ 1/10;
62; W.
Strong wind.

No savoys, endives &c: can be planted-out.

Sunday 30.
29½ 2/10; 63;
NW, W.
Fine, cloudy.

Shower in the night.

Monday 31.
29½ 2/10, 4/10;
63; W, N, NE.
Soft air, gentle
showers.
❧ *Lysimachia vulg:*,

Wasps begin to abound.

Hypericum elodes.
Vespa vulgaris.

AUGUST 1769

Tuesday 1.
30; 65; E.　　　　　　　The dry weather, some very inconsiderable showers excepted, has
Soft brown day.　　　　lasted five weeks.
⚘ *Scutellaria minor.*

Wednesday 2.
29½ 4/10½; 65,　　　　Male-ants flie away, & leave yᵉ nests.
68; W.
Bright, sun.
Tabanus bovinus.

Thursday 3.
29½ 4/10; 69; W.　　　Nuthatch chirps much.
Sultry.　　　　　　　　Swifts seem to be gone.
Papilio cinxia.

Friday 4.
29½ 3/10; 71, 75;
S, S.
Sultry air.
Musca mystacea.

Saturday 5.
29½ 1/10; 70,　　　　Stone-curlew cries.
77½; E, SW.　　　　　Apricots ripe.
Sultry day.
⚘ *Mentha longifolia.*
Vespa, Crabro.

Sunday 6.
29½; 71; S, W.　　　　Refreshing shower.
Rain, fine.　　　　　　Young goldfinches in their nests.

Monday 7.
29½ 3/10; 64; SW.　　Showers to the S. Wheat, rye, oats, barley cutting round the
Fine day.　　　　　　forest.

Tuesday 8.
29½ 3/10; 64; S.　　　Cucumbers bear well again.
Fine day.　　　　　　Grapes swell apace, & are large.

Wednesday 9.
29½ 2/10, 3/10;　　　Wheat begins to be cut at Selborne.

64; S, W, S. Small
rain, fine.

Swifts apear to be gone. Swallows congregate in trees with their
young & whistle much. Young martins begin to congregate on y^e
wallnut-trees.

Thursday 10.
29½ 2/10; 65; S,
W.
Fine, shower, fine.

Nuthatch chirps much. One swift appears. *Caprimulgus* chatters.

Mr Sheffield of Worcester Coll: went into Wolmer forest &
procured me a green sand-piper, *Tringa* Aldrov: *Tringa ochropus*
Lin: They were in pairs & had been seen about by many people on
the streams, & banks of the ponds.

Friday 11.
29½ 3/10; 65; W.
Hard shower, sun,
hard showers.

Stormy wet night.

Saturday 12.
29½ 2/10; 63; W,
SW.
Wind, cloudy, sun.

Yellow hammer sings.
Planted-out endives, & savoys.

Sunday 13.
29½ 1/10; 65; SW.
Clouds, shower,
clouds.
Ѱ *Agaricus
campestris*.

Monday 14.
29½ 2/10; 64; W.
Shower, fine,
shower.
Ѱ *Boletus albus*.
Papilio c: album!

Small showers: but the ground continues very harsh & dry: & no
transplanted thing in the garden grows at all.

Tuesday 15.
29½ 2/10; 63.
Pap: Semele.

Wednesday 16.
29½ 3/10; 62; W,
E, N.
Showers.

Thunder about.

Thursday 17.
29½ 4/10; 62; N.
Shower, fine.

Friday 18.
30; 61; W.
Sunny, soft air,
clouds.

Martins congregate on the roofs of houses.

Saturday 19.
29½ 2/10; 62; S,
W.
Very wet day.

No such wet day since tuesday June 27.

Sunday 20.
29½ 1/10; 58; W.
Fine, clouds.

Showers about.
Bulls begin to make their shrill autumnal note.

Monday 21.
29 4/10; 57; W.
Fine, shower, fine.

Yellow-hammer sings.
Vast showers about. People here housed all day. Vine leaves begin to turn purple.

Tuesday 22.
29 4/10; 59; W, N,
NW.
Fine, fine.

Vast showers about. Much wheat housed.
Regulus non crist: minor chirps. Nuthatch chirps. *Parus ater* chirps.

Wednesday 23.
29 4/10; 59; W, S,
E.
Hot, cloudy, heavy
rain.

Vast showers about all day. Much wheat housed in these last three days.

Thursday 24.
29½, 29½; 56½;
W, S.
Sun, clouds, fine.

Showers about.

Friday 25.
29½ 3/10; 59; W,
S.
Fine, showers.

Great showers about.
Male & female ants migrate at a great rate filling the ground & air.

Saturday 26.
29½ 2/10; 59; W,
SW.
Wet day.

Sunday 27.
29½ 1/10; 61½;
W, S.
Rain, sun.

Rain all night.

Monday 28.
29½ 1/10½; 60;
W.
Fine, sprinkling,
fine.

Much wheat abroad in this parish. Plums & pears crack with the rain.

Tuesday 29.
29½ 1/10; 59; SW.
Fine day.
Pap: Phlaeas.

Wheat housed.
Swallows sing.

Wednesday 30.
29 4/10; 61½; S, S.
Stormy wind, vast
showers.
Pap: paphia.

Thursday 31.
29½ 2/10; 62; W,
W.
Brisk wind, fine
day.
Phalaena pacta.

Some grapes begin to turn color.

SEPTEMBER 1769

Friday 1.
29½ 3/10; 59½;
W, N.
Heavy clouds, soft
air.
Phalaena russula.

1 September.
Swallows gathering.

Saturday 2.
30, 30¾d; 60, 65;
SE, W, S.
Sweet day.

Wheat harvest finished.

A comet, having a tail about six degrees in length, appears nightly in the constellation of Aries, between the 24, 29, & 51 stars of that constellation in the English catalogue.¶

Sunday 3.
30 ¾d; 61½, 65;
W, S.
Bright, sultry.
Papilio Atalanta!

Winged ants migrate from their nests.
Tame buzzard eats the winged ants.
Swallows congregate in vast flocks.

Monday 4.
29½ 3/10; 61, 66;
E.

Hop-picking begins. A very slender crop.

Bright, dark, soft
air.
Pap: Hyale!

Tuesday 5.
29½ 2/10; 63; NE,
SE.
Dark sky, sultry.
Chrysis ignita.

Beeches turn yellow at the top.
Glow-worm still appears.

Wednesday 6.
29½ 1/10; 64½;
W, S.
Dark, sweet day,
rain.

White sweet-water grapes begin to get clear; & the wasps to eat them.

Thursday 7.
29 3/10; 64½; NE,
N.
Dark, great rain.

Friday 8.
29 3/10, 29 4/10;
63; W, SW.
Dark & wet, sun,
wind.

Saturday 9.
29 4/10; 62; S, W,
E.
Vast showers, fine.

Sunday 10.
29 3/10; 59½; SW.
Soft, showers about.
Ortygometra.

Land rail.¶

Monday 11.
29 1/10; 60; NW.
Vast rain, stormy.

Tuesday 12.
W.
Shower.

Jynx torquilla.
Wheatears, *Oenanthe*, are still caught on yᵉ Sussex downs.

Wednesday 13.
SW.
Fair day, rain.
✿ *Colchicum*

RINGMER
Solidago virgaurea, centaurea calcitrapa on the road.

autumnale.

Thursday 14.
Wind & rain.   *Papilio Machaon*¶ is found here in May.

Friday 15.
S.   *Fringillago* sings. Lightening, hail.
Showers, wind, sun.

Saturday 16.
NW.   Grapes begin to ripen.
Fine day.

Sunday 17.
SW.   *Caprimulgus* still appears.
Showers.   *Gryllus gryllotalpa* works.
                                Rooks frequent their nest-trees, & repair their nests.

Monday 18.
SW.   Bustards¶ on the downs.
Fine day.

Tuesday 19.
SW.   *Caprimulgus.*
Fine day.

Wednesday 20.
NW.
Sweet day.

Thursday 21.
W.
Fog, sweet day.

Friday 22.
SW.   Storm in the night.
Fog, bright.   *Stoparola* appears.

Saturday 23.
SW, W.
Strong wind,
showers.

Sunday 24.
SW.   *Regulus non cristatus minor.*
Dark, showers.   Vast rain in the night.
                                Leaves fall. Young goldfinch.

Monday 25.
W.   Swallows, & martins.

Windy, dry.   Rooks repair their nests.

Tuesday 26.
W.   The sheep about Lewes are all without Horns, & have black
Sweet day.   faces, & legs.
                               Sheep have horns & white faces again west of Bramber.¶

Wednesday 27.
SW.
Rain all day.

Thursday 28.
SW.
Rain all day.

Friday 29.
W.   Swallows & martins all the way on the downs.
Fine day.

Saturday 30.   SELBORNE
30, 2/10; 58; NW.   Wood-lark sings sweetly.
Sweet day.
Merula torquata.   The ring-ouzels, *merulae torquatae*, are most punctual in their
                               migration, & appear again in a considerable flock.

OCTOBER 1769

Sunday 1.
30, 1/10; 52; NE.
Fine.

Monday 2.
30; 54; N.
Fine day, chill air.

Tuesday 3.
30; 50; N.   Some swallows.
Fine, chill air,
shower.

Wednesday 4.
29½, 4/10; 48; N,   Rocky clouds, & distant lightening.
E.
Fine, air chilly.

Thursday 5.
29½, 4/10; 46; E.   Some Hail.
Dark clouds, cold
air, small shower.

Friday 6.
29½, 3/10; 44½;
E.
Cold air.

Swallows, & martins.
Shattering shower.

Saturday 7.
29½, 3/10; 44; N.
Cold air.

Sunday 8.
29½, 3/10; 45;
NW.
Cold air, flying
shower.

Swallows, & martins.

Monday 9.
29½ 3/10; 46;
NW.
Fine, flying
showers, fine.

Skie-lark sings.

Tuesday 10.
30; 44; N.
White frost, fine.

Most sweet day.
Martins appear.

Wednesday 11.
30½ deg; 43; N,
W.
Frost, fine.
Turdus Iliacus.

Grapes begin to be very good.
Ground white & dirt a little crisped.

Thursday 12.
NE.
Sweet day.

Friday 13.
30, 3/10; NE, E.
Fine, sharp wind.
Scolopax.

The dry fit has lasted a fortnight, sprinklings excepted.
Oedicnemus whistles.

Saturday 14.
30, 1/10; 46; E, E.
Sun, sharp wind,
sun.

Shattering rain.
Roads dry, & dusty.

Sunday 15.
30, 29½ 4/10; 44;
E.
Severe wind, clouds.

Hedgesparrow whistles.
Sprinkling rain.
Three martins appear, & settle under the eves of the stable.

Monday 16.
29½ 2/10; 42; E,
SE.
Grey, showers.

Tuesday 17.
29½ 1/10; 47; E,   One martin appears.
SE.
Wet day.

Wednesday 18.
29½ 3/10; 53; E,
SE.
Soft fine day.

Thursday 19.
29½ 4/10; 53, 58;   Fog. Large flock of goldfinches.
E, SE.   The sun is very hot. The air is full of spider's webs.
Soft sweet day.

Friday 20.
29½ 4/10; 56; N,   Linnets, chaffinches, yellow-hammers congregate. Sky-lark sings
E, SE.   sweetly. Glow-worms appear.
Fog all day,
soft air.

Saturday 21.
29½ 2/10; 56; N,   *Merulae torquatae* still about: they abound more, & stay longer
E.   than in former autumns.
Soft, still day.   *Oedicnemus* clamours very loudly. Leaves fall apace. Barometer
                         falls apace.

Sunday 22.
29½ 2/10; 53; NE,
N.
Shower, dark
clouds.

Monday 23.
29½ 4/10; 49; N,   Paths very dry.
NE.
Sharp wind,
sun.

Tuesday 24.
30 1/10, 42 ½;   A vivid *aurora borealis*, which like a broad belt stretched across
NE.   the welkin from East to West. This extraordnary phenomenon
Ice, cutting wind,   was seen the same evening at Gibraltar.
sun.

Wednesday 25.
30 2/10; 40; NE.
Frost, sharp wind.

Thursday 26.
30 1/10; 45; NE.
Sun, sharp wind.

Friday 27.
29½ 4/10; 43; E,
SE.
Ice, warm day.

The weather has been dry just a month this day, one wet day
excepted. The fields are so dry, that farmers decline sowing.
The lapwing, *vannellus*, congregates in great flocks on the downs,
& uplands.

Saturday 28.
29½ 1/10; 45; SW,
S.
Sweet day.

Mrs J. W. sailed.¶

Sunday 29.
29 3/10; 50; SE, S.
Vast fog, wet.
Turdus pilaris.

North: lights every evening.

Monday 30.
29 2/10; 53; SE.
Great rain.

Six martins appeared flying under ye hanger.
Thunder & lightning with vast rain.

Tuesday 31.
29 4/10; 53; S.
Rain, rain.

Oedicnemus whistles.*
Swan's egg-pears¶ in high perfection.

*This was the last time the *Oedicnemus* was heard for this Year.

NOVEMBER 1769

Wednesday 1.
29; 53; W, SW.
Sun, small showers,
soft day.

Linnets congregate in flocks & sing sweetly.
Sky-lark sings.

Thursday 2.
29½ 2/10; 51; SE,
E.
Fog, rain, much
rain.

Golden-crowned wren on the tops of trees.

Friday 3.
29 1/10; 52; SE.

Five or six swallows appear.

Much rain.

Saturday 4.
29 1/10; 54½; S,
SW.
Great rain, stormy.

Vast storm that broke some boughs, & tore thatch.

Sunday 5.
29 4/10; 56; SW.
Strong wind, dry
day.

Grass grows.
Ricks much torn at Faringdon.

Monday 6.
29½; 53½; SW.
Small showers, soft
air.

Tuesday 7.
29 4/10; 53; SW.
Fine day.

Skylark sings.
Soft air.

Wednesday 8.
29 3/10; 53; SW.
Vast showers, fine.

Gold-finch, & Red-breast sing.

Thursday 9.
29½ 1/10; 49; SW,
E.
Rain, fog, rain.

Friday 10.
29½ 3/10; 47; NE.
Rain, fine day.
*Oenas, sive vinago.**

*A few stock-doves, or wood-pigeons, appear.
Gold-finch sings.

Saturday 11.
29½ 4/10; 42; E.
Clear, cold air.

Sunday 12.
29½; 39; NE.
Sharp air, fine.

Glass sinks very fast.
Sheep feed in the night.

Monday 13.
29 1/10; 38½; E.
Fog, cold, rain.

The hedge-sparrow makes it's winter-piping.

Tuesday 14.
29½, 29½ 1/10;

38; NW.
Sharp air, rain,
bright.

Wednesday 15.
29½ 3/10; 37;
NW, N.
Ice, sharp wind,
fine.

Thursday 16.
29½; 36; E.
Hard frost, sun.

Friday 17.
29½ 3/10; 36; E.
Frost, sun.

Saturday 18.
29½ 4/10; 34; N.　　　The ground as hard as a stone.
Hard frost.

Sunday 19.
30; 33½; N.　　　Bearing Ice.
Hard frost.

Monday 20.
30, 30; 34; W.
Fog, thaw, fog.

Tuesday 21.
29½ 4/10; 40; SW.
Soft air: wet.

Wednesday 22.
29 4/10; 45; SW.
Rain, rain, rain.

Thursday 23.
29 3/10, 29½ ¹/₁₀;　　　Wren whistles.
39¾; W, W.
Brisk air, fine.

Friday 24.
29½ 2/10; 40; W.
Brisk wind, wind.

Saturday 25.
29½ 1/10, 29½ 4/

10; 50; W, W.
Rain, wind, dry.

Sunday 26.
29½ 3/10; 44; S, S.
Rain, windy &
moist.

Monday 27.
30 2/10; 30 4/10;   Green-finches in a vast flock: they seem to feed on the seeds of the
44; W.   *echium vulgare.*
Dry & sunny.

Tuesday 28.
30 3/10; 44; SW.   In a dry chalky field far removed from any water was a water-rat
Sweet soft day.   plowed out which had formed for itself an hybernaculum curiously
                     constructed of leaves & grass. In one end of its burrow were piled
Wednesday 29.   up more than a gallon of potatoes. Was this amphibious animal
29½ 3/10; 47½;   determined in the choice of its place by the potatoes growing there;
W, W.   or does the water-rat habitually forsake the water-side during the
Brisk wind,   colder months of winter?
showers, wind.

Thursday 30.
30 2/10; 44; NW.
Dry air, sharp
wind.

DECEMBER 1769

Friday 1.
30 4/10; 42, NW.
Dry, fine day.

Saturday 2.
30 3/10; 38; NW.   Ice.
White frost, dry &
still.

Sunday 3.
30 3/10; 35; E, E.
Frost, fog, fog.

Monday 4.
30 3/10; 33; NW.   White water-wagtail appears.
Fog, grey day.

Tuesday 5.
30; 38; NE.   Still mild season.

Fog, fog.

Wednesday 6.
29½ 4/10; 37; SE.
Dark day, mist falls.

Thursday 7.
30½; 40; SE, SE.   Ground very dry.
Sun-shine.

Friday 8.
30; 42; SE, SE.   Soft air, no frost.
Sun, fine day.

Saturday 9.
29½ 3/10; 41; E.
Frost, fine day.

Sunday 10.
29½ 3/10; 40; SE.
Fog, rain, rain.

Monday 11.
29½ 4/10; 46, 47;   Damp moist air.
S.   Large broods of long-tailed titmice.
Rain, fog.

Tuesday 12.
30; 50; W, SW.   Shell-less snails crawl forth.
Sun-shine.   Red-breast, hedgesparrow, wren sing.
                          Worms come out on the turf by night. Great rain.

Wednesday 13.
30, 29½ 4/10; 46;
W.
Dry, fog, vast rain.

Thursday 14.
29½; 41; E, W,   Night *phalaenae*. Flood.
NW.
Vast rain, sun.

Friday 15.
29½ 3/10; 43; SW.
Windy, windy.

Saturday 16.
30; 50, 52; W.   *Phalaenae.*
Dark, fine day.

Sunday 17.
29½ 4/10, 30; 46,   Vast rock-like clouds.
43; W.
Showers, brisk
wind.

Monday 18.
29½ 3/10; 41; W.   Roses bud in hothouses; french-bean thrive: *Ananas* carry some
Drying air, wind.   late fruit.

Tuesday 19.
29½ 3/10; 48; 50;   Wood-pigeons abound in the fields. Some lambs fall.
W.
Brisk wind.

Wednesday 20.
29½ 2/10; 49; W.   Wood-pigeons.
Brisk wind.

Thursday 21.
29 3/10½; 48; S,   Song-thrush sings loudly.
SW.   Wren sings.
Wet, wet.

Friday 22.
29 2/10; 42; W.   Thunder, lightening & hail before day-break. Hen-chaffinches
Fine.   congregate.

Saturday 23.
28½, 28 4/10; 44,
45; SW.
Great rain, showers,
stormy: rain.

Sunday 24.
29 1/10, 29½ 1/10;
40; W.
Sharp air, bright
day.

Monday 25.
29 2/10; 45; SW.   Thrush sings.
Sad wet day.

Tuesday 26.
29 3/10; 45; SW.
Brisk wind blowing.

Wednesday 27.
29 4/10; 40; SW.
Fine, rain.

Here & there a lamb.

Thursday 28.
29½ 2/10, 30 1/10;
38; N.
Sleet, frost.

Friday 29.
30 2/10½; 32, 33;
NW.
Hard frost.

Saturday 30.
30 1/10; 31½; S,
SW.
Frost, sleet, rain,
thaw.

Papilio Io appears within doors, & is very brisk.

Sunday 31.
30 2/10; 37; NW.
Sun, grey
day.

— 1770 —

A proper antiseptic substance for the preservation of birds, &c.
Black pepper, & ginger, each one Ounce:
Camphire, cloves, each half an Oz:
Allom, one drachm:
Nitre, common salt, each half a drachm:
The intestines of the animal are to be drawn-out; & the abdomen is to be filled with this antiseptic mixture; or a layer of it, & a thin layer of tow alternately: then let the incision of the abdomen be sewed-up carefully. A little of the seasoning may also be thrust down the throat with a quill or skewer.

A motto for my Brother John's Naturalist's Journal kept at Gibraltar.
  Certe si aliquis Naturae consultus in maxime australi Hispania in aves observaret,
  quando accedant aut recedant austrum & septentrionem versus, notatis scilicet diebus
  mensis & speciebus; res haec adeo obscura brevi maxime illustraretur . . .
            Amaenit: academ: Vol: 4:¶

My Brotʳ John's birds are preserved with salt, allom, & pepper.

JANUARY

Monday 1.   BRADLEY
30 2/10; 38; SW.
Soft, fog.

Tuesday 2.
SW, W.   Storm-cock, *turdus viscivorus*, sings.
Grey, small rain.

Wednesday 3.
29½ 4/10; N.
Soft grey weather.

Thursday 4.
N.
Storms of Hail,
frost, fierce wind.

Friday 5.
29 1/10; N.
Frost, sun.

Saturday 6.   SELBORNE
29 3/10; 32; NW.
Frost, fierce wind,
snow, sleet.

Sunday 7.
29 4/10; 30; NW,
SE.
Frost, sun, grey.

Monday 8.
29½ 2/10; 26½;   Frost begins to come in a door. The thermometer abroad sunk to
NW.   25; & in the wine vault rose to 44.
Severe frost, snow.

Tuesday 9.
29½; 30; W, SW.   The sky promises for fall.
Dry, frost, sun, rain
& wind.
Cocks crow much.

Wednesday 10.
29 1/10; 32; NW.
Sleet in yᵉ night,
hard frost, snows
hard.

Thursday 11.
29½; 31½; N.
Considerable snow.

Wagtail appears.

Friday 12.
29½ 4/10; 33; NE.
Sharp wind, snow
lies.

Red-breast sings.

Saturday 13.
30; 33; N.
Still, sunny, snow
lies.

Wagtail.
Golden-crowned-wren.
Long-tailed titmouse.

Sunday 14.
29½ 4/10; 35, 39;
W, SW.
Thaw, fog, swift
thaw.

Snow melts away very fast.
House sparrows chirp.

Monday 15.
29½ 3/10; 38; W.
Frost, bright
sun.

Snow gone.

Tuesday 16.
29½ 1/10; 41; W.
Dark, rain.

Wednesday 17.
29½ 4/10, 30; 41;
N.
Frost, sweet day,
frost.

Red-breast whistles.
Cocks crow: hens chatter for laying.

Thursday 18.
30; 34, 36; W, S,
SE.
Hard frost, snow,
rain, fog.

Made a seedling hot bed for cucumbers.
Vast *aurora*: a red fiery broad belt from E: to W.

Friday 19.
29½ 2/10; 41; W.
Wet, fog.

Saturday 20.
27½ 3/10; 47;
SW.
Grey & mild.

Sunday 21.
29½ 4/10, 30½d;
43½; W.
Grey, sweet sunny
day.
❀ *Peziza
acetabulum.*

Skylark sings a little.

Monday 22.
29½ 4/10; 43; W.
Dark, damp.

Tuesday 23.
30 1/10; 48½; W.
Mist, fine, fog.
*Scarabaeus
stercorarius.*

Sowed cucumber-seeds.
Saw a bird which I suspected to be an *Aberdavine*, or siskin: it was
the *passer torquatus*, or reed sparrow.

Wednesday 24.
30, 3/10; W, SW.
Soft air, fog.
❀ *Helleborus
hyemalis, Anemone
hepatica.*

Woodlark, great titmouse, chaffinch sing. Blackbird whistles.
Wood lark sings in the air before daybreak. Thrush sings. Missel
bird sings.

Thursday 25.
30 3/10 ½; 45; S.
Fine, fog, soft air.
❀ *Lamium rubrum,
Galanthus nivalis.*

Chaffinches in vast flocks; mostly hens: some bramblings among
them.

Friday 26.
30, 3/10; 44; S, W.
Dark, soft air.
❀ *Primula vulgaris.*

Saturday 27.
30, 4/10; 41½; S,
NW.
Sweet summer-like
day.
❀ *Veronica agrestis.
Papilio urticae!*¶

Skylark sings: great titmouse.
Partial fog.

Sunday 28.
30 & an ½!! 44;
NW.
Dark & still, soft
air.

White wagtail sings a sort of a song.
Paths are steady.

✿ *Cheiranthus
cheiri.*

Monday 29.
inch: 30 & an half!!
45½; NW.
Falling fog all day.
✿ *Corylus avellana
masc: fem:*

Set beans, & sowed pease.
Heavy fog; yet the ground worked well.

Tuesday 30.
30 1/10½; 41½;
SW.
Cold wet fog.

Missel-bird sings.
Paths are dirty.

Wednesday 31.
29½ 4/10; 43½,
48; W.
Small rain.

FEBRUARY 1770

Thursday 1.
30 2/10; 44½;
NW.
Sweet sunny day.
✿ *Fragaria sterilis,
Ulex europaeus.*

The nuthatch, *sitta*, chatters.

Friday 2.
30 3/10; 40; NW.
Grey, cold wind.
✿ *Helleborus
foetidus.*

Saturday 3.
30 3/10; W.
Grey.

Sunday 4.
Sinks; SW.
Grey.

Monday 5.
Sinks; SW.
Grey.
✿ *Daphne mezereon.*

FYFIELD
Turn-pikes are dusty.

Tuesday 6.
29½ 3/10; 48;
NW.
Sun, colder air.
❦ *Crocus vernus*.

Hedge-sparrow, *curruca*, sings.
Vast halo round the moon.

Wednesday 7.
28½ 3/10, 29½
1/10; 29 abroad; S,
SW, N.
Rain, snow, violent
wind, frost.

Hedge-sparrow sings.
Most vehement wind with snow!!!
Wind blows off tiles, & thatch.

Thursday 8.
29½ 4/10, 30
1/10 ½; N.
Hard frost, sharp
wind.

Bunting, *emberiza alba*, in small flocks.
Halo round the moon.

Friday 9.
30 1/10½; NW.
Sun.

Chaffinch sings.
Still frost.
Rooks resort to their nest-trees.

Saturday 10.
30; W, SW.
Still & grey.
❦ *Leontodon*
taraxacum.

No frost.
Turkey-cock struts, & gobbles.

Sunday 11.
29½ 3/10; SW.
Grey & soft.

Linnets whistle inwardly as they sit in flocks.

Monday 12.
29½ 4/10, 30; S.
Soft & grey.
Apis mellifica.

Yellow-hammer, *emberiza flava*, sings. Bee gathers on the snow-
drops. Buntings sing.

Tuesday 13.
30 1/10; S, SW.
Soft & grey.

CHARLTON in Wilts.
Saw Bustards on Salisbury-plain: they much resemble fallow-deer
at a distance.

Wednesday 14.
SW.
Fog, sweet day.

Partridges pair.

Thursday 15.
29½ 3/10; SW.
Fog, fog.

FYFIELD
Wild-geese in the winter do great damage to the green wheat on
Salisbury plain.

Friday 16.
29½; S.
Spitting rain, fog.

Grey crows are not seen til we come about Andover from the eastward. As you go thence westward into Wilts they abound. Buntings abound in this part of Wilts.

Saturday 17.
28½ 1/10; 41; SW.
Storm, rain, sleet.

SELBORNE

Sunday 18.
28½ 4/10; 38; SW.
Storm, rain, snow.

Monday 19.
28½ 4/10.
Sun, wind,
March-like.
❀ *Helleborus viridis.*

Tuesday 20.
29 3/10;
Sun, wind.

Crocuss are blown out.

Wednesday 21.
29½; 37; N.
Sun, flight of snow.
  Ficaria verna.

Rock-like clouds.

Thursday 22.
29½; 36; N.
Frost, sun, clouds.

Friday 23.
29½ 1/10½; 35;
NE.
Frost, ice, sun,
clouds.

Blue mist. Vulg: called London smoke.

Quae: does this meteorous appearance shew itself on the N: E side of London when the wind is N: E? If that is the case then that mist cannot proceed from the smoke of the metropolis. This mist has a strong smell, & is supposed to occasion blights.

Saturday 24.
30 2/10; 35; N.
Frost, fine.

When such mists appear they are usually followed by dry weather. They have some what the smell of coal-smoke, & therefore are supposed to come from London, as they always come to us with a N: E: wind.

Sunday 25.
30 2/10; 35; NW.
Black frost, cold,
grey.

Monday 26.
30, sinks; 33; W,

SW.
Hard frost, white
dew, sun.
Phal: Tinea
vestianella.

Tuesday 27.
29½ 1/10; 37; S, S.
Soft, sun, rain.

Wednesday 28.
29½ 2/10; 41;   Rooks begin to build.
NW.   Made the bearing cucumᵗ-bed with eight cart-loads of dung.
Rain, moist, cloudy.

MARCH 1770

Thursday 1.
29½ 3/10½; 41;   *Calculus aegagropila* was found in the stomach of a fat ox. It was
W, SW.   black, shining, and round, & about the size of a large Sevil-
Spitting rain,   orange. See *Syst: Nat:* vol: 4: p: 176: n: 5.
fair.

Friday 2.
29½ 4/10; 47; W.
Dry, fine, brisk
wind.
⚘ *Viola odorata.*
Papilio rhamni;
Rana temporaria.

Saturday 3.
29½ 2/10; 48½;   Pheasant crows.
SW.
Spitting, fine,
spitting.

Sunday 4.
29 4/10; 49; W, N,   Ring dove, *palumbus torquatus*, cooes.
SW.   Rooks seem to have finished new nests.
Rain, dry, rain.
⚘ *Chrysosplenium*
oppositifolium.

Monday 5.
29½ 2/10; NW, N.   Crocuss make a gay appearance.
Moist & cloudy,
bright.

Tuesday 6.
29½ 1/10½; 37;
W.
White frost, fine.
❦ *Taxus baccata*.
Papilio Io.

Marsh-titmouse chirps, *parus palustris*.¶
This species is not so common as the great ox-eye, or the blue
nun. It frequents hedges, & bushes.

Wednesday 7.
29½; 37; E.
Ice, sharp frost, cold
air.

Rock-like clouds.

Thursday 8.
29 3/10; 35; E.
Frost, small snow.

Storm-cock sings.
Planted-out the cucumbers into the bearing-bed: some plants are
much drawn.

Friday 9.
29, 28½ 4/10; 35;
E, NE.
Sharp, grey, rain.

Cucumber-plants shew rudiments of fruit.

Saturday 10.
28½ 4/10; 40; E,
SE.
Grey, shower, vast
rain in yᵉ night.

Sunday 11.
29 2/10; 44½; W,
S, SW.
Heavy rain, dry,
great rain.

Monday 12.
29 3/10; 43½; SW.
Grey, shower, great
rain.

The golden-crowned wren, *regulus cristatus*, sings. His voice is as
minute as his body.

Tuesday 13.
29 3/10½; 45; E,
SE.
Rain, rain.
❦ *Cucumis sativus:*
Masc:

Ground well drenched.

Wednesday 14.
29½; 45; N. Dark,
rain & sleet, clear.

Thursday 15.
29½ 2/10; 34; N.
Hard frost, sun,
clouds.

Friday 16.
29½; 31½; NW.   Thick ice. Ground as hard as a stone.
Severe frost.
🌱 *Tussilago farfara.*

Saturday 17.
29 4/10; 31½; N.   † [Siskin, or *aberdavine* appears.]
Severe frost, sun.   Some flakes of snow. The bird above was the *passer torquatus*, or
                  reed-sparrow.

Sunday 18.
29 4/10; 31; NW.   Milk frozen in the pantry.
Severe frost, sun.   Vast rock-like clouds in the horizon.
                  Hard frost.

Monday 19.   BRADLEY
29 1/10; 31; N.   Viper appears.
Severe frost, sun.
Coluber Berus.

Tuesday 20.
N.   Swan-goose, *anser cygneus guineensis*, sits.
Hard frost, some   The peacock, *pavo*, exerts his gallantry when the hens appear:
snow.   . . . whose gay train
🌱 *Cucumis sativus:*   Adorns him color'd with the florid hue
fem: Of rain-bows, & starry eyes. Milton.¶

Wednesday 21.   SELBORNE
29½ 1/10 ½; 32½;
NE.
Frost, storms of
snow.

Thursday 22.
29½ 2/10; 31¾;   Ice very thick: ground growing dusty.
N, NE.   Blossom-buds of the pear-trees seem to be injured by the frost.
Dark, severe wind.
🌱 *Prunus armeniaca.*

Friday 23.
29½ 4/10; 31½;   Thermometer abroad sunk to 29.
N.   Plows are frozen out.
Severe frost, snow,   Great Northern *aurora*.
bright.
🌱 *Amygdalus persica.*

Saturday 24.
29½ 4/10; 33; N, NW.
Frost, still, sun.
⚘ *Anemone coronaria.*
Papilio rhamni, *Pap: urticae.*

Green finch, *chloris*, sings.
Roads & fields are dusty.

Sunday 25.
29½ 1/10; 36; SW, W, NW.
Sun, clouds & sleet, sun.
⚘ *Vinca minor.*

Viper appears.
Ice gone. Rock-like clouds about. Viper appears. Fields dusty.

Monday 26.
29 4/10; 36½; NW.
Cold air, fine day.

Sowed carrots, parsneps, onions, coss-lettuce, leeks, lark-spurs.

Tuesday 27.
29½ 4/10; 37½, 38; N, NE.
Frost, sun, snow, sun.

Planted potatoes, five rows. Flights of snow. Red-wings congregate on trees & whistle inwardly. In their breeding-country they are good songsters: see *Fauna Seucica.*

Wednesday 28.
29½ 4/10; 33½; NE, E.
Severe frost, bright day.
Papilio Iö.

Thursday 29.
29½ 2/10; 34½; E, SW.
Most severe, sweet day.
Pap. Iö.

Young cucumbers swell.
Dirt bears horse & man. Boys slide on the ice.

†[Many pairs of siskins or *aberdavines* appear in the hedges along the verge of the forest of Wulmere. By the deportment of the cocks towards their hens it is plain that they come hither for the purpose of breeding. The cock is handsome, but the hen is a little mean brown bird.]
These were reed-sparrows, *passeres torquati.*

Friday 30.
29½; 4½; W, NE.

Papilio rhamni sucks the bloom of ye primrose.

†Entry crossed out.

No frost, sun,   Polyanths coddled with ye frost.
colder air.

Saturday 31.
29 4/10; 46, 50; W.   Turkey & duck lay.
Showers, showers,   Goose sits.
windy, warm.

APRIL 1770

Sunday 1.
29½ 1/10; 43½;   Bat appears.
SW, W.
Sun, clouds, wind,
clear, fog.
✾ *Narcissus*
pseudonarcissus.
Oniscus asellus.

Monday 2.
29 3/10; 48; S, SW,   Fine soft rain.
W.
Shady, rain all day,
clear.
✾ *Veronica*
hederifolia.
Iülus terrestris.

Tuesday 3.
29 4/10, 29½; 43;   Snipe pipes in the moors.
W, NW.   Bat appears.
Cloudy & cold,
sleet, bright.
✾ *Glechoma*
hederacea.

Wednesday 4.
29 1/10½; 41½;   Stone curlew, *Oedicnemus*, is heard again.
W.   Vast shower of hail & sleet.
Cold, cloudy, great   Rock-like clouds.
Hailstorms.
✾ *Caltha palustris.*

Thursday 5.
28½ 4/10; 38; W.   Sour, cold day. Great storms about.
Hail, snow, snow.
✾ *Mercurialis*
perennis, Oxalis
acetosella.

Friday 6.
28½ 4/10½; 38;
NW.
Clouds, hail, snow.
✤ *Cardamine*
pratensis.
Apes bombinatrices.

Very sharp air.

Saturday 7.
29; 38; W, SW,
NW.
Frost, much snow,
fine.

Cut the first cucumber: full old.
Snow covers the ground.

Sunday 8.
29, 29 1/10; 37½;
W, SW, NW.
Cloudy, snow
about.

Sharp air.

Monday 9.
29 1/10½; 39½;
N, NE.
Frost, bright, dark,
rain & sleet.

No birds sing, & no insects appear during this wintry sharp
season.

Tuesday 10.
29½; 39; N, N.
Great snow, cold,
rain.

Cut a brace of fair cucumbers.
Snow pretty well gone.

Wednesday 11.
29½ 1/10½; 38;
N, NW.
Frost, cold air.
Hirundo domestica.

Kite sits.
Raven has young.
Swallows amidst frost & snow.

Thursday 12.
29½ 1/10; 40; N,
NE.
Deep snow, thaw,
snow, sun.

Rooks have young.
Snow melts away very fast.
Peaches & nectarines are in full bloom.
Apricot bloom seems to be cut-off.
Barley begins to be sown.

Friday 13.
29½ 4/10; 40; N,
NE, N.
Dark, sweet
afternoon.

Saturday 14.
29½ 4/10; 41; NE.
Cold morn, sweet
day.
❦ *Primula veris*,
Draba verna.

Butter flies abound.
Flies swarm.
Grass lamb.
Cut a brace more of large cucumbers.
Ants appear.

Sunday 15.
29½ 3/10; 44; W,
SW.
Grey, sun,
soft air.

Monday 16.
29½ 2/10; 47½;
W, SW.
Soft, sun.
*Regulus non cristatus
minor*.

WHITCHURCH
Green wood-pecker laughs at all the world.
Storm-cock sings.

Tuesday 17.
W.
Sun, windy,
showers.
Ruticilla.

Aberdavines in Oxfordshire.
These were *passeres torquati*, or reed-sparrows.

Wednesday 18

OXFORD

Thursday 19.

Friday 20.
Rain.

Saturday 21.
Rain, storm.

Vast storm that did much damage.

In my absence the ring-ouzels made their regular spring-visit
en passant; but they seemed to be few that passed this way.

Sunday 22.
N.
Snow storms.

WITNEY

Monday 23.
N.
Snow storms.

Tuesday 24.

Wednesday 25.
W, S.
Frost, rain.

Thursday 26.
S.
Rain, rain.
Hirundo apus.

Wood sorrel
growing on the Zig-zag.
25 April.

Friday 27.

Saturday 28.
NE.
Fine.

Sunday 29.
NE.   Two swifts.
Fine.

Monday 30.
NE.   Titlark sings: frogs migrate.
Sweet day.

MAY 1770

Tuesday 1.
N.
Wet, cold.

Wednesday 2.   OXFORD
Hail, sun, hail.   Swallows abound.
Cuculus.   Great snowstorm.

Thursday 3.
Hail, sun.   Rock-like clouds.
Hirundo agrestis.

Friday 4.
SW.   Nightingales abound.
Rain, rain.
Reg: non-crist: med:,
Luscinia.

Saturday 5.   SELBORNE
Clouds, great rain.

Sunday 6.
S, SW.   Young rooks perch.

Clouds, wind.   Great bat.
Hirundo riparia.

Monday 7.
29½; 47; S.   Grass-hopper-lark.
Shower, fine.
Alauda minima voce
locustae.

Tuesday 8.
49; W, SW.   Beeches on the hanger begin to leaf.
Fine, soft air.   *Whitethroat appears.
Ficedulae affinis   Black-cap.
*atricapella.**

Wednesday 9.
29½ 2/10; W, S.   Nightingales in my outlet.
Summer weather.
                             A brace of green sandpipers at James Knight's ponds. *Tringa*
                             Aldrov: *tringa ochropus* Lin:

Thursday 10.
SE, E.   *cantat voce stridula locustae.*
Fine, clouds.   Thunder.
Regulus non crist:
*major:**

Friday 11.
56, 61; E.   Thunder, & showers about.
Hot air, soft
showers.

Saturday 12.
63; S.
Soft air.
❀ *Lathraea*
squammaria.

Sunday 13.
29½ 1/10½; 58, S.   *Fly-catcher of *Brit: zool:* appears.
Shower, sweet day.   **Sedge-bird of *Brit: zool:* sings.
*Stoparola,** Passer*
arundinaceus
*minor.***

Monday 14.
58; NE, E, NE.   Vast rock-like clouds about.
Fine, hot day.   Vine begins to leaf. Lightening.
Papilio cardamines.

Tuesday 15.
60, 65; NE.
Fine, brisk air.
Scarabaeus
melolontha.

Blue mist.
Chafers begin to abound.
Grass-hopper-lark chirps.

Wednesday 16.
29½ 4/10; 60, 63;
N.
Mist, fine day.
*Gryllus gryllotalpa.**

*Mole-cricket churs.

Thursday 17.
29½ 4/10; 58; N.
Dark & cold,
bright.
Pap. aegeria,
Turtur.

No redstarts whistle yet about the village.

Friday 18.
29½ 3/10; 55; N.
Dark & cool.

Appletrees begin to open their bloom.

Saturday 19.
29½ 2/10; 54; W,
S, SE.
Dark, cool, sun.

Black-cap sings sweetly, but rather inwardly: it is a songster of
the first rate. It's notes are deep & sweet. Called in Norfolk the
mock-nightingale.

Sunday 20.
29½ 1/10; 52;
SE.
Frost, sun, soft rain,
sun.
Pap.[nes] *brascicae* &
napi.

Rooks have carry'd-off their young from the nest-trees.

Monday 21.
29½; 55; E.
Cloudy, soaking
rain.

No flesh-flies yet.
Cartway runs.

Tuesday 22.
29½ ½/10; 56; W,
S.
Showers, warm,
showers.

Growing weather.

Wednesday 23.
29½ 1/10½; 56; S,

Flesh-flies.

SW.   Chafers swarm.
Dripping, sweet
day.
Musca vomitoria.

Thursday 24.
29½ 3/10; 56; SW.   Heavy rock-like clouds.
Sun, heavy clouds,   Turtle cooes.
fine.   Showers about.
Tipulae, Gryllus
campestris.

Friday 25.
29½ 3/10; 60; E,   *Oedicnemus* lays.
NE.   Lapwing lays.
Mist, sweet day,   Nightingale lays.
cold wind.
🌱 *Pyrus malus,*   Cucumbers bear well again, after having produced scarce any for
Cucumis melo.   near three weeks. Cut eight brace.
Papilio c album.

Saturday 26.
29½ 3/10; 58; NE.   Melon shews rudiments of fruit.
Mist, cold & dark,
sun.   Chafers have not prevailed for some years, as now: they seldom
Caprimulgus   abound oftener than once in three or four years. When they swarm
sussurrat.   so, they deface the trees & hedges.

Sunday 27.
29½ 1/10; 58; NE.   Harsh hazy day.
Cold & black, sun.

Monday 28.
29½ 4/10; 52; NE.   Melon-fruit blows.
Cold & black, sun.

Tuesday 29.
N.   No dew.
Dark & sharp, sun.

Wednesday 30.
29½ 3/10; 52;   No dew.
NW.
Dark & cold, sun.

Thursday 31.
29 4/10½; 51; W,   Backward apples begin to blow.
S, SE.   The chafers seem much incommoded by the cold weather.
Cold, rain, rain.

JUNE 1770

Friday 1.
29½ 1/10; 51½;
NW, W.
Cold wind, sun.
❦ *Hieracium
murorum,
Menyanthes trifolia.*

St foin is large, & thick, & lodged by the rain.
Melon-fruit blows.

Saturday 2.
29½ 2/10; 53; W,
SW.
Sun, summer, small
rain.
❦ *Crataegus
oxyacantha.
Libellulae,
Hippobosca equina,
Pap: maera.*

Many sorts of dragon-flies appear for the first time. Swifts
devour the small dragon-flies as they first take their flight from
out their aurelias, which are lodged on the weeds of ponds.

Chafers are eaten by the turkey, the rook, & the house-sparrow.

Sunday 3.
29½ 1/10; 57; SW,
W.
Great rain, wind,
rain.

Chafers much suppressed by the cold, & rain.

Monday 4.
29½; 57; SW.
Great rain, wind.

Fleas (*pulex irritans*)¶ abound on the steep sand-banks where the
bank-martins build.

Tuesday 5.
29½ 3/10; 57; SW.
Vast showers, hail.

Wednesday 6.
29½ 3/10; 53; SW.
Great showers.
❦ *Sanicula
aeuropaea.*

Chafers abound.

Thursday 7.
29½ 4/10½; 56;
W.
Fine day, cool.
❦ *Polygala vulg:*

Mole-cricket churs.

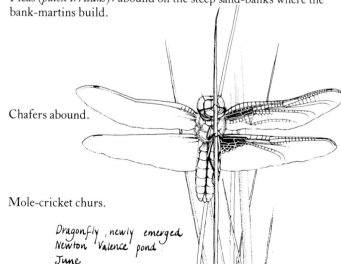

*Dragonfly, newly emerged
Newton Valence pond.
June.*

Friday 8.
29½ 3/10; 55; SE,

Melons begin to swell.

S, SW.
Sun, shady.
🜨 *Sorbus aucuparia.*
Scarabaeus auratus.

Sᵗ foin begins to blow.

Saturday 9.
Sinks, 29½ 2/10½;
59; S, SW.
Summer day.

Sunday 10.
59, 65; W, SW, S.
Sun, cloudy, sun.

Monday [11.]
Dark.

Hinds on Bagshot-heath.

LONDON to June 23.

Saturday 23.
29½ 2/10; 61; S.
Sun, clouds, sun.

SELBORNE
Wheat is very backward: hardly any ears appear.

It is worthy of notice that on my clayey soil horses prefer the grass
that grows on a sand walk, tho' shaded & dripped by a tall hedge,
to that which springs from the natural ground on a sunny & open
situation.

Sunday 24.
W.
Showers, showers.

Monday 25.
29½ 3/10.

Glow-worm appears.

Tuesday 26.
Dark, great rain.

FYFIELD
Sᵗ foin begins to be cut.

Wednesday 27.
Showers, showers.

Thursday 28.
Showers.

Trufles begin to be found.
Chafers still appear.

Friday 29.
W.
Showers, cold wind.

A pound of trufles were found by a trufle-hunter in my Brother's
grove.

Saturday 30.
NW.
Showers.

Farmers do not care to persist in cutting their Sᵗ foin.

The thermometer¶ fluctuates between 29 & 29 & ½.
The rooks pursue & catch the chafers as they flie. Whole woods of
oaks are stripped bare by the chafers.

JULY 1770

Sunday 1.
29½; N, NW.
Dark, fine.

Cuckow sings.
Quail calls.
Wheat begins to blow.

Monday 2.
29½ 2/10; N.
Dark, soft air.

Some hay is housed.

Tuesday 3.
29½ 2/10; 65; N,
W, S.
Dark, still, sun.

Red pinks begin to blow.
Blackcap sings sweetly.
Titlark sings, & black bird.

Wednesday 4.
29½ 1/10; S, NE,
SE.
Sun, clouds, rain,
rain.
✤ *Ophrys apifera.*

Sultry. Thunder-like clouds rising on all sides. Heavy rain.
Roses blow but poorly. Large titmouse makes his spring-note.

Thursday 5.
29½ 1/10; 73; S,
W, S.
Sun, clouds, soft
night.

Sultry. Showers at a distance.
The therm.ʳ 73 abroad in the shade.

Friday 6.
29½; 69; SW.
Sun, sultry, clouds,
sun.
✤ *Phallus impudicus
olet.*

Young daws come forth.
Cut my Sᵗ foin; a vast crop.
Vast showers about.

Saturday 7.
29½ 1/10; 64; SW.
Sultry, clouds.

SELBORNE
Wheat blows well.
Cuckow sings.
Showers about.

Orchis conopsea abounds in the dry banks of the corn-fields.
Wornils¶ are grown very large in the backs of cows. If they could
be watched, so as to be taken when going into the pupa state,
perhaps it might be discovered from what insect they are derived.
See Derham *Physico. theol:* ... wornils.

Sunday 8.
29½ 1/10; 58;
NW, W.

Showers at a distance, & thunder.

Sun, clouds, rain.

Monday 9.
29½ 3/10; 58; W   Vast showers about, & thunder.
Shower, shower.

Tuesday 10.
29½ 3/10; 58; W,   Very few apples, or pears.
SW.   Cherries hardly begin to turn.
Fine, clouds, rain,   Wood-straw berries turn.
cold.

Wednesday 11.
29½ 4/10; 56;   Vast showers about but no rain.
NW, W, SW, W.   Turn'd the S! foin twice, & cocked it in small-cock.
Dark, sun, heavy   Ricked five loads & ½ of S! foin in good order. Fern owl
clouds.   chatters.

Thursday 12.
30 1/10; 56; W.
Sun, clouds, sweet
day.

Friday 13.
30 1/10½; 60; W,   Cut my great mead, a good crop.
S.
Fog, sweet day.   Young bank-martins are flyers: this species every year is the first
                         that brings forth it's young. Quer: Do they feed their young flying,
                         or not?

Saturday 14.
30, 29½ 3/10; 64;   Hay makes very fast.
S, SE.   Grasshopper-lark chirps.
Hot sun, clouds.   Clouds threaten. Sultry.

Sunday 15.
29½, 29½ 1/10;   Heavy showers.
65; S, W, S.   Young frogs migrate from their ponds.
Hard rain, showers,   Young partridges.
fine.

Monday 16.
29; 2/10, 1/10; 65,   Elder in full bloom. Early shower.
65; W, S.   Ricked three loads of hay in good order.
Rain, sun, clouds,
misty rain.

Tuesday 17.
29½ 1/10; 62, 68;   First young swallows appear.
W, SW.   Young Goldfinches.

Misty rain, fine.
🌢 *Vitis vinifera*.

Turned the grass-cocks.

Vine begins to blow very late! in good summers about the last week in June.

Wednesday 18.
29½; 64; SE.
Rain, stormy wind.

Great rain, & wind.

Thursday 19.
29½ 1/10; 63; W.
Great shower,
shower, sun.

Great showers.
Grasshopper-lark chirps.

Friday 20.
29½ 3/10; 59, 62;
SW.
Sun, vast showers.

Spread the hay.
Stopped & tacked ye vines.
Cut the tall hedges.

Saturday 21.
29½ 4/10; 30/
½10; 59, 63; W, S,
W.
Sun, clouds,
sprinkling, sweet
evening.

Cut first melon. *Apis longicornis* carries wax on it's thighs into it's hole in the walks: in this wax it deposits it's eggs.
Cocked the hay in large cocks.

Martins tread in their nest, & flie-out one on the back of the other.

Sunday 22.
30, S, SW.
Sun, clouds, sweet
evening.

Monday 23.
29½ 4/10; 65, 71,
66; S.
Sun, clouds, sultry,
sweet eve.

Showers at a distance all day. Housed three loads of hay perfectly dry but discolored, & with little smell.

Tuesday 24.
29½ 3/10; 65 ½;
E.
Dark, showers,
showers.

Swallows begin to feed y^ir young ones flying.
Vast showers about.

Wednesday 25.
29½ 3/10; 67; E.
Sun, sultry, clouds,
fine.

Vast thunder-clouds about.
Glass rises.

I saw a young cuckow, nearly fledged, on the ground in the nest of a tit lark: it was become much too big for the nest . . . *in tenui re*

Majores pennas nido extendisse . . Hor: . . . ¶ was very pugnacious,
& would pursue a person's hand to some distance from the nest,
buffeting, & sparring, & sticking up it's feathers like a game-cock.
The dupe of a dam was attending at a distance in a solicitous
manner with food in her mouth.

Thursday 26.
29½ 3/10½; 65,
66; N, NW.
Dark, sultry, dark.

Turneps begin to be hoed.
Red-breast's note begins to be distinguishable, other birds being
more silent.

Friday 27.
29½ 4/10½; 65,
69; NW.
Dark, sultry, sun,
fog.
*Tabanus bovinus
macula trigona.*

Young swallows abound.

Saturday 28.
30; 66, 72; NW,
SW.
Sun, sultry, clouds,
mist.

Vine-bloom smells sweetly.
Strong gale & a misty rain.

Sunday 29.
29½ 4/10; 67, 73;
SW, W.
Fog, misty rain,
sun, fine.

Rain in the night.
Young swallows hawk for flies.
Strong gale.

Monday 30.
29½ 4/10; 64; W,
SW, W.
Clouds, sun,
showers.
✿ *Hypericum
Constantinopol:*

Cut my little mead.
Vines in bloom.
Many showers about.

Tuesday 31.
29½ 4/10; 63; W,
SW.
Clouds, sun, clouds.
✿ *Tilia Europaea.*

AUGUST 1770

Wednesday 1.
29½ 3/10; 63; W.

Hay makes in the afternoon.

Rain, clouds, thin
clouds, soft.

Cocked ye hay.
Martins (young) peep out of their nests.

Thursday 2.
30; 61; W, NW.
Clouds, strong
gales, sweet.

Bulfinches devour all the rasps. Ricked last load of hay in fine
order.

Friday 3.
30 ½ deg; 60; NW.
Sweet day.

Vast dew. Somewhat of an autumnal temperament seems to take
place.
Young martins come out.
Young swifts seem to be out.

Saturday 4.
30 1/10; 63; 68; E,
SE.
Sun, clouds,
sultry.

Great dew.
Nuthatch, *sitta Europ*: chatters.
Sweet weather.

Sunday 5
30½ dr.; 64, 69; E.
Sun, strong gale,
sweet.
❦ *Humulus lupulus.*

Hops promise well, & throw out branches at every joint.

Quer: Are not hops, which are dioecious plants, subject to blites, &
more frequent failures in their crops from the great over care that is
taken to root out every male plant? Male plants will not bear good
hops: but may not some of their farina be necessary towards
rendering the female productions more perfect?

Monday 6.
30; 68, 74; E, NE.
Fog, hot, brisk air,
sweet.

Levant weather: a brisk gale all day that dies away at sun set.

Tuesday 7.
30, 30; 69, 77; NE,
E.
Fog, hot, brisk air,
sweet.
*Plinus pectinicornis.**

Levant weather.

*Those maggots that make worm-holes in tables, chairs, bed posts
&c: & destroy wooden-furniture, especially where there is any sap,
are the larvae of the *Plinus pectinicornis*. This insect, it is probable,
deposits it's eggs on the surface & the worms eat their way in. In
their holes they turn into their pupa state, & so come forth winged
in July, eating their way thro' the valences or curtains of a bed, or
any other furniture that happens to obstruct their passage.
They seem to be most inclined to breed in beech: hence beech
will not make lasting utensils, or furniture. If their eggs are
deposited on the surface, frequent rubbings will preserve wooden
furniture.

Wednesday 8.
30, 29½ 4/10; 70,
75, 77; E, W.
Bright, still, sultry.
Oestrus σκολιθρος,
*sive curvicauda.**

Housed the grass of shrubbery.
*This fly,¶ which lays it's nits on the hairs of horses flanks & legs,
is very busy this sultry weather. See Derham's *Physico-theol*: 250.
This species of *Oestrus* seems to be unknown to Linnaeus &
Geoffroy.

Thursday 9.
29½ 2/10; 72½,
74, 76; NE, W, S.
Sprinkling, gale,
thunder.

Friday 10.
29½ 2/10½; 72;
SE.
Sun, strong gale,
showers.

Oedicnemi abound these moonshine nights on Selborne down:
they come most probably for worms.

Saturday 11.
29½ 3/10; 65, 66;
W.
Sun, clouds, gales,
showers, fine.

Sunday 12.
29½ 4/10; 62, 69;
SW.
Sweet day, gale.

Young swallows & martins begin to congregate.
Lapwings flie in parties to the downs as it grows dusk.

Monday 13.
29½ 4/10; 64, 74;
W, NW.
Sun, bright day.

Swifts seem to be partly gone.
Martins congregate.

Tuesday 14.
29½ 3/10; 66, 74,
72; S, E, NE.
Fog, bright sun,
hot.

Pease begin to be hacked.
Saw two swifts.

Wednesday 15.
29½ 2/10; 70, 69;
E, SE.
Cloudy, soft air,
rain.

Thunder at a distance.
Wheat-harvest begins.

Thursday 16.
29½ 2/10; 67, 70;

Nutchatch chirps much.

E, NE, SW.
Misty rain, fine.

Friday 17.
29½ 2/10; 64, 67,
66; SW.
Cloudy, still, fine.

Saturday 18.
29½ 3/10, 64, 69;
W.
Sweet day.

Sunday 19.
29½ 2/10; 64, 65;
SW.
Rainbow, clouds,
sprinklings, rain.

Ponds begin to fail.
Hops are perfectly free from lice.

Monday 20.
29½ 2/10; 65; S,
W.
Rain, sun, heavy
clouds.

Considerable rain.

Tuesday 21.
29½ 3/10; 62, 65;
NW.
Sun, clouds, fine,
clouds.

Sowed spinnage, & lettuces to stand ye winter.

Wednesday 22.
29½ 3/10½; 62;
NW.
Sun, brisk air.

Lapwings congregate.

Thursday 23.
29½ 3/10; 61; SW.
Clouds, sun, brisk
air.

Martins feed their young flying.

Friday 24.
29½ 3/10; 62; SW,
W.
Dark, fog.

Nuthatch chirps.

Saturday 25.
29½, 4/10; 66, 69;
SW, W.

Wheat begins to be housed.
Trenched out celeri.

Sun, misty rain,
fine.

Sunday 26.
30; 61½; W, NW.   Young swallows, & martins congregate in prodigious swarms.
Cold dew, sweet
day.

Monday 27.
30; 62, 65; N, NE.   Sweet harvest-weather. Wheat in general is light. Hops grow
Cool, sun, clouds.   very fast: a vast crop.

Tuesday 28.
30 ½ 10; 61½;   Delicate harvest-weather. Many loads of wheat housed. Great bat
NE.   appears; flies strongly & vigorously & very high. I call this rare
Cool, brisk air, sun.   species *vespertilio altivolans.*

Wednesday 29.
30 ½ 10; 58; NE.
Cold dew, bright
sun.

Thursday 30.
30; 59, 64; E.   *Regulus non cristatus* chirps.
Cool, sweet day.   China asters blow.
                    Mich: daisey blows.

Friday 31.
29½ 4/10; 60; NE.   Hop-picking begins.
Gale, sun, sun.   Plants in the garden suffer for want of moisture.

SEPTEMBER 1770

Saturday 1.
29½ 3/10; 60½;   Not one wasp appears notwithstanding the long dry season.
NE.   Aug 31. Great N: *Aurora* considering the bright moon.
Fog, grey, still.
                    Cuckows skim over the ponds at Oakhanger, & catch *libellulae* on
                    the weeds, & as they flie in the air. I can give no credit to the notion
                    that they are birds of prey. They have a weak bill, & no talons.

Sunday 2.
29½, 61, 65; E,
SE.
Grey, wind, sun,
hollow wind.

Monday 3.
29½; 63, 67; E, S.   Still soft night.
Rain, sweet
afternoon.

Tuesday 4.
29½ 1/10; 61; E,
NE.
Sun, grey, sun.
Turdus torquatus.
Lin: or
Merula torquata
Raÿ.

Vast rock-like clouds about all day.
Soft air.

The ring-ousel appears again in it's autumnal visit; but about twenty days earlier than usual.

Wednesday 5.
29½ 3/10; 63; NE.
Fog, sun, shower.

Swallows have second broods.
Vast rock-like clouds.

Thursday 6.
29½ 2/10 ½; 61;
E, SW.
Grey, cool, rain.

Martins feed their young flying.

Friday 7.
29½ 1/10; 61; W,
SW, S.
Sun, clouds,
showers.

Saturday 8.
29½; 61; W, SW,
NW.
Sun, vast clouds,
rain, fine.

Sunday 9.
29½ 2/10; 59;
NW.
Sun, clouds, sweet
afternoon.

Monday 10.
29½ 2/10; 58;
NW.
Sweet day.

FARNHAM CASTLE
The hop-picking at Farnham is just beginning. About 8000 people besides natives are employed.¶ A vast crop.

Tuesday 11.
Vast showers.

Much wall fruit at Farnham castle; but void of flavour.

Wednesday 12.
Great showers.

Thursday 13.
Showers.

FARNHAM CASTLE
Fly-catcher, & white throat appear.

Friday 14.
29½ 2/10; 61; S.
Showery, showers.

SELBORNE
Several fields of wheat unhoused.

Saturday 15.
29½ 3/10½; 62,
65; W, S, SE.
Small rain, fine.

Tyed-up a large plot of well-grown endive.
Young swallows come-out.
Peaches, but not well-flavoured.

Sunday 16.
29½ 3/10½; 64; S,
SW.
Hot, broken
clouds.

Titmice sings.
Reg: non crist: minor chirps.
Soft evening.

Monday 17.
29½ 3/10½; 66,
68; SE, S.
Broken clouds,
sultry.

Partial fogs.

Tuesday 18.
29½; 66; SW.
Brisk air, sun, sweet
even.

FYFIELD
Heavy showers after 'tis dark.

Wednesday 19.
29½; 66; SW.
Stormy winds,
showers.

Stormy all night.
Aequinoctial weather.
Wheat begins to be sown.

Thursday 20.
29 4/10; 64; SW.
Brisk wind.

Friday 21.
29 3/10; 64; SW.
Great rain.

Saturday 22.
29 2/10, 29½; 62,
59; SW.
Sun, frequent
showers, sun.

FYFIELD

Sunday 23.
29½ ½10; 57.
Wind, clouds,
fine.

SELBORNE
Grapes begin to turn.

Monday 24.
29½ 1/10; 58.
Dark, rain.

Tuesday 25.
S.   Barley grows in the swarth.
Great rain & wind.   Thunder lightening, & hail.

Wednesday 26.
29 1/10; 58; S, W.   Annuals are spoiled in the gardens.
Stormy, vast rain.

Thursday 27.
Rises; SW.   Gardens are torn to pieces, & great boughs off trees.
Showers, stormy
day.

Friday 28.
Rises; W.   Some barley housed.
Fine day.

Saturday 29.
30 1/10; 59; W.   Barley is housed.
Grey & soft, sun.   Barley much grown.
                           Martins feed y^{ir} young flying.

Sunday 30.
29½ 4/10; 58; S,   Sky-lark sings.
W.
Dark, soft air, rain.
❦ *Hedera helix*.

OCTOBER 1770

Monday 1.
30; 59; NW, NE.
Dark, sprinkling.
❦ *Arbutus unedo*.

Tuesday 2.   CHILGROVE
30 1/10½; 57; E.   Ring-ouzel on Harting hills.
Fog, sun.

Wednesday 3.
E.   Ring-ouzels again on the downs eastward.
Fine.

Thursday 4.   RINGMER
Sinks; SE.   Ring-ouzels near Ringmer.
Fog.   Swallows abound.

Friday 5.
SE.
Fog, grey, sun.

Crossbills, *loxiae curvirostrae*, among Mrs Snooke's Scotch pines.

Saturday 6.
W.
Grey, soft.

Harvest not finished.
Not one wasp or hornet.

Sunday 7.
NW.
Grey, sun, grey.

Swallows.
Grapes begin to grow black.

Monday 8.
NW, W.
Grey, sun, grey.

Tuesday 9.
SW.
Grey, soft, still.

Fog on the hills.

Wednesday 10.
Sinks; S, SW.
Sun, hot, clouds,
storm at night.

Several very young nestling swallows with square tails. *Oestrus curvicauda* still appears. Apples gathering.

Thursday 11.
NW, W.
Sun, sweet day.

Grapes begin to be eatable.
Swallows.

Friday 12.
Sun, clouds,
showers, wet.

Saturday 13.
Rain, sun, cold.

Swallows.

Sunday 14.
White frost, sharp,
sun, shower.

A few young swallows.

Monday 15.
Stormy, wet, vast
rain.

Many swallows.

Tuesday 16.
Rain, sun, showers.

Vast rock-like clouds.
Some swallows.

Wednesday 17.
Vast rain.

Thursday 18.
Dark, vast clouds,
rain, fine.
Cornix cinerea.

Swallows.
Some Martins at Findon.
Vast floods on the Sussex rivers: the meadows all under water.

Friday 19.
SW.
Wet morn:

CHILGROVE
Vast floods at Houghton.
Martins, crossbeaks.

Saturday 20.
White frost, sun,
vast clouds.
Turdus iliacus.

SELBORNE
Rain all night.

The Sussex rivers are very liable to floods, which occasion great loss
& inconvenience to the Farmers. The cattle from this time must be
taken in to the yards to live on straw, because the meads, which
would have maintained them many weeks longer, are all under
water. The standing grass is often flooded in summer. They call
their meads by the rivers-sides, brooks.

Sunday 21.
Rain, sun, shower.

Hen chaffinches begin to congregate.

Monday 22.
28½ 4/10; 45; SE.
White frost, heavy
rain.
Scolopax.

Tuesday 23.
42.
Dark, fine day.

Grapes are eatable.

Wednesday 24.
29 2/10; 42; W.
Sun.

Showers about, & vast clouds.

Thursday 25.
29 4/10; 45;
SW.
Sun, shower, sun,
shower.

A young swallow appears.

Friday 26.
29 4/10½; 48; W.
Sun, mild.

Saturday 27.
29½ 1/10; 42; W,
NW.

Ice. Ice.
Cobwebs float in the air & cover the ground.

White frost, sweet
day.

Sunday 28.
29 3/10; 41; S, SW.   Ice. Wet day.
White frost, rain,
fog.

Monday 29.
29 4/10½; 43; W.   Trees carry their leaves well for the season.
Drying wind, sun.

Tuesday 30.
29 3/10; 40; W,   Rooks & jays carry away the acorns from the oaks.
NW.
Sun, brisk air, fine
day.

Wednesday 31.
29½ 1/10½; 43;   Flights of skie-larks go westward.
NW.
Grey, fine.
Turdus pilaris.

NOVEMBER 1770

Thursday 1.
29½ 4/10; 39; N.
Frost, sun, fine day.

Friday 2.
29½ 4/10½; 38;   Wallnut, & ash leaves fall at a vast rate.
NW, W.
Frost, sweet day.

Saturday 3.
29½ 3/10; 45; S,
SW.
Misting rain all day.

Sunday 4.
29½ 3/10½; 50;   Great rain in the night.
NW, N.
Dark, bright.

Monday 5.
29½ 3/10; 47½;
SW.
Grey, wind.

Tuesday 6.
29½ 2/10½; 48;
SW.
Rain, fine, bright.

Great rain in the night.

Wednesday 7.
29 2/10 28½ 4/10;
44½; SW, E.
Grey, rain from
Noon.

Vast rain for many hours.
Leaves fall very fast.

Thursday 8.
28½ 1/10; 47½;
SW, W, S.
Rain continued til
noon, sun, showers.

Heavy rain for 24 hours. Vast flood at Gracious street, & dorton.
Heavy showers again in the evening.

Friday 9.
29 1/10; 46½; W,
SW.
Sun, great showers.

Lime-tree leaves fall all at once.
Floods: torrents & cataracts in the lanes.

Saturday 10.
29 2/10; 47; SW,
W.
Sun, brisk wind,
sun.

Drying air.

Sunday 11.
42; W, NW.
Cold, drying wind.

Monday 12.
S, S.
Driving rain, vast
showers.

Stormy.

Tuesday 13.
29½ 3/10; 51; SW.
Sun, small showers,
mild.

Wednesday 14.
29½ 2/10; 51; SW.
Driving rain,
warm.

Bee on the asters.

Thursday 15.
29½ 3/10; 51; E.

Vast rain at night.

Mist & driving   The ground so wet that no sowing goes forward. Much ground
rain.   unsown.

Friday 16.
29½ 2/10, 29½;   Vast rain in the night & all day. Again at night.
49; E.
Rain all day.

Saturday 17.
29 3/10; 47; W,   Sharp air.
NW.
Sun, showers,
bright.

Sunday 18.
29 4/10; 43; N,
NE.
Dark & cold.

Monday 19.
29 1/10½; 38; E.   Some few flakes of snow.
Black frost, dark
and cold.

Tuesday 20.
29 1/10, 29 4/10;   Severe wind. Plows are frozen out.
36; NE, NW.
Hard frost, sun,
clouds.

Wednesday 21.
29½ 4/10; 31; W,   Bearing Ice.
W.   Thaw.
Hard frost, sun,
dark.

Thursday 22.
29½ 2/10, 29 3/10;
36; S, W.
Rain, vast rain &
wind.

Friday 23.
29 2/10; 47; W.
Grey, wind.

Saturday 24.
29 3/10½; 47; W,   The wild wood pigeon, or stock-dove¶ begins to appear.
NW.

Dark, sweet sun,
shower, bright.
Oenas sive vinago.

They leave us all to a bird in the spring, & do not breed in these parts; perhaps not in this island. If they are birds of passage they are the last winter bird of passage that appears. The numbers that come to these parts are strangely diminished within these twenty years. For about that distance of time such multitudes used to be observed, as they went to & from roost, that they filled the air for a mile together: but now seldom more than 40 or 50 are to be anywhere seen. They feed on acorns, beech-mast, & turneps. They are much smaller than the ring dove, which stays with us all the year.

Sunday 25.
29; 47; SW.
Grey, sun, rain &
wind.

Linnets flock in prodigious numbers.

Monday 26.
28½ 1/10; 43½;
SW.
Sun, rain, snow,
sun.

Heavy rain; some snow.

Tuesday 27.
29½; 39; NW, N.
Frost, grey, sun.

Wednesday 28.
29½ 2/10¾; 35;
NW, NW.
Hard frost, sun,
still.

Very white.
The planet Mercury appears above the sun.

Thursday 29.
29½; 36; S, S.
Rain, rain, mist,
rain.

Friday 30.
29½ 3/10; 42; S, S.
Thick fog. Dº

Some spitting rain.

DECEMBER 1770

Saturday 1.
30; 41; NW, SW.
Frost, grey,
moonshine.

Some oaks have yet some green leaves.

Those oaks that were eaten bare by the chafers leafed again about midsumʳ & continued unusually green late into Novemʳ

Sunday 2.
29½ 3/10½; 43; S, SW.
Great rain, grey.

The earth in a sad wet condition. Wells strangely risen: one well runs over: our wells are about ten fathoms deep.

Monday 3.
29½ 3/10; 41; W, SW.
Grey & pleasant.

Some oaks very green still.

Tuesday 4.
29½ 4/10; 41; W, NW.
Grey, sun, rain, mild, fog.

Most owls seem to hoot exactly in B flat according to several pitch-pipes used in tuning of harpsichords, & sold as strictly at concert-pitch.

Wednesday 5.
29½ 3/10; 41; SW.
Grey, rain, vast rain.

Thursday 6.
29 3/10; 42; SW, W.
Sun.

Vast rain & tempest in the night.

Friday 7.
29½ 1/10; 40; W, NW.
Strong wind, small rain, wind.

Stormy wind all night.

Saturday 8.
29½ 1/10; 40; W, W.
Grey, sun, spitting rain, hail.

Wild fowl abound in the ponds on Woolmere forest: they lie in the great waters by day & feed in the streams & plashes by night.

Sunday 9.
29½ 2/10; 37½; NW, W.
Hard frost, sun shines.

Hail in the night. Frost almost constantly succeeds hail.

Monday 10.
29½ 1/10½; 34; W.
Severe frost, still & sun.

Ice bears.

Water cascading down
the old hollow lane to Alton.
December.

Tuesday 11.
29½ 2/10; 34½;
SW.
Frost, grey, small
rain, hard rain.

Wednesday 12.
29½ 3/10½; 42;
W, SW.
Sun, cold, drying
wind.

Great rain in the night with wind.

Thursday 13.
29½; 44½; W,
SW.
Rain, fog, rain.

Dark & dismal.

Friday 14.
29½ 2/10½; 41½;
SW.
Wh: frost, sun,
clouds.

Saturday 15.
29 2/10; 45½; SW,
W.
Grey, windy,
misling.¶

Vast rain in the night with wind.

It appears by a letter from my Nephew Sam Barker that in one
three weeks since the commencement of this wet fit there fell in the
country of Rutland 7½ of rain: which is more than has fallen in
any such space for more than 30 years past. The mean rain of a
twelve months in Rutland is 21 inch: & ½.

Sunday 16.
29½ 2/10; 48; SW.
Sun, rain, wind,
dry.

Monday 17.
29½ 1/10½; 44;
W.
Grey, sun, showers.

Young lambs begin to fall on the sands round the forest.

Tuesday 18.
29 3/10; 41½; SW,
SW, NW.
Dark, drizling,
showers, stormy.

Wood-pigeons, a large flock.

Wednesday 19.
29½ 3/10½; 43½;
W.
Sun, brisk wind,
still.

Tempestuous wind all night. This storm did great mischief at sea especially among the colliers.

Thursday 20.
29 1/10; 43½; SW,
SW.
Rain, windy,
stormy.

Great rain.

Friday 21.
29½; 39; W, NW.
Cold, rain, sun,
sleet, grey.

Musca tenax does not die as winter comes on, but lays itself up.

Saturday 22.
29½ 3/10; 35½;
NW, W.
Smart frost, sun,
grey, & creamy.

Trenched-up the quarters of the garden for the winter.

Sunday 23.
29 3/10; 40; S, SW.
Rain, sun, &
clouds.

Rain all night.
Skylarks flock.
Linnets flock, & haunt the oat-stubbles & pease-fields.

Monday 24.
29 3/10; 43; E, SE.
Spitting rain, fog,
rain.

Great rain in the night.
Wren whistles vigorously.

Tuesday 25.
29½ 3/10; 39, 37;
N, N.
Grey, sun, red sky,
frost.

Vast rain in the night, some snow towards morning.

Wednesday 26.
29½ 2/10, 29½
1/10½; 32, 35; W,
SW, W.

Hard frost, thaw, rain.

Thursday 27.
29½, 29½ 2/10; 43½; W, W.
Grey, wind, sun, grey.

Vast rain in the night.

Friday 28.
29½ 1/10; 43½; W.
Rain, fog, sun, moon shine.

The lavants, or land-springs run very strong between Faringdon & Chawton.

Saturday 29.
29½; 46½; SW, SW.
Fine day.

White wagtail.

Wrens whistle all the winter except in severe frost. Wrens whistle much more than any other English bird in a wild state. The redbreast sings great part of the year; but at intervals is silent.

Monday 31.
29½ 1/10; 46½; SW.
Dry, sun, windy, misly rain.

Warm air.

This year concludes with a very wet season, which has lasted from the middle of Oct! last, & has occasioned vast floods, & desolation both at home & abroad. Much wheat-land in wet countries remains unsown.

JANUARY   — 1771 —

Tuesday 1.
29½ 1/10; 48: W, SW.
Driving rain, stormy.

SELBORNE
Red-breast whistles.

Wednesday 2.
29 3/10½; 51; S.
Rain, sun, grey.

Vast rain.
Shell-less snails come forth.

Thursday 3.
29 2/10; 51; W, SW.
Great rain, large hail.

BRADLEY
Wood-lice, *onisci aselli*, appear all the winter in mild weather: spiders appear all the winter in moist weather; *lepismae* appear all the winter round hearths & in warm places.

Friday 4.
NW, W.
Crisp frost, sweet
day.

Saturday 5.
29½/1½10; 36½;
SW, NW.
Frost, sun, clouds,
stars.

SELBORNE
Some kinds of gnats appear all the winter in mild weather, as do
earth-worms, after it is dark, when there is no frost.

Sunday 6.
29½ 1/10, 29½ 3/
10; 34½, 32½; N,
N.
Hard frost, still &
fine, frost.

Large titmouse makes it's spring note.

Monday 7.
29½ 3/10; 30,
31½; W.
Severe frost, grey,
snow, freezes.

Some flakes of snow.

Tuesday 8.
29½ 1/10; 27½,
28½; NW.
Severe, sun, grey,
sharp wind.

Wednesday 9.
29½ 2/10; 28;
NW.
Severe frost, sun,
sharp wind.

Frost comes within doors. Thermometer within 28, in the wine
vault 43½, abroad 24.

Thursday 10.
29½; 28; NW.
Frost, sun, still,
pleasant.

Friday 11.
29 4/10½, 26½,
28; NE, E.
Severe, snow, sun,
severe wind.

Small snow on the ground.
Water-bottles freeze in chambers.

Saturday 12.
29½; 26½, 26½,

White wagtail.

26½; NE.
Severe biting wind,
grey.

Paths dusty.

Sunday 13.
29 4/10½; 25,
24½; 24; NE.
Severe, dark,
some snow, still,
clear.

Some flights of snow.

Monday 14.
29½ 1/10; 23½,
26; NE.
Still & bright, dark.

Tuesday 15.
29½ 1/10; 28, 30;
E.
Bright, & still.

Ways dusty.

Wednesday 16.
29 4/10½; 26½; E.
Rimes, sun, dark.

Thursday 17.
29½ 1/10; 28, 30;
NE.
Sun, blue mist,
still.

Paths very dusty.

Friday 18.
29 2/10½; 27¾,
30; NE.
Dark, sun, stars,
dark.

Barometer sinks apace.

Saturday 19.
29 1/10; 29½,
31½; E, SE.
Dark, sun, snow,
snow.

Small snow.
More snow.

By a letter from town it appears that in London in an hard frost
Martin's Thermometer it [is] just at the same pitch abroad in the
area, that it is with me in the dining-room without a fire.

Sunday 20.
29 3/10½; 31½;
SE, E.
Thick fog, thaw.

Snow melts.

Monday 21.
29½ 2/10½; 34½;
N, NE, N.
Dark, thaw, cold
wind.

Tuesday 22.
30; 35, 36½; N.　　　Frost goes off without rain.
Dark, thaw, sun,
dark.

Wednesday 23.
29½ 4/10½,30;
35; W, NW.
Grey, mild,
thaw.

Thursday 24.
29½ 2/10; 35, 38;　　　Sky strangely streaked with blue & red.
W, W.　　　　　　　　Wind & rain in the night.
Frost, sun, thaw,
wind.

Friday 25.
29½ 3/10½; 40½;　　　Larks rise & essay to sing.
W, SW, W.　　　　　　Daws begin to come to churches.¶
Sun, pleasant.

Saturday 26.
29 3/10; 40½; SW.　　Woodlark, red-breast, wren, great black titmouse sing.
Grey, sun, soft　　　　Lambs fall apace.
rain.

Sunday 27.
29½ 1/10½; 38½;
W, NW.
Frost, sun, & strong
wind, frost.

Monday 28.
29 2/10; 36½; E.　　　Turneps are very small this year, and are on the decay.
Snow, rain, fog,
rain.

Tuesday 29.
29½ 2/10; 36½; E,　　Small flights of snow.
SE.
Grey, snow, sun,
snow.

Wednesday 30.
29½ 1/10; 40; S,
SE.
Fog, wet, rain.

Hedge-sparrow essays to sing.

Thursday 31.
29½ 1/10½; 46,
47½; W, SW.
Rain, rain, rain &
wind.

FEBRUARY 1771

Friday 1.
29½ 2/10; 44½;
W.
Sun, brisk wind,
hail.

Spring-like weather.

Saturday 2.
29½ 4/10; 42; W.
Sun, showers, red
sky.

Made my seedling cucumber-bed.
Sky-larks rise a little way & sing.

Sunday 3.
30, 30 1/10; 41, 43;
W.
Fog, sun, sweet day.

Hens sit. Hedge-sparrow sings.
Soft, spring-like weather.
Rooks resort to their nest-trees.

Monday 4.
30 1/10; 42; W.
Grey & mild, sun,
sweet day.

Tuesday 5.
29½ 4/10½; 42;
SW.
Frost, fog, fog, sun.

FYFIELD
Warm fog.
Grey crows.
Creeping mist over the meadows.

Wednesday 6.
29½ 4/10; 41, 40;
S, E.
Frost, sun, fog,
rain, snow.

Bunting twitters.

Thursday 7.
29½ 3/10; 38; NE.
Frost, grey, sun,
frost.

Considerable snow on the ground.
Thermom.ʳ abroad 21½.

Friday 8.
29½ 3/10; 34,
32½; NE.
Hard frost, sun,
flying snow, dark.

Saturday 9.
29½ 4/10½; 32;   A decanter of water froze in my chamber.
NE.   Thermom. abroad 28.
Small flights of
snow, snow.   Eggs in the ovary of a turkey pullet about the size of mustard
                        seeds. Mem: to enquire when the pullets of the same brood will
                        begin to lay.

Sunday 10.
29½ 1/10; 31½;   Rooks flock to the farm yards.
NE.   Therm: abroad 12.
Severe, flying snow.

Monday 11.
29 3/10½; 31½; E.   Therm: abroad 25.
Small snow.   Small birds begin to cloak.¶
                       Therm: abroad 18.

                       Fieldfares, redwings, skielarks & tit-larks resort to yᵉ watered
                       meadows for food:¶ the latter wades up to it's belly in pursuit of
                       the pupae of insects, & runs along upon the floating grass & weeds.
                       Many gnats on the snow near the water: these support the birds in
                       part.

Tuesday 12.
29½; NE, NW.   Thermom. at sun rise abroad at 6. Wagtails white, grey, yellow.
Fierce frost, sun,   [Therm:] . . . at 10.
sun.

Wednesday 13.
29 3/10½; S, S.   Therm. at 24 early, night at 18.
Frost, rime, sun,   Red-wings die.
frost.

Thursday 14.
29 4/10; E, E.   Therm. abroad 10.
Fierce frost, sun   Sun hot, & melts the snow.
hot, frost.   Therm: . . . 9.

Friday 15.
29 4/10; E, E.   Therm: 21
Frost, rime, sun,   Sea gull down the stream.
grey.   Therm: . . . 32.

Saturday 16. 29 4/10, 29½ 1/10½; 37; E, E. Fog, warm, thaw, rain.	Therm^r within 37. . . . abroad 44. Turkey struts & gobbles. Gnats, & flies appear.
Sunday 17. 30; 40; S, SE. Grey & soft, wet mist.	Snow quite gone. Rooks return to y^ir nest-trees. Missle-thrush sings.
Monday 18. 30 1/10½; 45; SE, E. Sun, sweet day, fog. ✿ *Hepatica*, crocus, winter aconite. *Papilio urticae*.	Bees come out of their hives. Chaffinch, bunting, yellow hammer sing. Ravens build. Rooks attempt to build. Flies appear.
Tuesday 19. 29½ 4/10; 42; SE. Grey, sun, sweet day.	Trufles are found by the hunters in my brother's grove. *Aurora borealis*.
Wednesday 20. 29½ 1/10; 44½; SE. Sun, sweet day. *Papilio rhamni*.	Crisp frost, & very white dew. Bright *aurora*.
Thursday 21. 29½ ½/10; 46; SE, W. Hard frost, sun, sweet day.	Goldfinch sings. Bees come out round the hives as if swarming. Wind so still as not to move the cock.
Friday 22. 29½; 42; SE. Heavy fog, sweet afternoon.	BRADLEY Hen chaffinches congregate still. Very hot sun in the lanes.
Saturday 23. 29½ 1/10; 43; SW. Fog, grey, fog.	SELBORNE Blackbird whistles. The thaw surprisingly quick considering the small quantity of rain. Does not the warmth at such times come from below? The cold in still severe seasons seems to come down from above: for the coming over of a cloud in severe nights raises the thermom^r abroad

at once full ten degrees. The first notices of thaws often seem to appear in vaults, cellars, &c.

Sunday 24.
29½ 1/10; 41; SE.
Fog, sun, cold wind.

Ground very dry.

Monday 25.
29 2/10½; 45; SE.
Vast rain with wind.

Tuesday 26.
S.
Fog, spring weather, fog.

Song-thrush whistles.

Wednesday 27.
29½ 3/10; 46; SE.
Vast fog, grey.
🌱 *Crocus vernus.*

Thursday 28.
29½ 2/10½; 50; S.
Fog, soft & cloudy.
🌱 *Corylus avellana* masc: & fem: *Rana bufo.*

Blackbird whistles.
Helleborus viridis emerges, & shews it's flower-budds.

MARCH 1771

Friday 1.
29½ ½/10; 42½;
E.
Cold, & dark.

Paths get steady.
Cucumber-plants thrive.
Pease are sowing in the fields.

Saturday 2.
29 3/10½; 37½;
NE.
Dark, & cold.

Glass sinks steadily tho' yᵉ weather looks like dry.

Turneps are all rotten, & the wheat-fields look quite bare, & destitute of all verdure. Farmer parsons sows wheat in his fallow behind Beacher's shop, which was drowned in the winter. Mem: to observe what crop he gets from this spring-sowing. The spring-sowing round this village proved the finest wheat, & best crop.

Sunday 3.
29 2/10; 38; E, NE.

Considerable rain in the night.
Harsh wind.

Rain, dark & raw.

Monday 4.
29 4/10; 35; NE.
Ice, sleet, dark &
cold.

Great distress among the flocks: the turneps are all rotten, the ewes have little milk, & the lambs die.

Tuesday 5.
29 3/10; 34, 33;
NE.
Snow, sleety &
dark, frost.

Snow covers the ground.

Wednesday 6.
29 2/10; 34½; N.
Hard frost, sun,
snow, frost.

Thursday 7.
29 4/10½; 33½,
33; N, NW.
Hard frost, sun,
flights of snow.

Severe weather for the season.

Friday 8.
29½ 1/10; 31½,
32½; NW, NW.
Snow, severe wind,
dark, frost.

Large flocks of wild-geese go over the forest to the Eastward.

Saturday 9.
29½; 32; N, E.
Frost, grey, sun,
frost.

Sunday 10.
29½ 1/10; 30¾,
32; NE, E.
Hard frost, grey,
severe wind.

The ground thawed much in the middle of the day.
Rooks build notwithstanding the severe weather.

Monday 11.
29½ 2/10; 32; E,
E.
Hard frost, sharp
wind, & sun.

Crocuss at this time used to be in full bloom. Only one or two roots blowed before this frost began.

Made the bearing cucumber-bed with 8 cartloads of dung.

Tuesday 12.
29 3/10½; 35, 37;

E, SE.
Mist, rain, vast
rain.

Wednesday 13.
44½; S.
Showers, clouds &
wind.

BRAMSHOT
Wild fowls on Woollmere pond. Some large white fowls also:
qu: what? they had black heads.
Snipes begin to pipe in the moors.

Thursday 14.
S.
Soft sunny day.

Upon examination it seems probable that the gulls which I saw
were the pewit-gulls, or black caps, the *larus ridibundus* Linn:
They haunt, it seems, inland pools, & some times breed on them.
See *Brit: zoöl*: vol: 2nd.

Friday 15.
29½; SW.
Grey & mild.

Saturday 16.
29½ 1/10½; 44½;
E.
Mist, large rain.

SELBORNE
Crocuss begin to blow, & make a show.

Sunday 17.
30 ¼ 10; 42; N.
Cold, black
weather.

Monday 18.
30; 38; NE.
Dark, & still.

Paths dry.

Tuesday 19.
30 ½ 10; 38; NE.
Fog, dark & still,
sun.

Cucumber-plants thrive & shew the rudiments of bloom & fruit.
Farmer Turner sows wheat.
Crocuss figure.

Wednesday 20.
29½ 3/10½; 40;
W, S, SW.
Red sky, sun,
spitting rain.

Planted from their pots the cucumr-plants into their bearing bed.
Plants are strong.

Thursday 21.
30; 45; W,
NW, N.
Sun, fog, dark &
cold.

Strong wind.

Friday 22.
29½ 3/10; 37½;
N, NW, N.
Frost, dark, cold,
sleet, clear.

Sharp wind with frost.

Saturday 23.
29½ 2/10; 32½;
N, N.
Severe frost, sun, &
flights of snow.

Cutting wind.

Dr Johnson says,¶ "that in 1771 the season was so severe in the
Island of Sky that it is remembered by the name of the *black
spring*. The snow, which seldom lies at all, covered the ground for
eight weeks. Many cattle dyed, & those cows that survived were so
emaciated, & dispirited that they did not require the male at the
usual season." The case was just the same with us in the South:
never were so many barren cows known as in the spring following
that dreadful period. Whole dairies missed being in calf together.

Sunday 24.
29½ 2/10; 31½;
N.
Most severe, harsh
wind, flights of
snow.

Chaffinches & linnets flock still.

Monday 25.
29½ 2/10½; 29½;
N.
Most severe wind,
& snow.

Weather unusually severe. It freezes within. Plows are frozen
out: ice bears.

Tuesday 26.
29½ 1/10½; N, E.
Most severe, bright
sun.

Thermom^t at sunrise down at 17 abroad.
At 10 o'clock at night 25.
at sun rise . . . 23½.

Wednesday 27.
29½ 1/10; W, SW,
S.
Frost, clouds & sun.

Softer air.

Thursday 28.
29½ 2/10½; 36; E,
NE.
Frost, sun & clouds.

Snow in the night.
A flock of lapwings haunts about the common.

Friday 29.
29½ 3/10; 36; NE.
Frost, dark &

Hail in the night.
Severe wind which freezes all day.

harsh, sun.

Saturday 30.
30; 34; NE.
Frost, bright sun.

Ground hard, & thick ice.
Crocuss in full bloom.
Birds mate.
Some farmers feed y^{ir} sheep with bran & oates.

Sunday 31.
30 1/10; 38; NE,
N.
Sharp wind, sun,
moderate weather.
❀ *Cucumis sativus*,
Masc:, *Ficaria
verna*.

The face of the earth naked to a wonderful degree. Wheat hardly
to be seen & no signs of any grass: turneps all gone, & sheep in a
starving way.

APRIL 1771

Monday 1.
30; 40; NE, N.
Grey, sun, pleasant
day.

All provisions rising in price. Farmers cannot sow for want of
rain.

Mr Woods¶ of Chilgrove had on this day 27 acres of spring-sown
wheat not then sprouted out of the ground; & yet he had a good
crop from those fields, no less than 4 quarters on an acre!

Tuesday 2.
29½ 4/10; 40; NE.
Rime, sun, blue
mist, sun.

Butterflies appear again. Some flies begin to appear. Spring-like
day. Sharp in the morning.

Wednesday 3.
29½ 4/10½; 42½;
NE.
Fog, sun, blue mist,
clouds.
❀ *Cucumis sativus*
fem:

Planted potatoes, & sowed carrots, parsneps, onions, coss-lettuce,
leeks.

Thursday 4.
29½ 4/10; 40¼; E,
SE, S.
Hard frost, bright
sun.
❀ *Amygdalus persica*.
Apis bombinatrix.

Ring-ouzel.
Pleasant day, but every thing quite dryed up. No lambs frolic &
play as usual . . . *acrior illos Cura domat . . . . Virg*:¶

Friday 5.
29½ 2/10; 42½;
W, NW.

Birds begin to whistle a little.
Storm cock sings.

White, hot sun,
clouds, sun.
🌸 *Prunus armeniaca.*

Saturday 6.
30; 45½; NE.
Dark & harsh.

Began to be confined.

Sunday 7.
29½ 3/10½; 40;
NE.
Frost, Dark & cold,
sun.

Ring-ouzels begin to appear on their spring visit.

Monday 8.
29½ 2/10; 40; E.
Frost, dark, warm
sun.

Tuesday 9.
29½ 2/10½; 42½;
E.
Frost, rime, sun &
blue mist.
Jynx.

Wryneck pipes about in orchards. The first spring bird of
passage.

Wednesday 10.
29½ 4/10¾; 41½;
E.
White frost, harsh
wind, sun & clouds.

Thursday 11.
29½ 3/10¾; 39; E.
White frost, sunny,
& harsh
*Regulus non crist:
min:*

No rain since the 16ᵗʰ of March: dirty lanes all dryed-up.

Friday 12.
29½ 1/10½; 41½;
E, NW.
Fog, sun & blue
mist.

The second spring-bird of passage.

Saturday 13.
29½ 2/10½; 42½;
NW.
Small frost, sun, sun.

The dry weather has lasted just a month this day.

Dry weather is always supposed to help the wheat in the clays: but the wheat in general is so poor this year, that it is hardly seen on the ground. It will be worth remarking at harvest how the crop will turn-out.

Sunday 14.
29½; 45; W, W.
Sun, dark & cold,
clear.
Hirundo domestica.

Swallow appears as last year amidst frost & snow!
No frost.
Wind blows hollow.

Monday 15.
29½ 2/10; 39,
37½; N, NW.
Sun, severe air.

Hail in the night. Flights of snow at times: harsh biting day.
Thermom.ᵗ abroad at 10 at night down at 14 degrees!!!

Tuesday 16.
29½ 1/10¾; 32½,
36½; NW, W, N.
Intense frost,
severe wind, much
snow.

Froze within. Violent wind. Flying snow. Snow for many hours very heavy.

Wednesday 17.
30 1/10; 35, 42; N,
NW.
Sun, sharp
wind, shower of
snow.

Snow on the ground.
No *oedicnemus* (land curlew) has been heard yet.

Thursday 18.
30 2/10; 37, 43; N,
NE.
Frost, sun & sharp
wind.
Luscinia.

Cut the first cucumber; not a very fair fruit. Swallow. Colds & coughs universal.

Friday 19.
30; 43; N.
White frost, sun,
harsh wind.

Hay risen to four pounds per ton.
High rumbling wind.

Saturday 20.
29½ 4/10½; 42,
49; N, W.
Sun, grey & mild,
dark, sprinkling
rain.

The dry weather has lasted five weeks this day.

Just rain enough to discolour the pavement. Myriads of minute frogs, encouraged by those few drops of rain, migrate from the ponds & pools where they were hatched. Hence it appears that severe frost doth not interrupt the hatching & growth of young frogs.

Sunday 21.
29½ 3/10½; 46,
55½; W, S, SW.
Sun, grey: summer
like, mild & soft.

Crocuss that stand in the shade not out of bloom yet.
Sky shews for rain, & wind shifts about.

Monday 22.
29½ 1/10¼; 53;
W, SW.
Fog, dark & mild,
sun, heavy clouds.
*Alauda minima
locustae voce stridet.*

Nightingale. No more swallows appear.
Great showers about.

Tuesday 23.
29½ 1/10; 48, 50;
W, NW.
Sun, high clouds,
dark, shower,
bright.

Drying wind. Many showers about.
Small shower.

*Green helleboves on hedgerow bank.
Selborne Parish.
24 April.*

Wednesday 24.
29 4/10; 45; W, S,
W.
Sun, clouds,
showers, strong
wind.
*Oedicnemus.**

*Stone-curlew returns, & clamours.
The ground somewhat moistened.

Thursday 25.
29½ 4/10; 46, 50;
NW, W.
Sun, clouds,
shower, sun.
Hirundo riparia.

Titlark sings.
Small showers.
Heavy rock-like clouds.

Friday 26.
30 1/10; 44, 50;
NW, SE, S.
White frost, dark,
sun.
*Cuculus,**
*Ruticilla.***

Wheat begins to mead.
**Redstart whistles.

*Cuckow sings this year long before ye leaf appears.

Saturday 27.
30 ½/10; 45½; SE.
Sun, grey, mild.
*Regulus non crist:
medius.*

NEWTON
Ring-dove cooes.

Farmers feed their ewes with bran, & oats, or white pease. Some
few fat lambs are killed.

Wood-cock, & some field-fares still appear.

Sunday 28.
29½ 4/10; N.
Sun, clouds,
showers.
Bombylius medius,
Papilio brascicae.

Monday 29.
NE.   *White throat.
Grey, showers still.   Grass begins to grow.
*Ficedulae affinis,**
Hirundo apus.

Tuesday 30.
N, E, SE, E.
Sleet, rain, rain,
cold.
Hirundo agrestis.

MAY 1771

Wednesday 1.   SELBORNE
29½ 1/10½; 44;   Plenty of rain in the night.
N, NE.   Trees as bare as at Xmas.
Rain, fog, rain,
grey.

Thursday 2.
29½ 4/10; 43½;   House swallows abound.
NE, N.   Several martins.
Dark, cold, sun.   Ground well soaked.

Friday 3.
29½ 4/10½; 46½;   The turtle-dove returns & cooes.
S, SE.   Sowed white cucumber under an hand-glass.
Sun, dark, showers,
fine.
Turtur.

Saturday 4.
29½ 2/10; 47½; E,   Cucumbers swell away, & set apace.
NE.   Black-caps appear, & begin to sing.
Sun, dark,   Sowed white dwarf kidney-beans.
showers, spring
weather.
Atricapilla.

Sunday 5.
29½ 1/10; 52, 57;
E, S, E, SE.
Mist, sun, clouds,
sultry, thunder,
rain, sun.

Fine growing weather.
Several claps of thunder.
Moderate shower.

Monday 6.
29½; 51, 58; E, E.
Mist, dark, soft rain
half the day.

Great showers about.
Cucum.ʳˢ abound.
Most growing weather.

Tuesday 7.
29½; 53, 56; E,
SE.
Dark, soft rain.

Grass & corn grow very fast.
Soft rain most part of the day.

Wednesday 8.
29 4/10½; 55; E.
Warm, showers,
sun.
Caprimulgus.

Asparagus begin to sprout.
Fern-owl chatters.

Thursday 9.
29½ 2/10½; 56½,
60; W, S, S.
Sun, clouds, warm,
showers about.

Summer-like weather.
Some beeches begin to leaf.

Friday 10.
29½ 2/10½; 57½,
57½; N, N.
Dark, great
showers, dark.
Stoparola.

Fly-catcher. This bird is usually the last of the summer birds of
passage.

Saturday 11.
29½ 2/10; 54½,
54½; NE, NE.
Vast fog, dark &
foggy.
*Passer arundinaceus
minor.**

Cherry-trees begin to blossom.
*The sedge bird of the *Brit*: *zool*: sings about waters: variety of
notes; but the manner is hurrying.

Sunday 12.
29½ 2/10½; 53½,
55; S, SW, S.
Dark, rain, wind,
sun.

Ground very moist.
Barley, & all spring corn comes up well.
Vast *Aurora* for the NE & SE & all round.

Monday 13.
29½ 3/10; 49½; S,
SE, E.
White frost, sun,
clouds, sun, clouds.
*Regulus non crist
major cantat voce,* *
Stridula locustae.

Swallows & martins collect dirt for building.
*Usually a late bird of passage.
The horizon looks dark & louring.

Tuesday 14.
29½ 2/10¾; 54½,
62; E, NE, SW.
Shower, sun, hot
sun, thunder.

Vast rock-like clouds.
Loud thunder, & hail at eleven at night.
Much distant lightening.
Vines begin to sprout, & shew leaves.
Distant thunder, & showers about.

Wednesday 15.
29½ 1/10; 54½,
64; E, SW.
Sun, sultry, dark.

Thursday 16.
29 ½/10; 62½, 67;
E, SE, SW.
Sun, hot, brisk air,
clouds, soft.

Hanger in leaf this day: yesterday but a few trees were green.
Trees & hedges in general begin to leaf.

Friday 17.
29½ 1/10½; 63¾,
68; W, SW, W.
Dark, sun, dark,
cloud & rain.
Conops calcitrans.¶

Saturday 18.
29½ 4/10; 58½;
NW, NW.
Dark, sun, sweet
afternoon.
Hippobosca equina. *
*Gryllus
gryllotalpa.* **

Began to cut grass for the horses.
*The side-fly on horses.
**Mole-cricket churs in the moist meadows.

Sunday 19.
29½ 4/10½; 56½,
58; NW, SW, S,
SW.
Summer morn,
clouds, cool, chilly

evening.
Musca vomitoria.

Monday 20.
29½ 4/10½; 57;
SE, NE.
Dark, grey, sweet
weather, dark
clouds.

Still & soft.

Tuesday 21.
29½ 3/10½; 58½;
NE, W, S.
Sun, hot sun, cool
air, clouds.

Apple & pear-trees begin to blow out.

Wednesday 22.
29½ 4/10½; 59½;
NW.
Sun, clouds.

BRADLEY

Thursday 23.
N, SW.
Bright sun, brisk
air.
*Musca tenax, Musca
meridiana.*

Friday 24.
29½ 3/10½; 63½;
SW.
Bright sun, cool air.
*Musca carnaria,
Libellula.*

SELBORNE
Apple-trees much blown.

Saturday 25.
29½ 2/10; 58½;
SW, W, S.
Sun, brisk cool air.
*Gryllus campestris.**

*Field-cricket begins to shrill.
Cuckows abound this year.

We have round this church usually about 8 pairs of swifts: they do
not come all together, but in a straggling manner, a few at a time:
perhaps a pair many days before the rest.

Sunday 26.
29½ 1/10; 60; S, S.
Sun, clouds, strong
wind.
*Scarabaeus
melolontha.*

Few chafers appear.

Monday 27.
29½ 2/10½; S,
SW.
Blowing, misty
rain.

Tuesday 28.   RINGMER
29½; SW.   Apple trees in full bloom.
Sun, wind, sun.

Wednesday 29.
29½; SW.   Hawthorn blows.
Sun, clouds, brisk
wind.

Thursday 30.
29 3/10; SW.
Rain, strong wind,
sun, showers.

Friday 31.
29 4/10; SW.
Sun, clouds, rain.

JUNE 1771

Saturday 1.
29 4/10½; SW.
Rain, sun, clouds,
wind, showers.

Sunday 2.
29½ 3/10; NW.   Black-caps abound.
Sun, clouds,
showers, hail, fine.
Musca Caesar.

Monday 3.
29½ 2/10½; NW,
SW.
Sun, summer,
chilly.

Tuesday 4.
29½ 4/10; NW,
SW.
Dark, small rain,
still, cloudy.

Wednesday 5.
29½ 2/10; W, SW.
Bright, summer,
soft & still.

The nest of a *gryllo-talpa* full of eggs.

Thursday 6.
29½ 2/10; SW.
Sun, pleasant.
*Ephemera vulgata.**

**Meridie choreus aireas instituit, sursum recte tendens, rediensq eâdem fere viâ;¶* Scopoli.

A mole-cricket's nest full of small eggs was discovered just under the turf in the garden near the pond. They were of a dirty yellow colour, & of an oval shape, surrounded with a tough skin, & too small to have any rudiments of young within them, being full of viscous substance. There might be an hundred eggs in this one nest, they lay very shallow just under a little fresh-moved mould in an hollow formed for that purpose.

Friday 7.
Sun, hot, clouds.
Apis longicornis.

Mayfly by Shortheath Pond.

Saturday 8.
Cloudless, brisk
gale.

SELBORNE

Sunday 9.
29½ 3/10½; 67;
NE, SE.
Dark, sun, blue
mist, thunder
clouds.

Sultry.

Monday 10
29½ 3/10; 67; E.
Dark, grey, sultry.
Ephemera caudâ bisetâ.

WINTON

Small rain in the night. The angler's may-fly. Myriads of mayflies appear for the first time on the Alresford stream. The air was crouded with them, & the surface of the water covered. Large trouts sucked them in as they lay struggling on the surface of the stream, unable to rise til their wings were dryed. This appearance reconciled me in some measure to the wonderful account that Scopoli gives of the quantities emerging from the rivers of Carniola.
See his *Entomologia*

Tuesday 11.
NW.
Rain, dark, hot.

Wednesday 12.
29½ 1/10½; NW.
Showers, hot,
showers, dark.

FYFIELD

Thursday 13.
29½ 2/10; 66;
NW.
Dark, showers, dark
& moist.
Sphinx filipendula.¶

*Emerges from it's aurelia state. Fixes it's cods to dry twigs in hedges; is called in Hants the Sᵗ foin fly; & is in it's crawling state said to be very pernicious to that plant.

Friday 14.
29½ 2/10; 65;
NW.
Sun, clouds.

Saturday 15.
29 3/10½; 62;
NW, SW.
Great dew, dark,
rain, rain.

Bar: falls all day.
Wheat-ears peep.
Sᵗ foin begins to be cut.

Sunday 16.
29, 29, 3/10½; 56;
55; NW.
Wind, rain, wind,
rain.

Tempestuous wind, & vast rain for 22 hours.

Monday 17.
29 4/10; 56; NW.
Sun, wind, sun,
cold wind.

Tearing wind, which damages all the gardens.

Tuesday 18.
29½ 3/10½; 58;
NW.
Sun, clouds, brisk
wind, sweet even.

Strawberries.
Wheat-ears come out.
Nightingale sings.

Wednesday 19.
29½ 3/10½; 61;
W, NW.
Dark, brisk wind,
sun.

Swift sits, & comes out of an evening to feed for a few minutes.

Thursday 20.
29½ 4/10; 62;
NW.
Sun, brisk wind,
sun.

Sheep are shorn.
Sᵗ foin cut.

Friday 21.
29½ 3/10½; 64;

Sᵗ foin housed about Winton.

NW.
Hot sun, sultry.

Saturday 22.
30; 66; N.
Sun, brisk air, sweet
evening.

SELBORNE

Sunday 23.
30; 61; N.
Dark & cold, sun,
clouds.

Monday 24.
30; 60; N.
Dark, harsh.

BRADLEY
Cut my S^t foin.

Tuesday 25.
NE.
Sun, breeze, heavy
clouds.

Rain-bow. Rock-like clouds. Sweet evening. Moonshine.

Wednesday 26.
29½ 3/10; 69; NE,
E.
Sun, mist, vast
clouds.
❦ *Phallus impudicus
olet.*

SELBORNE
Showers about.

Thursday 27.
29½ 2/10; 70; NE.
Vast fog, sun,
clouds, shower, sun.

Distant thunder.
Sultry.

Friday 28.
29½ 2/10½; 64; N.
Dark & cool.

Hay makes slowly.

Saturday 29.
29½ 3/10¼; 58,
63; NE.
Cool, sun, sweet
day.

Ricked in two summer-cocks five jobbs of S^t foin in most curious
order.
Young martins hatched.
Apples, & pears but few.
Titlark whistles still.

Sunday 30.
29½ 3/10½; 59,
61½; NE.
Sun, dark & chilly.

Nothing grows in the garden.

JULY 1771

Monday 1.
29½ 3/10; 60½,
60½; NE.
Dark, & cold
wind.

Cut part of the mead: a good crop.
Young goldfinches.

Tuesday 2.
29½ 3/10¾; 58,
61½; N, NW.
Drops of rain,
clouds, sun, still.
🌱 *Triticum
hybernum.*

Cold weather damages the cucumbers. Hay makes slowly. Wheat
begins to blow.

Wednesday 3.
29½ 3/10½; 59;
NW.
Still & dark.

Thursday 4.
NW.
Sun, sweet even.

Ricked 6 jobbs of mead-hay in curious order, & added the Sᵗ foin
to it.

Friday 5.
30, 29½ 4/10½;
64, 69; W, NW.
Sun, clouds,
sprinkling.

Cut the slip & part of the mead.
Showers about.
Elder in full bloom.

Saturday 6.
29½ 4/10½; 65;
NW.
Sun, clouds, still &
dark.

Young swallows appear.
Cocked the hay in large cocks.

No kindly, regular dews all the summer; so that the walks & grass-
plots were seldom well mowed.

Sunday 7.
29½ 4/10½; 66;
SW, W.
Showers, showers,
fine.

Myriads of frogs, a second brood, migrate from J: Knight's
ponds.
Thunder about; & fine warm showers.

Monday 8.
29½ 3/10½; 66;
SW, W, SW.
Sun, clouds,
sprinklings.

Soft growing weather.
Threatning clouds all day.
Ricked the two jobbs of hay, & finish'd my rick in delicate order.

Tuesday 9.
29½ 2/10; 67; SW,
SW.
Sun & wind,
sprinkling.

Showers about.

Wednesday 10.
29½ 3/10; 67; W,
W.
Sun, clouds &
wind, still.
✤ *Vitis vinifera.*

Vine begins to blow. Very late again. it blowed last year on July 17. usually blows the last week in June.

Thursday 11.
29½ 2/10; 67; SW,
SW. Sun,
clouds & wind.

Sky threatens rain.

Friday 12.
29½ 1/10, 2/10½;
64½; SW, SW.
Shower, clouds,
wind, shower, fine.

Vine-bloom smells sweetly.
Threatning clouds

Saturday 13.
30 ½/10; 64; W,
SW, S, SW.
Sun, dark clouds,
sun, chilly.

No cucumbers for some weeks.
Much field-grass well made.

No dews.

Sunday 14.
30 1/10½; 67½;
NE, N, SW.
Glorious day.

Young martins, & swallows begin to congregate. Young swifts are fledge.

Monday 15.
30; 74; W, SE, S.
Beautiful day.

Lovely weather for the blowing of wheat.

Tuesday 16.
29½ 4/10¾; 75½;
SE, E.
Sultry, sunny day.

Good dew.
Gardens suffer for want of moisture.
Dark clouds round the horizon.

Wednesday 17.
29½ 3/10½; 71,
75; SE, SW.
Sun, sultry, sweet
even.

Good dew. Stopp'd the vines.
White cucumbers begin to bear: the green are still barren.
Clouds threaten.

Thursday 18.
29½ 1/10; 70, 69;
SW, SW.
Dark, small
showers, wind.

Dark heavy sky.
Blustering wind.

Friday 19.
29 4/10; 62, 64; W,
SW.
Sun, showers &
strong wind.
Tabanus bovinus.

Trenched out celeri.
Wind tears the hedges & flowers.

Saturday 20.
29½ 4/10; 60,
62½; NW.
Dark, harse[h]
wind.

Cold air.

Sunday 21.
29½ 4/10; 67;
NW, SW.
Dark, fine day.

Considerable rain in the night.
Frogs continue to migrate from the ponds.

Monday 22.
SW.
Small rain, hot sun.

FUNTINGTON

Tuesday 23.
NE, SW.
Sun, sultry, fine
even.

Pease begin to be cut.

Wednesday 24.
SE.
Dark, sun, fine
even.

Thursday 25.
SW.
Dark, rain.

Friday 26.
SW, W.
Hard showers,
stormy.

Turneps fail in many places, & are sown over again.

Saturday 27.
29½ 3/10; 68; SW,

SELBORNE
Cucumbers begin to bear again.

W.
Clouds & wind,
fine.

Sunday 28.
29½ 4/10; 64; W.　　Grasshopper-lark chirps.
Sun, clouds, dark,　Sweet evening.
shower, fine.

Monday 29.
30 1/10; 64; NW,
NW.
Sun, clouds, air,
sweet even.

Tuesday 30.
30, 29½ 3/10½;　　Cold white dew.
59; W, SW.
Sun, chilly, rain.

Wednesday 31.
29 4/10; 60, 62;　　Considerable rain in the night. Clap of thunder.
SW, W, NE.　　　Ground well soaked.
Rain, heavy
showers, showers.

AUGUST 1771

Thursday 1.
29½ 3/10; 57; W,　　Showers about.
NW.
Grey, drops, fine,
dew.
🌱 *Tremella nostoc.*

Friday 2.
29½ 4/10; 57, 60;　　Autumnal chill in the air.
NW, W.　　　　Showers about.
Dew, fine day.

Saturday 3.
29½ 4/10½; 60;　　Chilly air.
W, W.
Dark, dark &
chilly.

Sunday 4.
29½ 4/10; 61, 67;　　Swifts abound.
SW, W.

Small rain, dark,
sun & wind.

Monday 5.
29½ 3/10; 65; SW,   Young partridges strong flyers.
S, SW.   Soft showers.
Dew, dark,   Swifts. Pease are hacking.¶
showers, showers.

Tuesday 6.
29½ 1/10¾; 63,   Nuthatch chirps; is very loquacious at this time of the year.
66½; W, SW.   Large bat appears, *vespertilio altivolans*.¶
Dew, dark, sun,
warm.

Wednesday 7.
29½ ½/10; 65, 67;   Rye-harvest begins.
S, SW.   Procured the above-mentioned specimen of the bat, a male.
Sun, ripening
weather.

Thursday 8.
29½ 1/10; 64½,   Rain in the night with wind. Swifts.
67½; S, SW, W,   Sultry & moist: cucumbers bear abundantly.
SW.   Showers about.
Sun, sultry, clouds,   Procured a second large bat, a male.
hot & still.

Friday 9.
29½ 1/10; 64¾;   Good rain in the night with wind.
SW, W, SW.   Swifts.
Sun, clouds, wind,   Rain in the evening.
warm day.

Saturday 10.
29½ 3/10; 64; W,   Flying ants male & female.
SW, W.
Sun, clouds, &
wind, sun, still.

Sunday 11.
29½ 2/10; 63½;   Heavy clouds round the horizon.
W, SW.   Lambs play & frolick.
Sun, dark &
louring.

Monday 12.
29 2/10; 62; SE,   Rain most part of the night.
W, NW.   Thunder.

Rain, great showers.   Cartway runs. Swifts.

Tuesday 13.
29½ 1/10; 59; W,   Distant thunder.
NW, W.   Wheat-harvest begins.
Sun, clouds, heavy
showers.

Wednesday 14.
29½ 3/10; 59; W,
NW, W.
Sun, clouds, brisk
air, fine.

Thursday 15.
29½ 4/10; 58; W,   Swifts still. Air chilly.
SW.
Sun, clouds, dark
clouds.

Friday 16.
29½ 1/10½; 61;   Four swifts still.
W, SW.
Rain, driving rain,
dry.

Saturday 17.
29½ 3/10; 59, 62;   Drying wind. Swifts.
W, NW, SW.
Sun, strong wind,
still.

Sunday 18.
29½ ½/10; 59;   Swans flounce, & dive.
SW, SW.   Chilly & dark.
No dew, rain, rain,
rain.

Monday 19.
29 3/10; 61, 64;   Swifts abound. Swallows & martins bring out their second
SW, SW.   broods which are perchers.
Rain, rain, dry, vast   Thunder: wind.
shower.

Tuesday 20.
29½ ½/10; 59;   Swallows & martins in vast flocks.
SW, SW.   Swifts.
Sun, clouds, wind,
sun.

Wednesday 21.
29½ 3/10; 61; SW,
W, NW.
Sun, clouds, brisk
wind.

Swifts.
Showers about.

Thursday 22.
29½ 3/10; 59½;
SW, S.
Dew, sweet day,
fleecy sky.

Bank-martins bring out their second brood.
Swifts.
No swifts seen after this day.

Friday 23.
29½ 1/10; 61; S,
E. Cold dew,
dark & moist.

Young swallows & martins come-out every day. Still weather.
Wheat-harvest becomes pretty general.

Saturday 24.
29½ 1/10; 61, 58,
56; NE, N.
Rain, rain, rain.

Vast rain all day with a cold stormy wind.

Sunday 25.
29½ 3/10; 54, 56;
NW, NW.
Dark, cold, windy,
shower, bright.

Wheat not ripe at Faringdon. Winter weather. Oats & barley
ripe before wheat.

Monday 26.
29½ 4/10½; 54,
59½; NW, NW.
Sun, clouds & sun,
mild.

Nuthatch chirps much.
No swifts since 22nd.

Tuesday 27.
29½ 4/10½; 59,
64; SW, W.
Rain, hot sun, soft.

Rain in the night.
Good harvest weather.

Wednesday 28.
29½ 4/10½; 61;
SW, W.
Dark, grey & soft.

People bind their wheat.

Thursday 29.
29½ 4/10½; 65,
70½; W, SW.
Fog, sun, brisk
wind.

Sweet day.
Wheat begins to be housed.

Friday 30.
29½ 3/10; 64, 70;
SW, S.
Sun, hot & still.

Young Stoparolas abound.
Swallows congregate in vast flocks. Wheat housed.

Saturday 31.
29½ 1/10; 65, 71;
E, S, W.
Fog, sultry, cold,
fog.

Wheat housed all day.

SEPTEMBER 1771

Sunday 1.
29½ 3/10; 66; E,
NE.
Dark, grey, dark,
misty.

Monday 2.
29½ 4/10; 63; E,
NE.
Dew, dark, wind,
dark.

Corn is housed.
Swallows feed their young flying.

Tuesday 3.
29½ 3/10½; 61;
NE.
Dark, cold, dry.

Nuthatch chirps flying.
Some corn housed.
Swallows feed their young perchers.

Wednesday 4.
29½ 4/10; 61; NE.
Shower, dark,
shower, dark.

Hop-picking begins: hops small.
Much wheat not ripe yet.

Thursday 5.
29½ 4/10; 60½,
61; N.
Dark, sun, dark,
sun.

Wheat pretty well cut-down.
Soft & still.

Friday 6.
29½ 2/10; 60; W.
Sun, grey & soft.

Corn housed all day.
Swallows congregate in swarms.

Saturday 7.
29½, 29½ 1/10;
60½; W, NW.
Rain, dark, hard

Young perching swallows.

shower, bright.

Sunday 8.
29½ 1/10; 56½,
57½; W, SW.
Sun, clouds, rain,
wind.

Blowing & winter-like.

Monday 9.
29½ 4/10; 55; W,
NW.
Cold dew, clouds,
strong wind & sun.

Misslethrushes flock.
Corn housed.

Tuesday 10.
29½ 3/10; 55; W,
W.
Chilly, dark &
still.

Spring sown wheat is cut.
Hirundines swarm under the hanger.

Wednesday 11.
29½ 1/10½; 58,
60; SW, SW.
Grey, misty rain.

Spring-sown wheat the best crop.
Some corn housed.

Thursday 12.
29½ 2/10½; 60;
W, SW.
Rain, grey, sun,
grey.

Soft & still.

Friday 13.
29½ 2/10; 59; W,
SW, NW.
Rain, dark, rain,
rain.

Grapes begin to turn colour.
Mild.

Saturday 14.
29½ 3/10½; 58;
NW, W.
Rain, grey, sweet
day.

Great rain in the night.
Spring sown wheat still standing. *Regulus non cristatus minimus*
chirps.

Sunday 15.
29½ 3/10; 57,
61½; W, S, SE.
Great dew, sunny,
sweet day.

WINTON
Muscae & *papiliones* abound on the asters.

Monday 16.
29½ 1/10; 58; SE.
Rain, rain, sunny.

Tuesday 17.
NE.
Sweet day.

Wednesday 18.
Sun, sweet evening.

BRADLEY
Lapwings congregate on the downs.

Thursday 19.
SE.
Sun, wind, clouds,
wind.

Friday 20.
29½ 1/10; 61; S.
Dark, clouds, sun.

SELBORNE
Rain in the night.
Spring-sown wheat all housed.

Saturday 21.
29½ 1/10; 59, 61;
E, E.
Sun, fine day.

SELBORNE
Barley cart all day.

Sunday 22.
29½ 2/10; 59, 65;
E, NE.
Fog, sun, fine day.

Swallows abound.
Tops of the beeches are tinged with yellow.
Heavy clouds in the horizon.

This morning the swallows rendezvoused in a neighbour's wallnut tree. At the dawn of the day they arose altogether in infinite numbers, occasioning such a rushing with the strokes of their wings as might be heard to a considerable distance. Since that no flock has appeared, only some late broods, & stragglers.

Monday 23.
29½ 1/10; 61; N,
N. Dark, windy
& dark.
Merula torquata.*

Sprinkling rain, & rumbling wind.

Tuesday 24.
29½ 3/10½; 60,
61; N, NW.
Dark, sun & sweet
day.
⚘ *Hedera helix.*

Hardly any swallows have appeared since sunday.

Wednesday 25.
30 1/10; 58½, 60;
N, N.
Grey, sun, shower,
fine.
Merula torquata.*

Shower in the night.
Two swallows.
Hedge sparrow begins its winter note.
Soft & still.

Thursday 26.
30 1/10; 54; N, N.
Sun, grey, sun,
chilly air.

*Ring-ouzels begin to appear on their autumnal migration.
Several swallows.

Friday 27.
30 1/10½; 55, 58;
NE, NE.
Sun, brisk wind,
sun.

Few swallows, black cap, few bank-martins over oak-hanger
ponds. Woodlark whistles.

September 30
Looking towards the Great Meadow
from Wool Lane.

Saturday 28.
30 ½/10; 55, 56;
NE, NE.
Sun, fine, clouds,
fine.

Few swallows.

Sunday 29.
29½ 4/10; 54; NE,
N.
Grey, cold air, grey.
Scolopax.

Woodcock appears early.
Glow worms shine.

Monday 30.
29½ 3/10½; 54½,
55; NE.
Grey, sun, grey &
mild.

Several swallows.
Great bat appears.

OCTOBER 1771

Tuesday 1.
29½ 4/10; 54½,
57; NE.
Sun, sharp wind,
sun.

Ground very dry.
Muscae & *papiliones* congregate on the asters.

Wednesday 2.
29½ 3/10½; 50,
54½; NE.
White frost, sun,
still & fine.

Wood-lark whistles, few swallows.
One martin's nest with young in it.¶ Some few martins about.

Thursday 3.
29 4/10; 52; NE.
Dark & still.

Grapes turn black. Vetches, & seed-clover housed. Baromʳ sinks very fast. Ring-ouzels. Apples are gathering.

Friday 4.
29½; 50; N.
Rain & mist, sun,
sharp wind.

Swallows.

Saturday 5.
29½ 3/10½; 48;
NW.
White frost, grey &
clouds.

Ashen leaves begin to fall.

Ringouzels affect to perch on the top twigs of tall trees, like field-fares. When they flie off they chatter like black birds.

Sunday 6.
29½ 1/10; 47½;
SW, S.
Sun, clouds, wind,
rain.

Many swallows & martins.
Stormy wind, much rain.

Monday 7.
29½ 1/10; 56¾;
SW, W, S.
Rain all day with
gusts of wind.

Many swallows, & martins.

Tuesday 8.
29 3/10; 57; SW, S.
Vast rain, stormy
wind.

Wednesday 9.
29 4/10; 57½; W,
SW.
Clouds, wind,
showers.

Several swallows, & martins.

Thursday 10.
29½ 3/10; 56;
NW, W.
Sun, brisk air, fine
day.

Great rain in the night.

Friday 11.
29½ 2/10; 52; S,
SE.
Dark, showers, sun,
showers, sun.

Several martins.

Saturday 12.
29½ 1/10; 51; W,
W.
Sun, brisk air,
pleasant day.

Sunday 13.
29; 55; S, S, S.   Stormy winds, & gluts of rain. Floods.
Stormy wind, vast
rain.

Monday 14.
29 2/10½;54; S,   Some swallows. Grapes large & black, but not high-flavoured
W.   yet.
Stormy, sun,   Several martins.
showers, clear.

Tuesday 15.
29 2/10; 49½; S,   Several martins.
SE.
Fine, showers,
showers.

Wednesday 16.
29½ 3/10; 45½;
W.
Fine day, shower.

Thursday 17.
29 3/10½; 48, 53;   Vast rains all day.
SW, SW.
Stormy wind &
heavy rain.

Friday 18.
29½ 3/10; 50; W,   Grapes not high-flavoured.
W.   Some martins.
Mild & still, sun,
fine.

Saturday 19.
29½ 1/10¾; 52½;   Some martins.
S, E, W, SW.
Grey, rain, & wind.

Sunday 20.
30 2/10; 57½; W,   Sweet day.
N.   Large halo round the moon.
Mild, & sun.

Monday 21.
30 2/10; 47½; E,
S.
White frost, soft,
still.

FYFIELD
Ice.

Tuesday 22.
29½ 1/10; 54;
NW.
Misty rain, soft,
fine.

Wednesday 23.
29 4/10; 54; S, SW.
Misty rain, soft.

Thursday 24.
29½ 2/10; 51; SW.
Sun, sweet day.

Friday 25.
29½ 1/10½; 46;
SW.
White frost, sun,
tempest.

Vast rain & wind.

Saturday 26.
29½ 4/10½; 49½;
NW.
Fine day.

SELBORNE

Sunday 27.
30; 46½; SW.
Shower, sun, mist,
fine.

Monday 28.
30?;¶ 49; S, W,
S.
Misty rain, fine.

Soft, & moist.

Tuesday 29.
29½ 4/10½; 51; S.
Fine, mild.

CHILGROVE
Soft & sunny.

Wednesday 30.
30 2/10; 48; NE.
Wh: frost,
cloudless.

Curlews have cryed here within these few days.
Haws fail here.

Thursday 31.
30 2/10; 47; NE.,
Wh: frost. Sweet
day.

M⁛ Woods saw many redwings about the 31. of Octob⁛

NOVEMBER 1771

Friday 1
29½ 4/10; SE, E.
Vast fog, sweet day.
Cornix cinerea
frugilega.

RINGMER *near Lewes*
An imperfect rain bow on the fog; a more vivid one on the dewy
grass.
Grey crows near South Wick.

Mʳˢ Snooke's tortoise begins to scrape an hole in the ground in
order for laying up.

Saturday 2.
29½ 3/10; SW,
NW, SW.
Sun, sweet day,
clouds, still.

The vale of Bramber, & the River eveloped in a vast fog: the
downs were clear.

Mʳˢ Snooke's tortoise begins to dig in order to hide himself for the
winter.

Sunday 3.
29½ 2/10; W.
Grey, brisk wind,
clouds, small rain.

Monday 4.
29½ 2/10½; NW.
Sun, brisk wind,
clouds.

Saw three house-swallows flying briskly at Newhaven at the
mouth of the Lewes river!!

Tuesday 5.
30; N, W, SW.
Frost, ice, sun, dark
clouds.

Phyteuma orbicularis¶ in bloom on the downs S. of Lewes.

Wednesday 6.
29½ 1/10½; W.
Hard frost, sun,
clouds, clear.

Whitings in high season: herrings going out.

Thursday 7.
29½ 3/10½; N.
Grey, sharp wind,
bright.

Friday 8.
30 1/10; N.
Hard frost,

Few petrifactions about Ringmer & Lewes. Ringmer soil not
clay at top but brick-loam: bears good apples, pears, & grapes.

cloudless, still &
pleasant.

Clay under which holds water like a dish. The trees are mostly elms.

Saturday 9.
30 2/10; W, SW.
Hard frost, sun,
clouds, mild &
dark.

Sunday 10.
29½ 4/10; SW.
Sun, mild,
cloudless.

Monday 11.
29½; SW.
Sun, wind, dark &
windy.

Tortoise comes-out in the sun about noon, but soon returns to his work of digging a hole to retire into.

Tuesday 12.
29 2/10; SW.
Wet & stormy.

Wednesday 13.
29½ 1/10½; N.
Sun, soft, fine day.

Saw 16 forked-tail kites¶ at once on the downs.

Thursday 14.
29½ 3/10½; 45;
SW.
Wh: frost, sun,
louring.

CHILGROVE
An epidemic disease among the dogs in Sussex, which proves fatal to many. They pine away, & die moping.

Friday 15.
29½ 2/10½, 29½
2/10½; 45; SW.
Grey, sun, dark &
wet.

SELBORNE
Tortoise at Ringmer had not finish'd his hybernaculum, being interrupted by the sunny weather, which tempted him out.

Saturday 16.
29½ 4/10½; 51;
SW.
Wet, grey.

Sunday 17.
29½ 4/10; 52½;
SW, NE.
Wet, dark, wet,
windy.

A most astonishing, & destructive flood at Newcastle on Tyne.

Monday 18.
30 4/10½; 42; N.
Sun, sprinkling,
sun, frost.

Crocuss begin to spring.

Tuesday 19.
30 2/10½; 37½;
NW, NW.
Frost, sun, sun,
creamy.

Hen chaffinches begin to congregate.

Wednesday 20.
30 2/10¾; 42;
NW.
Grey, mild &
agreeable.

Bat appears still at times.

Thursday 21.
30 3/10; 44; N,
NW.
Sun, sweet day,
frost.

Friday 22.
30 ⅓/10; 37; NW.
Frost, misty rain,
raw.

Saturday 23.
29½ 3/10½; 44;
NW.
Grey, brisk wind,
misty rain.
Turdus pilaris.

Hardly any field-fares appear: there are no haws.

Sunday 24.
30 1/10; 44, 45; N.
Grey, sun, soft &
still.

Sweet day.

Monday 25.
30 1/10; 44; SW,
W.
Grey, soft & still.

Tuesday 26.
30 1/10; 45, 47; W.
Sun, soft, sweet
day.

September-like weather.
Footpaths dry like March.

Wednesday 27.
30 1/10⅓; 46; W.
Dark & mild.
Turdus iliacus.

A large flock of red-wings appear.
Still & soft.

Thursday 28.
30; 43; SE, E.
Spitting, fog, dark
& cold.

The reed-sparrow, *passer torquatus*¶, forsaking the reeds, &
waterside in the winter, roves about among the fields, & hedges.
This bird which I sometimes saw but never could procure 'til
now, I mistook for the *aberdavine*.

Friday 29.
29½ 3/10; 45; E.
Grey, dry & cold.

Saturday 30.
29½ 3/10¾; 46,
49; S, SE.
Sun, summer-like
day.

DECEMBER 1771

Sunday 1.
29½ 3/10½; 48,
50; SW, E.
Sun, summer-like,
clouds.

Hot sun. Cloudless & still. Dark clouds to the S:W.
Bats about.

Monday 2.
29½ 3/10; 47; 49;
E.
Fog, sunny & soft,
fog.

Cole-mouse roosts in the eaves of a thatched house.

Tuesday 3.
29½; 47, 48; E.
Thick fog.

Wednesday 4.
29 3/10½; 47½; E.
Fog, sun, mild.

Thursday 5.
29 4/10; 47½; E.
Fog, grey, sun,
grey.

Friday 6.
29 2/10; 49; S.

Dark, grey &
windy.

Saturday 7.
29, 29 3/10; 49, 50;
S.
Rain, clouds &
wind.

Sunday 8.
4/10, 29 3/10; 47;   Vast rain, & wind all night.
W, SW.
Sun, clouds, wind
& rain.

Monday 9.
29, 29 2/10; 49;
SE, SW.
Rain, heavy rain,
rain.

Tuesday 10.
29½; 48; W.
Sun, fine.

Wednesday 11.
29½ 1/10, 29½;   Much rain towards morning.
50, 52; W, SW.   Redwings.
Sun, clouds &
wind, rain.

Thursday 12.
29½ 3/10; 50½;   Rain & wind in the night.
W.   Ground full of water.
Sun, fine, clouds to
the south, bright.

Friday 13.
29½ 3/10½, 3/10;
41; W, SW.
White frost, sun,
fine.

Saturday 14.
29½; 44; SE, E.   Glass sinks all day.
Wh: frost, sun, fine
& mild, clouds.

Sunday 15.
28½ 2/10; 43; S, SE.
Wh: frost, showers, tempest, & vast rain.

Song thrush sings.
Daisey, wallflower, *hepatica*, Mesereon, pot-marigold, spring flower blow.

Monday 16.
28½ 4/10½; 44; W.
Sun, fine day.

Thrush sings.

Tuesday 17.
29 2/10; 42; NW, N.
Sun, fine, showers about.

Mild & soft.
Thrush sings.

Wednesday 18.
29 4/10½; 37½; NW, W, SW.
Hard frost, sun, clouds, sprinkling, fine.

Thursday 19.
29 3/10½, 4/10½; 39; W.
Rain, sun, fine, dark.

Friday 20.
29 3/10; 41½; S, SW.
Rain, rain, dark & blowing.

Mild.

Saturday 21.
29 ½/10; 47, 49; SW.
Sun, fine, clouds, rain.

Storm, rain & hail, thunder.

Sunday 22.
29 3/10; 41½; SW.
Sun, fine, rain & wind.

Ground very wet.

Monday 23.
29 1/10½; 41½; S.
Dark, rain, rain &
wind.

Tuesday 24.
29 2/10½; 44; SW,   Many sorts of flies are out, & very brisk.
W.
Sun, fine, clear.

Wednesday 25.
29½ 1/10; 40; SW.   Thrush sings.
Frost, fine, dark.   Hedge-sparrow sings.

Thursday 26.
29½ 1/10½; 44; S,   Thrush & redbreast sing.
W, SW.   Bunting, *emberiza alba*, at Faringdon: I never saw one in the
Wet fog, rain, dark,   parish of Selborne. They affect a champion country,¶ & abound
rain.   in the downy open parts.

Friday 27.
29½ 2/10¾; 49½;   Thrush sings.
SW, NW.
Rain, sun, rain,
bright.

Saturday 28.
29½ 3/10½; 37½;   Ducks. teals, & wigeons have appeared on Wulmere-pond about
SW.   three weeks: one pewit-gull, *larus cinereus*,¶ appears. A pike was
Frost, ice, sun,   taken lately in this pond measuring 3 feet & 3 inch: in length; &
snow, clear.   21 inch: in circumference: in it's belly were 3 considerable carps.
                          When fit for the table it weighed 24 pounds.

Sunday 29.
30 ½/10; 38, 38;   Thrush sings.
N, N. Grey & still.

Monday 30.
30 ¾/10; 38; NE,   Lambs begin to fall.
NE.   Harsh wind all day.
Sun, fine, sharp
wind.

Tuesday 31.
30 1/10; 37½; NE.   Sharp wind.
Dark & harsh.

FEBRUARY 1771
Br^or Henry's field opposite his house was fallowed for barley before the two frosts, all save
the headlands: mem: to enquire if the earlier fallowing in that part proved of any advantage.

JANUARY   — 1772 —

Wednesday 1.
30 ½/10; 37½;
NE.
Dark & harsh.

SELBORNE
Severe wind.

Thursday 2.
30 1/10½; 37½;
NE.
Frost, clouds,
sprinkling, dark.

Cold wind.

Friday 3.
30; 37½; N.
Frost, grey & still.

Saturday 4.
30; 36¾; N.
Grey & sharp.

Sunday 5.
29½ 4/10½; 36,
35; NW.
Still & dark.

Hedge-sparrow whistles.
Paths get dry.

Monday 6.
29½ 2/10; 35; W.
Still & dark, wind
& wet.

BRADLEY
An extraordinary concussion in the air which shook peoples
windows, & doors round the neighbourhood.

Tuesday 7.
W, NW.
Sun, heavy clouds,
snow, wind, hail.

The concussion felt Jan: 6 was occasioned by the blowing-up of the
powder-mills near Hounslow. Incredible damage was done in that
neighbourhood.

Wednesday 8.
28½ 3/10; N.
Frost, sun, snow,
vast clouds.

Small birds flock.

Thursday 9.
NW, W. Frost,
sun, ground hard.

Snow on the ground, & thick ice.

Friday 10.
29 4/10½; 36; SW.
Frost, thaw, dark,
rain.

SELBORNE

Saturday 11.
29 1/10½; 41; S,
SW.
Great rain all day.

Flood.

Sunday 12.
29 3/10½; 47½;
SW.
Misty, dark, moist
& mild.

Hedge-sprarrow, & red-breast whistle.

Monday 13.
30; 41; N, NE.
Wh: frost, sun, fine
day.

Tuesday 14.
30 1/10½, 29½
3/10½; 36; N.
Hard frost, sun,
clouds, rain.

Vast white dew.

Wednesday 15.
28½ 4/10; 37½; S,
SW.
Continual rain all
day.

Great rain all night.

Thursday 16.
28½ 2/10, 4/10½;
42½, 47; NW, N,
NW.
Dark, sleet, driving
snow.

Severe air. Icicles. Cutting wind & frost.

Friday 17.
29 2/10; 33½, 32;
N, N.
Hard frost, sun,
clouds, freezes.

Snow on the ground.

Saturday 18.
29 2/10¼; 32, 32;
NW.
Snow, dark & still.

Snow covers the ground.
Larks congregate in vast flocks.

Sunday 19.
29½; 32, 30¾; N,
E, SE, E.

Much snow towards morning.
Snow very deep on the ground.

Great snow, snow, snow, clear & freezing.

Monday 20.
29½ 1/10½; 27, 28½; E, NE. Severe frost, sun, grey.

Thermom.^r abroad at sun rise 11: in the wine-vault 43. Snow dry & frozen: very deep.

Tuesday 21.
29½ 1/10½; 28, 30; NE, N. Grey & still.

Snow does not melt. Snipes come up the stream.

Wednesday 22.
29½ 1/10; 28, 32½; NE. Dark, grey & still.

Snow melts but little.

Thursday 23.
29½ 1/10; 33, 33½; NE. Dark, small snow, snow.

A gentle thaw all day. Eaves drip all day.

Friday 24.
29 4/10; 33½; NE, N. Snow, small snow, dark.

Thaw. Wettish snow covers the ground.

Saturday 25.
29 4/10; 33¾; NE. Frost, dark & still.

Gentle thaw: mist.

Sunday 26.
29 4/10; 34; NE. Grey, still, sun, dark, snow.

Monday 27
N. Dark, fog & thaw.

WINTON

Tuesday 28.
NE, SE, NW. Sun, fog, snow, sun.

NEWTON

Wednesday 29.
29 4/10½; 29;
NW.
Severe frost, sun.

SELBORNE
Thermom.ͬ abroad before sun rise at 11.
Bright sun.

Thursday 30.
29 4/10; 30; NW.
Frost, bright sun.

Much snow on the ground.

Friday 31.
29 1/10½; 32; E.
Frost, dark.

FEBRUARY 1772

Saturday 1.
28½ 3/10½; 31;
NE, E.
Snow, fog, rain &
thaw.

Snow all night.

Sunday 2.
29; 30½; NW,
NW.
Heavy snow, thaw,
sun, clouds, frost,
dark.

Much old snow remaining, & the bare places now covered again.
Tom-tit attempts it's spring note.

Monday 3.
29 3/10; 32; NW,
W, SW, W.
Hard frost, sun,
dark, wind & snow.

Therm.ͬ abroad 24.
Roads covered with ice.
Driving snow after dark.

In the evening of Feb: the 3rd the sheep were ravenous after their
hay: & before bed-time came a great flight of snow with wind.
Sheep are desirous of filling their bellies against bad weather: & are
by their voraciousness prognostic of that bad weather. They also
frolic & gambol about at such seasons.

Tuesday 4.
29½; 35; W, W.
Fog, warm sun,
frost.

Considerable driving snow in the night, which powdered the
trees & woods in a most beautiful, & romantic manner. Ground
all covered.

Wednesday 5.
29 4/10; 35; E,
NE.
Hard snow,

Snow in the night.
Snow thick on the ground.

snow, dark.

Thursday 6.
29½ 1/10; 30; NE.
Hard frost,
sunshine, frost.

Deep snow covers the ground.
Beautiful winter-pieces.

Friday 7.
29½ 3/10½; 31,
40; W.
Rain, fog, swift
thaw.

Cole-mouse picks bones in the yard.
The snow has lain on the ground this evening just 21 days: a long
period for England!

Saturday 8.
29½ 4/10½; 44½;
W, SW.
Grey, mild & still.

Snow gone below the hills.
Redbreast whistles. Mild.

Sunday 9.
29½ 1/10; 43; S,
SE.
Dark, grey & mild.

Redbreasts, & hedge-sprarrows whistle.
Snow gone save under hedges.
Ravens seem paired.

Monday 10.
29 3/10; 42; E, SE.
Fog, rain, rain,
rain.

Made cucumber-bed.
Snow gone on the hills.
Winter-aconite blows.

Tuesday 11.
29½ 1/10½; 41½;
W, S.
Frost, sweet day,
clouds, dropping.

Large titmouse sings.
Chaffinch sings.
Hot sunshine.
Snowdrops blow.

Wednesday 12.
29 3/10; 41½; S,
SW, W.
Dark, rain, rain.

Thursday 13.
29 2/10; 42; SW,
SW.
Grey, sunny & soft,
shower, fine.

Wood-pecker laughs.¶
Spring-like weather.
Skylark mounts, & sings.
Crocus begins to blow.

Friday 14.
29 1/10½; S, SW.
Sun & showers,
spring-like.

Saturday 15.
29 4/10½; 40; W, NW.
Grey, flights of snow, sun, frost.

Mild.
Harsh & sowr.
Sowed cucumber-seeds.

An ash-colored butcher-bird was shot this winter in Rotherfield park: *lanius ... seu collurio cinereus major*: the only one I ever heard of in these parts.¶

Sunday 16.
29 3/10; 37½; S, SE.
Hard frost, shower, stormy & wet, sun.

Chaffinch sings.
Harsh air.
Vast halo round the moon.

Monday 17.
29 4/10; 37; S, SE.
Frost, vast fog, sun, clear evening.

Larks rise & sing much. Missle thrush (storm-cock in Hants), *turdus viscivorus*, sings. Vast clouds in the horizon.

Tuesday 18.
29 3/10; 38½; E, NE.
Grey, sun, drying air.

March-like weather.
Vast clouds in the wind: now & then a flake or two of snow.
Birds sing.

Wednesday 19.
29 3/10½; 36, 36; N, N.
Dark, cold, drying wind.

Thursday 20.
29 4/10½; 35; NW, NW.
Dark, grey & still, sleet.

Sharp air.

Friday 21.
29½; 34; NW.
Frost, sun, heavy snow, frost.

Saturday 22.
29 1/10; 37.
Rain, rain & snow, fog.

No snow lies on the ground.

Sunday 23.
29 3/10; 34; W, N.

Frost all day in the shade.

Hard frost, sun, &
clouds, sharp wind,
frost.

Monday 24.   LONDON
29 3/10; 30; E.
Hard frost.

Tuesday 25.¶

Wednesday 26.

Thursday 27.

Friday 28.

Saturday 29.

MARCH 1772

Friday 13.   NEWTON
NE.   Water-bottle freezes.
Flights of snow,
severe wind.

Saturday 14.   SELBORNE
29½ 1/10½; 31;   Plows are frozen out.
NE.   Dirt carries horse, & man.
Most severe, flights
of snow.

Sunday 15.
29 4/10; 29, 31;   Abroad thermᵗ 27.
NE.
Severe, grey, sun,
cutting wind.

A bunch of snowdrops,
Gilbert White's grave.
Mid March.

Monday 16.
29 1/10; 31; NE.   Snow covers the ground.
Dark & harsh,
snow.

Tuesday 17.
28½ 4/10; 31½,   Wild geese appear in a vast flock flying to the Southward.
34½; N, NW,
W.
Deep snow, snow,
snow, thaw.

Wednesday 18.
29 3/10; 31, 41; W,   Snow covers the ground.
SE, S.   Thaw.
Frost, sun, hot sun,
thaw, spitting.

Thursday 19.
29 3/10½; 41, 45;   Snow almost gone.
S, SE.
Sun, warm sun,
heavy clouds.
❧ *Ficaria verna.*
Apis mellifica,
Papillio urticae.

Friday 20.
29 3/10; 44, 47; S,
W, SW.
Rain, sun, soft fine
day.

Saturday 21.
29, 44½, 46; E,
SE.
Rain, rain, dark,
rain.

Sunday 22.
28½ 3/10; 46½,   *Least uncrest: wren appears. First summer bird of passage.
50; S, SW.   Flood. Loud thunder.
Great rain, rain,
sun, thunder, rain
& wind.
Regulus non crist:
minimus.

Monday 23.
29 1/10; 46½; S,   Considerable mischief was done by this storm near & in London.
SW.
Sun, clouds,
showers & hail,
bright.
❧ *Tussilago farfara.*

Tuesday 24.
29 2/10; 47; S,
SE.
Sun, sun, sun,
heavy clouds.

Wednesday 25.
29 2/10; 45½,
47½; SE, SE.
Sun, fine day,
shower.
Papilio rhamni.

Thursday 26.
29 3/10; 46; S, W.
Showers, wind &
showers.

Planted-out some stout cucum^r plants into the bearing beds.
Rudiments of fruit shew.

Friday 27.
29 2/10; 46, 48; S,
E, W.
Dark, heavy rains,
heavy rains.

Strong wind.

Saturday 28.
29 3/10½; 48; W,
S.
Sun, fine day.

The ground too wet for ploughing.

Sunday 29.
28½ 4/10; 48; E,
SW, W.
Great rain, rain,
wind.

Flood. Thunder.
Black-bird whistles.

Monday 30.
29 2/10; 45; S, W.
Rain, rain, sun &
heavy showers.
*Merula torquata.**

*On it's spring visit.
Thunder.

One cock ring-ouzel appears on Nore-Hill in it's spring visit, but
earlier than common.

Tuesday 31.
29½; 42; NW,
NE.
Grey, sun, & sweet
day.
✵ *Viola odorata.*

APRIL 1772

Wednesday 1.
29 4/10; 41; NE.
Cold, rain, snow,
snow.

Wet snow.

Thursday 2.
29½ 3/10; 39; NE.
Grey, cold, wind,
sun.

Friday 3.
30; 37; N, NW.   Fine weather with a sharp wind.
Frost, clouds & sun.

Saturday 4.
29½ 4/10; 44; W,   Mackrel sky, wheel round the sun.
S.   Clouds in horison.
Hard frost, sun,
sweet day.

Sunday 5.
29½ 2/10; 44; E,   Uncrested wren chirps.
E.   Barometer falls apace.
Wh: frost, sun, fine   Ants appear.
day.
Formicae.

Monday 6.
29½ 2/10; 49; E,   Wood lark sits.
W, SW.   *Swallow comes early.
Grey & soft, moist,
sweet day, moist air.   Cock snipe pipes & humms in the air. Is the latter sound
Hirundo domestica!   ventriloquous, or from the rapid motion of the wings? The bird
                        always descends when that noise is made, & the wings are violently
                        agitated.¶

Tuesday 7.
29½ 1/10¾; 48; S,   *Death-watch vulg:
W.
Rain, small rain,
sun & soft.
❀ *Cucumis sativus*
Mas:.
Termes pulsatorium
raps.*

Wednesday 8.
29 4/10½; 51; W,   Swallow.
SW.
Rain, showers,
showers, mild.
❀ *Cucumis sativus*
Fem:

Thursday 9.
29½ 3/10; 49; W,
NW, NE.
Rain, clouds, grey,
sun.

Titlark whistles.

Friday 10.
29½ 4/10; 48; N,
W, S.
Grey & pleasant,
dark.
⚘ *Prunus armeniaca.*

Saturday 11.
29 3/10½; 46; S,
SW.
Rain, rain, rain.
⚘ *Amygdalus persica.*

Grass grows apace.

The great black & white Gull, *larus maximus ex albo & nigro seu caeruleo nigricante varius* Raii, was shot lately near Chawton: *Larus marinus* Linn: The head & part of the neck of this bird is dotted with black small spots.

Sunday 12.
29 2/10½; 48, 53;
S, SW.
Rain, sun, showers,
hot sun.
*Cuculus.**

*The cuckow is heard in the forest of Bere.
Growing weather.

Monday 13.
29½; 48; S, W,
NE.
Bright,
clouds, showers,
dark.
*Ruticilla.**

*Redstart appears, & whistles.
Swallow.
Garden too wet for sowing.

Tuesday 14.
29½ 1/10; 48½;
NE.
Rain, rain, rain,
dark.

Began mowing the grass-walks.

Wednesday 15.
29½ 1/10; 48; NE,
N.
Rain, dark, sun,
dark clouds.
*Luscinia!**

*Nightingale sings sweetly.
Grass grows. Wheat looks well.

Thursday 16.
29½; 46½, 45;
NE.
Great rain, rain,
dark & cold.

The ground in a sad wet condition; & the farmers much behind in their spring-sowing. No seeds sown yet in my garden. An high rumbling wind.

Friday 17.
29½ 3/10; 47, 45;
N, S.
Bright, clouds, sun
& clouds.
*Regulus non crist:
medius,* Hirundo
agrestis.***

*A pretty plaintive note.
Chilly air.
**Martins appear.

Saturday 18.
29½; 41; S, W, N.
Frost, sun, clouds,
dark, snow.

Ice.
Snow covers the ground.

Sunday 19.
29½ 2/10; 37; N,
N, NW.
Severe frost, sun,
snow, snow.

Severe wind.
Snow on the ground.
Swallows abound.

Monday 20.
29½ 3/10½; 34½;
NW, NW.
Severe frost, sun,
clouds, fine.

Thick ice.
No swallows appear.

Tuesday 21.
29½ 3/10; 39; W,
SW, W.
Small rain, grey, &
mild.
*Turtur.***

*The turtle dove returns.
Swallows again.

Wednesday 22.
30; 45; N, N.
Dark, grey, sunny,
mild.

The bloom of the fruit-trees on the wall does not seem to be destroyed. Sowed all sorts of garden seeds as carrots, parsneps, &c.
Cucumbers swell.

Thursday 23.
30 1/10; 51; NE,
N, S.
Wh: frost, sun,

sweet day, clouds.
Bombylius medius.

Friday 24.
30; 48, 52; W,
NW.
Grey, sun & clouds,
sweet day.
Apis hyphorum,
Atricipilla,* Musca
tenax, Hirundo
apus.**

Martins appear, but do not frequent houses.
*Black cap whistles.
Showers about.
**Swift returns.

Planted potatoes, four rows. Sowed box of polyanth-seed from London. Sowed annuals.

Saturday 25.
30 ½/10; 51; NW,
NE.
Sun, clouds & sun,
drying air.
Conops calcitrans.

Grass very forward in the field.

The ring dove cooes, & hangs about on the wing in the air in a toying manner.

Sunday 26.
29½ 3/10; 49; SE,
S, E.
Sun, clouds,
sprinkling, chilly.

Barley-fields like to be very wet, & lumpy.

Monday 27.
29½ 1/10; 45; E,
NE.
Dark, grey, &
harsh wind.

Ground dries, & binds up very hard.

Tuesday 28.
29½ 2/10; 44; NE,
NE.
Grey, sun, sun, sun.

Drying & cold.
Black-caps abound.

Wednesday 29.
29½; 43½; NE,
NE.
Hard frost, sun, &
drying wind.

Grass crisp with white frost.
Cut first cucumber, a large fruit.
Harsh wind. Sowed annuals.

Thursday 30.
29 4/10; 29½; 46,
50; NE, NE.
Dark, sun, & harsh
drying wind.
Ficedulae affinis.*

Cuckow.
*White-throat returns & whistles.
Golden-crowned wren whistles: his note is as minute as his person.

MAY 1772

Friday 1.
29½ 4/10½; 46½;
N, N.
Dark, sun &
cloudy, harsh wind.

Some few beeches in the Hanger shew a small tinge of verdure.

Saturday 2.
30 1/10½; 46; NE,
NE.
White frost, hot
sun, & cold air,
cloudless.
Hirundo riparia.

Sand-martins abound at the sand-pit at short-heath.

Sunday 3.
30 2/10; 38; NE,
NE.
Wh: frost, sun &
harsh wind,
cloudless.
*Regulus non crist:
major cantat voce
stridula locustae.*

Shaking it's wings it makes at intervals a sibilous noise on the tops of the tallest beeches.

Monday 4.
30 2/10; 37½, 57;
NE, NE.
Wh: frost, sun,
cloudless, sweet day.
⚥ *Lathraea
squammaria.*¶

Cut a brace of cucum^{rs}
Ground very hard, & cloddy; & wants rain before it can be sown.

Tuesday 5.
30 1/10½; 53½,
61; NE, NE.
Dew, sun, dark
clouds, sultry, dark.

Wednesday 6.
30; 46½; NE, NE.
Dark, sun hot &
harsh air.

Rumbling wind.

Thursday 7.
29½ 4/10; 56, 61;
NE, NE.
Sun, hot sun, &

No dews: so that the grass-walks get rough for want of mowing.
Gardens suffer for want of rain.

harsh wind.

Friday 8.
30 ½/10; 53; NE,
N.
Very cold, sun, sun,
& harsh wind.

Fields & gardens suffer by the severe, harsh winds.

Saturday 9.
30; 50; NE, N.
Harsh wind, sun,
hail, bright.

Farmers in stiff ground can sow no barley: not one grain is yet sown on Newton great farm.

Sunday 10.
29½ 4/10½; 45;
N, N.
Frost, sun, dark,
harsh & severe.

Drought has lasted three weeks this day.

Monday 11.
29½ 3/10; 45½;
N, SW, S.
Grey, soft, dark &
mild.

Showers about.

Tuesday 12.
29½ 3/10; 47; SE,
E, SE.
Frost, sun, fine.
*Passer arundinaceus
minor.**

*The sedge-bird sings: variety of notes, but it's manner is hurrying.

Wednesday 13.
29½ 3/10; 47½; E,
NE.
Hard frost, sun, hot
sun, dark clouds.
Musca vomitoria.

Mason's morter frozen.
Wheat looks yellow.
Fruit-trees of all sorts blow much.

Thursday 14.
29½ 4/10; 53; NE.
Dark, sun, sweet
afternoon.

Chill air.

Friday 15.
30 ½/10; 47½;
NE, SE.
Hard frost,
cloudless, hot,

The country dry as powder.

sweet afternoon.

Saturday 16.
30 ½/10; 53; N,
NW, W.
Dew, sun, grey,
sweet & summer
like.

20 horses with vast labour cannot on moderate ground sow more
than three acres of barley in a day, instead of seven or eight. The
ground wants endless rolling & dragging.
The drought has lasted one month.

Sunday 17.
29½ 4/10; 56; W,
SW, NW.
Dark, dark & mild,
spitting.

Very little barley above ground.

Monday 18.
29½ 4/10; 58; W,
SE, E.
Dark, mist &
showers.

Tuesday 19.
29½ 3/10½; 57; E.
Small rain.

Wednesday 20.
29½ 3/10; 57; E.
Moist & dark, fog.
Hippobosca equina.

MIDHURST & FINDON

Thursday 21.
29 4/10½; SE.
Fog, showers,
soaking shower.

BRIGHTON, RINGMER

Friday 22.
29½ 1/10; NW,
W.
Sun & clouds,
warm.
Stoparola, Gyrinus
natator, Musca
meridiana.*

Tortoise eats.
*Fly catcher appears, & builds.

Saturday 23.
29 4/10; SE.
Brisk wind.
Libellulae, Jynx.

Wry-neck pipes.

The Ringmer tortoise came forth from it's hybernaculum on the 6th
of April; but did not appear to eat 'til May the 5th; it does not eat

but on hot days. As far as I could find it has no perceptible pulse.
    The mole-cricket seems to chur all night.

Sunday 24.
29 2/10; SW.
Great rain, wind &
showers.

Monday 25.
SW.
Rain in the night,
sun & wind, soft
showers.

Tuesday 26.
29 4/10; W, NW.
Dark clouds,
showers about,
shower.

Wednesday 27.
29½ 2/10; NE.
Dark & cold,
shower, red
evening.

Thursday 28.
N, SW.
White frosty dew,
chilly evening, dew.

Friday 29.
29½; S.   Grass-hopper-lark chirps.
Brisk wind, sun &
clouds, dark.
*Scarabaeus
melolontha, Alauda
minima voce locustae
stridet.*

Saturday 30.
29½.   Tortoise eats all day.
Showers, sun &
clouds, sultry, dark
clouds, summer's
day.

Sunday 31.
29½; NE.   In Mrs Snooke's ponds are vast spiders, which dive & conceal
Dark & cold, fog on   themselves on the underside of plants, lying on the water: perhaps
hills.   *aranea aquatica* Linn: *urinatoria.*

JUNE 1772

Monday 1.
29 4/10; NE, SW.
Dark & mild, fog
on the downs.

The swallow seems to be the only bird which washes itself as it flies, by dropping into the water.

Tuesday 2.
29½ 1/10; W.
Dark, sun, clouds &
wind.

Wednesday 3.
29½ 1/10½; NW,
SW.
Brisk wind, &
clouds.

ARUNDEL

Thursday 4.
29½; 62; SW.
Rain, dark &
windy, driving rain,
stormy.

CHILGROVE

Friday 5.
29½ 2/10; 62; W.
Windy, showers.

SELBORNE

Saturday 6.
29½ 2/10; 58½;
W, SW.
Showers, showers,
clouds & wind.

Sunday 7.
30½; 62; W.
Sun, wind &
clouds, hollow
wind, fog.
Gryllus campestris.

Field cricket makes it's shrilling noise.

Monday 8.
30 1/10; 67½; W,
S.
Sun, perfect
summer's day.

Tuesday 9.
30 1/10½; 67; W.

The long-horned bees bore their nests in the ground where it is

Sun, brisk wind,
summer weather.
Apis longicornis.

trodden the hardest.

Wednesday 10.
30 1/10; 61, 68;
NW, W.
Sun, brisk wind,
summer weather.

Brisk wind all day which falls with the sun.

Thursday 11.
30 1/10; 63, 69¾;
NW, NE.
Cloudless, sweet
summer weather.

Friday 12.
30 1/10½; 66½;
NE.
Sun, clouds, fine day
with brisk air.

S^t foin blows, & gets very tall.

Saturday 13.
31 1/10½; 63½,
68; NE.
Fine summer
weather.

Sunday 14.
30 1/10; 63; NE.
Bright, sweet
afternoon.

BRADLEY

Monday 15.
29½ 1/10½; NW,
SW.
Hot, brisk air,
sweet day.
❀ *Carduus nutans*,
Digitalis purpurea.

FYFIELD
Sheep shorn.

Tuesday 16.
29½ 1/10; 66; SW.
Great dew,
cloudless, rock-like
clouds, dark clouds.

Wednesday 17.
29½ 2/10; W, SW.

CHARLTON, in Wilts
Colchicum autumnale in seed.

Sun, soft air, rock-like clouds.
♄ *Polygonum bistorta*.

Ephemerae & *phryganeae* abound on the stream.

Bro.ʳ John¶ set out on horse-back for Cadiz.

Thursday 18.
29½ 2/10½; 66;
W, SW.
Sun, clouds, sultry,
showers about.

FYFIELD
Thomas cut my Sᵗ foin.

Friday 19.
29½; 1/10½; SE.
Vast fog, hot sun.

WINTON
Thermʳ abroad in the shade 78.

Arrived at Cadiz.

Saturday 20.
29½ 3/10; 70; SE.
Fog, cloudy, sultry,
fog.

WINTON, SELBORNE
Ephmerae innumerable on the Alresford stream.

When the swifts play very low over the water they are feeding on *ephemerae* & *phryganeae*.

Sunday 21.
29½ 3/10¾; 67,
70; S, SW.
Vivid rainbow,
clouds &
sprinkling, brisk
wind, fine.

Baromʳ sunk in the night.
Brother John sailed from Cadiz for England.

Monday 22.
30; 65, 70; W, S.
Sun, sun & clouds,
brisk air, bright.

Sweet hay-making day.
Put all the Sᵗ foin up in a large cock in excellent order: four large jobs.

Tuesday 23.
29½ 4/10; 65,
69½; SE, S.
Sun, large clouds,
bright, & sweet.

A brood of swallows, flyers, appear for the first time.
Cut great part of the great meadow.

Wednesday 24.
29½ 4/10; 65½,
73½; E, SE, S, W.
Sun, clouds & sun,
sultry, bright, dark
mist scuds over.
♄ *Sambucus nigra*.

Hay makes well. Flisky clouds, & some rock-like clouds.
When the elder blows summer is established.

Thursday 25.
30; 68, 69½; W, S,
W.
Sun, dark sky, dark,
sweet evening.

Hay in beautiful order.
Gardens suffer much for want of rain.

Friday 26.
29½ 3/10½; 68,
70, 76½; W, E,
SE, SW.
Sun, sultry,
cloudless, severe
heat.

Hottest day.
Ricked all the hay save one job in most excellent order. Ground
much burnt.

Saturday 27.
29½ 1/10½; 70,
73; W, S, SW.
Sun, sun & clouds,
sultry, dark &
showers about,
bright, heavy clouds
to the SE.
♀ *Triticum
hybernum*.

Wheat begins to blow.
Finished my hay, which is curious.
Watered the garden: nothing grows.
Cucumbers cease to bear.
The drought has lasted three weeks this day.

Sunday 28.
29½ ½/10, 29½
1/10½; 69, 72;
SW, SW.
Small shower, sun
& clouds, shower,
fine.

Not rain enough to lay the dust.

Monday 29.
29½ 4/10; 64;
NW, N.
Sun, dark, showers,
showers, fine.
♀ *Stachys germanica*.

Light showers, not enough to lay the dust. Chilly.

Tuesday 30.
30; 59, 64½; N,
NE.
Cold dew, sun,
dark, sun & clouds.

Ground much chopped, & burnt.
Gave the garden many hoghs:¶ of water: watered the rasps well
with the engine.

Young frogs migrating.
Shortheath Pond.
27 June.

JULY 1772

Wednesday 1.
29½ 4/10¾; 62,   Watered the pease.
63½; NE, NW, N.   Some nectarines & peaches.
Dew, sun, sun,   Two or three apricots.
sprinkling, fine.

Thursday 2.
30 ¾/10; 62, 64½;   Few apples & pears.
NE.   Small walnuts fall off by thousands. Few nuts. Chilly.
Sun, dark, dark,
sun & clouds, fine.

Friday 3.
30 1/10; 61, 65;   Field-pease suffer.
NE.   Watered the garden well.
Cold white dew,
fog, sun & clouds,
fine.

Saturday 4.
30 1/10; 63; NE,   Dry weather has lasted just a month.
N, NW, N.   Ground not wetted in half an inch.
Shattering, soft
showers all day.

Sunday 5.
30 1/10; 60½, 67;   Frogs migrate with the showers of yesterday.
NE.   Dust flies. No appearances of rain left.
Harsh wind, & sun.

Monday 6.
30; 62; NE.   Young partridges are flyers.
Dark, grey & still.   Vines continue to blow.
♀ Monotropa   *emerges, & blows.
hypopithys.*

Tuesday 7.
30; 62; NE, N.   Watered the ground for planting of annuals.
Dark, grey, sun,   Watered the garden plentifully.
grey & still.   Planted out a double row of China-asters.

Wednesday 8.
29½ 4/10; 63, 70;   Planted out African & french marrigolds.
NE, SW.   Watered the annuals.
Dark, sun, sultry,   Brisk wind.
cloudless.

Thursday 9.
29½ 3/10; 65,
71½; W, N, NW,
E.
Sun, sultry, rocklike
clouds, serene &
cloudless.

Meadow-hay begins to be cut.
Some barley in ear. Wheat uneven.
Watered annuals. Finished cutting the tall hedges.

Friday 10.
29½ 1/10½; 65,
70; NE, N, NE.
Sun, sultry, dark
clouds.

Wood strawberries come.
Rasps begin to ripen.
Sprinkling shower. Showers at a distance.

Saturday 11.
29½ 3/10½; 66;
71; NE, W.
Sun, sultry, brisk
gale.

Drought has continued five weeks this day.
Watered the rasps, & annuals well.

There is a sort of wild bee,¶ frequenting the garden-campion for the sake of it's tomentum, which probably it turns to some purpose in the business of nidification. It is very pleasant to see with what address it strips off the pubes, running from the top to the bottom of a branch, and shaving it bare with all the dexterity of an hoop-shaver. When it has got a vast bundle, almost as large as itself, it flies away, holding it secure between it's chin, & it's fore legs.

Sunday 12.
29½ 3/10½; 66,
70; W, NW.
Sun, brisk air, dark
clouds, brisk wind,
red sky.

Barley & pease suffer much. Frogs continue to migrate from the ponds.

Monday 13.
30; 62½; W, NW,
SW.
Sun, brisk drying
wind, serene.
❀ *Tilia Europaea.*

Lime blows & smells sweetly, & is much frequented by bees.
Rasps ripen.

Tuesday 14.
29½ 4/10; 66, 74;
W, SW.
Dark, sun, sultry,
brisk air.

The grass-walks burnt to powder.

Wednesday 15.
29½ 3/10½; 69,

*The fern-owl preys on the fern-chafer.

73½; W, NW.　　　　　　Watered the garden.
Dark & spitting,
sun, dark, serene.
Scarabaeus
solstitialis. *

Thursday 16.
29½ 2/10¾; 65,　　　　Rasps & strawberries abound.
68; W, SW, S, W.
Sun, sun, brisk
wind, dark clouds,
serene.

Friday 17.
29½ 2/10; 65,
66½; W, S, SW, S.
Dark, spitting,
wind & clouds.

Saturday 18.
29½ ½/10; 65½;　　　　Frequent sprinklings, but not enough all day to lay the dust.
W, S, SW, S.　　　　　The dry fit has lasted six weeks this day.
Small showers,
small showers, sun,
dark.

Sunday 19.
29½ 1/10; 62; W,　　　Some thunder & hail. Smart showers.
SW, SW.
Bright sun, clouds,
showers, showers,
showers, bright.

Monday 20.
29½ 1/10½; 59;　　　　Vast showers about to the SE, & NW.
SW, SW, W.　　　　　Dust hardly laid in the roads.
Bright sun, clouds,
soft rain, red
evening.

Tuesday 21.
29½ 3/10½; 57½;　　　Heavy clouds around.
W, SW.　　　　　　　Roads are dusty.
Cold dew, sun,
clouds, serene &
fine.

Wednesday 22.
29½ 4/10; 61, 65;　　　Pease begin to be hacked.

W, SW, S.
Sun, dark, soft day,
sweet evening.

Thursday 23.
30 ¹/₂/10; 61; SE,
E, NE.
Sun, sultry, sweet
evening.

Young martins begin to congregate on the tower.
Cucumbers begin to bear again.

Friday 24.
30; 62; SE, S, W.
Sun, burning ,
grey, soft.

Cherries & Rasps are in perfection.
Watered the annuals well.

Saturday 25.
29½ 1/10; 66; SE,
W, S.
Sun, grey, dark,
rain with wind.

Wheat turns yellowish.
Mercury falls very fast.

Sunday 26.
29 3/10; 65, 71;
SW, S, SW.
Sun, clouds &
wind, vast clouds.
❦ *Sambucus ebulus*.

Fine shower in the night.
Distant thunder.
Frogs migrate in myriads from the ponds.

Monday 27.
29 2/10; 65; SW.
Sun, clouds,
showers, showers,
chilly with wind.
❦ *Humulus lupulus*.

BRADLEY
Small shower at Selborne.
Young swallows abound.

Brother John arrived at Gravesend in 37 days from Cadiz. He went
from Gibraltar to Cadiz by land to get a ship.

Tuesday 28.
29½ 3/10; 65; W,
SW.
Bright, clouds,
showers, fine.
❦ *Veratrum rubrum*.

SELBORNE
Ponds fail.
Wheat turns.
Hardly any rain at Selb:

Wednesday 29.
29½ 2/10; 62, 68;
SE, S, SE.
Fog, bright, grey,
brisk air, soft &
grey.
❦ *Dipsacus pilosus*.

Sky looks turbid.
Field-cricket chirps.

Thursday 30.
29½ 3/10; 68; SW,
W.
Sun, fine, ripening
day.

Vast *aurora borealis*.

Friday 31.
29½ 3/10½; 63,
64; W, SW, W.
Sun, clouds, dark
with sprinklings,
fine.

The ground dryed to powder.

AUGUST 1772

Saturday 1.
29½ 1/10; 62; SW,
S.
Sun, clouds, dark,
rain & wind, great
rain.

Clouds of dust attend the drags & harrows.
No such rain at this place since June 6th.

Sunday 2.
29½ 1/10; 64; SW,
SW.
Sun, clouds &
wind, sprinklings,
sun.

Ground well moistened.
The frogs from James Knight's ponds travel in troops to the top
of the Hanger.

Monday 3.
29½ 2/10; 61½;
SW, W, SW.
Sun, clouds,
sprinklings, fine.

Red-breast sings. Hops are perfectly free from distemper, &
promise a moderate crop.

Tuesday 4.
30; 61; W, NW.
Sun, ripening hot,
dry air.

Young black-caps abound, & eat the rasps. ¶
Trimmed the vines of their side-shoots.

Wednesday 5.
30 1/10; 63, 68; W.
Grey, hot sun, grey.

Grass-walks look the better for the rain.

Thursday 6.
30 1/10; 67, 71; W,
NW, SE, S.
Dark, sultry, close
& sultry.

Wheat begins to be cut.
Not a breath of air.
The nights are hot.

Friday 7.
29½ 4/10½; 69,
71½; W, W.
Dew, sun, sultry,
sprinkling, fine.

Heavy showers to the NW: & N.

Saturday 8.
29½ 3/10; 68,
72½; W, SW, W.
Fog, sun & brisk
wind, serene.

Ripening weather.
Young martins (the first brood) congregate & are very numerous:
the old ones breed again.

Sunday 9.
29½ 4/10; 63;
NW, N.
Sun, sun & cool
wind, serene.

Grapes swell.

Monday 10.
29½ 4/10; 62;
NW, NW.
Sun, clouds, serene
& beautiful.

An autumnal coolness begins to take place morning & evening.

Tuesday 11.
29½ 4/10; 63, 65;
W, NW, N.
Dew, sun, dark
heavy clouds, sun,
serene.

Wheat-harvest becomes pretty general.
Barom: sinks & rises to it's former pitch.

Wednesday 12.
30 1/10; 60; N.
Cold white dew,
sun, & clouds,
serene.

Thursday 13.
30; 60, 64; W, NW.
Dew, sun, ripening
fine harvest weather.

Some few wasps begin to appear.

Friday 14.
30; 61½; N.
Cloudless, sultry,
dark.

MEONSTOKE

Saturday 15.
29½ 3/10; 65;

BP'S WALTHAM, SELBORNE
On this day at 10 in the morn: some sober & intelligent people

N.
Grey, sultry, dark
& cool.

felt at Noar hill what they thought to be a slight shock of any earth-quake. A mother & her son perceived the house to tremble at the same time while one was above stairs & the other below; & each called to the other to know what was the matter. A young man in the field near, heard a strange rumbling.

Notwithstanding the long severe drought the little pond on the common¶ contains a considerable share of water in spite of evaporation, & the multitude of cattle that drink at it. Have ponds on such high situations a power, unknown to us, of recruiting from the air? Evaporation is probably less on the tops of hills; but cattle must use a vast proportion of the whole stock of water of a small pond.

Sunday 16.
29½ 3/10½; 63;
N.
Fog, sun, harsh
wind, delicate
evening.

Several birds begin to reassume their spring notes, such as the wren, redbreast, smaller *Reg: non crist:*

Monday 17.
29½ 4/10; 64½,
71; SW, S.
Dark, sun, sultry,
serene.

Wheat begins to be housed.

Tuesday 18.
29½ 3/10½; 64½,
69; SW, NE, N, S.
Dew, sun, sultry,
sweet evening.

The swifts seem for some days to have taken their leave. Apricots. None seen after that time.

Wednesday 19.
29½ 2/10; 64½,
72; W, NE, S.
White dew, sun,
sultry, serene &
cloudless.

All the pastures are burnt up, & scarce any butter made. Wheat in fine order, & heavy.

Thursday 20.
29 3/10½; 65; S,
E, S.
Grey, sun, sultry,
vast clouds, soft
shower, showers.

Barometer falls very fast.
Vast rock-like clouds around.
The drought lasted 10 weeks & four days.

Friday 21.
29½; 64½; W.

Young swallows come forth.

Grey, sun, heavy
shower with
thunder, brisk
wind, fine.

Orleans plums¶ begin to change color.
Dark clouds in the S:E.

Saturday 22.
29½ ½/10; 63;
SW, W, SW.
Heavy shower,
shower, sun &
wind, shower, fine.

Planted-out endive, & trenched some celeri.
Ground strangely hard, & bound: will require much rain to
soften it.

Invigorated by this burning season such legions of *Chrysomelae
oleraceae saltatoriae* (vulg: called turnep-flies) swarm in the fields
that they destroy every turnep as fast as it springs: they abound
also in gardens, & devour not only the tender plants, but the tough
outer leaves of cabbages. When disturbed on the cabbages they
leap in such multitudes as to make a pattering noise on the leaves
like a shower of rain. They seem to relish the leaves of horse-
radish.

Sunday 23.
29 2/10½; 63; S,
SW.
Sun, showers with
wind, vast showers,
wind.

Young stoparolas come forth.

Monday 24.
29 3/10; 61; SW,
SW.
Sun, shower,
blustering
wind, rain &
wind.
۞ *Tremella nostoc.*

Trenched more celeri.
Sowed spinage.
Hops suffer by the wind.
Planted small cabbages.

Tuesday 25.
29 4/10¾; 61; SW,
SW, W.
Heavy showers
with wind,
showers, showers,
dry.

Much wheat abroad.
Strong gusts. Much rain.
The ground is well-moistened.

Wednesday 26.
29½ 3/10; 59; SW,
W.
Sun & showers,
showers, fine
afternoon.

Wheat begins to grow under hedges.

Thursday 27.
29½ 2/10¾; 59;   Much wheat abroad in this district.
W, E, SE.
Fine day, rain.

Friday 28.
29½ 3/10; 66; SE,   Wheat housed all day.
SE. Clouds, grey &
soft, clouds.

Saturday 29.
29½ 2/10½; 65,   Hop-picking begins.
68; SE, S, SW.   Sultry.
Fog, hot sun, sultry,   Wheat housed in cold condition.
clouds & rain, fine   Orleans plums become ripe.
afternoon.

Sunday 30.
29½ 1/10; 65½; S,   Mich: daisey begins to blow.
SW, SE.
Sun & clouds, soft
day.
✾ *Aster Chinensis.*

Monday 31.
29 3/10½; 65½; S,   Some wheat out still.
SE, SW.
Dark, great rains,
dry with wind,
shower.
✾ *Agaricus*
campestris.

SEPTEMBER 1772

Tuesday 1.
29 3/10; 62; W, W,
NW.
Vast rain with
thunder, strong
wind with showers.
✾ *Solidago*
canadensis.

Wednesday 2.
29½ 2/10; 60;   Grapes begin to change colour.
NW, NW.   Some wheat still out.
Fine, still day,   The weather bad for hop-picking.
clouds,

sprinklings, fine.
❀ *Hibiscus syriacus*.

Thursday 3.
29½ 2/10; 61; S,
W, SW.
Misty rain, rain,
sun & clouds, fog.
❀ *Lycoperdon
bovista*.

Some wasps appear.
Muscle-plums¶ become ripe.

Friday 4.
29½ 2/10; 64; S,
SW, S.
Rain, dark & misty,
rain.

Spring corn in a bad way where cut.
Barley in general not ripe.
Hot & moist. Grass grows.

Saturday 5.
29½ 1/10; 65½; S,
SW, SW.
Rain, dark & soft
with showers,
stormy.

Oats grow as they lie.
Some wheat abroad.
Bad for hop-picking.
A strange yellow tinge in the sky at sun set.
Distant thunder & lightening in the evening.

Sunday 6.
29½ 2/10; 64½;
SW, S.
Soft & grey, clouds,
rain.

The hops by the late winds are much injured & blow into flyers:
at best they are very brown. Crop large in some gardens.
Distant thunder & lightening.

Monday 7.
.29½ 1/10¾; 64½;
S, SW.
Bright, showers,
sun & clouds, fine,
clouds.

Peaches begin to ripen.

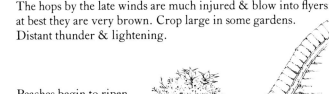

Small tortoiseshell on asters.
Fruit wall at the Wares.
8 September.

Tuesday 8.
29 4/10½; 63; SE,
E.
Fine, fog, sun &
soft, dark clouds,
rain.
Papilio Atalanta.

Wednesday 9.
29½; 62½; NE, E,
S, SW. Rain, rain,
fine, clouds.

Vast rains in the night.

Thursday 10.
29½; 61; NE, N.
Sun, fine, dark
clouds, rain, rain.

Swallows & martins congregate in vast clouds.

Friday 11.
29½ 4/10; 57½;
NW, N.
Grey, sun, dark &
chilly, fine evening.
Turdus torquatus.

Ring-ouzel appears on it's autumnal visit: several seen.
Stoparolas seem to be gone for three days past.

Nasturtiums scrambling up yew hedge, the Wakes.
15 September.

Saturday 12.
29½ 4/10½; 57½,
61; NE, NE.
Sprinkling, sun &
clouds, fine evening.

Sunday 13.
29½ 1/10½; 59; E,
SE.
Fog, sun & clouds,
vast rock-like
clouds.

Sultry.
Vast rains with thunder & lightening.

Monday 14.
29½ ½/10; 62; SE,
SE.
Sun, sun & clouds,
vast rains with
thunder, fine.

Oats rot as they lie: a very poor scanty crop.
Little barley cut; but dead ripe.

Tuesday 15.
29½ 2/10; 61;
NW, N.
Sun, fine day, sweet
evening.

Papilio Atalanta abounds.¶
Vast rock-like clouds in the horison.

Wednesday 16.
29½ 2/10; 60;
NW, W, NW.
Fog, sun, fine day,
chilly air.

Vast dews. *Chrysomelae oleraceae* still abound on the cabbages.
Some corn housed.

Thursday 17.
29½ 2/10; 60;
NW, W, NW.
Grey, dark, sun &
clouds.

Grapes turn apace.
Corn housed.

Friday 18.
29½ 3/10; 57;
NW, NW.
Grey, sun, fine day,
chilly air, spitting.
⚘ *Hedera helix.*

Ivy¶ begins to blow; & is the last flower which supports the
hymenopterous, & dipterous Insects. ¶ On sunny days quite on to
Nov.ʳ they swarm on trees covered with this plant; & when they
disappear probably retire under the shelter of it's leaves,
concealing themselves between it's fibres, & the tree that it
entwines.

Saturday 19.
29½ 4/10; 59;
NW, NW.
Dark, spitting, sun,
fine afternoon.

Sunday 20.
58; NW, SW.
Grey, soft & sun,
grey & mild.

Monday 21.
29½ 3/10; 60; W,
SW, W.
Grey, spitting, fine
& warm, wind,
shower.

Few swallows about.

Tuesday 22.
29½ 1/10¼; 60;
SW, SW.
Grey, dark clouds,
small showers, wind
& clouds.

Began parlour-fires.
Martins abound under the hanger.
No swallows.

Wednesday 23.
29; 58; S, S.
Rain, wind & rain,
rain, rain, stormy.

A miserable crop of barley round these parts.
Grapes eatable.

Thursday 24.
28½ 4/10; 58; SW,
S, SE.
Sun, grey, clouds,
great rain, stormy.

Some swallows & many martins under the hanger.

Friday 25.
29 4/10; 52; W,
SW, SW.
Bright sun, sun, sun
& rock-like clouds,
shower, fine.

Vast tempest in the night that broke boughs from the trees, &
blowed down much of the apples & pears. Gathered some apples.

The tempest on thursday night did considerable damage in
London, & at Oxford, & in many parts of the Kingdom.

Saturday 26.
29½ 3/10; 53; W,
W. White frost,
sun, fine day.

Apples & pears large & fine.
Chilly air.
Swallows & martins.

Sunday 27.
29½ 3/10¼; 51;
W, SW. White
frost, sun, fine day.

Swallows, & martins.

Monday 28.
29½ 2/10; 51; SW,
NE, N.
Dark, rain, rain,
dark with wind.

Swallows & martins.
Gathered first grapes: large & good.
Some wasps damage them.

Tuesday 29.
29 4/10; 54; NE,
NE.
Thick fog, dark,
still & warm.

Wednesday 30.
29½ 1/10½; 58;
NE, NW, W.
Fog, small rain, hot
sun, grey, dark.

OCTOBER 1772

Thursday 1.
29½ 3/10; 56; W.
Sun, soft air.

LASSAM
Martins.
Young martins in their nest at Lassam.

Friday 2.

OXFORD

Saturday 3.

[Monday 19.]

OXFORD, LASSAM

Tuesday 20.
30; 57; SE.
Grey, soft, fine
afternoon.
*Scolopax, Turdus
iliacus.*¶

SELBORNE
Woodcock returns.
Papiliones & *muscae* abound on the asters.
Redwings return.

Wednesday 21.
29½ 3/10½; 59;

Under the eaves of a neighbouring house is a martin's nest full of

SE.
Grey, sun, hot sun,
serene & summer-
like weather.

young just ready to flie. The old ones hawk for flies with great
alertness.

Thursday 22.
29½ 1/10½; 55;
SE.
Fog, grey, sun &
soft.

This morning the young martins forsook their nest & were flying
round the village.
Grapes delicate, & plenty.

Friday 23.
29½; 55; SE.
Dark, grey, rain,
rain.

The martins about.

Saturday 24.
29 2/10½; 58; SE.
Dark, grey, sun,
heavy rain.

Glow-worms shine.

A baker at Lewes assur'd me, that about seven years ago ring-
ouzels¶ abounded so about that town in the autumn that he killed
16 himself in one afternoon: he added further that some had
appeared since every autumn: but that he could not find that any
had been observed before the season in which he shot so many. I
myself have found the birds in little parties in the autumn all along
the Sussex downs from Chichester to Lewes, particularly in

Sunday 25.
SW.
Grey, dark,
thunder, vast rain,
vast showers.

Autumn 1770. Persons worthy of credit assure me that Ring-
ouzels were seen at Xmass 1770 in the forest of Bere in this county:
from whence we may conclude that their migrations are only
internal, & not extended to the continent southward; if they do at
first come at all to us from yᵉ N: parts of this island, & not from the
N: of Europe.

Monday 26.
29 3/10; 55; SW.
Sun, showers,
showers, fine.

Swallow appears still.
Vast rains.

Tuesday 27.
29 2/10½; 55; SW.
Grey, dark, rain,
rain.

Grapes decay with the rain: are most highly ripened.

Wednesday 28.
29½; 52½; N, S.
Rain, mist, dark,
rain & wind.

Thursday 29.
29 3/10½; 56; S,

Vast quantities of rain has fallen lately.

SE.
Stormy with rain,
rain, vast rains with
stormy gusts.

Friday 30.
29½; 58½, 60; S,
SW.
Showers, fine, hot
air, soft, & mild.

Grass grows.
Medlars shaken off the tree by the wind.

Saturday 31.
29 3/10½; 58½,
60; S, SE, SW.
Cloudy, shower,
rain, yellow
evening, wind.

Ring-ouzels still appear. They usually finish their autumnal visit
before this time. Qu: if this delay is owing to the unusual
mildness of the season?
Grapes rot.

NOVEMBER 1772

Sunday 1.
29½ 2/10½; 51½;
W, W.
Dew, sun, clouds,
sun & fine.

Monday 2.
29½ 4/10; 52½;
SE.
Sun, grey with
drying wind, vast
rain.
Turdus pilaris.

Fieldfare is seen.

Tuesday 3.
29½; 51; SW.
Sun, shower, fine
day.

20 or perhaps 30 martins were playing all day along by the side of
the hanger; & over my fields.¶

Will these house-martins, some of which were nestlings 12 days
ago, shift their quarters at this late season of the Year to the other
side of the northern tropic! Or rather is it not more probable that
the next church ruin, cliff, sandbank, (a Northern naturalist would
say) lake or pool will prove their hybernaculum, & afford them a
ready, & obvious retreat?

Wednesday 4.
29½ 3/10; 44½;
W, NW.
Sun, cold air, sunny

Saw one martin.

fine day.

Thursday 5.
29½ 1/10¾; 50;
SW.
Wet, wet & windy
day, foggy.

Friday 6.
29½ 2/10; 56; S,
SW.
Dark & warm, vast
rain.

Saturday 7.
29 4/10; 58; SW,
SW.
Grey, rain, rain &
wind.

Warm air.
Flesh-flies blow the meat in the larder still.

Sunday 8.
29 3/10; 58; SW,
SW.
Sun, shower, sun,
rain, windy & clear.

Monday 9.
29½ 2/10; 47; SW,
W, SW.
Grey with wind,
rain, rain with
wind.

Tuesday 10.
29 3/10½; 55; SW,
SW.
Rain, rain, rain &
wind, rain.

Vast quantities of rain!

Wednesday 11.
29 3/10½; 53; SW,
SW.
Sun & strong wind,
strong wind.

Nasturtiums & other Indian flowers¶ still in bloom: a sure token
that there has been no frost.

Thursday 12.
29½ 2/10; 48, W,
NW.
Shower, sun &

*The stock-dove, or wood-pigeon appears. Where they breed is
uncertain. They leave us in spring, & do not return 'til about this
time. Before the beechen woods were so much destroyed we had

wind, calm, red
evening.
*Oenas, sive vinago.**

every winter prodigious flocks, reaching for a mile together as
they went out from their roost of a morning. Hartley-wood used
to swarm with them. They are considerably less than the ring-
dove or queest, which breeds with us, & stays the whole Year
round.

Friday 13.
29½ 3/10; 46;
NW, NW.
White dew, sun,
fine day, shower,
fine.

Saturday 14.
30; 43; N, N.
White dew, sun,
dry, & sharp wind.

Sunday 15.
30; 44; NE, NE.
Sprinkling, clouds,
rain, dark, dark.

Harsh air.

Monday 16.
29½ 3/10; 44;
NW, N.
Dark, harsh &
lowering.
*Elvela mitra.**

*Appears in my fields . . . *Elvela pileo deflexo, adnato, lobato,
difformi:* Linn: *flo: Suec: Elvela petiolata, lamina in formam
capituli deorsum plicato laciniata & crispa; petiolo fistuloso,
striato, & rimoso:* Gleditsch *methodus fungorum.*¶

Tuesday 17.
29½ 4/10; 41; NE,
NE.
White frost,
sprinkling, harsh &
lowering.

Wednesday 18.
29½ 2/10; 43; N,
NW.
Dark & still.

Nasturtiums blow yet: some few leaves are decayed.
Grapes delicate, but many bunches decay.
Paths dry.

Thursday 19.
29½ 1/10½; 42;
W, W.
Dark & still, sweet,
sunny afternoon.

Paths very good.

Friday 20.
29 3/10; 45; S, S.

Snipes come up into the meadows.

Showers, showers,
rain with wind.

Saturday 21.
29; 49; SW, SW.   Stormy in the night.
Showers, hail, rain   Much hail.
& wind.

Sunday 22.
29½ 1/10½; 40½;
SW, SW.
White frost, sun,
clouds, fine
afternoon.

Monday 23.
29 1/10½; 48; SW,   Distant lightening with thunder.
SW.
Rain & wind all
day.

Tuesday 24.
29 4/10½; 45½; S,   Nasturtiums nipped, but still in bloom.
W, S.
Showers, showers,
sunny, shower,
starry.

Wednesday 25.   BRAMSHOT PLACE
29½ 2/10½; 41;
W.
White frost, fine,
rain with wind.

Thursday 26.
SE, W.   At Mr Pink's at Faringdon is a rook's nest with young in it.
Very wet, rain, fine,
rain.

Friday 27.   SELBORNE
29 3/10; 43; SW.   Vast flocks of wild fowls in the forest.
White frost, fine   They are probably migraters newly arrived.
day, rain.

Saturday 28.
28½ 4/10 3/10; 44; Vast rains in the night!
SE, SE.   Some few grapes left on the vines.
Rain, rain, dark &
windy, rain.

Sunday 29.
29 4/10½; 45½;   Vast rains in the night.
NE, N, NW.
Dark, grey with vast
clouds, spitting.

Monday 30.
29½ 1/10½; 45½;   Thrush whistles.
SE, SE.
Fog, bright sun,
dark, rain.

DECEMBER 1772

Tuesday 1.
29½ 1/10½; 51;
S, S.
Driving rain,`
dark & moist,
spitting.

Wednesday 2.
29½ 1/10; 47½;   Trimmed the vines. Their shoots were by no means good, nor
E, E.   well-ripened, notwithstanding the hot summer.
Sun, grey & cold
wind.

Thursday 3.
29½ 1/10½; 45;   Paths dry & pleasant.
NE, NE.   Several flies stirring.
Grey, sun, sweet
mid-day, grey &
pleasant.

Friday 4.
29½ 1/10¾; 44½;   Nasturtiums blow yet.
E, E.   Indian flowers in Dec!
Dark & spitting.   Song-thrush sings.

Saturday 5.
29½ 3/10¾; 43;   Thrush sings.
NE, NE.
Grey & still.

Sunday 6.
29½ 2/10; 42; NE,   Thrush sings: redbreast sings.
NE.   A dead young rook about half-grown was found in a nest on one
Still, dark & dry.   of Mr Pink's trees near his house.

Monday 7.
29½ 2/10; 40; NE,
NE.
Cold, fog, dark &
spitting.

Earthed asparagus beds.
No ice yet.

Tuesday 8.
29½ 3/10; 41; NE,
NE.
Cold, wet, fog.

Brother & sister John arrived.

Wednesday 9.
29½ 1/10¾; 41;
SE, S, W.
Dark, grey, bright,
wet fog.

Thursday 10.
29 4/10; 43; SW,
W.
Rain, rain, dry,
fine.

Thrush sings.

Friday 11.
29½ 2/10; 44; W,
NE.
Fine, sun, grey.

Young lamb falls.

Saturday 12.
29 1/10; 42½; SE,
SW.
Rain, rain, rain,
dark and windy.

Bats appear, & many *phalaenae*.

Sunday 13.
29½ 3/10½; 48!;
NW, W.
Grey, sun, sweet
day.

Female chaffinches congregate.

Monday 14.
30; 46; W, W.
Grey, sun, sweet
day.

Nasturtiums blow still.

Tuesday 15.
29 3/10, 29½
3/10½; 49½!;
SW, S, W.

Mild & soft.

Rain, rain, rain,
fine.

Wednesday 16.
29½ 2/10; 47½;   Missel-thrush, or storm-cock sings.
SW, SW.   Polyanth, & annual stock blow.
Grey & soft, dark,
spitting.

Thursday 17.
29½ 3/10; 48½;
SW, SW.
Grey, sun &
showers, rain.

Friday 18.
30 ½ of 10; 50;   Thrush whistles.
SW, SW.
Sun, sweet day,
grey.

Saturday 19.
29½ 4/10; 52; SW,   Thrush whistles.
SW.
Dark &
moist, dark &
mild.

Sunday 20.
29½ 2/10½; 52!;
SW, SW.
Dark & mild, sun,
dark.

Monday 21.
30; 51; SW, NE.
Fog, rain, dark &
moist.

Tuesday 22.
30 1/10; 45, 43;   Nasturtiums still.
NE.
Vast fog.

Wednesday 23.
30 1/10½; 38½,   First ice! Icicles. Ground very white.
38½; NE.   Nasturtiums cut all down, & rotten.
Hard frost, bright,
frost.

Thursday 24.
30 2/10¾; 33½;
NE.
Hard frost, bright
sun.

Ground very white.
Thermom^r abroad 27.

Friday 25.
30 2/10; abroad 27,
27; NE.
Rime & frost, sun,
fog, fog.

Saturday 26.
30 1/10; 35, 36;
NE.
Rime, dark, thaw,
dark, & thaw.

Sunday 27.
30; 35; NE.
Dark, frost, thaw,
fog.

Monday 28.
30 ½/10; 35; NE.
Dark & frosty, fog,
rimes.

Tuesday 29.
30; 36; NE, E.
Dark with rime,
grey & still.

Wednesday 30.
29½ 2/10½; 36½;
36½; NE, NE.
Dark, grey & still.

Thursday 31.
29½; 36½, W,
SW.
Sun, clouds, rain,
bright.

JANUARY

— 1773 —

Friday 1.
29½; 37; NW.
Frost, sun, clouds.

SELBORNE

Saturday 2.
29½ ½/10; 36;
NW, W.
Snow, sun, clouds,
snow, dark.

Sunday 3.
29½ 3/10; 34;
NW, NW.
Frost, sun, sun,
frost.

Monday 4.
30 2/10½; 34; N,
N.
Frost, warm sun,
fog.

Tuesday 5.
30 2/10; 35, 32; N,
N.
Fog & frost, fog,
clear with frost.

Wednesday 6.
30 1/10¾; 30½;   Great rime.
W, SW, W.
Hard frost, warm
sun, dark.

Thursday 7.
30 2/10; 36½; W,
W.
Fog, warm sun,
fog.

Friday 8.
30 ½/10; 37; W, S.
Frost, thaw, thaw.

Saturday 9.
29½ 3/10½; 40½;
S, S.
Dark, spitting,
dark.

Sunday 10.
30 1/10; 42, 37;   Nuthatch chirps.

SW, SW.
Frost, sweet sun,
frost.

Monday 11.
29½ 4/10; 41, 47;   Hen chaffinches congregate in vast flocks.
SW.
Cloudy, moist air,
windy.

Tuesday 12.
29½ 3/10; 46½,
49; SW.
Dark, sprinkling,
windy.

Wednesday 13.
29½ 2/10½; 48,   Soft air.
47½; W.
Rain, rain, windy.

Thursday 14.
29½; 49; W, NW.
Dark, rain & wind,
rain, windy & fair.

Friday 15.
29½ 2/10½; 40¾;
NW, NW.
Sun, fine day, bright
evening.

Saturday 16.
29 1/10; 42; SE,
SE, S.
Dark, rain, rain,
wind.

Sunday 17.
28½ 2/10; 46½;   Vast rain.
NE, E, SW.   Black bird whistles.
Rain, rain, rain,
rain.

Monday 18.
29 3/10½; 42; SW,
W.
Bright sun, wind.

Tuesday 19.
29 4/10; 42, 42;
SW, SW.
Rain, rain, rain,
windy.

Wednesday 20.
29½ 3/10; 44; SW.
Dark & mild with
wind.

Thursday 21.
29½ 2/10; 46, 47;   Thrush sings.
SW.   Titmouse begins it's spring first note.
Grey & mild,
spitting rain.

Friday 22.
29½ 2/10; 47, 46;   Thrush whistles.
SW, W.
Dew, sunny & soft.
❀ *Helleborus*
hyemalis.

Saturday 23.
29½; 46, 45; E,
NE.
Fog, spitting rain,
dark & mild.
❀ *Helleborus*
foetidus.

Sunday 24.
29½; 48, 46; W,   *Parus major* sings.
SW.   Hedge sparrow essays to sing.
Rain, grey, sun &
windy.
❀ *Corylus avellana*,
Bellis perennis,
Galanthus nivalis.

Monday 25.
29½; 44½, 49; W,
SW.
Bright sun, misty
rain.

Tuesday 26.
29½ 1/10; 49, 50;   Mild.

SW.
Grey, sun, misty
rain.

Wednesday 27.
29 1/10½; 49½;   Wood-lark sings.
SE.
Grey, windy, rain.

Thursday 28.
29½ 2/10½; 42,
40; W, NW.
Grey, sprinkling,
wind & rain.

Friday 29.
30 1/10, ½/10; 37;   Vast halo round the moon.
NW, W.
Frost, bright sun,
clouds.
⚘ *Crocus sativus.*

Saturday 30.
30 1/10½; 36, 38,
36; N, N.
Frost, hot sun,
frost.

Sunday 31.
30 2/10; 32, 34½;   Vast halo round the moon.
NW.
Frost, sunny & still,
cloudy.

FEBRUARY 1773

Monday 1.
29½ 4/10; 33½;
W, SW.
Frost, sun, dark.

Tuesday 2.
30 ½/10; 39; NE,   No snow lies.
NW.
Rain & sleet, snow,
sun, bright.

Wednesday 3.
30 3/10½, 4/10½;   Ice within doors.

Church Meadow,
February.

31, 32½; NE, E,
E.
Severe frost. Bright
sun. Vast clouds.
Bright.

Thursday 4.
31; 29½, 32½;
NE, E.
Severe frost, sun,
sun, clouds.

Larks congregate.

Friday 5.
30 ½/10; 29¾,
31½; NE, W.
Severe frost, dark &
sharp, snow.
♉ *Primula vulgaris*.

Ground hard frozen.

Saturday 6.
29½ 4/10½; 32,
35; SW, E.
Frost, dark, sun,
frost.

Snow all melted in the morning.
Vast flocks of hen chaffinches.

Sunday 7.
29½ 3/10; 30,
32½; E, NE.
Severe frost, sun,
dark & harsh.

Frost all day. No snow.

Monday 8.
29½ 1/10½; 32,
33, E, E.
Severe frost, dark,
dark, sun.

Ground hard all day.

Tuesday 9.
29½ 1/10½; 32;
NE, N.
Snow, sun, sun,
clear.

Made hot bed.

Wednesday 10.
29½ 1/10; 29, 30,
32; NW, W, SW,
S, SE.
Severe frost, sun,
sun & clouds, sharp

Bottles of water freeze in chambers.
Snow in the night. Cutting air.

air, snow about.

Thursday 11.
29½ 2/10½; 33,
35; E.
Frost, snow on the
ground, sun, dark.

Reduced my barometer to the true standard of 28 inches, lowering
it about two degrees.

Friday 12.
29½ 4/10; 33, 40,
39; E, E.
Frost, sun, swift
thaw, mild, dark.

Saturday 13.
29½ 3/10; 37½,
37½; SE, SE.
Dark, frost, dark &
thaw, dark & misty.

Sunday 14.
29½ 2/10¾; 40,
44; SW, SW.
Mist, soft rain,
gentle thaw, misty.

Monday 15.
29½ 3/10; 46, SW.
Soft & mild.
☙ Helleborus
viridis.*

*emerges & blows.
Chaffinch sings.

Tuesday 16.
SW.
Sweet soft day.

FYFIELD
Grey crows near Andover.

Wednesday 17.
29½ 2/10; 48; SW,
NW.
Misty rain.

Thursday 18.
29½ 2/10½; 43;
N.
Misty rain.

Lambs fall strong, & thrive very fast.
Last year numbers perished.

Friday 19.
29½ 1/10; NE.
Misty rain.

Saturday 20.
29 2/10; 40; S, SW.
Rain, sunny, rain.

Sunday 21.
29; 45.
Sun, heavy clouds,
sun & showers,
lightening.

Monday 22.
28½ 3/10; 36; S,
N.
Rain, sun, hail,
bright.

Tuesday 23.
28 4/10; 48; SW.
Stormy, vast rains,
lightening.

Wednesday 24.
29 1/10; 40; SW,
W.
Rain & hail,
showers, sun.

Thursday 25.
29 1/10½; SW,
SE.
Frost, sun, dark.

Friday 26.
28 3/10; S, SW.
Stormy night with
vast rains.
Fierce wind all day.

Saturday 27.
29 3/10; 49; SW,
SW.
Sun, sun & clouds,
showers & wind.

Sunday 28.
29½ 1/10; 46; SW.
Sun, clouds, sweet
afternoon.
♥ *Tussilago farfara.*

Trufles continue to be found ¶ in my Bro: Henry's grove of beeches: tho' the season is near at an end. It is supposed that seven or eight pounds are taken annually in that little spot. My Bro: & the trufle-hunter divide them equally between them.

WINTON
This storm did considerable damage in many places.

SELBORNE

MARCH 1773

Monday 1.
29 4/10½; 46; SW.
Sun, grey, wet
evening.
❦ *Ficaria verna.*

Tuesday 2.
29½ 1/10; 48; SW,   Crocuss in high beauty.
S.
Sun, fine soft day.

Wednesday 3.
29 3/10; 51; SE,
SE.
Sun, great fog,
sweet afternoon.

Thursday 4.
29 4/10½; 54; SW,
S.
Soft showers, sweet
day.
❦ *Pulmonaria
officinalis.*
Papilio rhamni.

Friday 5.
29½ 3/10; 51; N,   The rooks at Faringdon have built several nests since sunday.
NE.
Sun, dark, dark,
spitting.

Saturday 6.
30; 45; NE, NE.   Mild, still, pleasant weather.
Dark, grey, sun.

Sunday 7.
29½ 3/10¾; 41;
NE, E.
White frost,
fog, bright &
sharp air.

Monday 8.
29½ 3/10; 41½;   Seed barley sells at 38$^{s.}$ p^{r} quarter! a price never heard of before.
NE.
Fine day, air sharp.

Tuesday 9.
29½ 2/10; 39; NE.
Dark with some
snow & sleet, grey
& dry.

Wednesday 10.
29½ 1/10½; 38½;
NE.
Dark & cold,
spitting rain.

Thursday 11.
29½ 4/10; 41; E,
E.
Bright, sunny day
with sharp wind.
❀ *Leontodon*
taraxacum.

Sun begins to look down the hanger.

Friday 12.
30; 39½; E, NE.
Wh: frost, & ice,
bright sun, stars.
❀ *Populus tremula*.
Papilio urticae.

Saturday 13.
29½ 4/10; 39½;
NE.
Thick ice, cloudless
day.

Bees abound on the crocuss.
Humble-bees & some flies appear.
Made the bearing cucumber-bed.

Sunday 14.
29½ 2/10; 39; NE,
N, W.
Wh: frost, thick ice,
cloudless sky.
❀ *Viola odorata*.

Skylarks rise & sing a little.

Monday 15.
29½ 2/10¼; 42;
NW.
Mild & grey, sun.
Chrysomela
Gottingensis.*

Ants.
*This insect is very common with us.

Tuesday 16.
29½ 3/10½; 41,

Fine season for the sowing of spring-corn.

45; N, W.
Frost, sun, grey,
grey & mild.

Wednesday 17.
29½ 3/10¼; 40,
45; NW, W.
Frost, bright sun.

Beautiful season.

Thursday 18.
29½ 3/10¾; 39;
NW, S.
Frost, bright sun.

Many sorts of Insects begin to come out.
Water-insects begin to move.
Milvus aeruginosus? Hot in the sun.

Friday 19.
29½ 3/10; 43, 53;
S, SE.
Grey, sun, soft &
mild.

Saturday 20.
29½ 1/10¾; 41;
SE, S, SW.
Hard frost, sultry
sun.
Lacerta.

Sky thickens with flisky clouds.

Sunday 21.
29½ 2/10; 45; W,
W.
Grey, mild &
pleasant.
⚘ *Prunus armeniaca,*
Amygdalus persica.

Black bird sings.

Monday 22.
29½ 2/10¾; 44,
57½; W, SW.
Sun, hot & summer
like.

Gossamer floats about.

Tuesday 23.
29½ 2/10½; 47,
57; SW, SE, S.
Wh: frost,
cloudless, cloudless,
dark horison.
⚘ *Fragaria sterilis.*
Coluber natrix.

Summer weather with a brisk wind.
Cock & hen wheatear.

Wednesday 24.
29½ 2/10½; 48,
56; SE, S.
Bright, summerlike
& cloudless.
Rana bufo.

Bat appears.

Thursday 25.
29 1/10½; 48, 62;
W, W.
Bright, cloudless &
hot sun with brisk
air.
*Regulus non cristatus
minimus.*

Least uncrested wren chirps; the first summer bird of passage.
Was heard first last year March 22.

Friday 26.
29½ 2/10; 52, 53;
NW, N.
Grey, sun, sweet
day.

Grass begins to grow.

A large flock of titlarks¶ on the common, feeding & flitting on,
probably going down to the forest to the moory moist places.

Saturday 27.
29½ 4/10; 48, 49;
NE, N.
Grey, sun,
small sleet with
cold air.

Bearing cucumber-bed still in a burning condition. Plants in the
pots much drawn.

Sunday 28.
29½ 3/10¾; 39½,
44; NE, SE, S.
Hard frost, thick
ice, sun, dark &
hazy.

Sharp air.
Three swallows were seen I hear this day over the paper-mill
pond at Bramshot.

Monday 29.
29½ 4/10; 41, 46;
E, E.
Frost, cloudless with
sharp air.

Turned out the cucumbers into their hills.
Bed still too hot.
The dry weather has lasted just a month.
Roads all dried up.

Tuesday 30.
29½ 3/10¼; 38,
46; NE, NE.
Hard frost, ice,
cloudless,
sharp wind,
frost.

No larks in the fields, & few birds to be heard or seen: probably
this harsh dry air renders their food scarce & sends them to the
lower moister grounds.

Wednesday 31.
29 4/10½; 38, 43;
W, NW, N.
Frost, small snow,
small rain, harsh.

APRIL 1773

Thursday 1.
29 4/10½; 37, 39,
41; N, N.
Frost, dark with
flights of snow, &
harsh wind.

Friday 2.
29 1/10; 36, 40, 41;
NW, W, SW, S.
Harsh with sleet,
sun, small shower,
rain.

Saturday 3.
28½ 4/10¾; 42,   Apricot-blossoms seem mostly cut-off: peaches & nectarines are
47; SW, S.   well-blown, & look well.
Dark & mild, small   Sowed a box of polyanth-seed, & a bed of Celeri.
rain, rain.

Sunday 4.
28½ 4/10, D°; 47,   Air soft.
50; SW, W.   Cucumbᵣ plants shew rudiments of fruit.
Sun, clouds &
wind, sun, dark
clouds.
✤ *Cucumis sativus:*
mas.

Monday 5.
28½ 2/10, 4/10;   Fine showers with sunshine. Hail.
47, 47; SW, W.
Showers, showers,
brisk wind, sun &
clouds, bright.
✤ *Caltha*
palustris.

Tuesday 6.
29 3/10½; 44, 47;   I am informed that three swallows appeared over a mill-pond at
W, NW.   Bramshot on Sunday March 28. They were seen over the paper-

Sun, frequent showers & hail, bright.

mill pond by Mr. Pym.

Wednesday 7.
29½ 1/10¼; 43, 50; NW, N.
Wh: frost, sharp air, bright day, dark.

Thursday 8.
29½ 2/10; 47, 50; NW, NW.
Rain, cloudy, cloudy.
♆ *Fritillaria imperialis . . . Meleagris.*

Friday 9.
29½ 3/10; 47½, 56; E, SE, S.
Grey, sun, sweet day.
♆ *Cucumis sativus* fem:

Saturday 10.
29½ 1/10¾; 48, 54; S.
Wh. frost, sunny & spring-like, dark, misty rain.
♆ *Adoxa moschatellina, Oxalis acetosella. Oedicnemus.**

Grass begins to grow.
*Stone-curlew returns, & whistles.
Stormy wind.

It appears from good information that sometimes the osprey,¶ *falco haliaetus* Linn: is known to haunt the great pond at Frinsham. It darts down with great violence on a fish, so as to plunge itself quite under water. The man at the ale-house adjoining shot one as it was devouring its prey on the handle of a plough. This man shot also a sea-pie, *haematopus ostralegus*, on the banks of this pond.

Sunday 11.
29 3/10½; 49; SW, W, SW.
Clouds, & windy.
♆ *Anemone nemorosa, Cardamine pratensis.*

Goose-berry bushes in leaf.

Monday 12.
29½; 47, 51; SW,
W, NW.
Sun, hail storms, &
sun, sun.
Hirundo domestica.

Swallow appears.

Tuesday 13.
29 4/10¼; 47, 50;
W, SW.
Shower, dark, rain,
rain, bright.
❦ *Primula veris.*

Swallow.
Growing showers.

Wednesday 14.
28½ 4/10½; 44,
47; SW, SE, SW.
Frost, ice, dark,
shower, rain, rain,
dark.

Great showers.
Bat appears.

Thursday 15.
29 1/10½; 46½,
50; NE, E, W.
Dark, soft showers,
sun, showers about.

Titlark begins to whistle.
Wind changing with every shower.
Soft growing weather.

Friday 16.
29 4/10; 47; SW,
W, NW.
Dark & mild, soft
showers, dark.
❦ *Lamium album.*
Ruticilla, * *Conops
calcitrans.*

*Redstart returns.
Most soft growing weather.
Thomas begins to mow the walks.

Saturday 17.
29½ 1/10¾; 46;
W, S.
Bright, sweet day.
❦ *Prunus spinosa.*
Hirundo riparia, *
Hirundo agrestis, **
Merula torquata. ***

*Bank martin appears.
**House martin appears.
Redstart whistles.
Many swallows.
Grass grows very fast.
Young cucumbers swell.

***Ring-ouzels are first seen in their spring migration. They are
late in their visit this year.

Sunday 18.
29½ 1/10; 51; S,
W.

Ground very wet.
Nightingale sings.

Soft rain, rain, sun,
bright.
Luscinia.

Monday 19.
29½ ½/10; 44, 48;
W, SW, S.
Frost, sun, clouds,
soft rain, clouds &
rain.
🌱 *Mercurialis
perennis, Stellaria
holostea, Pedicularis
sylvatica.*
Atricapilla.

Black cap sings.
The sedge-bird, a delicate polyglott.

Tuesday 20.
29½ 1/10¾; 47,
55; W, S, S.
Vast dew, bright,
summer's day.
🌱 *Hyacinthus non
scriptus.*
*Regulus non cristatus
medius,* *
Bombylius major.

*Sings: a pretty plaintive note: some call it a joyous note; it begins
with an high note & runs down.

Wednesday 21.
29½ 3/10; 52 54;
W, SW.
Grey & mild, brisk
wind, sprinkling,
sun.
*Alauda minima
locustae voce stridet,* *
Gryllus campestris.

The titlark, a sweet songster,¶ not only sings flying in its descent,
& on trees; but also on the ground, as it walks about feeding in
pastures.
*Grasshopper-lark chirps.

Field-crickets have opened their holes: they are full-grown, but
have only the rudiments of wings, & are probably in their larva
state; yet they certainly eat, as appears by their dung. It seems
likely that they die every winter, leaving eggs behind them. About
Septemʳ all the mouths of their holes are obliterated. They do not
cry 'til about the middle of May. Their noise is shrill & loud. This is
by no means a common insect. They probably cast an other coat
before their wings are perfect, & they are capable of shrilling.

Thursday 22.
30, 30; 48½, 57;
NW, NW.
Great dew, bright,
sweet summer
weather.
Cuculus.

Bat. Apricots begin to set.
Cut first cucumber.

Friday 23.
31, 31; 52½; NW.
Wh: frost, sweet
summer weather,
dark & mild.
❧ *Prunus cerasus,*
Pyrus communis.

Four ring-ouzels appear on the common; they feed on ivy-berries: are wild & shy: have probably been shot at. Are very late in their passage.

Saturday 24.
30; 52, 56; NW,
NE.
Bright summer's
day, dark clouds.
Musca meridiana.

Spring-corn comes up well. Wheat thrives much.
Sowed carrots: planted potatoes.
Mild & still.

Sunday 25.
29½ 4/10; 52, 55;
NW, NE.
Bright, sun, dark,
sun.

Monday 26.¶

LONDON
Went to London with Bro: & Sister J: W.

Whooping coughs have been general among children the winter thro': & now putrid sore throats begin to be common among young people of the female sex.
   In the wings of the ring-ouzel eight of the secondary feathers have an unusual sharp point at the extremity: is not this irregularity peculiar to this species? It seems to me that some peculiarity attends the ends of the secondaries of most birds. Might not this be used as a specific by nice observers.

MAY 1773

Wednesday 12.

First swifts were seen, many together. On May 19 at night was a vast rain with thunder & lightening: frequent showers before & since, so that the ground is very moist; & the corn & grass grow. The floods are much out at Staines.

In the beginning of the month there were frosts, hail, & some snow. Apricots continue to fall off: peaches, & nectarines decent crop. Apples blow well: pears seem hurt by the frosts. Vine shoots very backward: they were pinched by the frost.

Friday 21.
29 4/10; 59.
Dark, sun & clouds.

SELBORNE

Snakeshead fritillavies
Baker's Hill
9 May

Saturday 22.
29 4/10½;
58, 57½.
Sun, & clouds,
bright.

Stoparola builds.

Sunday 23.
29 3/10½; 53,
58½; SE, SE.
Sun & clouds,
showers about, vast
rock-like clouds,
sweet growing
weather.

Lathraea squammaria in seed.
Turtle-dove about.
Measles prevail in this neighbourhood.

Monday 24.
29 3/10; 57½; NE,
N.
Dark, rain, dark,
rain & fog.
🌱 *Pinus sylvestris*,
Pinus abies.

Scotch & spruce firs beautifully illuminated by the male &
female blossoms!

Tuesday 25.
29 1/10½; 56½;
N, N.
Rain, rain, rain.

Wednesday 26.
29 4/10; W, W.
Rain, rain, brisk
air, fine evening.
🌱 *Crataegus
oxyacantha*.

Thursday 27.
29 3/10¾; 56½;
W, W.
Rain, wind, stormy
with rain.

Friday 28.
29½ 3/10½; 59½;   *bores it's nest in the field-walks.
NW, NW.
Bright, sun, sweet
afternoon.
*Apis longicornis.**

Saturday 29.
30; 60½; NE, NE.
Fog, sun, sweet day.

Sunday 30.
30; 63½; N, N.
Fog, sun, harsh air,
sweet evening.

Monday 31.
29½ 3/10½; 60,   Ashes & walnut-trees naked yet.
66; NE, NE.   Fern-owl chatters.
Sun, sultry out of yᵉ   Thunder.
wind, soft.
Libellula,
Ephemerae.

JUNE 1773

Tuesday 1.
29½ 1/10; 62, 68;   *Field cricket sings: sings all night. Thunder.
NE, NE.
Sun, brisk air,
sultry, still.
*Gryllus campestris.**

Wednesday 2.
29 3/10½; 62; NE,   Thunder & lightening & moderate rain half the night.
NE.   The corn & grass & gardens look well after the rain.
Dark, sun, sweet
evening.
Lampyris noctiluca.

Thursday 3.
29½ 1/10; 58½;   A dozen pair of swifts appear at times.

NE, NE.
Rain, dark, sun,
bright afternoon.

Some heads of S^t foin begin to blow.

Friday 4.
29½ 1/10½; 54,
61½; W, NW.
Cold dew, sun &
cold air.
♆ *Crataegus aria.* *

Began to tack the vines, which are backward.

*blows beautifully.

Saturday 5.
29½ 1/10¾; 56½;
NW, NW.
Sun & clouds, cold
air.

Some wall fruit.

Sunday 6.
29½ 1/10½; 60½;
SW, SW.
White dew, sun,
cool air, dark.

Here & there a single chafer this year.

Monday 7.
29½ 1/10¼; 59½;
63½; W, NW.
Clouds & sun,
showers about,
dark, sweet
evening.

Tuesday 8.
29½ 2/10; 66;
NW, S.
Fog, sun, summer
weather.

Rye in ear.

Wednesday 9.
29½ 2/10; 60¼,
67½; W, SW.
Sun, sultry, dark,
red evening.

Swifts sit hard.

Thursday 10.
29½ 2/10½; 62;
NW, NW.
Sun, brisk air, soft
evening.

Friday 11.
29 4/10½; 58¼;
W, SW.
Sun, dark, showers,
showers, showers.
❧ *Sambucus nigra*.

Elder begins to blow. When the elder blows-out the summer is at it's height.

Saturday 12.
29 3/10¼; 60¼;
SW, S.
Dark, showers,
showers.

Sunday 13.
29 2/10½; 68; E,
NE.
Fog, sun & strong
gale all day.
❧ *Sanicula europaea*,
*Lysimachia
nemorum*.

Bees swarm.
Pease in the fields thrive wonderfully.
Thunder.

Monday 14.
29 3/10; 68; NE,
NE.
Fog, hot sun with
brisk air, heavy
showers.

Thunder.

Tuesday 15.
29½; 60, 66; W, S.
Dark, sun, sweet
afternoon.

Great rains in the night.
Planted-out a bed of Savoys.
No apples or pears.

Wednesday 16.
29½; 60, 62; E, S.
Dark, sun, sweet
afternoon.

Sheep are shorn.

Thursday 17.
29 4/10; 60, 62; W,
SW.
Sun & clouds,
showers about.
❧ *Rosa canina*.

Friday 18.
29½; 58; W, NW,
W.

Some ears of wheat begin to appear.

Sun, clouds,
showers about,
shower, fine.

Saturday 19.
29½ 2/10½; 56,
60; NW, NW.
Sun & clouds,
showers about, sweet
evening.

Chill air.

Measles epidemic to a wonderful degree: whole families down at a
time. Several children that had been reduced by the whooping
cough dyed of them.

Sunday 20.
29½ 3/10; 57,
61½; W, SW.
Sun, clouds & cold
wind, sun, & dark.
⚘ *Carduus nutans*.

Young wild-ducks, or flappers are taken at Oakhanger-pond; & a
small *Anas* alive, which seemed to me to be a young teal: turned it
into James Knight's ponds.

Monday 21.
29½ 2/10¼; 61;
SW, SW.
⚘ *Carduus palustris*.

First brood of young swallows comes forth more early than usual.
They commonly appear about the first week in July.

Tuesday 22.
29½ 2/10; 61½,
67; SW, SW.
Shower, sun &
brisk air, sweet
evening.
⚘ *Digitalis
purpurea, Triticum
hybernum*.

The King came down to Portsmouth to see the fleet.

Wednesday 23.
29½ 2/10; 67½;
SW, SW, S.
Vast dew, cloudless,
summer's day.
⚘ *Vitis vinifera*.*

Cut my S! foin.

*begins to blow.

Thursday 24.
29½ 1/10¾; 65,
61; W, SW, SW.
Sun, sultry, rain,
rain, fog.

22: 23: 24. The firings at Spithead were so great that they shook
this house. They were heard on those days at Ringmer two miles
east of Lewes in Sussex; & at Epsom in Surrey.

Friday 25.
29 3/10½; 61¼,
63; NW, W, SW.

Sun, clouds, rain,
rain, bright.

Saturday 26.
1/10, 29 ½/10; 58,   Great hail-storm at Alton.
60; W, SW, SE,   S^t foin not yet turned.
NW.
Sun, clouds, vast
showers, fine.

Sunday 27.
29 1/10¼; 57,   Great showers about.
60¼; NW, NW.
Sun, dark heavy
clouds, shower,
dark.

Monday 28.
29 3/10½; 59;   S^t foin begins to be damaged.
NW, NW.
Showers, dark,
grey, showers, dark.

Tuesday 29.
29 4/10¾; 58½;   Turned the S^t foin.
NW, NW.
Dark & still.
🌢 *Agrimonia*
eupatoria.

Wednesday 30.
29 3/10¾; 56½,   Young stoparolas, fly-catchers.
57; NE, NE.
No dew, dark,
showers, showers,
showers.

JULY 1773

Thursday 1.
29 4/10, 29½; 55,   Portugal-laurel blows in a most beautiful manner.
57½; NE, NW.
Sun & clouds,
clouds, sun, chill
air.
🌢 *Prunus lusitanica*.

Friday 2.
29½ 2/10; 55, 59;   Cold air. Turned S^t foin.

N, N.
Sun, sun, dark
clouds, shower.

Showers about.

Saturday 3.
29½ 3/10; 57½,
60¾; NW, NW.
Sun & brisk air,
sun, sweet
afternoon, clouds.

Ricked my S^t foin, five jobbs, into a large cock. It has suffered
less than could be expected. Has lost its smell. Is got full of coarse
grass. This is the sixth crop.

Sunday 4.
29½ 1/10; 58,
60½; W, SW.
Bright & warm,
dark & cold,
showers.

Frogs migrate from the ponds.

Hops do not cover their poles well, checked perhaps by the cold,
black weather: they are pretty much infested by aphides, that
begin to abound.

Monday 5.
29½ ½/10; 58½,
60½; W, SW, W.
Cold & dark, cold,
sun.
𝕎 *Phallus impudicus.*

Cold starving weather: nothing grows.

Tuesday 6.
29½ 1/10½; 56,
59; NW, NW.
Cloudless & cold,
cold wind, still &
cold.

All vegetation in gardens seems to stand still.

Wednesday 7.
29½ 1/10½; 56,
59½; NW, E, S.
Dark, bright
& hot, dark,
sprinkling.

Cut great part of my great mead.

Robin in herb garden,
the Wares.
July.

Thursday 8.
29½ 2/10; 58½,
62½; E, NE.
Showers, hot sun,
vast clouds, shower,
bright.

Friday 9.
29½ 2/10¼; 59½,
62¼; NE, N.

Hay makes well.
Flocks of lapwings on the common. After breeding they forsake

Vast dew, bright,   the moory places; & take to the high grounds.
heavy clouds, sweet
afternoon.

Saturday 10.
29½ 4/10; 67½;   Wood strawberries begin to ripen.
NE, N, S, SW.   Hay makes well. Cocked great part of the hay in very large cock.
Sun, clouds, sweet   Many young bank-martins seem to be flown in the forest: the old
summer's day.   ones carry dragonflies into their nests for their young.

Sunday 11.
29½ 4/10½; 62½,   Partridges, young, flyers.
72; SW, S, SW.
Bright, summer's
day, flisky clouds,
brisk gale.

Monday 12.
30, 29½ 4/10;   Ricked all my hay. The S^t foin has lost all smell: the meadow hay
63¾, 75; SW, S.   is most delicate. A large crop.
Cloudless, brisk
gale, sweet day.

Tuesday 13.
29½ 1/10½; 76½;   Finished stopping the vines. Much bloom & some fruit set.
SW, S.   Finished cutting the tall hedges.
Great dew,
cloudless, sultry,
sweet evening.

Wednesday 14.
29½ 1/10, 1/10½;   Swallows & martins bring-out their first broods of young very
67½, 62½; N,   fast.
NE.
Bright, dark,
sprinkling, bright
& cold.

Thursday 15.
29½ 3/10; 64¾;
N, NE, S.
Fog, sun, hot sun
with blue mist,
sweet evening.

Friday 16.
29½ 3/10½; 68½;   Much hay brought-in in delicate order.
E, NE, SE.
Fog, grey, sunny

hot day.
*Scarabaeus
solstitialis.*

Saturday 17.
2/10½, 29½
1/10¼; 61½, 71;
E, E.
Sun, brisk air &
sun.

Much hay carted.
Showers about. Lightening.

Most of the Sᵗ foin & clover this year much damaged by rain: most of the meadow-hay ricked in very curious condition. Good hay sold this year in the place for 25ˢ pʳ load: last year for £2:7s:0d pʳ load in the place.

Sunday 18.
29 4/10½; 66½,
64½; E, W.
Loud thunder,
shower, showers,
showers.

Mʳˢ Snooke at Ringmer near Lewes had a coach-horse killed by this tempest: the horse was at grass just before the house. Very gentle showers.

Monday 19.
29½ 1/10; 63½,
63½; W, W.
Showers, grey, fine
day.
⚘ *Betonica
officinalis.*

Tuesday 20.
29½ 1/10; 61½;
W, S.
Dark, misty rain,
showers, misty rain.
⚘ *Stachys germanica.*

Wednesday 21.
½/10, 29½ 1/10;
63; NW, W.
Bright, fine day.

A bunting, *emberiza alba*, sitting about on the bushes in the North field. Probably has a nest there. This is a very rare bird in this parish: a very common one in the open champain country. I am not sure that I ever saw one before in Selborne.

Thursday 22.
29½ 1/10½; 60½,
65; N, NE.
Bright, rock-like
clouds, dark &
louring.
⚘ *Tilia europaea.*

Wheat is now at 17 pᵈˢ per load, & very little left in the kingdom.

Friday 23.
29½ 2/10¼; 62,

Turnips begin to be hoed. In general a good crop.

66; N, N.
Dark & still, grey,
sweet evening.

The young clover among the corn is fine this year.

Saturday 24.
29½ 2/10½; 63¾,
66; NW.
Bright, grey & soft,
dark & mild.

Wheat at Farnham £17:12s: 6d. p^r load.

Several fields of cone,¶ or bearded wheat growing this year round the village: the bloom of this wheat is of a brimstone colour. The bloom of some beardless wheat is purple. Qu: what sort? The bloom of wheat in general is whitish.

Sunday 25.
29½ 2/10½; 68;
NW, W.
Grey, sun, dark &
still.

Some hops much infested with aphides.

Monday 26.
29½ ½/10; 65¾,
68; SW, SW.
Grey, sun & sultry,
showers about,
dark, sprinkling.
❦ *Sambucus ebulus.*

Young martins abound.

Tuesday 27.
29½ ¼/10; 62½;
NW, SW.
Grey, clouds with
chilly air, dark.

Some wheat seems to be blighted.

Wednesday 28.
29 4/10¼; 59½,
60½; SW, NW.
Sprinkling, dark &
sprinkling, red
evening, sprinkling.

Chilly air.

Thursday 29.
29½ 1/10; 56¾,
59½; NW, NW.
Sun, cold air, sun &
clouds, showers
about.

Friday 30.
29½ ¼, 29 3/10½;
57, 59½; S, SE, E,

Distant thunder.
Much wheat lodged.

W, NW.
Dark, rain, rain,
sun, dark clouds.

Saturday 31.
29½, 29½ 1/10½;
56½, 62; W, NW.
Dark, showers,
showers, sun.

The lightening beat down a chimney on the Burnet: no person
was hurt.
Measles still about.

Thro' this month the *Caprimulgi* are busy every evening in
catching the solstitial chafers which abound in chalky soils on the
tops of hills. These birds certainly do, as I suspected last year, take
these insects with their feet, & pick them to pieces as they flie
along; & so pouch them for their young. Any person that has a
quick eye may see them bend their heads downwards, & push out
their short feet forwards as they pull their prey to pieces. The
chafer may also be discerned in their claws. The serrated claw
therefore on their longest toe is no doubt for the purpose of holding
their prey. This is the only insectivorous bird that I know which
takes it's prey flying with it's feet.

AUGUST 1773

Sunday 1.
29½ 2/10, 1/10¼;
58, 62; SW, S.
Sun, clouds, dark,
wet & windy.
ॐ *Geranium
pratense*.

Turneps thrive at a vast rate: a fine crop.
A prospect of much after-grass.
Many young swallows & martins come out.

Monday 2.
29½ 3/10; 72½;
NW, NW.
Dark, sun & sultry,
distant thunder
clouds, rain.
ॐ *Humulus lupulus*.
Apis manicata.

This bee is never observed by me 'til the *Stachys germanica* blows,
on which it feeds all day: tho' doubtless it had other plants to feed
on before I introduced that *Stachys*.

Tuesday 3.
29½ 3/10½; 69½;
E, E.
Grey, dark &
spitting, sweet
evening.

Young swallows, & martins begin to congregate on the roofs.
Distant thunder clouds.

Wednesday 4.
29½ 1/10½; 69½;
E, E.
Fog, sweet day.

Thursday 5.
29½ 2/10; 66; E.
Delicate ripening
weather.

Friday 6.
29½ 2/10¼; 73; E,
NE.
Sun, hot, sunny
weather.

The male, & female ants of the little dusky sort come forth by
myriads, & course about with great agility.

Saturday 7.
29½ 3/10; 72; NE,
E, S.
Sun, sultry with
rock-like clouds,
brisk air, sweet
evening.

The flight of the *scarabaeus solstitialis* seems to be over.
Measles still in some families.

Sunday 8.
29½ 3/10; 68½; E,
S.
Grey, sun & brisk
air, sweet even:

Hops have been some time in bloom, & do not promise for much
of a crop: they are lousy, & have not run the poles well.

Monday 9.
29½ 3/10; 65¾,
72¾; SE.
Cloudless, brisk air,
sultry.

MEONSTOKE
Wheat harvest begins.
Apricots ripen.

Tuesday 10.
SE.
Cloudless, air, dark,
sun.

Most sultry night.

Wednesday 11.
W.
Fog, sun, sultry,
sweet even.

Thursday 12.
W, SW, SE.
Cloudless, air.

Friday 13.
78½, 76½; SE, S.
Sun, brisk air,
sultry, thunder.

Great thunder, & lightening.

Saturday 14.
29½ 1/10, 29½;
74½; N, W.
Dark, sun & clouds,
sultry.

SELBORNE
Wheat-harvest pretty general.
Dark heavy clouds to the N:W.

Heat unusually severe all this week! This storm did great damage
in & about London.

Sunday 15.
29 4/10½; 66½,
67; W, SW, S.
Sun, sun & clouds,
dark.

Hops visibly improved by the thunder-shower on friday
evening.

If the swifts are gone, as they seem to be, they can never breed but
once in a summer; since the swallows & martins in general are now
but laying their eggs for a second brood. As young swifts never
perch or congregate on buildings I can never be sure exactly when
they come forth. The retreat of swifts so early is a wonderful fact:
& yet it is more strange still, that they withdraw full as soon in the
summer at Gibraltar. Swifts sat hard June 9th.

Monday 16.
29 3/10½; 65, 55,
64; SE, SW.
Rain, rain & strong
wind, wind.

Wind covers the walks with leaves, & blows down the annuals.

Tuesday 17.
29½; 60, 65; W, S.
Fine day, fine.

Swifts seem to be gone; very early.
Vast clouds in the horizon.
Wheat bound.

Wednesday 18
29 ½/10; 61, 61;
E, NE, N.
Dark &
windy, rain, vast
rains.

Wheat lies in a bad way. Much cut, little bound, & scarce any
housed.

Thursday 19.
29 ½/10; 3/10½;
58; N, NW, W.
Heavy rain with
storms, rains, sun &
clouds.

Terrible storm all night, which made sad havock among the
hops, & broke off boughs from the trees.

Friday 20.
29½ 1/10; 59; W,
NW.
Sun, sun & clouds,
good harvest day.
Vespa communis.

Wasps begin to appear.
No swifts since last week.

Saturday 21.
29½ 2/10½; 57,
61½; NW, W.
Sun, clouds & sun,
sweet harvest day.

With respect to the singing of birds Aug: is much the most silent
month: for many species begin to reassume their notes in Septemʳ
The goldfinch sings now every day.
Wheat housed all this afternoon.

Sunday 22.
29½ 3/10½; 55,
61; N, S.
White frost, sun,
rock-like clouds,
sweet afternoon.

Monday 23.
29½ 3/10½; 60;
W, SW.
Sun, fine harvest
weather.

Some heavy clouds about.
Wheat housed all day.

Tuesday 24.
29½ 1/10½; 59,
65; W, SE.
Vast dew, cloudless,
heavy clouds,
dusky.

Peaches & nectarines redden.
China-asters begin to blow.
Baromʳ sinks fast.

Wild strawberry growing
from a crevice in
the fruit wall.
the Wakes
26 August.

Wednesday 25.
29½ ½/10, 1/10;
62, 67; SE, S.
Sun, sultry with
clouds, sweet
afternoon.

Baromʳ sinks.
Much wheat housed.
Tho' there was a brisk air from the S: all the afternoon; yet the
clouds in an upper-region flew swiftly all the while from yᵉ N: in
great quantities.

Thursday 26.
29 4/10½; 62; SW.
Sun, fog, dark,
misty rain, shower.

Friday 27.
29 4/10½; 60½;
SW, W.
Sun, clouds & brisk

Vast quantities of Nuts & filberts.

wind, showers,
strong gale.

Saturday 28.
29½ 1/10; 57½,
63½; NW, W.
Sun & clouds, sweet
harvest day.

Some few grapes begin to turn red.
Peaches begin to ripen, & are large & good.
Nectarines look well: they are very ruddy & large.

Sunday 29.
29½ 1/10½; 60;
W, SW.
Sun & clouds, sweet
day.

A little black *curculio* damages the peaches¶ by boring holes in
them before they are quite ripe. I do not remember this insect on
my wall-fruit before. They damage the leaves.

Monday 30:
29½; 60¾, 68½;
E, NE.
Sun, fine harvest
day.

Tyed up endives.
Peaches ripen, & are also fine.
Some people have finished wheat-harvest.

Tuesday 31.
29 4/10, 29½; 63,
65½; E, SE, SW.
Dark &
louring, sweet
afternoon.

Much wheat housed.

SEPTEMBER 1773

Wednesday 1
29 4/10; 63½, 65;
SE, S, SW.
Fog, bright &
sultry, sprinklings,
vast clouds, hard
rain.

Orleans plums¶ begin to ripen.
Hops continue small & have not grown kindly since the storm.

Thursday 2.
29½; 64; S, SW.
Sun, dark, showers,
sun & clouds.

Some perennial asters begin to blow.
Grapes rather small as yet. Several bunches begin to turn.

Friday 3.
29½; 65; SE, SW.
Hard showers,
showers, sun &
clouds.

Young wagtails come out.
Delicate peaches, & nectarines in plenty.

Saturday 4.
29 4/10¼, 29½;
59½; NW, W,
SW.
Rain, rain, rain,
sun, bright.

The beards of cone-wheat do not long preserve the grain from sparrows: for as the corn gets ripe those *aristae* are shaken off by the wind.

Sunday 5.
29 3/10¾; 58.
Great dew, sun,
heavy clouds, dark
& threatning.

Rock-like clouds in the horizon.

Monday 6.
29 1/10½, 3/10;
60; SE, SW.
Rain, rain, sun &
wind.

Tuesday 7.
29 3/10½; 59; SW.
Sun, showers.

WINTON
People begin to pick hops.

Wednesday 8.
28½ 4/10; 59½;
SW.
Sun, showers &
wind, showers.

Showers.
Wheat about still.

Thursday 9.
29, 29 4/10¾; SW,
W.
Sun, dry day.

SELBORNE
Little barley housed.

Friday 10.
29 4/10; 59; SW,
W.
Showers, showers &
wind, dark.

Sad harvest, & hop-picking weather!
Rain damages the wall fruit.

Saturday 11.
29½ 2/10½; 57½,
59; W, W.
Sun, sun & cold
brisk wind.

Wasps increase, & injure peaches & nect:
& begin on the grapes.
Young martins come out.

Sunday 12.
29½; W, SW.

Young martins in the nest.

Wh: frost, sun,
dark & chilly.

Monday 13.
29 2/10½, 3/10½;
59; W, NW.
Rain, sun &
showers, bright.

Young swallows in the nest.
Hops very ordinary: very small.

Tuesday 14.
29½ 2/10½; 56½;
W, SW, W.
Sun, louring, fine
afternoon.

Young swallows come out.
Barley & oats housed.
Some wheat out still.

Wednesday 15.
29½ 2/10; 56; W,
W.
No dew, rain, rain,
sun, chilly.

Peaches & nectarines very fine.

Thursday 16.
29 3/10½; 55; SW,
S.
Sun, soft air, dark
& harsh.

Gathered first grapes: small but good.
Last wheat housed.

Friday 17.
29 2/10½; 58; SW,
W.
Rain, rain, rain,
dry, sun.

Miserable harvest-weather.
Peach: & nect: very fine.

Saturday 18.
29½; SW, SW.
Grey, sun, showers
about.

Linnets begin to congregate: they feed on the seeds of *centaurea jacea*.
Cold & damp. Ground very moist.

Sunday 19.
29½ 2/10; 55; SW,
SW.
Fog, grey, sun,
dark.

Monday 20.
29½ 1/10; 61; SW.
Bright, sun,
pleasant day.

Tuesday 21.
29; 61; SE, SE.
Grey, dark,
showers, showers,
stormy.

Wednesday 22.   LASHAM
28 4/10; 58; W.
Stormy with rain,
sun, shower, windy.

Thursday 23.   BASINGSTOKE, LASHAM
Wh: frost, showers.

Friday 24.
Showers.

Saturday 25.   SELBORNE
29 4/10; 57.   Much barley abroad.
Showers.   Wet fit ever since the first of Sep.[r]
☙ *Hedera helix.*   Wall-fruit fine still.

Sunday 26.
29 3/10; SE, SE.   Barley not so much damaged as might be expected, being soon
Grey, dark &   dried by continual wind.
windy, rain, rain.

Monday 27.
29½ ¾/10; 54;   Gathered the last nectarines: very good.
SW, SW.   Large *aurora*: very vivid in the S:W.
Bright, clouds,
showers, showers,
bright.

Tuesday 28.
29½ 3/10; 52; SW,   *Stoparola*, flycatcher, still appears.
SE, SW.
Grey, sun, dark,
fine afternoon.
Papilio Atalanta.

Wednesday 29.
29½ 2/10; 57¼;   Multitudes of martins, but I think not many swallows.
SW, S, SE.   Grapes are eatable, but not curious yet: are damaged by the
Grey, clouds, sun,   wasps.
grey & mild.   Much barley abroad.

Thursday 30.
29½ 2/10; 60;   Some barley abroad that has been cut a month. Earwigs cast their

SW, S.
Grey, dark & mild,
spitting, spitting,
mild.
Merula torquata.

skins & come forth white. 10 or 12 ring-ouzels appear on their autumn migration round Noar hill.

OCTOBER 1773

Friday 1.
29½; SW, SW.
Grey, mild &
pleasant, dark &
windy.

Martins are seldom seen at any distance from neighbourhoods. They feed over waters or under the shelter of an hanging wood. Swallows often hawk about on naked downs & fields, even in very windy seasons at a great distance from houses.

Saturday 2.
29½; 54¾; NW,
W, SW.
Grey, sun, still &
pleasant.

Swallows do not resort to chimneys for some time before they retire.
Titlarks abound on the common.

Martins are the shortest-winged, & least agile of all the swallow-tribe. They take their prey in a middle region, not so high as the swifts: nor do they usually sweep the ground so low as the swallows. Breed the latest of all the swallow genus: last year they had young nestling to the 21 of Oct.ʳ They usually stay later than their congeners. Last year 20 or 30 were playing all day long by the side of the hanger, & over my fields on Novʳ 3ʳᵈ. After that they were seen no more.

Sunday 3.
28½ 4/10¾; 5 5¾;
SE, SW.
Grey, dark showers,
showers & wind,
dry & windy.

Swallows.
Glass falls at a vast rate.

Monday 4.
28½ 3/10½; 5 5½;
SW, SW.
Shower, sun &
soft air, showers,
bright.

Vetches & pease are mostly spoiled. Martins.
Mʳ Yalden has yet 10 acres of barley abroad.

Tuesday 5.
29 2/10½; 5 1½;
SW, SW.
Red morn, fine,
showers, showers,
fine.

Grapes good.

Wednesday 6.
29 3/10½; 49; SW,
SE.
White dew, fine,
clouds, showers,
vast shower.

Thursday 7.
29½ ½/10; 53; N,
NW.
Dark, sun & clouds,
bright.

Wasps cease to appear.
Swallows & Martins seem to be gone.

Friday 8.
29 4/10½; 57; S, S.
Grey & windy,
dark, great rain.

No swallows, or martins.
Rooks frequent wallnut-trees, & carry-off the fruit.

Saturday 9.
29½; 58; S, SE.
Sun, sun & clouds,
warm & still.

Many martins appear again.
Mr Yalden's barley abroad: it was large corn, & full of clover.

The breed of partridges was good this year: pheasants are very
scarce; hardly any eyes to be found¶. We abound usually in
pheasants. In some counties pheasants are so scarce that the Gent:
have agreed to refrain from killing any.
Rains ever since the first of Sep^r

Sunday 10.
29 1/10½, 4/10½;
57; S, SW.
Stormy with great
rain, fine, fine.

Storm that broke boughs from the hedges.
Many swallows & martins.
Much barley & vetches abroad.

Monday 11.
29½ 2/10¾.
Fine day, clouds &
wind at night.

WORTING
The housed & ricked barley in wet condition: it heats much.

From Octr to Oct. 21st inclusive the journal was kept by John White
at Selborne.¶

Tuesday 12.
29½ 3/10, 29½
1/10; 51½; W, N,
W.
Clouds, showers,
fine.

OXFORD
Hops sold at Weyhill fair much cheaper than people expected:
from £6.10.0 to £7.10.0.

Wednesday 13.
29½ 1/10½; 50;

W, SE.
Fine, heavy
showers, distant
lightening.

Thursday 14.
29½ 2/10, 3/10½;
48; W, S.
Fine, shower, fine.

Friday 15.
29½ 4/10; 51½;
W.
Fine day.

Saturday 16.
29½ 2/10½; 54½;
W.
Fine day.

Mr Yalden finished his barley-harvest, some of which had been cut more than six weeks. In general the grain is not spoiled, but by drying & frequent turning in a floor will be tollerable.

Sunday 17.
29½ 1/10½; 55¼;
SW.
Heavy clouds, soft,
heavy showers.

Monday 18.
29½ 1/10; 55½;
W, W.
Fine, wet evening.

Tuesday 19.
29½ 4/10½; 49¾;
W.
Fine day, frost.

Venus is become an evening star: Vivid *Aurora bor:*

Wednesday 20.
29½ 4/10; 48½.
White frost, fine.

Aurora.

Thursday 21.
29½ 2/10.
White frost, sweet
sunny day.

WORTING
No swallows or martins observed.

Saw several martins at Dorchester in Oxfordshire round the church. It is remarkable that the swallow kind appear full as late in the midland counties, as in the maritime: a circumstance this more favourable to hiding than migration.

As it proved these were the last martins that I saw.

Friday 22.
29½ 1/10½; SE,
SW.
Fog, rain, fog, fog.

Saturday 23.
29½; 57; S, SE.
Fog, fog, grey &
soft.

SELBORNE
Grapes are now delicate.

Sunday 24.
29½ 1/10¾; 57,
58½; S, NW, E.
Sweet morning,
dark & still
& mild.

Woodlark sings.
Great titmouse reassumes it's spring note.

Monday 25.
29½ 4/10; 57, 58;
S, SE.
Fog, spitting fog,
rain & wind.

Began levelling my grass-plot & walks at the garden-door, &
bringing them down to the level of the floor of my house.

Tuesday 26.
29 4/10½; 58; S,
SW, SW.
Grey, rain, gusts,
fine.

Grapes are excellent in spite of continual wet.
Bat appears on evenings.

Wednesday 27.
29 3/10; 56½; S,
SE, SW.
Rain, dark, rain,
dark & windy.

Hares abound, but pheasants are very scarce this year. One of the
vines to the SW: casts it's leaves, & looks sickly.

Thursday 28.
29½; 54½; S, SW,
S.
Bright, warm sun,
showers, bright.

Vast rain in the night.

Friday 29.
29 1/10; 56½; S,
SW.
Shower, fine, fine,
stormy.

Saturday 30.
28 4/10; 51½; SW,
SW, SW.
Vast rain in the
night, sun, showers,
showers.

Grapes are very curious.

Sunday 31.
29 2/10½; 46½;
SW, SW.
Fine, sun & heavy
clouds, shower,
fine.

Yellow-hammer sings.

NOVEMBER 1773

Monday 1.
29 4/10½; 44; SW,
W.
Cold dew, sun, fine
with vast clouds in
the horizon.

Seed-clover cutting.
A ring-ouzel was shot in the high wood with a russet gorget, &
russet spots on it's wings. Three or four more were seen.

Tuesday 2.
SW, SE.
Sun, fine day, rain
with wind.

NEWTON

Wednesday 3.
28½ 4/10½; 54;
SW.
Driving rain, vast
showers, rain.
*Oenas sive vinago,**
*Turdus iliacus.***

SELBORNE
*Stock-dove, or wood-pigeon appears.
**Red wing appears.

Thursday 4.
29 2/10½; 47; W.
Sun, sun & wind,
dark, heavy
showers.
*Scolopax.**

*Woodcock returns.

Friday 5.
29 4/10; 47; W, W.
Frost, sun &
pleasant, dark.
*Cornix cinerea.**

*Flying over Faringdon heath. The first grey crow¶ that I ever
saw in the district of Selborne. They are common on the downs
about Andover: about Winton, & Bagshot.

Saturday 6.
29 2/10; 49½; W,
S.
Much rain in the
night, fine & soft,
dark.

Most of the earth to be removed in levelling in the garden is taken
away; in some places to the depth of 18 inches. The continual rains
much interrupt the work, & make it a nasty jobb. The best mould
is laid on the quarters of the garden, the clayey soil is wheeled into
the meadow.

Sunday 7.
28½ 2/10; 50¾; S,
SE.
Rain, rain, dark &
vast clouds, rain.

Hedge-sparrow sings.
Grapes delicate still.
Vast rain.

Monday 8.
28½; 49½; SW, S.
Fine, sun, clouds,
showers, stormy,
vast rain.
Turdus pilaris.

Snipes leave the moors & marshes which are flooded, & get up
into the uplands.

Tuesday 9.
28 4/10, 28½ 2/10;
SW, SW.
Vast rains, showers,
shower, bright.

Ground to be levelled is under water.
Woodcocks pretty common.
The country all in a flood.

Wednesday 10.
28½ 3/10½; 45½;
S, SW.
Frost, bright, heavy
showers, dry.

Rains have lasted ten weeks.
Saw a flock of seven or 8 stone curlews.
These birds generally retire before this time.

Thursday 11.
28 2/10½; 47; S,
SW, S.
Bright, clouds, rain,
vast rain with wind.

Grapes are still very fine.
All our levelling work is under water.
The barom' has been unusually low for many days past; & yet
with little wind: but the rains have been prodigious. Most of the
rain has fallen by night.

Friday 12.
28 ¾/10, 29 1/10;
W.
Thunder in the
night, vast rains,
sun & wind.

Saturday 13.
29 1/10¾; 45; W,
W.
Sun, clouds & brisk
wind, bright, wind.

The turfing the levelled ground goes on briskly.

No late Martins have appeared this Nov' a flight sometimes is seen
about the first week in this month.

Sunday 14.
29 4/10½; 43; W,
SW.
Bright, dry with

Green plovers now appear in small companies on the uplands.
They flie high & make a whistling. Do not breed in these parts.

brisk wind.

Monday 15.
28½ 2/10, 29 1/10;
43; SW, W, NW.
Vast rain with wind,
dry, bright.

Helleborus foetidus buds for bloom.

Tuesday 16.
29½; 40; W, NW.
White frost, sun &
drying wind, dark
& still.

Two grey crows flew over my garden to the hanger: a sight I
never saw before.

Wednesday 17.
29½ 1/10, ½/10;
39¾; W, S.
Frost, ice, sun,
dark, spitting fog.

The turfing the walks advances apace.

Thursday 18.
29½ 1/10¾; 46;
NW, NW.
Grey, sun, soft day,
bright.

Some Curlews appear still on Temple farm.

Friday 19.
29½ 2/10½; 39;
W, NE, N.
Frost, ground hard,
sunny & still, frost.

Ring-ouzels still remain.
Gathered-in the last grapes: yᵉ crop was very large, & the grapes
delicate. And yet the vine shoots were much pinched at their top
by frost the first week in May: & more-over Septemʳ was a season
of continual clouds & rain!

Saturday 20.
29½ 1/10¾; 36½;
N, N. White frost,
fog, freezing fog.

Ring-ouzels, & stone-curlews stay late with us this year.

Sunday 21.
29 4/10½; 36;
NW, NW.
Dark, rimes, rimes,
clear.

Yellow water wagtail.¶

Monday 22.
29 3/10; 35½, 36;
N, SE, S.
Hard frost, bright
& still, clouds &
moonshine.

Beautiful rimes all day on the hanger.

Tuesday 23.
29 2/10½; 37; W,
NW, W.
Sun, fine still day,
frost.

While my people move earth in the garden the red-breasts in pursuit of worms are very tame, & familiar, settling on the very wheel-barrow, while filling.

Wednesday 24.
29; 37; W.
Rain, flight
of snow, dark,
bright.

Finished the levelling, & turfing the garden. The alteration has a good effect. The weather & rains considered the turf lies pretty well.

Thursday 25.
29 3/10¾; 36; N,
NW.
Snow, snow, dark,
thaw, freezes.

Considerable snow on the ground.

Friday 26.
29½ 1/10; W.
Swift thaw,
pleasant.

ALTON
A profusion of turneps probably all the kingdom over: on which account lean sheep are very dear. Hops at present lie on hand: were carryed to Weyhill, then to Andover: & now are bringing home again.
Snow gone except under hedges.

Saturday 27.
29½; 43; SW, W.
Fog, warm &
sunny, dark.

SELBORNE

Birds do not seem to touch the berries of the *tamus communis*, 'tho they look very red, & inviting: the berries also of the *bryonia alba* seem not to be meddled with. Perhaps they are too acrid.
     There is a fine crop of clover of last spring: the frequent showers of last summer occasioned also a vast growth of grass.

Sunday 28.
29½ 3/10¾; 45¼;
SW, SW.
Dark, still &
mild.

Bat appears.

Monday 29.
29½ 3/10¾; 46;
SW, SW.
Dark, still, mild,
rain.

The tortoise in Mrs Snooke's garden went under ground Novr 21: came-out on the 30th for one day, & retired to the same hole: lies in a wet border in mud & mire! with it's back bare.
     In the late floods the water at Houghton ran over the clappers:¶ & at Bramber in to men's ovens.

Tuesday 30.
30 1/10, 30½; W.
Bright, sunny, soft.

CHILGROVE

DECEMBER 1773

Wednesday 1.
SW.
Dark & still.

STENNING
Birds on the downs are rooks, larks, stone-chats, kites, gulls:
some fieldfares, some hawks.

Thursday 2.
SW.
Partial fogs, dark &
still.

RINGMER
Not one wheat-ear to be seen on the downs.
The grubs of the *scarabaeus solstitialis* abound on the downs: the
rooks dig them out. On what do they feed when they come forth?
for there are no trees on the South downs.

Friday 3.
SW, W.
Grey, sun, rain.

Saturday 4.
W.
Rain & wind, rain
& wind.

The county of Sussex abounds in turneps.

Sunday 5.
SW.
Sunny, pleasant,
shower.

Rooks spend most of their time in mild weather on their nest-
trees: some stares & jack-daws attend them.

Monday 6.
NW.
Frost, ice, sunny,
sharp.

White wagtail.¶

Tuesday 7.
NW, W.
Frost, sun, wet &
cold.

Wednesday 8.
N.
Fine, cold air.

Much wheat still sowing.

Thursday 9.
N.
Hard frost, bright,
still.

Rooks attend their nest trees in frost only morning & evening.

Friday 10.
N.
Hard frost, bearing
ice, sun, clouds in
horizon.

Saturday 11.
S.
Dark, spitting,
grey, thaw.

Flocks of chaffinches; & multitudes of buntings at the foot of
mount Caborn.

Sunday 12.
S, SW.
Rain, dark & still.

Rooks visit their nest-trees every morning just at the dawn of the
day, being preceeded a few minutes by a flight of daws: & again
about sunset. At the close of day they retire into deep woods to
roost.

Monday 13.
SE.
Gentle showers,
rain.

Tuesday 14.
E.
Dark, rain, bright,
grey & still.

Wednesday 15.
SE.
Grey, soft, still,
rain.

FINDON
Large gulls on the downs. Some bustards are bred in the parish of
Findon. Fieldfares.

Thursday 16.
29 2/10½; 48; SE.
Dark, grey, still,
some fog.

CHILGROVE
They, the shepherds, do not take any wheatears W: of Houghton
bridge. Fieldfares.

Friday 17.
29; SE.
Fog, rain, fog.

Chaffinches, many cocks among them.
Black rabbits are pretty common on Chilgrove warren.

Saturday 18.
29; SE.
Great rain, bright,
dark & still.

SELBORNE

The parish-well in Findon-village is 200 feet deep: at Montham on
the down the well is full 350 feet. Mͬ Woods's well at Chilgrove is
156 feet deep; & yet in some very wet seasons is brim full: his
cellars are some times full.

Sunday 19.
28½ 3/10; 48; E.
Dark, spitting, fog
& rain, rain.

Monday 20.
29 1/10½; 48; W,
SW.
Great rain, dark,

sun, grey.

Tuesday 21.
28½ 4/10½; 49½;
E.
Grey & mild, still.

Wednesday 22.
28½ 2/10¼; 50¾;
S, SE.
Dark, grey & mild,
rain, much rain.

Thursday 23.
29 1/10½; 44;
NW.
Dark, rain, rain,
dark.

Friday 24.
29 3/10; 39½;
NW.
Cold rain, cold rain.

Saturday 25.
29½; 40; NW.   Yellow-water-wagtail¶ frequents the shallow parts of the stream.
Dark, spitting,
gleams, dark.

Sunday 26.
29½ 1/10; 38;   White water wagtail.
NW.
Dark & still.

Monday 27.
29½ 1/10; 38½;
SE, SE.
Frost, bright, rock-
like fliskly clouds.

Tuesday 28.
29 4/10; 45; SW,
W, SW.
Rain, showers, fine
& soft.

Wednesday 29.
29 1/10; 43; NE,
NE.

Rain, rain, great
rain.

Thursday 30.
29 3/4/10; 38½; W,
W.
Dark, sun, bright &
sharp.

Friday 31.   Frost all day.
29 2/10½; 32½;
NW, NW.
Hard frost, bright,
brisk wind, hard
frost.

N O T E S

G A R D E N   K A L E N D A R

In order to avoid repetition the following abbreviations have been used:
GW = Gilbert White
FS = *Flora Selborniensis*
NHS = *The Natural History of Selborne*

1751 Events and journeys
In early June Gilbert White went to Oxford and thence to Chipping Norton. He set off again on 1 July on a journey to Oxford and round the north-west of England to Lyndon and Stamford, returning on 24 August. During September he went to both Oxford and Portsmouth. On 25 October, Gilbert White became Curate-in-charge at Selborne for Dr Bristow, who was absent owing to ill health, and stayed at the Vicarage at Selborne.

January	7.	Spanish-Beans A variety of broad bean, possibly the Seville long-pod.
	7.	Turner's plot This was a large vegetable plot on Baker's Hill, to the NE of the original garden.
	23.	loaf-Cabbage The sugar-loaf cabbage, a productive, early variety which has a long oblong head, looking something like a Cos lettuce.
	24.	little Garden GW is referring to the original garden behind The Wakes.
February	23.	large, white, Dutch-Currants An old variety, and one of the palest whites. In his *Gardener's Dictionary*, published between 1731 and 1739, Philip Miller comments that Dutch reds and whites are prolific and preferred for their looks and size, though the common kinds are better flavoured.
March	7.	U: White GW's uncle, Charles White, Rector of Bradley and Vicar of Swarraton, where GW was his curate.
	22.	Hot-bed Cucumber There was a great fashion for cucumber growing in the 18th century. Miller's *Gardener's Dictionary* has four large pages of detailed instructions on the subject. They were often eaten cooked as well as raw – a later entry refers to 'a dish of 20 stewed cucumbers'.
		Mays-seed Also called Indian wheat by GW (see 7 March 1752) and now known as maize or sweet corn. Seven kinds are mentioned by Miller with the remark: 'Seldom propagated in England but as a Curiosity.'
		The Grange This was the granary of the former Selborne Priory.
		Chardoons Now generally known as cardoons, these are a kind of vegetable thistle, closely related to globe artichokes and grown for their fleshy stems. Shortly before harvesting, the plants need to be closely wrapped around with straw in order to blanch the stems; GW refers to this as 'basketing' (12 September 1751).

	27.	Winsor beans A variety of broad bean.
April	1.	marrow-fat pease A large, rich-flavoured kind of pea which is still available (e.g. 'Onward'). A farming book published in 1766 rated marrowfat 'the best tasted of all the large kinds of peas'.
	6.	Salsafy, Skirret, Scorzonera Three old-fashioned root vegetables. Salsafy is now usually written as 'salsify'.
		Sea-cale Not widely cultivated until the end of the century. GW obtained his when visiting his friend the Revd Nathan Wells at East Allington in the autumn of 1750, possibly from the wild stock growing along the Devon coast.
		sliped . . . the artichoke beds The gaps were filled in with slips or cuttings of young plants.
	13.	purslain Purslane, *Portulaca oleracea*, is naturalised in Britain. Its leaves may be cooked or eaten raw in salad.
		a cover of oiled paper This would be an early kind of cloche made from good-quality paper and greased to render it translucent and weatherproof.
	27.	Lassams A cottage at the southern end of the main street of Selborne, probably belonging to the Lassam (or Lasham) family. An orchard belonging to the cottage was bought by GW.
May	23.	basons in the field These were large beds excavated and filled with good soil: Selborne soil is poor.
October	5.	Stock-gilliflowers A name used for both wallflowers and stocks; in this case it was probably the former, as they were being planted in October.
November	6.	Scorpion senna Crown vetch (*Coronilla emerus*), an erect, green-twigged shrub with twisted seed pods, suggestive of scorpions.
December	2: 3.	Earthed-up Artichoke-beds These would be globe artichokes, as 6 April. If blanched the stems and leaves may be eaten as well as the flower-head scales.

1752 Events and journeys

This was the year in which Gilbert White, a Fellow of Oriel College, became Junior Proctor at Oxford, an office which he took up on 8 April, having resigned his curacy of Selborne in March. The university appointment which his friend John Mulso called his 'Oxford confinement' entailed residence in the city, and although he returned to Selborne as frequently as possible, his *Garden Kalendar* for this year runs to only four pages, with the period from 8 April to 14 May entered by his brother, Thomas White.

March	5.	Quincunx of firs A group of trees planted in the form of a five-dot domino with one in each corner of a square and one centred. This was a traditional pattern for tree planting, consisting either of one set, as here, or of several to make an orchard or grove.
	10.	Plashed . . . the Quickset Pleached, that is, weaving in the horizontal part of a layed hedge. Quickset nowadays means hawthorn, but in the past it was used to distinguish it from a 'dead' hedge of man-made construction, such as the rod hedge mentioned on 13 April.
April	10.	Put . . . plants under the Hand Glasses Handglasses – the antecedents of modern cloches – seem to have been available in several shapes and sizes.
	13: 15.	Cups These were smallish, round depressions dug into the soil, used here both for raising seedlings and in May for growing cucumbers in the hot bed.
		Rod Hedge A 'dead' hedge, probably made of willow rods woven together.
	16.	Sowed Radishes with the Stocks as Miller directs It was suggested that these would be eaten in preference to the stocks by 'a Sort of Fly' which attacks the young plants in warm dry weather. This probably refers to aphids, pests shared by radishes and stocks.
May	19.	Removed four plants Cucumber plants. It is a measure of GW's obsession with hot-bed cultivation of cucumbers (and later of melons) that he forgets to write down the name of the plant.
July	29.	Turneps for spring greens Turnips were cultivated as a culinary vegetable and for feeding sheep. As at present, the green leaves were known as turnip tops or spring greens. The practice of fattening sheep on this root vegetable was so prevalent in the 18th and 19th centuries that the word was used as a verb meaning fed or fattened on turnips. It was usually sheep who were 'turnipped', although

		it was a practice which was also sometimes applied to hogs or cattle.
September	15.	N:S: New Style. This referred to the new style of calendar, the Gregorian calendar, which Britain and her dominions adopted in 1752 on 3 September. This then became 14 September. There was a considerable outcry about this loss of eleven days.

1753 Events and journeys

In February of this year Benjamin White, Gilbert's brother, married Ann Yalden, daughter of the Revd Edmund Yalden, Vicar of Newton Valence. Gilbert's period of duty in the office of Proctor finished on 2 May, and at the end of the month he set out for 'London, Sunbury [to see John Mulso] and Selborne'. Later, in July, he visited the 'Hot well'¶ at Bristol, staying there for seven weeks. In September, Gilbert White became Curate of the rural parish of Durley near Bishop's Waltham in Hampshire.

The *Garden Kalendar* for this year is exceptionally brief, scarcely a page of manuscript. A new edition of Philip Miller's *Gardener's Dictionary* and possibly also John Ray's *Synopsis Methodica Stirpium Britannicarum* appear to have been purchased in this year. It was during the winter of 1752–3 that the steep path known as the Zig-zag which climbs Selborne Hanger was made, the principal engineer being Gilbert's brother John.

July		Hot well The Hot Well at Bristol was a popular watering place or spa which was visited for the healing powers of the waters. There is an engraving of the Hot Wells by Paul Sandby in Rashleigh Holt-White's *Life and Letters of Gilbert White of Selborne*.
October	25.	Laid-down several Branches of the Laurus-tinus This refers to propagation by layering.

1754 Events and journeys

The year began with very bad weather, so Gilbert did not get back to Selborne until late February. Early in the year John White, Gilbert's father, was ill, but recovered. In June Gilbert visited his friend John Mulso, during which time his brother Thomas White contributed a *Kalendar* entry. While visiting Oxford in mid-October it seems that Gilbert had an accident, injuring his leg, which kept him in Oxford until mid-November. He left the day after his brother Harry was elected at Oriel to Bishop Robinson's Exhibition. Meanwhile, Thomas White had been staying at Selborne and made the *Kalendar* entries from 15 October to 10 November.

April	4.	Hot-bed for . . . melon frame Not only cucumbers were fashionable plants. Philip Miller in his *Gardener's Dictionary* (1731–9), referring to melons, observed: 'There is not any Plant cultivated in the Kitchen-Garden, which the Gardeners near London have a greater Ambition to produce early and in Plenty.' His advice on their cultivation runs to several pages, and includes the making, renewing and widening of hot-beds, and considerable detail on the intensive care that these plants require. Should the young plants become too steamy inside their frame, gardeners are instructed to 'raise the light with a Stone about an Inch high, which will make way for the Steam of the bed to pass off', though as GW implies, in very cold weather a draught of cold air would be equally undesirable.
	10.	Planted six laurels near the pitching in the old orchard The pitching was a kind of paving or stone facing on an earth slope.
	11.	Covered with a paper light Probably the same as the 'oiled paper' used as a cloche (see note for 13/4/51).
May	22.	wattle hedge . . . round the melon beds This would be a low fence made out of longish sticks woven horizontally in and out of stout vertical rods, used to shore up the melon beds where they were widened.
June	28.	Lin'd the Cockscomb-bed Lining a cooling hot-bed with dung or straw, that is, covering it all over, was the standard method of warming it up again. In this case, it was effective within four days – 'Cockscomb-bed very hot with the new lining' despite 'shady, showery weather'.
October	21.	Cloves Clove gilliflowers. This was an old-fashioned variety of pink (*Dianthus*) with a spicy scent.
	24.	St Peter's Wort The name usually applied to the cowslip, but it was also a country name for the primrose and occasionally *Hypericum* species. The legend is that St Peter dropped the keys to heaven when he heard that duplicates had been made, and cowslips grew in the place where they fell. Other names are Bunch of Keys, St

Peter's Keys and Cove Keys. The plant resembles old-fashioned keys much more closely than modern ones.

November   20.   Mazagon beans Several kinds of broad bean were cultivated under this name. They vary in height and earliness but have in common small seeds and erect, slightly flattened pods, which they bear prolifically. GW believed himself to be the first to sow at least one kind of Mazagon (see 2 November 1755), but there is no note as to their source, or whether they were the same variety as sown in 1754. Perhaps the first crop failed: on 27 June 1756 there is an entry 'Gather'd Mazagan Beans', with no other comment. They were offered for sale in a nursery catalogue of 1782, but the Vilmorin-Andrieux review of beans in *The Vegetable Garden* (1905) dismissed the Mazagon type as 'the worst and most useless of its race'.

             21.   Made, earth'd, and thatch'd a musroom-bed . . . according to Miller This was to be made with layers of horse manure and rich earth, overlaid with 6 inches of dry litter.

1755 Events and journeys
In January Rebecca White, Gilbert's grandmother, died at the age of 91. Gilbert made his usual visit to Oxford at Easter and afterwards took up a temporary curacy at West Dean in Wiltshire for the Revd Edmund Yalden, Vicar of West Dean and Newton Valence. Before departing for Wiltshire in July Gilbert spent another seven weeks at the Hot Well at Bristol. Though residing at West Dean, he returned often to Selborne: his account book itemises frequent purchases of riding breeches. In the autumn, Gilbert did duty for Mr Yalden once more, this time at nearby Newton Valence.

March   15.   Carry'd Mr Garnier's Cantaleupe-seed . . . 6 or 8 weeks There was a belief that melon seed should be several years old before being sown – hence GW's remark (23 July 1754) on the failure of Missen's melons, '. . . besides the seed was but one year old'. In his *Gardener's Dictionary* Miller advises that great care should be taken in choosing good seed which should then be preserved carefully for two or three years (better still, three or four), but if this were not possible, 'carry it in your Breeches pocket . . . two months before it be sown'.

          20.   two stoneless barberies The barbery *Berberis vulgaris*, a shrub native to Europe, produces piquant red berries which were often used for garnishes and sauces. It is now not often seen having been much destroyed because it is a secondary host of wheat rust.
                  Pine, & Chili-Strawberries John Parkinson wrote in 1629 about growing Chile strawberries, an early imported species which, though it had larger fruit than the native kind, was of indifferent flavour and produced a sparse crop. A hundred years later, Miller was similarly unimpressed. Continuous cross-breeding of imported species, however, produced sweet, prolific hybrids, and these were the ancestors of today's cultivars. The Pine or pineapple strawberry was one of the first good hybrids, with light red fruits and dark green foliage.

          21.   Planted Ivy round the little-house This was to screen the lavatory building.

April   3.   Planted 13 Laurels round the necessary This referred to the same building as in the previous note, 21/3/55.

          16.   three-thorned Acacia seed The honey locust, *Gleditsia triacanthos*, was introduced from Central United States in about 1700. It is extremely tough in poor soil and hot conditions but in Britain will thrive only in mild south-eastern counties.

          22.   earth'd the basons with Dorton-mould Dorton lies to the NE of Selborne and it was from here that GW obtained the Dorton earth or mould that he describes in Letter I to Thomas Pennant in *The Natural History of Selborne* as 'a warm, forward, crumbling mould, called black malm, which seems highly saturated with vegetable and animal manure'.

          23.   hoop'd and matted it Bound together and covered the dung with garden matting. This was made from the inner bark of lime.

          29.   two storax trees sent me by Will: Yalden It is suggested by David Elliston Allen in a paper as yet unpublished that this Will Yalden may have been not the ironmonger in business with GW's brother Thomas, but from the Winchester branch of the Yalden family, the father of Thomas Yalden (1750–1777) who collected the earliest known Guernsey plant specimens, and who visited GW at Selborne.

1756 Events and journeys

There was a very full *Garden Kalendar* for this year which Gilbert spent mostly at home, except for visits to Oxford at Easter and in October, and a visit to John Mulso at Sunbury in June following his friend's recent marriage. Gilbert White took on the curacy of Selborne for Dr Bristow probably from November, when he concluded his duties at West Dean and Newton Valence on behalf of Mr Yalden.

Work on the grounds of the Wakes continued apace, with the erection of vases (oil jars), the opening of vistas and the planting of the 'bason in the field'.

February	14.	Farina might not mix Farina is pollen. It is possible for cucumbers and melons to cross-pollinate.
March	15.	four-wheel'd post-chaise to y^c door Selborne roads were frequently impassable during the winter months. It was due to the extraordinary weather – the 'hot, sunny days, & fierce frosts at night' that so heavy a vehicle could be brought in.
	22.	Syringa Though *Syringa* is the botanical name for lilac species, it is possible that here GW was using it as the common name for *Philadelphus coronarius*, a custom which still causes confusion. In *Flora Selborniensis* on 17/4/66 he refers to privet-leaved lilac as Persian jessamin, yet the entry for 24/10/59 of the *Garden Kalendar* relates Persian jessamin (jasmine) to the white or common jasmine, *Jasminum officinale*. Since this entry for 22/3/56 includes in the list of plants both lilac and Persian jasmine, as well as syringa, *Philadelphus* seems the most likely possibility here.
		Lavender cotton *Santolina chamaecyparissus*, also known as cotton lavender, is a fragrant, low-growing shrub grown in England since the 16th century.
April	5.	radishes for the bugs See note for 15/4/52.
	6.	Venetian mallow A Gloucestershire nursery catalogue of 1753 lists a plant called Venation Mallo, but its identity is obscure.
May	14.	Oil-jar Vase Huge oil jars set on plinths to make an eye-catching urn-like feature were fashionable at this period. They would later be planted with creepers and climbing roses.
June	3.	Best cantaleupe knit for bloom Knit means to set fruit. The sense here indicates that the best cantaloup melons are set to bloom, with the proto-melon showing behind the female flower.
August	3.	turn'd, & tiled The melons were turned to present another face to the sun to assist ripening, and a tile was set beneath each of them to prevent rot.
	24.	Turn'd colour before it began to smell Miller observes in his *Gardener's Dictionary* that ripeness in a melon is shown by a crack near to the stalk and the smell of the fruit; those which change colour are over-ripe.

1757 Events and journeys

By the end of January Gilbert's ambition to become the next Provost of Oriel was thwarted by the election of Chardin Musgrave to the post. Gilbert made his usual visit to Oxford in April, and was at Sunbury in August.

He continued to act as Curate to the ailing Dr Bristow. For September and much of October he was Curate of West Dean and Newton Valence. The living of Moreton Pinkney in Northamptonshire became vacant in October, and in December it was given to Gilbert. His intention not to reside there was accepted.

March	4.	Bush'd Protected by a covering of bushes or cut brushwood.
	14.	melon paper-House This was made by pasting best-quality paper to the frame, and subsequently oiling it to make it both waterproof and translucent.
	22.	Sowed the clover in the wheat The presence of clover, rich in nitrogen, would increase the quantity and probably improve the quality of the grain as well as providing a useful fodder crop after the wheat had been harvested. Not only that, it would constitute valuable green manure when ploughed in at the end of the season.
September	19.	planted . . . some [Xiphiums] in a row under my Father's window Any personal note is usually avoided in the *Kalendar*, but in this entry it might be surmised that Gilbert was trying to create some pleasure for his ill and depressed father by planting new flowers beneath his window, and that his emphasis on 'my Father's window' was not just to fix the location.

| | 27. | Mrs Mulso Mrs John Mulso, wife of GW's old friend. From 1760 onwards another Mrs Mulso may also have visited Selborne. She is the wife of John Mulso's brother Thomas. |

27. Mrs Mulso Mrs John Mulso, wife of GW's old friend. From 1760 onwards another Mrs Mulso may also have visited Selborne. She is the wife of John Mulso's brother Thomas.

October

1. Lord Keeper The Lord Keeper at this time was Sir Robert Henley, a Hampshire neighbour and friend of the White family who later became Lord Chancellor.

11. Cut . . . Cantaleupes for Mangoes By this GW meant a pickle made of melons or cucumbers which resembles mango chutney. Nowadays it is more usually made with marrows.

November

6. Cut-up a Cantaleupe . . . & laid in the Buffet to ripen The Buffet was an alcove, cupboard or niche where china and glasses were kept.

1758 Events and journeys

The *Kalendar* entry for this year is the longest so far. Improvements were made to the Zig-zag and to the Hermitage. During the year, Gilbert was in London between 1 and 12 May, and probably made his trip to Oxford at Easter as was his custom. In July Dr Bristow, the Vicar of Selborne for whom Gilbert had been acting as Curate, died and on 29 September Gilbert's father, John White, also died. Towards the end of the year Gilbert's supposed inheritance of wealth began to cause problems over his Oxford fellowship, but by Christmas the Provost, Chardin Musgrave, appears to have been fully persuaded that Gilbert White was far from wealthy and that the fellowship was justified.

January

17. earth-house This was used to store 'mould', a kind of composted top soil described in a treatise of 1797 as 'loams, mixed with animal and vegetable remains, particularly from putrefaction'.

19. ash-house Used for storing ash. Some of this was bought from forest workings (see entry for 30 January). The *Museum rusticum et commerciale: or Select Papers on Agriculture* (1763–6) notes that certain kinds of ashes which 'are called pot-ash muck make excellent manure for some kinds of soil'. GW's soil, which was heavy clay, undoubtedly came into this category.

29. . . . the mercury in the weather glasses The Whites seem to have had weather glasses or barometers in several places. This high reading shows unusually settled conditions for January, with high pressure pushing the mercury well up the tube.

February

8. Trimm'd, & tack'd the vines . . . according to Hitt's directions GW was referring to T. A. Hitt's *Treatise of Fruit Trees*, published in 1755.

14. 20 bushels of tan from Alton Tan was the bark of young oaks which was used in the tanning of leather. Miller in his *Gardener's Dictionary* advised using the spent tan from tan pits for the garden: 'The best sort of tan for Hotbeds is that which is ground of a middling Size.'

25. Laid a leaden-pipe . . . according to Dr Hales's proposal Stephen Hales (1677–1761) was Curate of Teddington and also Rector of Faringdon, when GW later became his curate. He was a close friend of the White family. His major botanical work *Vegetable Staticks*, published in 1727, disproved the current belief that there was a circulation of sap in plants analogous to that of blood in animals. His series of remarkable experiments gave new insight into the water economy of plants, and made some of the earliest hypotheses about the importance of light and air in plant nutrition, leading the way to the discovery of photosynthesis about 50 years later. He experimented with, wrote about and invented artificial ventilators, and several prisons adopted his methods. It is this aspect of his work to which GW is referring here.

March

18. Earth'd up Cucumber hillocks Ridge cucumbers were so called because they were grown on a 'ridge', a name for a raised hot-bed.

23. Planted . . . from Mr Budd The Black Belgic rose is a variety now lost, probably an old dark red gallica rose. Capability Brown planted some at Petworth in 1757. The Marbled rose is probably one of the mottled old gallicas of which there were many. The monthly rose is a form of *Rosa chinensis*, the autumn damask now called *Rosa x bifera*.

25. Tryed an experiment . . . GW was following the example of Dr Hales.

28. sowed . . . with black-seed Black medick, *Medicago lupulina*, is still sown in one-year leys along with grasses.

April

4. Sowed . . . Carrot-seed, mixed with Coss-lettuce Carrot seed was frequently mixed with that of lettuce, onion, parsnip and radish. According to his *Gardener's*

		Dictionary Miller disapproves; he recommends sowing a *row* of lettuce next to early carrots.
	9.	Saw two swallows This is the first observation on birds in these journals, notable that it is about swallows, birds that GW was particularly fond of.
	27.	. . . according to Hit See note for 8 February above.
July	24.	Stringed pine strawberries Removed the runners from the strawberry bed.
August	25.	The Hermitage A mock rustic arbour newly built halfway up the Zig-zag path to the Hanger.
October	2: 3.	Chip'd the best of yᵉ Polyanths It was the practice to mark the best-flowering plants and to divide them for the next year. Polyanthuses do not come true from seed.
	21.	Polyanth-Narcissus Probably the cluster-flowered narcissus group. They are not completely hardy, and of those GW receives from his brother Thomas (16 November) some have been grown under glass.
November	2.	A large flock of House-Martens This is the second reference to birds, and once again it is to hirundines.
	24.	The pound field Villagers now know this field as the Punfle. The new path to the Zig-zag goes through it.

1759 Events and journeys

In January Gilbert White spent ten days in Oxford and the question as to whether he was entitled to retain his fellowship was entirely resolved. He visited Oxford again at Easter, and in June there was a trip to see his friend John Mulso at Sunbury. He journeyed further afield in November to visit his sister Anne and brother-in-law Thomas Barker at Lyndon in Rutland. He seems to have been impressed with a journal of facts and observations kept by Thomas Barker since 1736 (he kept it up until 1801). This was a long visit which extended into the new year.

Once again Gilbert served as Curate at Selborne until October when the new Vicar, Mr Andrew Etty, took over the duties.

March	6.	Ventured to mat-down the Cucumber-frames untriged To trig means to support or prop: the frames were therefore left closed and covered with protective mats.
	19.	double-flowering Sweet Briar This seems likely to have been the double Eglantine rose or Williams Sweet-briar described by H. C. Andrews (*Roses*, 1817). The history of this rose stretches back to the beginning of the 17th century and before, and it was 'the only eglantine rose known with perfectly double flowers'.
	31.	Finished a bastion, & Haha . . . & a conical mount These were landscape improvements in the picturesque style fashionable at the time. The bastion was a sort of rampart, the ha-ha not the one surviving but a smaller version which was supported by wooden piles, and the mount was a small artificial hillock. These were also fashionable in the 15th and 16th centuries.
May	20.	lettuce . . . finely loav'd That is, they formed the solid, oblong hearts typical of sugar-loaf lettuces.
	28: 29.	the bats crumble These are peat bats, brick-shaped turves of peat.
June	23.	Mr Miller at Chelsea Philip Miller at the Chelsea Physic Garden, the author of *The Gardener's Dictionary* 1731–1739.
September	8.	Tyed-up . . . best bunches of Grapes in Crape-bags This was a method of protecting the fruit from the ravages of wasps.
October	24.	French willows Willowherbs (*Epilobium* species) were grown as garden plants in GW's time. Rosebay willowherb, *Epilobium angustifolium* (now *Chamaenerion angustifolium*) was for sale in a contemporary catalogue and the similar *C. dodonaei*, which has a shorter leafy inflorescence, was also grown in gardens.
November	6.	Grapes . . . hung up in the study Presumably this was in order to ripen them.
	15.	Duke cherries Semi-sweet cherry, intermediate between sweet and sour cherries, and partly self-fertile.

1760 Events and journeys

Gilbert White did not return to Selborne until May from his trip to Rutland, visiting his brother Thomas in London on the way home. This meant he had been away for six months, his longest period of absence from Selborne. In June, he purchased the upper part of Lassam's orchard which was a useful addition to the Wakes grounds, and upon which work was started immediately.

May	18.	Hail . . . batter'd the vine shoots This year much attention is given to the growing of grapes. Vines grew well in Selborne.
June	15.	Wood-strawberries GW probably cultivated plants transplanted from the wild as was the practice. In cultivation, wild strawberries grow bigger and more succulent and GW obviously valued them as well as the new imported kinds he was also growing.
August	4.	Mezereon *Daphne mezereum*, which grew on Selborne Hanger. Philip Miller doubted that it was wild there and gave the impression that he thought it might have been sown, but it is now generally accepted that *Daphne mezereum*, though now very rare, is a native wild plant. GW describes it in NHS Letter XLI to Daines Barrington.
October	14.	fallows . . . full of water In one meaning, fallows are fields ploughed and ready for sowing, and they therefore have ridges and hollows where water collects.
	2.	Dᵣ Hill's mummy This is a kind of wax used in the transplanting and grafting of trees and shrubs. It is described in Ellis's *Philosophical Transactions* (1759) as 'Gardener's mummy, consisting of a mixture of bees-wax, rosin & pitch'. Dr Hill is Sir John Hill, author of *The British Herbal* (1759) and many other medical, vegetable and literary works.

1761 Events and journeys

The dry wall of the Ha-ha was finished in January. This ha-ha still survives. So does part of the fruit wall which was also built in this year, the sundial, post and slab. In April a further piece of land was purchased from Magdalen College, owner of the manor of Selborne. During August Gilbert was at Ringmer for three weeks with his aunt, Mrs Rebecca Snooke, and at Michaelmas he took up the post of Curate to Dr Roman, Rector of Faringdon, a village adjoining Selborne. Gilbert's sister Rebecca married her cousin Henry Woods on 17 November, leaving her brother alone at Selborne, and in December Gilbert made a journey to his living in Moreton Pinkney in Northamptonshire.

January	19.	marl Soil which consists principally of clay and carbonate of lime, and which is valuable as a fertiliser.
	24.	finished the dry wall of the Haha . . . built of blue rags A ha-ha is a wall built into the side of a deep ditch so that it does not create any visible break in the landscape when viewed from the house. Ragstone is a dense blue coarse stone which breaks up into flat pieces and can be used as roofing slates.
March	25.	makes the turf stare and chop Causes the turf to stick up and the ground to crack up.
	30.	Cions Scions are the young shoots which are used for grafting on to a stock.
April	4.	red cowslip A red sport of the cowslip (*Primula veris*). Nowadays it is known in the south west as 'Devon red', and valued as a rare cottage garden plant.
	11.	cutting the edges of the turf round the water-tables The meaning is obscure. Possibly these were ornamental receptacles for water.
May	20.	My Brother Tho: This long entry on crickets was largely re-used in Letter XLVI to Daines Barrington in *The Natural History of Selborne*. The *Garden Kalendar* entry has several alterations changing personal and specific observations into more generalised and indirect language. 'All the month of May in the short Lythe' becomes 'all the summer months in many places in the south of England', and 'We easily discovered' is changed to 'It was easy to discover'. This rather more pedantic tone is absent from the Selborne letter, where not only does the short Lythe reappear, but an anecdote is included, and several latinate phrases are taken out in favour of a simpler, more direct approach. For example, *a long terebra* becomes 'a long sword-shaped weapon', and *strongtooth'd Malae (like the sheers of lobster's claws)* is put more simply as 'their strong jaws toothed like the shears of a lobster's claws'.
		This is an unusually long entry for the *Kalendar*, especially since it is confined to one subject. GW was, of course, aware that little was known about this creature *Gryllus campestris* and I would suggest that in exploring new territory and having Thomas with whom to discuss and extend his thoughts, he was moved to record their observations at greater length and to be self-conscious about style even when

June	8.	he was preparing his note-form, personal *Kalendar*.
		perchers Young rooks are called perchers or branchers at the stage when they are fledged and have left the nest but are not yet independent.
November	2: 3.	golden-pippens A variety of apple much loved in the 18th century, as shown in this Midas-touch couplet by Swift:

'A codling e'er it went his lip in
Would strait become a golden Pippin.'

December	26.	Dutch-medlar, & a Service There have never been many varieties of medlar. The Dutch, a small, slightly weeping tree is a very old form and is still esteemed. The service tree here may be *Sorbus domestica*, though I would have thought that GW would have noted whether it was the one with apple-shaped or pear-shaped fruits. It may be a wild service (*Sorbus torminalis*) which bears clusters of small edible fruits. The fruits of both medlars and services of all kinds need to be bletted or allowed to go soft after frost before they take on their delicious flavour.
	30.	Sweet-water vine A variety of grape.
		Roman nectar and Newington nectar Varieties of nectarine. Roman Nectarine is one of the oldest known varieties; it was mentioned in 1629.

1762 Events and journeys

Garden improvements continued apace. In April, Gilbert visited his brother Harry White at Tidworth in Wiltshire, a last visit before his brother's upward move to take on new duties as the Rector of Fyfield, near Andover in Hampshire. During this year Gilbert's uncle Charles White became progressively more ill, and his nephew visited Bradley frequently to see him.

January	14.	Obliged to keep the light tilted a nights The frame lights had to be propped open at night to prevent the hot-bed overheating. See note for 6/3/59.
February	21.	Many people froze to death Not such a callous note as it appears in print. It is clear from the manuscript that this sentence was squeezed in at a later date in a small space which dictated brevity. I would place this observation in the same order as GW's generalised weather notes as something he had read in a journal or newspaper, and not something that had occurred at Selborne.
March	1.	Chaumontelle, Virgoleuse Varieties of pear, replacing those planted on 14 March 1761. These new ones were very probably espaliers too and, like the earlier trees, planted against the fruit wall of the new garden.
	13.	Cut-down all the wall trees That is, all the fruit trees trained along the wall were pruned.
July	5.	Set-out for Tidworth This was to visit GW's brother Harry White who had been appointed to the living of Fyfield.
		Country is burnt-up . . . beyond what any middle-aged person remembers GW was at this time nearly 42, coming into middle age, and the latter phrase implies a discussion of the unusual weather conditions with a number of his contemporaries.
September	18.	nonpareils & golden-rennets Apple varieties. The Non Pareil has been known in England since about 1600 as a good, greenish eater. Golden Rennet, now known as Golden Reinette, is a golden-red variety which does well on clay.
November	3.	ragwort Probably a garden species of *Senecio*.

1763 Events and journeys

In March 1763 Gilbert's uncle, Charles White, died and Gilbert inherited the Wakes. He applied to Lord Chancellor Henley who had presented the livings of Swarraton and Bradley to his uncle, a personal friend, for the living of Bradley but was refused, apparently because he had seemed lukewarm in his support of the Chancellor over an Oxford vote. During the summer of this year large groups of visitors stayed at both the Wakes and the Vicarage where they were guests of the Ettys. Unusually for him, Gilbert mentions in the *Kalendar* the visit of his friend Thomas Mulso and his wife and his brother Edward Mulso and a friend from July 13. Gilbert's aunt Mrs Rebecca Snooke and two of his nieces also stayed at the Wakes for some of this time, and so did his brother Harry.

| March | 19. | Matted-down the bed See note for 23/4/55. |
| | | trigg'd the lights a little He raised the top of the frame and propped it open. See also note for 6/3/59. |

April	7–22.	These entries are in GW's hand although he was in London from 5 to 22 April. Probably notes were taken in his absence and then written in by him on his return.
July	4.	Tyled the Succades A tile was slipped under the developing melon fruit to keep it off the soil and prevent it rotting.
	13.	Mr Tho: Mulso, & Lady, & Mʳ Edw: Mulso Thomas Mulso was John Mulso's eldest brother, and Edward another brother who was unmarried. This is the only time in the *Kalendar* that details of GW's personal domestic life are entered in this diary-like fashion. It must have been a momentous visit.
	27.	Pheasant-eyed pinks Probably a variety of *Dianthus plumarius*.
	28.	The Hermit This was GW's brother Harry dressed up in disguise for the entertainment of the company.
September	18.	pd Kelsey . . . from the dunghill This suggests that GW paid Kelsey for five loads of *fresh* manure straight from the stable with three loads of old, well-rotted dung.

1764 Events and journeys

Gilbert's aunt, Mrs Rebecca Snooke, stayed on at the Wakes into the new year. Gilbert made his usual visit to Oxford, and visited his brother Harry at Fyfield twice during the summer.

February	7.	Tunn'd the strong beer Beer was distinguished from ale by the fact that hops were added to the fermented malt, sugar and water mixture. Small beer is a weak brew, only lightly fermented. Strong beer is considerably more alcoholic.
	13.	To mantle in the glass To froth in the glass.
March	12.	landsprings are much abated These are springs which flow only after heavy rains. GW notes elsewhere that in the Selborne neighbourhood they are known also as 'lavants'.
	20.	swarth Old and dialect form of 'swath', meaning the space covered by the stroke of a scythe and, by extension, the grass cut by the scythe stroke.
	24.	fraxinella-seeds *Dictamnus alba* (syn. *D. fraxinella*), also known as burning bush. It is strongly aromatic and on a warm summer evening it is possible to ignite the halo of volatised oil, especially around the older flowerheads. It has pinnate leaves.
April	27.	Iraquois-Gourds New varieties of gourd were continually being brought over from North America at this period. They were probably used for culinary purposes.
		sowed . . . a little plot of burnet Salad burnet, *Poterium sanguisorba* (*Sanguisorba minor*), a culinary herb which has a pleasing cucumber taste.
August	24.	Warner's black Hambro' seems . . . to be some ordinary sort of white Grape This seems to have been another disappointing purchase.
September	18.	In the night . . . melons and Cucumbers were pulled all to pieces Apparently a solitary act of vandalism. There seems to have been no recurrence and no further comment on the incident.
October	26.	Gather'd 6 medlars This was the first fruit from the tree GW planted in December 1761.
November	23.	Queen-claud plum An anglicisation of the variety Reine Claude, one of the delicious greengage plums.

1765 Events and journeys

A letter from John Mulso in January indicates that he thought it possible that Gilbert White might be given the living of Cholderton on the Wiltshire/Hampshire border, but this proved to be unfounded. Gilbert visited his brother Harry in the summer, returning early in July and botanising along the route. This was the year that he bought Hudson's *Flora Anglica*, an important botanical work and John Hill's *British Herbal* (1756).

In August, a new volume of the *Garden Kalendar* is headed 'A Calendar of Flora, & the Garden . . .' and during this year and the next, Gilbert gives much of his attention to identifying plants, especially those growing in and around Selborne. It is interesting to note that he continues to use Ray's descriptions rather than adopting the Linnaean nomenclature as Hudson does. He visited his aunt Mrs Rebecca Snooke at Ringmer in September, and in October he went to Oxford, noting those plants he found along the way and also those in the Oxford Botanic Garden.

| April | 13. | sow a crop of Sᵗ foin along with his Corn See note for 22/3/57. Sainfoin has |

similar properties to clover and was used as a fodder crop.

May   14.   Let it [raisin-elder wine] stand one night in the Kiver A kiver is a wooden tub
which seems to have been used for various household tasks, for kneading in, as a
receptacle in which the butter is made and also, it seems, one used in brewing and
wine-making. A newspaper item of 1884 catalogued 'brew vat & stands, oval
kiver, two 5-gallon casks'.

           24.   Put 10 field-crickets in the bank of the terrass This colony was probably the one
recorded in the NHS Letter XLVI to Daines Barrington. 'I endeavoured to
transplant a colony to the terrace in my garden, by boring deep holes in the
sloping turf. The new inhabitants stayed some time, and fed and sung; but
wandered away by degrees, and were heard at a farther distance every morning; so
that it appears that on this emergency they made use of their wings in attempting
to return to the spot from which they were taken.'

July   6.   The downs . . . are full of Burnet This plant is still sold by at least one seed
merchant as Burnet (*Poterium polyganum* or fodder burnet) in grass mixtures
because as GW observed, it thrives on poor, dry soils and is eaten freely by cows
and sheep. It is said to give an agreeable flavour to butter which has been made
from animals grazed on it, and also to benefit sheep affected by scour.
P^d Will Dewey for 8 Doz: of young sparrows   Destroyed presumably because
they were believed to be damaging the plants.

           13.   Farmer Knight, having plowed Baker's Hill . . . stirr'd it across The practice of
ploughing across the furrows in order to improve the quality of the tilth is known
as 'stirring' and was recommended as far back as the first half of the 16th century.
In this case there seems to have been dubious success with the heavy land 'as rough
as the sea in an hard Gale: the Clods . . . as high as one's knees.'

           16.   fern-owls or Goat-suckers Vernacular names for the nightjar, *Caprimulgus
europaeus*, and echoed in its scientific name – *capri*, goat; *mulgeo*, to milk.

           27.   Housed my billet in curious order A billet was wood cut for fuel. 'Curious' is
used in a sense where today we would say 'good' or 'nice', or even 'excellent', as
applied for example to melons.

August   9.   A Calendar of Flora, & the Garden Here GW begins a new notebook and alters
the title to accommodate his developing interest in the local flora. Perhaps he
intended to include other botanical notes for he appears to have left three clear
pages although he has only written notes on '*Scirpi* & *Junci*' and filled in the
remainder with the *Kalendar* entries of November 25 to the end of the year, for
which he had not enough space when he reached the end of the book. Though the
second title reverts simply to '*Garden Calendar*', he incorporates botanical and
garden notes within it as he later includes garden notes in his *Naturalist's Journal*.
        At this point it may be noticed that he also begins to spell 'calendar' in the
modern fashion.
Entries from 25 November In preparing this edition for print, I have moved the
section from 25 November to the year end from here, its squeezed-in position in
the manuscript, to its rightful place. The notes on the differentiation between the
Junci and *Scirpi* have been left in their original position, since I believe them to
have been written in August when GW started his new notebook.

           14.   white-apples . . . fit to make pies August is very early for apples. The only variety
we know today which is called 'white apple' is the Hawthornden, which was raised
about the time of GW and seems to have first appeared in catalogues in 1780. It is
an exceptionally good cooking apple but it ripens mid-season, that is to say
October-December. It was common practice to make pies out of the apples which
dropped early (often called codlins) and it is possible that these were rather young
white apples, just ready for pie making.
Tremella abounds now on the walks The first of several observations on the
appearance of the blue-green alga *Nostoc*. Elsewhere GW notes '*Tremella nostoc*
. . . abounds on the grass walks' (*Naturalist's Journal* 10/5/80) and remarks on
its strange, jelly-like substance (4/10/83). The name *Tremella* is now used
for a group of jelly-like fungi. *Nostoc* was named by Paracelsus and there
are many references to its having been an emanation from the stars, but by the
mid-18th century more rational descriptions of its origin were being sought,

for example by Chambers.

16.   stone curlues clamour The stone curlew, *Burhinus oedicnemus*. Hampshire is one of the few counties where this now rare bird may still be found.

25: 26.   Martens . . . late hatchings . . . rather in favour of hiding than migration These are the first observations GW makes on a theme which was to occupy him for the rest of his life.

27.   Earth-nuts More usually this is the common name for pig-nut, *Conopodium majus*, but in Hampshire it is also a vernacular name for *Oenanthe pimpinelloides*, the corky-fruited water dropwort, and as this continues flowering into August, while the pignut usually drops off in June, the water dropwort is probably the one indicated here.

September   5.   fungus kind that seemed . . . to be poured over the ground This is thought to be a common slime fungus known as 'flowers of the tan', *Fuligo septica*, which would be growing out of the tan with which the melon beds had been dressed, as GW implies in his observation.
This was ladies traces An old form of lady's tresses, likely in this case to be autumn lady's tresses, *Spiranthes spiralis*. This sentence has been written in at a later date. Hill is John Hill, author of *British Herbal* (1756). He puts the flowering time several months early.

9.   that peculiar plant the sun-dew *Drosera* species, carnivorous plants which entrap insects in their sticky leaves and absorb them.
Owls hiss round the Church These would be barn owls, which have a characteristic hissing cry.

17: 18.   Burnet rose Almost certainly this was the species – an exact description.

24.   the ground had been devonshired An anachronistic usage, more common in the shortened 'denshire', also known as 'burn-beating'. It means paring off the turf, stubble and weeds, burning them and then spreading the ashes on the land.

October   1.   Began gathering the white apples See note 14/8/65 above. This, then, was the main crop.

5.   Examined the wild black Hellebore . . . very common in Selborne-wood Both native hellebores are to be found around Selborne. In NHS Letter XLI to Daines Barrington GW remarks that *Helleborus foetidus* is common in the nearby woods, and anyway *H. viridis*, the green hellebore, would have died back for the winter by this time. It is the stinking hellebore 'a great branching plant the winter through . . . and very ornamental' of which he writes in this instance, and makes many observations at this season in years to come.

28.   Plants still in bloom Blue-bottles: both harebells and viper's bugloss go by this country name. So do bluebells and cornflowers, but the season is wrong. Throatworts: bellflowers, *Campanula* spp., probably the nettle-leaved species. All-heal: this is almost certainly self-heal, *Prunella vulgaris*. Valerian, which also goes by this name, would be over by this time.

November   25.   See note for 9/8/65 on position of entries.

1766 Events and journeys

In this year Gilbert separated his gardening notes which continued as the *Garden Calendar*, reverting to its original title but with a modernised spelling of calendar, and his botanical identifications which he put together in a book entitled *Flora Selborniensis*. This consisted of little more than a catalogue of plants found in and around Selborne. Also in 1766, Gilbert moved his large barn to the upper end of the orchard – a considerable undertaking, since it was 40ft long.

At midsummer, he stayed for a week in Fyfield with his brother Harry and his family and, late in August, set out to spend a fortnight with his aunt, Mrs Rebecca Snooke at Ringmer.

April   26.   making new sills Preparing large timbers to support the walls of the barn.
pulling down the skillings Removing lean-to structures. There is a modern Australian word for this: 'skillion'.

November   17.   Nectarine-tree . . . Violet GW apparently forgot what name Armstrong, the nurseryman, had mentioned and had meant to go back and fill in this space later. This tree might be the famous Violette Hative, or possibly the Violet Nectarine of England, described by Bunyard in 1930 'about whose origins little is known except that it has been grown for many years'.

1767 Events and journeys

In April of this year, John Mulso became Vicar and Rector of Witney in Oxfordshire, putting himself within fairly easy reach of Gilbert. The now-famous correspondence with Thomas Pennant began in the summer, the first letter being sent on 10 August 1767 (dated August 4 in *The Natural History of Selborne*). Gilbert visited the Mulsos in October, botanising on the way and around the district of Witney. In December, he describes the harvest mouse – 'a species very common in these parts' – the first time this creature had been recognised as an individual species and described.

Seventeen sixty-six and seven were the last years in which Gilbert kept assiduous gardening records. Henceforth, gardening notes are incorporated occasionally in the *Naturalist's Journal*, though for the first few years they take second place to the wild-life observations.

April	4.	Motacilla trochilus Lin: Regulus non cristatus Raii: Here GW cites the names used by Linnaeus and Ray to identify a migrant warbler, probably the chiff-chaff. It is not clear here from the context. By 1768 GW was certain that there were three kinds of leaf-warbler (see Letter XVI of April 18 to Thomas Pennant, *The Natural History of Selborne*): he was the first observer to distinguish between them.
		Colemouse The coal tit. The scientific name is the same now as it was then, *Parus ater*.
July	3.	Alauda minima locusta voce This is the grasshopper warbler, *Locustella naevia*.
	20.	Ananas Pineapples are still worth a special mention, a century after the first pineapple is said to have been raised successfully in England.
September	17.	yellow centory The plant is now known as yellow wort, *Blackstonia perfoliata*, after Hudson's naming.
	24.	Ear-wig . . . mistake; there are two species This note was written in later. The two species would seem likely to be the common earwig *Forficula auricularia*, which though it has wings rarely flies and the lesser earwig, *Labia minor*, common in rough herbage in many parts of the British Isles and which flies actively in August and September.
October	20.	base hoarhound Downy woundwort, *Stachys germinica*, is now to be found only in Oxfordshire.
November	23.	Celeri . . . begins to pipe That is, the stems begin to become hollow.
December	1.	Sent two field-mice . . . to Thomas Pennant See Letter XII of *The Natural History of Selborne*. GW was the first to identify harvest mice, and this observation is of particular importance for its note on their nesting in thistles as well as wheatfields. Owing to modern harvesting techniques, the arable habitat is no longer suitable and harvest mice are again being found in field edges, hedgerows and gardens.
	6.	Planted one golden-rennet Golden Reinette, a variety of apple, known in England since the mid-1600s. See note for 18/9/62.
		Entry for 6 March 1771 The whole of the *Kalendar* has been written neatly and almost without error; it is uncharacteristic that the last entry of all should have a word obscured by a heavy blot of ink.

FLORA SELBORNIENSIS

	1766	Title page The works that GW refers to are *Synopsis Methodica Stirpium Britannicarum* 3rd edition (1724) by John Ray, ed. J.J. Dillenius, and *Ornithology in Three Books . . . translated into English and enlarged by John Ray 1678*, Francis Willughby and John Ray.
February	22.	Primula veris Ray called the primrose *Primula veris vulgaris* to which GW refers here, and the cowslip *P. veris major*. In modern usage the primrose is *Primula vulgaris* and the cowslip *P. veris*.
March	3.	Great black Hellebore The Latin epithet indicates that this is stinking hellebore, *Helleborus foetidus*, as described in John Ray's *Synopsis*. The vernacular names can refer to either of the wild species, but bear's foot is usually the green hellebore,

<table>
<tbody>
<tr><td></td><td>4.</td><td>Helleborus viridis, while setterwort is Helleborus foetidus. See also the note for 5/10/65.</td></tr>
<tr><td></td><td>9.</td><td>Gryllus sylvestris This would seem to be the creature which is elsewhere called Gryllus campestris. As GW supposed, these early spring crickets were the nymphs emerging from hibernation – these would go on to mature in May and die off in August, having laid their eggs in summer.</td></tr>
<tr><td></td><td>12.</td><td>Periwinkle, vinca pervinca minor Vinca minor, the lesser periwinkle, also found in Selborne Hanger (see NHS Letter XLI to Daines Barrington).
Mezereon See note for 4/8/60.</td></tr>
<tr><td></td><td>17.</td><td>Weeping willow This would be the species Salix babylonica which is not entirely hardy in Britain. The weeping tree which is commonly seen nowadays has a golden-green foliage and is a hybrid, Salix x chrysocoma.
This was sanicle This entry would seem to be a correction added at a later date.
Moschatel itself was seen on 11 April 1766.</td></tr>
<tr><td></td><td>19.</td><td>Daffodils This is the first reference to daffodils which are clearly wild ones. These are still to be found, though in small numbers, in the woodlands around Selborne.</td></tr>
<tr><td>April</td><td>4.</td><td>O.S. This refers to the Old Style calendar – see note for 15/9/52.</td></tr>
<tr><td></td><td>17.</td><td>Persian jasmine There is some ambiguity between this entry and those of the Garden Kalendar for 9/3/51 and 24/10/59, where GW seems to be identifying Persian jessamin (jasmine) as white jasmine, Jasminum officinale. Here, however, he clearly refers to Persian jasmine as privet-leaved lilac which he knew as Syringa ligustri folio, now called Persian lilac, Syringa persica.</td></tr>
<tr><td></td><td>19.</td><td>Wood pease Lathyrus montanus, which is still to be found in the woods on Selborne Hanger.</td></tr>
<tr><td></td><td>19; 20.</td><td>Words crossed out: this suggests that GW was learning by trial and error.</td></tr>
<tr><td></td><td>21.</td><td>Ravens Now very much rarer than in the 18th century, these birds are no longer present at Selborne.</td></tr>
<tr><td></td><td>28.</td><td>Meadows glow A strikingly poetic observation in this catalogue-like journal, displaying an aptness of language which GW develops further in the Naturalist's Journal. It is also a true description, and remains so today.</td></tr>
<tr><td>May</td><td>2.</td><td>Herb Paris Though it is rare now, this plant can still be found plentifully in some woodland lanes near Selborne.
Wood anemony, flore rubro Ray's Synopsis notes a red anemone occurring in Devon. This variation in colour still occurs in some populations.</td></tr>
<tr><td></td><td>16.</td><td>field crane's bill The species is not certain: this was not the meadow cranesbill unless it was in flower rather early. Perhaps the plant was dove's-foot cranesbill, Geranium molle, or cut-leaved cranesbill, G. dissectum.
agrifolium A mistake for aquifolium.</td></tr>
<tr><td>June</td><td>11.</td><td>Water elder Glossaries and dialect dictionaries give this as guelder rose, but GW has already noted on 25 May 'Guelder rose, opulus blooms', so it seems unlikely to be the right identification here.</td></tr>
<tr><td></td><td>20.</td><td>Base rocket Ray in his Synopsis lists this as Reseda vulgaris (now Reseda lutea), wild mignonette which is not scented, unlike the species GW observed in FS on 8/7/66¶ which was fragrant.</td></tr>
<tr><td>July</td><td>2.</td><td>Regulus non-cristatus Leaf warblers are insectivorous so this is a rare occasion when GW appears to have been mistaken in what he observed. They are unlikely to have been 'mischievous among pease & cherries'.</td></tr>
<tr><td></td><td>7.</td><td>Hypopitys A rare reference to his friend Thomas Mulso who found this strange plant. It is still found near Selborne.</td></tr>
<tr><td></td><td>8.</td><td>Mignonette This flower described as small and fragrant was the sweet mignonette Reseda odorata, an Egyptian plant. Introduced through a Dutch contact by Philip Miller in 1739 or 1740, it became tremendously popular on account of its strong scent.</td></tr>
</tbody>
</table>

NATURALIST'S JOURNAL

1768 Events and journeys

This was the year in which Gilbert White began his *Naturalist's Journal* – an elaborate notebook for which the layout had been designed by Daines Barrington, a friend of Thomas Pennant, and published by Gilbert's brother, Benjamin White. An unpublished part of a letter to Pennant which became Letter XIII in *The Natural History of Selborne* mentions that Mr Barrington, whom Gilbert had not then met, had made him a gift of the Journal – later, of course, Daines Barrington was to become the second correspondent of *The Natural History of Selborne*.

In February, Gilbert followed a visit to his brothers in London with a trip to Oxford, where the Provost of Oriel had recently died. He was in London again for ten days in May, and in July visited his brother Harry at Fyfield for a fortnight, where Thomas joined them on 14 July, bringing with him succade melons from Selborne. In October Gilbert made another visit to Oxford.

		Inscriptions to the Naturalist's Journal title pages
		A full description of everything which God has made in this world or which has been subsequently developed by the forces of Nature cannot be achieved in the span of one man's life. The following distinguished treatises therefore contain only the most useful Flora and Fauna.
		Virgil, Aeneid VI 730: Their seeds have the strength of fire and a divine origin.
		Horace, Carmina 4.2.27: I am like a bee from Mount Matinus laboriously gathering its favourite thyme from the woods and banks of the watery Tiber.
January	3.	Horses are still falling with their general disorder These hard-winter notes are elaborated in Letter LXI NHS to Daines Barrington where the illness affecting the horses is termed 'an epidemic distemper'.
	9.	titmice pull straws from the eaves According to the NHS Letter XLI to Pennant, the purpose of this behaviour is to catch the flies that conceal themselves among the thatch straws.
February	15.	Crocus sativus A name now used for the saffron crocus, but GW meant the spring crocus, *Crocus purpureus* (and possibly other kinds). He seems to be especially fond of these early spring flowers and in 1778, when he was absent from home in February, remarks that thanks to the late season that year, his crocuses are still in bloom.
	19.	Arbutus This was damaged more seriously than supposed and never recovered.
March	26.	physic-garden at Oxford The Oxford Botanic Gardens, established in 1621.
	30.	Canes foeminae catuliunt The bitches are on heat.
April	2.	Musca bombyliiformis . . . See note for 6/4/69.
	3.	Tulipa Gesneriana praecox An early-flowering tulip named after the notable naturalist Conrad Gesner, who is given the credit for introducing the tulip as a prized garden plant to Western Europe after having seen them growing in Bavaria. It took only a decade or so for tulip growing to have become a passion, with fortunes being made – a single bulb fetched 100,000 florins in Holland, where in 1637 the government took action to end such speculation.
	4.	Vespertilio murinus Referred to in NHS Letter XI as 'the common *Vespertilio murinus*', this is almost certainly the pipistrelle bat (*Pipistrellus pipistrellus*). The bat which now goes by the name *Vespertilio murinus* is the parti-coloured bat of which there is only a handful of authenticated British records.
	9.	Titlark sings The tree pipit *Anthus trivialis* and the meadow pipit *Anthus pratensis* were not clearly described as distinct species until Montagu's *Ornithological Dictionary* 1808. GW was probably describing the tree pipit here and in the NHS Letter XXXIX to Pennant.
	15.	Second willow wren Also called the middle willow wren by GW, this is the willow warbler *Phylloscopus trochilus*.
	17.	Fork-tailed Kite The red kite *Milvus milvus* is now restricted to a small area in Wales.
	20.	St Foin Sainfoin, *Onobrychis viciifolia*, was used as a fodder crop. In *Systema Agriculturae*, published in 1669, John Worlidge wrote of it, 'This St Foyn or Holy-hay hath in several places of England obtained the preference above clover-grass for that it . . . is so great an improvement on our barren lands.'

May	21.	red-backed butcher bird The red-backed shrike, now a rare breeding bird in Britain. Its numbers have been declining and its range contracting for more than a century. Up until 1961, Hampshire held about a quarter of the British population (centred in the New Forest) but after this date there was a population crash and by the mid-1970s there were thought to be less than 50 breeding pairs throughout the whole of Britain.
	26.	Cantharis noctiluca The glow worm, now called *Lampyris noctiluca*, is a very much less common sight than in the 18th century.
	29.	Aristotle *Historia Animalium* quotation: The viper is oviparous on the inside [pre-birth] but viviparous on the outside [post-birth].
June	3.	Alis caeruleo-atris . . . with dark blue-black wings and antennae which are more than twice the length of its body.
	4.	Snipes play . . . hum as they are descending The phrasing is almost exactly as in the NHS Letter XVI to Pennant, dated 18 April 1768. In fact, as was ascertained about a century later, the snipe 'drumming' is made by the vibration of the outer tail feathers, thrust out at right angles to the body during the swift plunges of the display flight.
	6.	Corpore caeruleo nitido . . . A blue-black shiny body with greeny-blue erect wings.
July	23.	Martins congregate on the maypole This was situated on the Plestor – the village green. It was mended and repainted in 1779 but has since disappeared.
	24.	Hippobosca equina The forest fly, now rare except in the New Forest and a few other parts of Hampshire and of Dorset and Wales. It attaches itself to horses, donkeys, cattle, dogs and people who pass through the bracken, causing irritation.
August	3.	Oestrus bovis: the whame or burrel fly of Derham The reference is to Revd W. Derham (1657–1735), to whose *Physico-theology* GW gives a page reference in NHS Letter XXXIV to Pennant. Derham stated that 'the whame or burrel fly is vexatious to horses in summer'. Another authority (Bailey 1721) noted that it was 'an insect very troublesome to working cattle'. In Letter XXXIV GW suggests that the insect is the same as that described as *Oestrus curvicauda* (a name which GW also uses in the *Naturalist's Journal*) by the eminent Elizabethan Dr Thomas Muffet in his *Theatre of Insects*. (See note for 8/8/70). The species in question may have been a kind of horse-fly, *Tabanus bovinus*, or the bot-fly, *Gasterophilus intestinalis*.
September	1.	Transplanted . . . Helleborus viridis GW had often observed this colony of plants. He waited until the foliage had died before transplanting them.
	23.	See note above for 3/8/68.
	25.	Merula torquata Ring ouzels, *Turdus torquatus*, on migratory passage southwards to southern Europe and North Africa.
December	7.	Lavants A Sussex and Hampshire name for springs which arise suddenly in the hills. See also note for 12/3/64.
	15.	Immundi meminere sues jactare maniplos Virgil *Georgics* I 400. †The unclean swine remember to toss the bundles of straw.
	22.	Pines are still cutting The first pineapple raised in Britain is said to have been grown by John Rose in Charles II's reign. There were several growers in the 18th century, and the first notes published on cultivation were John Giles's *Ananas or a Treatise on the Pine Apple*.

1769 Events and journeys

Gilbert spent 10 to 28 January at Fyfield with his brother Harry. At the end of March he visited his friend John Mulso at Witney, going from there to Oxford, and returning to Selborne on 8 April. Before the month was out, he was in London to stay a little over a fortnight. It was during this period that he made personal acquaintance with Daines Barrington, and on 30 June his correspondence with this gentleman was begun.

Gilbert was at 'Newton' between 25 June and 10 July which means, probably, that he was doing duty as Curate at Newton Valence. On 11 July he was at Whitchurch which was Mr Etty's new living, and he returned there again for a day's visit after spending three days in Oxford. On his return to Selborne he entertained Mr Skinner of Corpus Christi College and Mr Sheffield of Worcester College, both of whom were naturalists. For

---

†A misquote, or a pun, perhaps?

the last two weeks in September, Gilbert was with his aunt Mrs Rebecca Snooke at Ringmer.

A personal note is recorded in the Journal at the end of October when 'Mrs J. W. sails'. That is his brother John's wife, who was returning to Gibraltar where her husband was Chaplain to the garrison. She had brought their only child Jack to England.

January	1.	This year GW began to keep more detailed barometric records. On the scale each inch is divided into 10. One tenth of an inch is quite easily subdivided by eye, and that is what GW has done. One inch is equal to about 35 millibars in today's meterological terms.
February	4.	The dates in brackets [ ] are the correct ones. GW misnumbered after turning a page and corrected himself on 12 February.
	26.	Vast aurora borealis This is mentioned and described several times in these journals. The 'northern lights' are associated with an unusually active period in the sun's cycle, and may appear as a simple glow or shimmering arcs or draperies of colour. It has been calculated that an *aurora* may be visible from the southern counties of England on about five per cent of all clear moonless nights at times of maximum sunspot.
March	6.	The cock swan A slight misquotation, probably written from memory, from Paradise Lost VII 438–9 '. . . the swan with arched neck,/ Between her white wings proudly rows.' (Milton).
	10.	Ews and lambs are turned in to the wheat to eat it down An agricultural practice known as 'tillering'. It was done to encourage the shoots to branch out and increase the yield, on the same principle as pinching out the shoots of a plant to make it bushy.
April	6.	Musca bombyliiformis . . . This fly is like a bumble-bee. It is covered in thick black hair, has a squat body and red sides. It occasionally extends a very long sting or tongue out of its mouth.
	13.	ring-ouzels These could have been birds on their way to northern Europe or northern England returning from the south where they had wintered.
	22.	large . . . bat In the NHS Letter XI to Thomas Pennant GW says: 'At present, I know only two species of bats, the common *vespertilio murinus* [pipistrelle] and the *vespertilio auribus* [long-eared].'
	30.	Jynx The wryneck, *Jynx torquilla*. There are several mentions of this now rather rare bird, but this observation, from London, is the most remarkable.
May	13.	salicaria Sedge warbler *Acrocephalus scirpaceus* – described in detail in the NHS Letter XXIV to Thomas Pennant dated 29 May 1769.
	14.	GW has repeated a day. The correct dates are in square brackets.
July	13.	charwell This is the River Charwell.
	18.	Moor buzzard Marsh harrier *Circus aeruginosus*. This is now a rare breeder in Britain. After becoming extinct here in the 19th century, they re-established themselves in small numbers in East Anglia in the 1920s.
September	2.	comet This comet was distinguished by its brilliance and the great arc of its tail. It was first noted by Charles Messier, the French astronomer, and nicknamed the 'comet Ferret' by Louis XV.
	10.	Land rail The corncrake, *Crex crex*, is now an uncommon bird in the British Isles (except in Ireland) owing to the destruction of its habitat and changes in agricultural practice.
	14.	Papilo Machaen The swallowtail butterfly, now a rarity.
	18.	Bustards These were great bustards, which are now extinct in Britain.
	26.	sheep This observation is developed in NHS Letter XVII to Daines Barrington on 9 December 1773.
October	28.	Mrs J. W. sailed GW's sister-in-law, Mrs John White, returned to Gibraltar to join her husband.
	31.	Swan's egg pears 'A middle-sized pear, in shape like an egg; it is of green colour thinly covered with brown; the flesh is melting and full of a pleasant musky juice. It comes in eating in November.' (Forsyth, 1806).

1770 Events and journeys

In February, Gilbert visited his brother Harry in Fyfield, also spending two days at Charlton (south of

Salisbury), and made some observations on the birds of the Plain and elsewhere in Wiltshire. He was briefly away at Bradley in March, and in April visited Whitchurch, Witney and Oxford, returning to Selborne on 5 May. In April he wrote a letter to Daines Barrington (Letter V NHS) which is revealing of his ideas on method, remarking that in the environs of Selborne 'there is endless room for observation . . . yet investigation (where a man endeavours to be sure of his facts) can make but slow progress; and all that one could collect in many years would go into a very narrow compass.'

A visit to London in June was followed by a stay at Selborne by the Mulsos. In September, Gilbert was briefly at Farnham Castle, and with his brother Harry at Fyfield again for a few days. His autumn visit to Mrs Snooke, his father's sister, was made in October, and he called in at his relatives by marriage, the Woods at Chilgrove, breaking his journey on the way there and the way back.

January		Certe si aliquis . . . Certainly an experienced Naturalist, who was watching the exact times, days and months that migratory birds appeared over southern Spain, would find this obscure matter clarified in no time at all.
	27.	Papilio urticae! Small tortoiseshell butterfly. These hibernate in the imago form, and were probably disturbed in this relatively mild weather.
March	6.	March titmouse This name covered both the marsh tit (Parus palustris) and willow tit until 1900 when they were separately distinguished and the willow tit was given the species name Parus montanus. However, since marsh tits are the more numerous and obvious in broad-leaved woodland, and begin singing early in the year, it is likely that GW was correct in his identification.
	21.	Quotation from Milton Paradise Lost VII again 11 444–7.
June	4.	Pulex irritans The so-called human flea which is, in fact, found on many animals besides humans.
	30.	thermometer Written in error for barometer?
July	7.	wornils These are now known as warbles, and the insect which causes these swellings on the backs of cattle is the warble fly, Hypoderma bovis.
	25.	Quotation from Horace: . . . spreading wings that are greater than its humble nest.
August	8.	Oestrus sive curvicauda Possible the bot-fly Gasterophilus intestinalis. The females have long ovipositors with which they attach their eggs to the hairs on the shoulders, belly and flanks of horses. See also note for 3/8/68. Literal translation: This fly has a crooked or curved tail.
September	10.	The hop picking at Farnham . . . a vast crop A century later Dickens wrote about hop picking: 'The whole countryside will swarm with hopping tramps,' and even with mechanisation Londoners still go down to the country for the hop harvest.
November	24.	stock dove A species which expanded its range significantly in the early 19th century. They are not considered migrant birds in England where they nest in almost every part, but they prefer to nest in open parkland rather than woodland.
December	15.	misling Mizzling: a dialect word for drizzling.

1771 Events and journeys
Early in the year, Gilbert's sister Mrs Rebecca Woods died, an event which seems to have caused him great distress. Gilbert spent just over a fortnight in February, the month of her death, in Fyfield. He made a great number of short visits during this year, writing to Pennant in July of a 'roving unsettled life'. He visited his brother-in-law Henry Woods at Chilgrove in the autumn, when as usual he paused there on his way to and from his fortnight's stay with his aunt at Ringmer. There are two observations noted by Mr Woods entered in the journal for this year. In November John Mulso left Witney and moved to the Rectory of Meonstoke, so that he was now only seventeen miles south-west of Selborne.

January	25.	Daws . . . come to churches Church towers are a favoured nesting site for jackdaws.
February	11.	Small birds begin to cloak An archaic phrase: small birds begin to take shelter. Fieldfares . . . resort to watered meadows Water meadows, which are flooded during the winter months.
March	23.	Dr Johnson says This note was written at the foot of the diary page, possibly added much later. Johnson's Journey to the Western Isles was published in 1775.
April	1.	Mr Woods This was Mr John Woods, father-in-law of GW's sister, Rebecca. This footnote was clearly added at a later date.

	4.	Virgil quotation *Georgics III 538–9*: . . . a more pressing care subdued them.
May	17.	Conops calcitrans The stable fly *Stomoxys calcitrans*. It resembles a housefly, but it bites and sucks blood. It prefers to feed on cattle and horses but also, sometimes, on people.
June	6.	Scopoli quotation: At midday it begins its aerial dance, rising straight up and then falling back the way it came.
	13.	Sphinx filipendula The six-spot burnet moth. It lays its eggs on vetches and pea species, including sainfoin.
August	5.	Peas are hacking cf. Worlidge *Systema agriculturae: the Mystery of Husbandry Discovered* (1669): 'To cut up [reap] Pease or other Haw[m]ly stuff by the roots.'
	6.	large bat The noctule bat, *Nyctalus noctula*. GW is credited with the first English description of this bat which was first described by Daubenton.
October	2.	martin's nest with young A very late brood, but it seems to have survived, since there is no further mention of it.
	28.	There is a large blot on the barometer measurement: it is impossible to be sure of the figures.
November	5.	Phyteuma orbicularis Probably the round-headed rampion, *Phyteuma tenerum*. *Rapunculus scabiosae* (16/7/66 FS) is sheep's-bit, *Jasione montana*.
	13.	16 . . . kites Red kites, *Milvus milvus*. See note for 17/4/68.
	28.	reed-sparrow GW's reed sparrow is now known as the reed bunting *Emberiza schoeniclus* and the aberdavine as the siskin *Carduelis spinus*.
December	26.	bunting(s) . . . affect a champion [champain] country That is, corn buntings (*Emberiza calandra*) prefer open country.
	28.	pewit-gull larus cinereus Black-headed gull, earlier noted under the scientific name *Larus ridibundus* (13/3/71), which is still the name used for this species.

1772 Events and journeys

In the spring of the year Gilbert's brother John White was presented to the Vicarage of Blackburn in Lancashire. John arrived in England on 27 July, having taken 37 days to reach Gravesend from Cadiz. He and his wife spent the winter of 1772–1773 with Gilbert at Selborne and their son Jack White stayed on as his amanuensis. Also in this year Gilbert's brother Harry White received the living of the small parish of Uphaven in Wiltshire which he held with his Fyfield living.

Altogether in 1772 Gilbert made nine journeys away from home, some of only a day or so, such as to Bradley or Newton Valence, and others longer. He visited his aunt, Mrs Rebecca Snooke, from 20 May to early June, and later that month journeyed to Fyfield and back. He made a longer stay in Oxford than was usual from 1 to 20 October, while in August he paid a brief call on his friend John Mulso at Meonstoke.

February	13.	Woodpecker laughs The green woodpecker's laughing call.
	15.	ash-coloured butcher-bird The great grey shrike, *Lanius excubitor*, is a casual visitor, mainly in eastern England. The note appears as a footnote to the week's entries. The place where it was shot, Rotherfield Park, is referred to as Tisted Park in NHS Letter XXXIX to Pennant. The Park still goes by the name of Rotherfield, and is situated to the east of the village of East Tisted, which GW perhaps thought was a better landmark for a wider readership.
February to March	25 12.	GW is in London. There are no journal entries for this period. An unusual gap; perhaps he was unable to arrange for anyone to keep the records in his absence.
April	6.	Cock snipe . . . hums in the air See note for 4/6/68.
May	4.	Lathraea squammaria Toothwort, *Lathraea squamaria*, is still to be found in the wooded lanes close by Selborne, its pinkish-cream flowers in a one-sided spike. It is a parasite, mostly growing on hazel and elm suckers.
June	17.	Bro^r John GW's brother John was the Chaplain to the garrison at Gibraltar.
	30.	hoghs: A hogshead is a liquid measurement usually relating to alcoholic beverages. It represents 54 imperial gallons of beer or 52.5 gallons of wine.
July	11.	a sort of wild bee *Anthidium manicatum*, called the 'hoop shaver' or 'wool carder' because of its habit of stripping flowers in the way described, and also stems and leaves. As GW guessed, it lines its nest with this 'wool', having rolled it into a ball and carried it back to its hole.

August	4.	black-caps . . . eat the rasps. Although they feed largely on insects, blackcaps are also fond of flowers, berries and fruit to a very much greater extent than most other warblers. They will also eat gooseberries, picking out the seeds – possibly they did the same with GW's raspberries.
	15.	the little pond on the common This point is discussed in the NHS Letter XXIX to Daines Barrington on dew ponds.
	21.	Orleans plums An old French variety, believed to date back to the time of Louis XIV and named after the Duke of Orleans. It is a medium-sized cooking plum, blue-black in colour.
September	3.	muscle-plums An old variety of plum, blue-purple in colour,
	15.	Papilio Atalanta The red admiral, *Vanessa atalanta*, abounds in the southern counties in early autumn as the butterflies fly southwards to hibernate across the Channel.
	18.	Ivy A most important shelter and food plant for insects, as well as for birds and bats.
		the last flower which supports the hymenopterous and dipterous Insects Hymenopterous: belonging to the order *Hymenoptera*, which includes bees, wasps, ants and sawflies and is distinguished by having two pairs of membranous wings and a specialised ovipositor. Dipterous: belonging to the order *Diptera* which includes flies, mosquitos, craneflies and midges and is distinguished by having a single pair of wings and sucking or piercing mouth parts.
October	20.	Turdus iliacus Redwings return on winter migration to Britain.
	24.	ring-ouzels See note for 4/9/70.
November	3.	martins The very late appearance of these martins is referred to in the NHS Letter XVI to Daines Barrington, and the matter of the house martin's withdrawal is left ambiguous. However, following later observations GW seems to be more inclined to accept the idea of hibernation for the late-hatched birds, if not for all (NHS Letter XXXVI of 1777 and Letter LV of 1781 to Daines Barrington).
	11.	Nasturtiums & other Indian flowers Nasturtiums, in fact, come from South America.
	16.	Elvela pileo deflexo . . . The elvela [*Helvella*] grows with a bent, lobed and misshapen cap. This fungus grows upon a stalk and has a jagged and curled gill which is folded down into the shape of a pileus. The stalk is grooved and full of holes and cracks.
		Gleditsch methodus fungorum Johann Gottlieb Gleditsch (1714–1786) was the Director of the Berlin Botanic Garden. The honey locust tree *Gleditsia triacanthos* was named after him.

1773 Events and journeys

Early in the year Gilbert was at Fyfield for ten days with his brother Harry and his family. At the end of April, he journeyed to London with his 'brother and sister John White', returning on 21 May. He went to Oxford in the autumn again, spending 12 to 21 October there, and his fortnight's visit to Ringmer was made very late in the year. From summer onwards, his nephew Jack White was at Selborne, where he was nursed back to health after an attack of measles in the middle of the year. By August, John White was installed in his house at Blackburn and Gilbert was writing to him there to tell him that he was expecting their other brothers, Thomas and Harry. A letter from Gilbert to John, written from Ringmer in December, discloses that a letter to Daines Barrington on the subject of house martins was to be read before the Royal Society.

February	20.	Truffles continue to be found . . . There are 30 references to truffles in GW's various journals. *Lycoperdon tuber*, a Linnaean binomial, is the name used by GW in 5/3/90 and the species in question is probably that now known as *Tuber aestivum*. This truffle grows underground in woods, especially beechwoods. Resembling a hard, irregular ball, it can be between 1 to 4 inches across, its flesh white turning to buff with a network of white veins, and is regarded as the best-tasting of the British truffles. On four occasions GW mentions the truffle hunters' dogs: the usual method of finding truffles is for a dog to sniff them out. Hogs are also mentioned in a later entry (12/11/86), but these seem to have been truffling on their own account.
March and April	26. 21.	titlarks The tree pipit and the meadow pipit were not identified as separate species at this time. GW's description of a bird which sings sweetly from trees and in the

		descending flight conforms to the general habits of the tree pipit; meadow pipits more frequently sing as they rise from the ground.
April	10.	osprey The ospreys observed near Selborne would be individuals migrating from their African wintering grounds back to Scotland and Scandinavia. They often remain at a suitable lake, river or reservoir for several days or more during passage.
	26.	There were no daily journal notings for the period 26 April to 12 May while GW was in London, though notes on whooping cough and swifts were added at the foot of two pages.
July	24.	fields of cone Cone-wheat (also called simply cone or cones) is so called because of the conical form of the bearded spike.
August	29.	little black curculio This is a member of the *Curculionidae*, the weevil family, of which about 500 species are known in Britian. Their larvae are legless and most feed enclosed in roots, stems, seeds, nuts or fruit.
September	1.	Orleans plums See note for 21/8/72.
October	9.	hardly any eyes to be found Nesting holes. Pheasants lay their eggs in a hollow scraped out by the female and lined with a few grass stems or dead leaves.
	11.	From Octr: 11th to Oct. 21st the journal was kept by John White at Selborne This note is in GW's handwriting, as are all the entries for these dates. Observations of this period are both of Selborne and 'abroad' – it would seem that GW took the journal with him, and later made additions to it based upon John White's notes.
November	5.	The first grey crow Hooded crows, or Royston crows as they are sometimes called (*Corvus cornix*), occasionally still appear in Hampshire. This one is a winter visitor.
	21.	yellow water wagtail In his list of species given in NHS Letter I to Daines Barrington, GW includes the yellow wagtail as one of the birds resident all year. In fact, the yellow wagtail (*Motacilla flava*) is a summer visitor to England, so GW's observations made in the winter months, were probably of the grey wagtail *Motacilla cinerea* which has a yellow breast. This species was also noted in Letter I. The male grey wagtail differs from the female in having a black throat and being brighter yellow when in breeding plumage. It is possible that GW mistook the male and female for different species, calling the male the 'yellow water-wagtail'.
	29.	clappers A simple bridge, or a raised side-walk, often made of planks, across a stream.
December	6.	White wagtail Also referred to by GW as the grey and white wagtail, this is the pied wagtail *Motacilla alba yarrellii*. A very few of the European race of white wagtails *Motacilla alba alba* breed in Britain.
	25.	See note for 21/11/73 above.

G L O S S A R Y · I N D E X

Included in this glossary/index are words or ideas which might perplex the modern reader: scientific names, unfamiliar common names, archaic or idiomatic terms, and names of people and places. Some species may be mentioned frequently so only the first date reference has been given, unless another entry is particularly significant or is accompanied by reference to a note ¶, in which case this date is also given.

In order to avoid repetition the following abbreviations have been used:
GW = Gilbert White
FS = *Flora Selborniensis*
NHS = *The Natural History of Selborne*

Entries are indexed as they appear in the text, with their date. Then follows the present-day common name and scientific name, with other names also used by Gilbert White shown afterwards in brackets.

Examples

Toad flax, yellow: 30/8/65 Common toadflax *Linaria vulgaris*

i.e. The plant referred to by Gilbert White as 'yellow toad flax' is now known as common toadflax, scientific name *Linaria vulgaris*. If the species is referred to by an out-of-date scientific name only, that would be the index entry, and it would appear thus:

Cornus frugilega: 7/3/66 FS Rook *Corvus frugilegus* (*Cornix frugilega*)

i.e. The bird referred to as *Cornus frugilega* is the rook, present-day scientific name *Corvus frugilegus*. On other occasions Gilbert White also refers to this bird as *Cornix frugilega*, so this name is shown in brackets.

An entry may appear with a note mark ¶ beside the date, which indicates that there is further information to be found in the *Notes* under that date.

Example

Kiver 14/5/65¶ Wooden tub

Aberdavine: 23/1/70, 28/11/71¶ Siskin *Carduelis spinus*
Acacia: 16/4/55 *Acacia dealbata*
Acer campestre: 12/5/66 FS, 16/5/68 Field maple (Acer minus)
Acer pseudoplatanus: 6/3/66 FS Sycamore (*Acer majus*)
Achillea ptarmica: 30/6/68 Sneezewort
Aconite, winter: 18/2/71 *Eranthis hyemalis* (*Helleborus hyemalis*)
Aconitum purpureum: 15/6/66 FS, 29/5/68 Monkshood *Aconitum napellus*
Aconitum uncinatum: 29/5/68
Adder's-tongue: 17/5/66 FS *Ophioglossum vulgatum*
Adonis annua: 1/7/68 Pheasant's-eye
Adoxa moschatellina: 7/4/68 Moschatel
Aesculus hippo-cast: 22/5/68 Horse chestnut *Aesculus hippocastanum*
Aestrus: 8/8/70 See Oestrus
Aethusa cynapium: 14/7/68 Fool's parsley *Aethusa cynapium*
Agaricus campestris: 26/6/68 Field mushroom
Agrimonia eupatoria: 4/4/66 FS, 27/6/66 FS Agrimony
Agrimony: 27/6/66 FS *Agrimonia eupatoria*
Agrimony, least water hemp-: 9/9/66 FS Nodding bur-marigold *?Bidens cernua* (*Verbesina minima*)
Agrimony, trifid water hemp-: 2/8/66 FS *Bidens tripartita* (*Verbesina . . .*)
Agrostemma githaco: 2/7/68 Corncockle
Ajuga reptans: 16/10/65 Bugle
Alaternus: 25/5/66 FS Mediterranean buckthorn *Rhamnus alaternus*
Alauda arborea: 30/10/65 Wood-lark *Lullula arborea*
Alauda locustae voce: 16/4/68 Grasshopper warbler *Locustella naevia*
Alauda minima locustae voce: 3/7/67¶ Grasshopper warbler *Locustella naevia* (grasshopper lark)
Alauda pratorum: 19/4/66 FS Tree pipit (+ meadow?) *Anthus trivialis*
Alauda vulgaris: 22/2/66 Skylark (Skie-lark)
Alcove: Small summerhouse
Alder: 30/8/65 *Alnus glutinosa*
Alisma plantago: 24/7/68 Common water-plantain *Alisma plantago-aquatica*
All-good: 3/5/66 FS Good King Henry *Chenopodium bonus-henricus*
All-heal, broad-leaved: 28/10/65¶ ?Self-heal *Prunella vulgaris*
All-heal, broad-leaved, little: 30/10/65 ?Ground ivy *Glechoma hederacea* (*Sideritis humilis . . .*)
All-heal, clown's: 2/8/66 FS *?Stachys palustris* (*Sideritis*)

Alliaria petiolata: 12/3/66 FS Garlic Mustard, Jack-by-the-hedge
Allium ursinum: 9/4/66 FS Ramsons (*Allium sylvestre* . . .)
Alopecurus myosuroides: 25/7/68 Slender fox-tail or Black grass
Althaea frutex: 22/3/56 Shrub althaea *Hibiscus syriacus*
Amaranth, pendulous: 21/5/54 Love lies bleeding *Amaranthus caudatus*
Amarillis: 10/10/66 FS ?sp. *Amaryllis* family (Guernsey lilly)
Amygdalus persica: 26/4/68 Peach *Prunus persica*
Anagallis flore phoeniceo: 17/6/66 FS Scarlet pimpernel *Anagallis arvensis* (Male or
    red-flowered)
Ananas: 20/7/67¶, 22/12/68¶ Pineapple *Ananas comosus*
Anas crecca: 20/6/73 Teal
Anblatum . . . aphyllon: 24/4/66 FS Toothwort *Lathraea squamaria*
Anemone nemorosa: 6/4/60, 31/3/66 FS Wood anemone
Anemony, wood (flore rubro): 2/5/66 FS¶ Wood anemone *Anemone nemorosa* var *flore rubro*
Angelica sylvatica erratica: 2/4/65, 9/6/66 FS Ground elder *Aegopodium podograria*
Angelica sylvestris: 12/8/66 FS Angelica
Anonis: 20/9/65 Prickly rest-harrow *Ononis spinosa*
Ant, wood: 12/10/65 *Formica rufa*
Anthemis nobilis: 30/7/68 Chamomile *Chamaemelum nobile*
Anthyllis vulnaria: 4/6/68 Kidney vetch *Anthyllis vulneraria*
Antirrhinum angustifolium . . .: 29/9/66 FS Lesser snapdragon *Antirrhinum orontium*
Antirrhinum cymbalarea: 16/10/65 Ivy-leaved toadflax *Cymbalaria muralis*
Antirrhinum linaria: 1/7/66 FS Common toadflax *Linaria vulgaris* (least toad's flax)
Antirrhinum majus: 28/6/66 FS Snapdragon (Great purple snapdragon)
Aparine vulgaris: 6/3/66 FS Goose-grass *Galium aparine*
Aphaca: 19/7/68 Yellow vetchling *Lathyrus alphaca*
Apis domesticae: 4/3/66 FS Honey-bee *Apis mellifera*
Apis hyphorum: 24/4/72
Apis longicornis: 2/6/66 FS Wild bee sp. *Eucera longicornis*
Apis manicata: 11/7/72¶ Wool carder or hoop shaver bee *Anthidium manicatum*
Apis mellifica: 12/1/70 ?Honey bee *Apis mellifera*
Apis mellifera: 19/5/66 FS Honey bee
Apium palustre: 5/7/66 FS Wild celery *Apium graveolens* (smallage)
Apple, thorney: 24/10/66 FS Thorn-apple *Datura stramonium*
Aranea aquatica: 31/5/72 *Argyroneta aquatica* Water spider
Aranea scenica saliens: 4/3/69 ?sp.
Aranaeus niger: 4/3/69 Black spider ?sp.
Arbor-Judae: 2/4/56 Judas tree *Cercis siliquastrum*
Arbor-vitae: *Thuya orientalis*
Arbutus: 14/3/55, 19/2/68¶ Strawberry tree *Arbutus unedo*
Arenaria trinervia: 8/6/69 Three-veined sandwort *Moehringia trinervia*
Arctium lappa: 8/7/68 Greater burdock
Arrow-head: 1/8/66 FS *Sagittaria sagittifolia* (*Sagitta*)
Arsmart, dead or spotted: 8/9/66 FS Redshank *Polygonum persicaria* (*Persicaria maculosa*)
Arsmart, pale: 2/8/66 FS Pale persicaria *Polygonum lapithifolium* (*Persicaria mitis* . . .)
Arsmart, perennial: 22/7/66 Amphibious bistort *Polygonum amphibium* (*Polygonum salicis* . . .)
Artemisia absinthium: 8/8/68 Wormwood
Artemesia vulgaris: 8/8/68 Mugwort *Artemisia vulgaris*
Artichoke, globe: 6/4/51 *Cynara scolymus*
Arum: 6/3/66 FS Cuckoo pint *Arum italicum* (Cuckow pint)
Arum: 15/9/66 FS Lords and Ladies *Arum maculatum*
Ash-house: 19/1/58¶
Ash, mountain: 28/5/66 FS *Sorbus aucuparia* (*Sorbus sylvestris* . . .)
Asparagus, culinary: 8/3/51 FS *Asparagus officinalis*

Aspen: 17/3/66 FS *Populus tremula*
Asperula odorata: 12/3/66 FS Woodruff *Galium odoratum*
Aster amellus: 18/8/66 FS Italian starwort (Virgil's amello)
Aster Chinensis: 21/9/66 FS China aster *Callistephus chinensis*
Aster, late garden: 4/10/66 FS ?Michaelmas daisy *Aster novi-belgii*
Aster, sea: 12/9/66 FS *Aster tripolium* (*Aster maritimus*)
Atricapilla: 9/4/68 Blackcap *Sylvia atricapilla*
Atropa bella donna: 9/9/65 Deadly nightshade
Avens, caryophyllata: 6/3/66 FS Wood avens *Geum urbanum*
Ballota nigra: 16/10/65 Black horehound
Balm: 28/9/54 Lemon balm *Melissa officinalis*
Balm of Gilead fir: 12/5/56 ?*Pinus balsamea*
Balsams: 13/4/51 *Impatiens balsamina* (Balssam)
Barbarea vulgaris: 14/4/66 FS Winter-cress
Barberies: 20/3/55¶ Barberry *Berberis vulgaris*
Barker, Sam: GW's nephew, son of his sister Anne and Thomas Barker
Barker, Thomas: (Brother Barker in Rutland) Husband of GW's sister Anne
Barometer: 1/1/68¶
Base horehound: 20/10/67¶ Downy woundwort *Stachys germanica* (*Stachys fuchsii*)
Base rocket: 20/6/66 FS¶ *Reseda lutea*
Basil, great wild: 22/7/66 FS *Clinopodium origano* (*Calamintha adscendens?*)
Basil, tufted: 28/10/65 Wild basil *Clinopodium vulgare*
Basil, wild: 30/8/65 *Clinopodium vulgare* (Tufted basil *Acinos multis*)
Basoms: 11/4/61 ?Balsams *Impatiens balsamina*
Basons: 23/5/51¶
Bat, large species: 22/4/69,¶ 6/8/71¶
Battie, Anne: Cousin of Mrs Etty: later married Admiral Sir George Young
Battie, Catherine: 28/7/63 Friend of GW, cousin of Mrs Etty. 1771 married John Rashleigh
Battie, Philadelphia: 28/7/63 Cousin of Mrs Etty. Later married Sir John Call, Bart
Baum: 14/8/65 Lemon balm *Melissa officinalis*
Beans, African: 19/10/52 Broad beans
Beans, common: 14/5/51 Probably Windsor type of broad bean, *Vicia faba*
Beans, French: 7/5/51 *Phaseolus vulgaris*
Beans, kidney: 1/10/65 *Phaseolus vulgaris*
Beans, Magazon: 20/11/54¶
Beans, Spanish: 7/1/51¶
Beans, Winsor: 27/3/51 Type of broad bean *Vicia faba*
Bean's pond: 13/9/65, 16/5/66 FS Pond in Woolmer forest (Bin's pond)
Bearsfoot: 22/10/54 Hellebore *Helleborus foetidus* or *H. viridis*¶ 3/3/66 FS
Bedstraw, white ladies: 26/6/66 FS Hedge bedstraw (*Molluginis vulgatioris . . .*)
Bedstraw, mountain ladies: 29/4/66 FS Heath bedstraw *Galium saxatile* (*Mollugo montana*)
Bees, honey: 4/3/66 FS *Apis mellifera* (*Apis domestica*)
Bee, wild: 11/7/72¶ Hoop-shaver or wool-carder bee *Anthidium manicatum*
Beet: 22/3/51 *Beta vulgaris*
Beetle, death-watch: 7/4/72 *Xestobium rufovillosum* (*Termes pulsatorium*)
Beetle, horned: 25/6/66 FS Stag beetle *Lucanus cervus*
Behn, white: 28/10/65 ?Baum
Bellis perennis: 15/1/68 Daisy
Belvedere: 23/9/55 Summer cypress, Burning bush *Kochia scoparia* var. *trichophylla*
Benham, Mr: Selborne farmer
Berberis vulgaris: 17/5/68 Barberry
Berriman, John: 22/10/54 Selborne farmer
Betony: 30/8/65 *Betonica officinalis*
Betony, water-: 5/7/66 FS *Scrophularia aquatica* (Water figwort)

Betula: 12/3/66 Birch spp.

Billet: 27/7/65¶ Cut wood for fuel

Bindweed, black: 28/7/66 FS *Polygonum convolvulus* (*Fegopyrum scandens sylvestre, Polygonum fagopyrum*)

Bines: 8/9/61 Stems

Bird-cherry: 16/4/55 *Prunus padus*

Bistort (greater): 9/4/66 FS Common bistort *Polygonim bistorta*

Bittern: 14/1/74 *Botaurus stellaris*

Blackberry: 15/9/66 FS *Rubus fruticosus* (*Rubus vulg.*)

Black cap: 10/4/67, 4/8/72¶ *Sylvia atricapilla* (*Motacilla atricapilla*)

Black-seed: 28/3/58¶ Black medick *Medicago lupulina*

Blackstonia perfoliata: 18/7/68 Yellow-wort

Bladder-nut tree: 8/9/66 FS *Staphylea pinnata* (*Staphylodendron*)

Blow: 9/10/56 To bloom

Blue-bottles: 28/10/65¶

Boletus albus: 14/8/69 Fungus ?sp.

Bombylius: 12/3/66 FS Bee fly

Bombylius medius: 2/4/68, 6/4/69 Bee fly *Bombylius discolor*

Bombinatrices: 6/4/68 ?Bumble-bees

Boorcole: 16/4/55 Borecole or Kale *Brassica oleracea* v. *Acephala*

Borago officinalis: 9/7/66 FS Borage (*Borrago hortensis*)

Boschas major: 24/4/66 FS ?Mallard *Anas platyrhynchos* (Wild duck)

Box (planted): 9/11/54 *Buxus sempervirens*

Bradley: 5/10/51 Village 5m NW of Alton. Uncle Charles White was Vicar of Swarraton and Bradley.

Bramber: 2/10/71 Village in River Adur valley, W, Sussex.

Bramble: 28/10/65 *Rubus fruticosus* agg.

Brambling: 16/4/67 *Fringilla montifringilla*

Bramshot: 28/3/73 Village 1m N of Liphook in Hampshire.

Bridger, Mr: 17/10/57 Selborne farmer

Brighthelmstone: 17–18/9/65 Brighton (archaism)

Briony, black: 13/6/66 FS Black bryony *Tamus communis* (*Tamnus*)

Bristow, Dr: 24/10/54 Vicar of Selborne until 1758. GW became Curate in 1751 when he was ill.

Broccoli: 25/5/51 *Brassica oleracea*

Bromelia: 8/4/68 Bromeliad – pineapple family

Bromelia ananas: 18/5/69 Pineapple *Ananas comosus*

Brooklime: 22/5/66 FS *Veronica beccabunga*

Broom, butcher's: 19/3/66 FS *Ruscus aculeatus*

Brown owl: 29/4/69 Tawny owl *Strix aluco*

Bryonia alba: 20/4/66, 9/6/68 White bryony *Bryonica dioica*

Buckthorn: 27/10/57 *Rhamnus cathartica*

Buckwheat: 1/8/66 FS *Fagopyrum* spp. (*fegopyrum*)

Bufo bufo: 13/3/66 FS Common toad

Bugle: 16/10/65 *Ajuga reptans*

Bugloss, small wild: 2/11/65 Bugloss *Anchusa arvensis*

Bugloss: 30/9/65 Viper's bugloss *Echium vulgare*

Bulls: 20/8/69 Bullfinches *Pyrrhula pyrrhula*

Bunium bulbocastanum: 17/3/66 FS Great pignut

Bupleurum rotundifolium: 21/6/66 FS Thorow-wax (*Bupleurum perfoliatum . . .*)

Burbey, Mr: Kept a shop in Selborne

Burdock: 22/8/65, 26/7/66 FS *Arctium lappa* (*Lappa major*)

Burnet: 14/8/65, 6/7/65¶, 20/5/66 FS¶ Fodder burnet *Poterium polygamum*

Burnet, garden: 27/4/64¶ Salad burnet *Poterium sanguisorba* (*Sanguisorba minor*)

Burnet, large sort: 26/10/65 *Sanguisorba officinalis*
Burnet ose: 17:18/9/65¶ *Rosa pimpinellifolia* (*Rosa spinosissima*)
Bustard: 18/9/69¶ Great bustard *Otis tarda*
Butcher-bird, ash-coloured: 15/2/72¶ Great grey shrike *Lanius excubitor*
Butcher-bird, red-backed: 21/5/68¶ Red-backed shrike *Lanius collurio* (Flusher)
Butcher's yard/garden: 31/3/56 Old butcher's shop opposite the Wakes
Butomus umbellatus: 11/7/69 Flowering rush
Buttercups: 28/10/65 *Ranunculus* spp.
Buttercup, bulbous: 10/5/66 FS *Ranunculus bulbosa*
Buxus: 3/4/68 Box *Buxus sempervirens*
Buzzard, moor: 18/7/69¶ Marsh harrier *Circus aeruginosus* (*Milvus aeruginosus*)
Cabbage: 4/3/52 *Brassica oleracea*
Cabbage, red: 22/3/51
Calamint, common: 1/9/66 FS *Calamintha adscendens* (*Calamintha vulgaris*)
Calamint, field: 26/8/66 FS Lesser calamint *Calamintha nepeta* (*Calamintha odore pulegii*)
Caltha palustris: 14/3/66 FS Marsh marigold
Campanula glomerata: 29/10/65 Clustered bellflower (Little throatwort or cluster-flowered throatwort)
Campanula hybrida: 15/8/68 Venus's looking glass *Legousia speculum-veneris*
Campanula latifolia: 19/7/68 Giant bellflower
Campanula, pyramidal: 15/10/54, 13/8/66 FS Chimney bellflower *Campanula pyramidalis*
Campanula rotundifolia: 16/7/66 FS Harebell
Campanula trachelium: 5/8/68 Nettle-leaved bellflower
Campion, bladder: 14/6/66 FS *Silene alba* (*Lychnis sylvestris* . . .)
Campion, red: 28/10/65 *Silene dioica*
Campion, rose: 13/2/59 *Lychnis coronaria*
Campion, wild white: 30/5/66 FS *Silene alba* (*Lychnis sylvestris* . . .)
Candytuft: 17/4/55 *Iberis umbellata*
Cane, Basil: 21/7/59 Cousin of GW, Curate of Ludgershall, Wiltshire, 7m NW of Andover.
Canterbury bells: 30/10/55 *Campanula medium*
Cantharis noctiluca: 26/5/68¶ Glow-worm *Lampyris noctiluca*
Caprifolium: 3/3/66 FS Perfoliate honeysuckle
Caprimulgus: 11/5/66 FS Nightjar *Caprimulgus europaeus* (Goatsucker, fern-owl)
Capsicums: 19/3/54 Peppers
Caraway: 19/5/66 FS *Carum carvi*
Cardamine impatiens: 11/6/66 FS Hairy bittercress
Cardamine pratensis: 14/4/66 FS Cuckooflower
Carduelis carduelis: 27/4/66 FS Goldfinch
Carduus acanthoides: 29/6/68 Welted thistle
Carduus acaulos: 16/7/66 Dwarf thistle *Cirsium acaulon*
Carduus crispus: 29/6/68 Welted thistle also known as *Carduus acanthoides*
Carduus eriophorus corona fratrum: 12/7/68 Woolly thistle *Cirsium eriophorum* (Woolly headed thistle)
Carduus lanceolatus: 15/7/66 FS Spear thistle *Cirsium vulgare*
Carduus marianus: 24/8/68 ?Slender thistle *C. tenuiflorus*
Carduus nutans: 15/7/66 FS Musk thistle
Carduus spinosissimus: 6/9/66 FS Welted thistle *Carduus acanthoides*
Carduus tormentosus: 2/8/66 FS Woolly thistle *Cirsium eriophorum*
Carlina vulgaris: 16/7/66 FS Carline thistle
Carpenter, Will: 29/3/65 Cobbler who lived close to GW in Selborne
Carrots: 6/4/51 *Daucus carota*
Carthumus tinctorius: 15/8/68 Yellow star-thistle *Carthamus tinctorius* (casual from Asia)
Catch-fly, narrow-leaved: 14/6/66 FS Red German catchfly *Lychnis viscaria* (*Lychnis angustifolia viscosa* . . .)

Cat-mint: 16/6/66 FS *Nepeta cataria* (*Nepeta major*)

Caucalis Anthriscus: 13/7/68 Bur chervil *Anthriscus caucalis*

Cauliflower: 21/5/54 *Brassica oleracea*

Cedar of Libanus: 21/3/55 Cedar of Lebanon *Cedrus libani*

Celandine, greater: 25/11/65 *Chelidonium majus* (*C. papaver*)

Celandine, less (Pilewort): 25/11/65 *Ranunculus ficaria* (*Chelidonium minus*)

Celeri, Celery: 14/1/51 *Apium graveolens*

Celeriac: 13/4/51 *Apium graveolens* v. *rapaceum*

Centaurea calcitrapa: 16/7/68 Red star-thistle

Centaurea cyanus: 5/7/68 Cornflower

Centaurea jacea: 28/6/68 Brown knapweed

Centaurea scabiosa: 25/6/68 Greater knapweed

Centaurea solstitialis: 10/8/68 Yellow star-thistle

Centaurium luteum perfoliatum: 17/9/67¶ Yellow wort *Blackstonia perfoliata* (Centory)

Centaurium minus: 10/10/65 Lesser centaury *Centaurium pulchellum*

Centaury, small: 10/10/65 Lesser centaury *Centaurium pulchellum* (*Centaurium minus*)

Centaury, yellow: 17/9/67¶ Yellow-wort *Blackstonia perfoliata* (yellow centory)

Centory: 17/9/67 Centaury

Cerasus: Dwarf cherry *Prunus cerasus*

Chafer: 27/4/66 FS ?Cock chafer or maybug *Melolontha melolontha*

Chaffinch: 22/2/66 FS *Fringilla coelebs*

Chamaemelium odoratissimum: 9/8/66 FS Chamomile *Chamaemelum nobile*

Chardoons: 22/3/51¶ Cardoon *Cynara cardunculus* (Chardon)

Charlock: 29/10/65 *Sinapsis arvensis* (*Rapistrum arvorum*)

Cheiranthus cheiri: 1/4/68 Wallflower

Chelidonium majus: 14/5/68 Greater celandine

Chelidonium minus: 16/5/66 FS Lesser celandine *Ranunculus ficaria* (pilewort)

Chenopodium Bonus Henricus: 8/7/68 Good King Henry *Chenopodium bonus-henricus*

Chenopodium folius integris: 20/9/66 FS *Chenopodium polyspermum* (green bite)

Cherry, wild, black: 22/4/66 FS ?Bird cherry *Prunus padus*

Cherrysucker: 4/5/59 Spotted flycatcher *Muscicapa striata*

Chervil, garden: 12/6/66 FS *Anthriscus cerefolium* (*cerefolium sativum*)

Chervil, wild: 25/11/65 Rough chervil *Chaerophyllum temulentum* (*Cicutaria vulgaris: sive Myrrhis sylvestris . . .*, chervil, wild Cicely, cow-weed)

Chestnut, horse: 25/5/66 FS *Aesculus hippocastanum*

Chestnut, Spanish: 10/3/62 *Castanea sativa*

Chilgrove, W. Sussex: 1/4/71 Village 3m west of Singleton, family home of GW's sister Rebecca and her husband Henry Woods

China-Arbor-Vitae: 2/4/56 Chinese Thuya *Thuja orientalis*

China aster: 17/4/55 *Callistephus chinensis* (*Aster Chinensis*)

Chops: 25/3/61¶ Cracks

Chrysis ignita: 5/9/69 Ruby-tail wasp

Chrysomela Gottingensis: 15/3/73 Leaf beetle ?sp.

Chrysomelae oleraceae: 22/8/72 Turnip flies *Phyllotreta nemorum*

Chrysosplenium oppositifolium: 9/4/68 Opposite-leaved golden saxifrage (opposite-leaved saxifrage)

Cicada spumaria: 16/6/68 Frog hopper *Philaenus spumarius*

Cichoreum sylvestre: 23/8/66 FS Chicory *Cichorium intybus* (Wild succory)

Cicely, wild: 25/11/65 Cow parsley *Anthriscus sylvestris*

Cicutaria tenuifolia: 5/3/66 FS Fool's parsley *Aethusa cynapium*

Cicutaria vulgaris: 25/11/65 Cow parsley *Anthriscus sylvestris*

Cimex lectularius: 4/5/68 Bedbug

Cinquefoil, common: 1/7/66 FS Creeping cinquefoil *Potentilla reptans* (five-leaved grass)

Cinquefoil, purple marsh: 11/8/67 FS *Potentilla palustris* (*Pentaphylloides palustre . . .*)

Cinque-foil, shrubby: 15/6/66 FS *Potentilla fruticosa*
Cions: 30/3/61¶ Scions
Circaea: 3/10/65 Enchanter's nightshade *Circaea lutetiana*
Circaea lutetiana: 18/7/68 Enchanter's nightshade
Cistus, dwarf: 24/10/66 FS see *Helianthemum chamaecistus*
Cistus helianthemum: 22/5/66 FS, 25/4/68 Rock rose *Helianthemum chamaecistus*
Clary, wild: 16/6/66 FS *Salvia horminoides (Hormium sylvestre . . .)*
Clematis vitalba: 25/7/66 FS Traveller's joy *(Clematis latifolia . . .)*
Clement, Mr & Mrs, of Alton: Mrs Clement was GW's niece
Clover, white: 20/9/54 *Trifolium repens*
Cloves: 21/10/54¶ Clove gilliflowers (pinks) *Dianthus* spp.
Cluster-pines: 18/7/55 *Pinus pinaster*
Cobnuts: 19/12/63 *Corylus avellana* var. *grandis*
Coccigyra: 31/3/56 *Cotinus coggygria (Rhus cotinus)*
Coccinella bipunctata: 16/4/68 Two-spot ladybird *Adalia bipunctata*
Cochlearia officinalis: 27/4/69 Scurvy grass
Cockle: 22/7/66 FS Corn cockle *Agrostemma githago (Lychnis segetum major)*
Cockscombs: 12/3/54 *Celosia argentea v. cristata* (Amaranths)
Cods: 13/6/71 Cocoons
Colchicum autumnale: 23/8/66 FS 13/9/69 Autumn crocus, Meadow saffron *(Colchicum commune)*
Colemouse: 4/4/67¶ Coal tit *Parus ater*
Coluber berus: 23/3/69 Adder
Coluba natrix: 30/3/68 Grass snake *Natrix natrix*
Columba oenas: 24/11/70¶ Stock dove
Columbine: 5/3/52 *Aquilegia vulgaris* (Cullumbines)
Colutea scorpiodes: 6/11/51,¶ 12/5/66 FS Scorpion-senna *Coronilla emerus*
Comarum palustre: 23/7/68 Marsh cinquefoil *Potentilla palustris*
Comfrey: 16/10/65 *Symphytum officinale (Symphytum magnum)*
Common beans: Broad beans *Vicia faba*
Conium maculatum: 13/7/68 Hemlock
Conops calcitrans: 17/5/71¶ Stable fly *Stomoxys calcitrans*
Convulvulus arvensis: 22/6/68 Field bindweed *Convolvulus arvensis* (small bindweed)
Convulvulus major: 14/5/66 FS Hedge bindweed *Calystegia sepium* (great bindweed)
Conysa squarrosa: 18/8/68 Canadian fleabane *Conyza canadensis*
Corn, Indian: 15/4/52 Sweet corn, maize *Zea mays* (Indian wheat)
Corn-flags: 24/10/61 ?Gladioli
Cornix cinerea frugilega: 23/10/68, 5/11/73 Hooded crow, Royston crow *Corvus corone cornix*
Cornix frugilega: 7/3/66 FS Rook *Corvus frugilegus*
Cornus sanguinea: 20/6/66 FS Dogwood *Cornus foemina* (Female cornel, dog-berry tree)
Coronae Imperialis: 16/11/58 Crown imperial fritillary *Fritillaria imperialis*
Coronilla emerus: 2/11/51¶ Scorpion senna *(Colutea scorpiodes)*
Corni: 21/4/66 FS¶ Raven *Corvus corax*
Corydalis solida: 7/4/66 FS Bulbous corydalis (garden plant)
Corylus avellana: 10/2/68 Hazel
Corylus sylvestris: 22/2/66 see *Corylus avellana*
Coturnix: 4/7/68 Quail *Coturnix coturnix*
Coltus gobio: 19/11/66 FS Miller's thumb
Cow-parsnep: 4/4/66 FS *Heracleum sphondylium*
Cowslip: 22/2/66 FS¶ *Primula veris (Paralysis vulgaris pratensis . . .)*
Cowslip, red: 4/4/61¶
Cow-weed: 25/11/65 ?Cow parsley *Anthriscus sylvestris* (wild Cicely, *Cicutaria vulgaris*)
Cow-wheat, yellow: 17/6/66 Common cow-wheat *Melampyrum pratense*
Crabro: 5/8/69 Digger wasp *Crabro cribrarius*

Crambe maritima: 30/5/66 FS Sea kale (Sea colewort)

Cranberry: 9/9/65 *Vaccinium vitis-idaea* (*Oxycoccus*)

Crane's-bill: 28/10/65 *Geranium* spp.

Crane's-bill, alpine: 12/10/65 *Geranium* sp. ?*G. endressii* (*Geranium argenteum Alpinum*)

Crane's-bill, crow's foot: 29/10/65 Meadow cranesbill *Geranium pratense*

Crane's-bill, dove's foot: 7/5/66 FS ?*Geranium molle* or *Geranium columbinum*

Crane's-bill, dove's foot, with jagged leaves: 6/6/66 FS ?Cut-leaved cranesbill *Geranium dissectum*

Crane's-bill, field: 16/5/66 FS¶ Common storksbill *Erodium cicutarium* (*Geranium cicuta . . .*)

Crataegus aria: 4/6/73 Whitebeam *Sorbus aria*

Cratagus oxyacantha: 23/5/68, 12/4/66 FS Hawthorn *Crataegus monogyna*

Cratagus torminalis: 27/5/68 Wild service tree *Sorbus torminalis*

Cricket: 20/5/61¶, 24/5/65 Field cricket *Gryllus campestris*

Cricket, mole: 23/5/69 *Gryllotalpa gryllotalpa*

Crocus, autumn: 13/9/69 *Crocus nudiflorus*

Crocus sativus: 15/2/68¶ Spring crocus *Crocus purpureus*

Crocus (Yellow and purple): 21/9/54, 15/2/68¶Spring crocus *Crocus purpureus* (*Crocus sativus*)

Crossbill: 5/10/70 *Loxia curvirostra*

Crosswort: 16/10/65 *Galium cruciata* (*Cruciata hirsuta . . .*)

Crow-foot, field, with small flower: 22/5/66 FS Small-flowered buttercup *Ranunculus parviflorus*

Crow, grey: 23/10/68, 5/11/73¶ Hooded crow, Royston crow *Corvus corone cornix* (*Cornix cinerea frugilega*)

Crow, Royston: 25/1/69 Hooded crow *Corvus corone cornix*

Crowfoot, bulbose: 10/5/66 FS, 30/5/68 Bulbous buttercup *Ranunculus bulbosus*

Crown imperial: 24/1/51 *Fritillaria imperialis*

Cucubalus behen: 9/6/68 ?Berry catchfly *Cucubalus baccifer*

Cuculus: 20/4/66 Cuckoo *Cuculus canorus* (Cuckow)

Cucumis melo: 13/3/69 Melon

Cucumber: 22/3/51¶ *Cucumis sativus*

Cudweed, common: 6/9/66 FS ?Small cudweed *Filago minima* (*Gnaphalium minus*)

Cups: 13/4/52¶ Small, round depressions

Curculio: 29/8/73¶ Weevil family *Curculionidae*

Curious: 28/7/62, 27/7/65¶ Good, excellent

Curlew, stone-: 16/8/65¶, 5/8/66 FS *Burhinus oedicnemus* (Stone curlues, *Oedicnemus*)

Currants: 6/11/51 *Ribes* spp.

Currants, White Dutch: 23/2/51 White currants *Ribes rubrum* agg.

Currant, large Dutch 11/3/52

Curruca: 9/3/66 FS Hedge-sparrow *Prunella modularis*

Cuscuta Europaea: 29/8/66 FS, 20/7/68 Greater dodder *Cuscuta europaea* (*Cuscuta major*)

Cyanus: 20/6/66 FS Cornflower *Centaurea cyanus*

Cymbalaria hederaceo . . .: 16/10/65 Ivy-leaved toadflax *Cymbalaria muralis*

Cynocrambe: 9/3/66 FS Dog's mercury *Mercurialis perennis*

Cynoglossum officinale: 12/3/66 FS Hound's tongue

Cyperus-grass, great vernal ?Greater pond-sedge *Carex riparia*

Cypress: *Cupressus* spp.

Cytisus, evergreen: 1/5/56 Broom ?sp.

Cytisus laburnum: 18/5/68 ?Laburnum *Laburnum anagyroides*

Daffodil: 19/3/66 FS¶ *Narcissus pseudo-narcissus* (*Narcissus palidus . . .*)

Daisy, common: 28/10/65 Bellis perennis

Daisy, great or ox-eye: 28/10/65 Ox-eye daisy *Chrysanthemum leucanthemum*

Dama: 14/10/66 FS Fallow deer *Dama dama*

Dandelion: 28/10/65 *Taraxacum officinale* agg.

Daphne laureola: 1/4/68 Spurge laurel

Daphne mezereum: 3/3/68 Mezereon

Daucus carota: 9/7/66 FS Wild carrot (bird's nest, *Daucus vulgaris*)

Dentaria aphyllos . . .: 5/9/65¶ Lady's tresses *Spiranthes spiralis* (Ladies traces)

Devonshired: 24/9/56¶

Devil's bit, blue: 24/10/66 FS Devilsbit scabious *Succisa pratensis* (*Scabiosa succisa*)

Dianthus barbatus: 8/6/68 Sweet William

Dianthus caryophyllus: 7/6/68 Clove pink

Dier's broom: 20/9/65, 11/6/66 FS *Genista tinctoria* (Dier's weed, wood-waxen *Genistella tinctoria*)

Digitalis purpurea: 10/6/68 Foxglove

Dipsacus: 10/3/66 see *Dipsacus sylvestris*

Dipsacus minor . . .: 14/8/66 FS Small teasel *Dipsacus pilosus*

Dipsacus pilosus: 28/7/68 Small teasel

Dipsacus sylvestris: 10/3/66 FS Teasel *Dipsacus fullonum*

Dock: 1/7/66 FS *Rumex obtusifolius* (*Lapathum vulgaris*)

Dog's mercury: 11/10/65 *Mercurialis perennis* (*Cynocrambe*)

Dogwood: 22/3/56 *Cornus* spp.

Dorchester: 21/10/73 village on R. Thames 4m NW of Wallingford

Dorton-earth: 3/4/56 Dorton-mould 22/4/55¶

Dove, ring: 9/3/66 FS Wood pigeon *Columba palumbus*

Dove, stock: 24/11/70¶ *Columba oenas*

Dove, turtle: 28/5/66 FS *Streptopelia turtur* (*Turtur*)

Dragon: 21/7/66 FS ?*Dracunculus vulgaris* (*Dracontium vulg:*)

Drosera rotundifolia: 22/7/68 Common sundew

Dwarf elder: 21/4/66 FS *Sambucus ebulus*

Durley: Small rural parish of which GW was Curate from 1753–55

Dyer's weed/Weld: 9/9/65 *Reseda luteola* (*luteola*, Wild wold, yellow weed)

Earth nuts: 27/8/65¶ ?Water dropwort *Oenanthe pimpinelloides*

Earwigs: 21/8/65 *Forficulae*

Echium vulgare: 19/6/68 Viper's bugloss

Elder: 3/2/66 FS *Sambucus nigra*

Elder, parsley: 12/11/59 Cut-leaved elder *Sambucus nigra* var. *laciniata*

Elder, water-: 11/6/66 FS¶ ?Guelder rose *Viburnum opulus*

Elder, white: 14/3/57 ?White-berried elder *Sambucus nigra*

Elecampane: 22/7/66 FS *Inula helenium* (*Helenium*)

Elvela mitra: 16/11/72 fungus sp. ?*Helvella crispa*

Emberiza alba: 9/1/69 Corn bunting *Emberiza calandra*

Emberiza flava: 14/8/65 Yellow-hammer *Emberiza citrinella*

Endive, Batavian: Plain-leaved endive, Batavian *Cichorium endivia*

Endive, curled: 7/5/51 *Cichorium endivia*

English Mercury: 3/5/66 FS Good King Henry *Chenopodium bonus-henricus*

Ephemera cauda biseta: 10/6/71 ?Mayfly

Ephemera vulgata: 3/6/68 The angler's mayfly *Ephemera danica*

Epilobium angustifolium: 12/6/68 Rosebay willowherb

Epilobium montanum: 22/6/68 Broad-leaved willowherb

Epilobium ramosum: 17/7/68 Willowherb ?sp.

Equisetum, majus: 2/5/66 FS Marsh horse-tail *Equisetum palustre* (Great water horse-tail)

Equisetum segetale: 2/5/66 FS Common horse-tail *Equisetum arvense* (Corn horse-tail)

Eryngium maritimum: 14/8/66 Sea holly

Erysimum alliaria: 23/4/69 Garlic mustard *Alliaria petiolata*

Esshallots: 7/4/52 Shallots

Etty, Revd Andrew: Vicar of Selborne from 1759 to 1784, and friend of GW

Etty, Charles: Son of Andrew Etty

Euonymus europaeus: 17/6/66 FS Spindle tree

Eupatorium cannabinum: 8/9/66 FS Hemp agrimony (Dutch agrimony)
Euphorbia amygdaloides: 1/6/68 Wood spurge
Euphrasia odontites: 2/7/68 ?sp.
Everlasting-pea: 11/4/58 *Lathyrus latifolius*
Eye-bright: 30/8/65 *Euphrasia* spp.
Fagus sylvatica: 28/4/68 Beech
Faringdon: villages (Upper and Lower) near Alton
Fell-wort: 3/9/68 Felwort or Autumn gentian *Gentianella amarella*
Fennel: 18/8/66 FS *Foeniculum vulgare*
Fern, common (brakes): 27/4/66 FS ?Lady fern *Athyrium filix-femina*
Fern, hart's-tongue: 31/10/65 *Phyllitis scolopendrium*
Fern, male: 31/10/65 *Dryopteris filix-mas.*
Fern, prickly, male-: 11/3/66 FS Hard shield-fern *Polystichum aculeatum* (*Filex aculeata mas*)
Fern-owl: 16/7/65¶ Nightjar *Caprimulgus europaeus* (Goatsucker)
Ficaria verna: 8/3/68 Lesser celandine *Ranunculus ficaria*
Fieldfare: 15/10/65, 11/2/71¶ *Turdus pilaris*
Field-cricket: 24/5/65¶
Field garden, old/new 12/4/68 see p.12
Fig: *Ficus carica*
Figwort, common: 11/10/65 *Scrophularia nodosa* (knobby rooted figwort)
Figwort, water: 16/10/65 *Scrophularia aquatica*
Filberts: 6/1/55 Hazel *Corylus avellana*
Filex elegans: 25/11/65 *Asplenium adiantum-nigrum* (*Adianto nigro accedens . . .*)
Filipendula Ulmaria: 14/3/66 FS Meadowsweet
Filipendula vulgaris: 21/6/66 FS Dropwort
Finochia: 18/5/52 Florence fennel, finocchio *Foeniculum vulgare v. dulce* (fenochia)
Fir, silver: 1/5/56 *Abies alba*
Firs, spruce: 26/10/51 *Picea* spp. ?*Picea abies*
Flax, wild blue: 15/7/66 FS *Linum perenne* (*Linum sylvestre caeruleum*)
Fleabane, middle: 9/8/66 FS Common fleabane *Pulicaria dysenterica* (*Conyza media*)
Flisky: 24/6/72 Dialect word, fitfully scudding
Fluellin, round-leaved: 30/10/65 Round-leaved fluellen *Kicksia spuria*
Fluellin, sharp-pointed: 30/10/65 Sharp-leaved fluellen *Kicksia elatine*
Fool's-stones, male: 29/4/66 FS Early-purple orchid *Orchis mascula*
Formica: 5/3/66 FS Ant
Formica herculeana: 18/4/68 ?Wood ant *Formica rufa*
Formica nigra: 22/4/68 Common black ant *Lasius niger*
Formica rufa: 12/10/65 Wood ant
Foxglove: 22/10/54 *Digitalis purpurea*
Fragaria sterilis: 26/3/68 Barren strawberry *Potentilla sterilis*
Fragarai vesca: 9/3/66 FS Wild Strawberry (wood strawberry)
Fraxinella, sown: 24/10/54, 24/3/64¶ Burning bush *Dictamnus alba* (White dittany)
Fraxinus excelsior: 13/5/66 FS Ash
Fringilla: 22/2/66 FS Chaffinch *Fringilla coelebs*
Fringilla montifringilla: 16/4/67 Brambling
Fringillago: 28/1/68 Great tit *Parus major* (Great titmouse)
Fritillaria Imperialis: 8/4/68 Crown Imperial
Fritillaria meleagris: 8/4/73 Snakeshead fritillary
Froyle: 9/9/66 Villages Upper and Lower Froyle 4m NE of Alton
Fumaria bulbosa: 19/3/68 ?Bulbous corydalis *Corydalis bulbosa*
Fumitory, common: 10/10/65 *Fumaria officinalis*
Fumitory, hollow rooted: 7/4/66 FS *Corydalis solida*
Funtington, W. Sussex: 22/7/71 Village 5m NW Chichester
Fyfield, Wiltshire: Village W of Marlborough, where GW's brother Henry (Harry)

held the living from 1762–1788.

Galanthus nivalis: 13/2/68 Snowdrop

Galega officinalis: 17/7/68 Goat's rue

Galium cruciata: 16/10/65 Crosswort (*Cruciata*)

Galeopsis galeobdolon: 14/5/68 Yellow archangel *Lamiastrum galeobdolon*

Galium palustre: 29/6/68 Marsh bedstraw

Galium verum: 15/3/66 FS Lady's bedstraw

Gallinago minor: 24/4/66 FS Snipe *Gallinago gallinago*

Gallinula: 29/3/66 FS Moorhen, water-hen *Gallinula chloropus*

Garlick: 14/4/54 Garlic *Allium sativum*

Genista spinosa vulgaris: 12/3/66 FS Gorse, furze *Ulex europaeus*

Genista tinctoria: 28/6/68 Dyer's greenweed

Gentiana amarella: 3/9/68 Autumn gentian *Gentianella amarella*

Gentiana centaureum: 20/7/68 Common centaury *Centaurium erythraea*

Gentian, autumn: 29/8/66 *Gentianella amarella* (*Gentianella pratensis* . . .)

Geranium, alphine: 12/6/66 FS *Geranium argenteum*

Geranium argenteum Alpinum: 12/10/65 Silvery alpine cranesbill *Geranium argenteum*

Geranium cicuta . . .: 16/5/66 FS Common storksbill *Erodium cicutarium* (Field geranium)

Geranium columbinum: 7/5/66 FS ?Dovesfoot cranesbill *Geranium molle* or long-stalked cranesbill *Geranium columbinum*

Geranium, crow-foot: 25/6/66 FS Meadow cranesbill *Geranium pratense*

Geranium pratense: 25/6/66 FS, 8/6/69 Meadow cranesbill (Crow-foot geranium)

Geranium Robertianum: 29/4/66 FS Herb Robert

Geum urbanum: 28/5/68 Herb Bennet

Gladiolus communis: 12/6/68 *Gladiolus illyricus*

Gladwin, stinking: 16/10/65 *Iris foetidissima*

Glechoma hederacea: 4/4/68 Ground ivy

Gleditsch . . .: 16/11/72¶

Glow worm: 8/8/65, 26/5/68¶ *Lampyris noctiluca* (*Cicindela, Cantharis noctiluca*)

Goatsucker: 16/7/65¶ Nightjar *Caprimulgus europaeus* (Fern owl)

Golden-crowned wren: 12/3/69 Goldcrest *Regulus regulus*

Golden rod: 14/7/66 FS *Solidago virgaurea* (*virga aurea*)

Goldylocks: 24/10/57 Goldilocks *Aster linosyris* (*Linosyris vulgaris*)

Gooseberries: 6/11/51 *Grossularia uva-crispa*

Goosefoot, common: 20/9/66 FS ?*Chenopodium rubrum* or *C. album*

Goose-grass: 6/3/66 FS *Galium aparine* (*Aparine vulgaris*)

Gorse: 28/10/65 Furze *Ulex* spp.

Gould: Revd William Gould wrote *Account of English Ants* 1747

Gourd: 17/4/55, 27/4/64¶ *Cucurbita pepo*

Grasshopper: 28/3/66 FS *Locusta* spp. family *Acrididae*

Greenfinch: 27/4/66 FS *Carduelis chloris*

Green geese: 9/5/69 Immature geese

Grimm, Hieronymous (1733–94) Itinerant topographical artist, specialising in rural and antiquarian subjects.

Gripes: Trenches or ditches

Gromel: 2/11/65 Gromwell *Lithospermum* spp. (Gromill)

Gromwell: 10/10/65 ?*Lithospermum officinale*

Groundsel-tree: 30/12/61 *Baccharis halimifolia*

Grounsel: 1/3/66 FS *Senecio vulgaris*

Guelder rose: 22/3/56, 11/6/66 FS¶ *Viburnum opulus*

Gryllus campestris: 20/5/61¶, 24/5/65¶ Field cricket

Gryllus gryllotalpa: 16/5/66 FS Mole cricket *Gryllotalpa gryllotalpa*

Gryllus sylvestris: 9/3/66 FS¶ Wood cricket *Nemobius sylvestris* (Field cricket)

Gyrinus natator: 22/5/72 Whirligig beetle *Gyrinus substriatus*

Haematopus ostralegus: 10/4/73 Oystercatcher (Sea-pie)

Hale, Mr: 31/1/59, 3/2/59 of Hambledon, village 5m SE of Meonstoke

Hale, Mr: A Selborne farmer

Hales, Dr Steven: 23/2/58¶ Rector of Faringdon and friend of the White family

Halimus: 30/12/61 Tree purslane ?*Atriplex halimus*

Hampton, Goody, also written Hammond: GW's regular weeding woman

Hartley: large estate 3m south of Selborne

Hart's-tongue: 31/10/65 *Phyllitis scolopendrium*

Hasel: 14/8/65 Hazel *Corylus avellana*

Hawkley: Village 2m NW of Liss

Hawkweed: 22/8/65 *Hieracium* spp.

Hawkweed, long-rooted: 14/6/66 FS Common cat's-ear *Hypochoeris radicata* (*Hieracium longius radicatum*)

Hawkweed, rough: 10/6/66 FS *Picris echioides* (*Hieracium asperum*)

Hawkweed, smooth succory-: 6/7/66 FS Smooth hawk's-beard *Crepis capillaris* (*Hieracium luteum glabrum*)

Hawkweed, yellow Devil's bit: 3/6/66 FS *Leontodon autumnale* (*Hieracium minus*)

Hawthorn: 12/4/66 FS *Crataegus monogyna*

Heath, cross-leaved: 16/7/66 FS *Erica tetralix* (*Erica brabantica* . . .)

Hedera: 30/9/65 Ivy *Hedera helix*

Hedley: 1/7/66 FS Headley, Hampshire, village 4m north of Bramshott

Hedysarum onobrychis: 28/5/68 French honeysuckle *Hedysarum coronarium*

Helianthemum vulgare: 22/5/66 FS Common rock-rose *Helianthemum chamaecistus*

Helianthus multiflorus: 31/7/68 Sunflower

Hellebore, black: 5/10/65¶, 3/3/66 FS¶ Stinking hellebore *Helleborus foetidus*

Hellebore, white: 5/3/66 Green hellebore *Helleborus viridis*

Hellebore, wild black: 5/10/65¶, 23/5/66 Stinking hellebore *Helleborus foetidus*

Helleborine latifolia: 2/8/66 FS Broad-leaved helleborine Epipactis helleborine (*Helleborine latifolia* . . .)

Helleborus albus: 5/3/66 FS Green hellebore *Helleborus viridis*

Helleborus foetidus: 3/3/66 FS¶, 14/2/68 Stinking hellebore

Helleborus hyemalis: 11/2/68 Winter aconite *Eranthis hyemalis*

Helleborus niger: 5/10/65 Stinking hellebore *Helleborus foetidus*

Helleborus viridis: 1/9/68¶ Green hellebore

Hemerocallis spp: 17/6/66 FS Day lily (Yellow asphodel lily and Alpine bastard lily)

Hemlock: 14/7/66 FS *Conium maculatum* (*Cicuta*)

Hemp agrimony: 8/9/66 FS *Eupatorium cannabinum*

Hemp agrimony, least water-: 9/9/66 FS ?Nodding bur-marigold *Bidens cernua* (*Verbesina minima*)

Hemp-agrimony, trifid water with divided leaf: 2/8/66 FS, 11/8/67 FS Trifid bur-marigold *Bidens tripartita* (*Verbesina seu cannabina aquat* . . .)

Hemp agrimony, water, with undivided leaf: 11/8/67 FS Nodding bur-marigold *Bidens cernua* (*Verbesina pulchriore flore luteo*)

Hen-bit, great: Henbit dead-nettle *Lamium amplexicaule* (*lamium folio caulem* . . .)

Henbit, small: 25/11/65 *Veronica hederifolia* (Ivy-leaved speedwell, *Veronica flosculis* . . .)

Hepatica: 25/1/66 ?*Hepatica triloba*

Hepatica Polyanthus: 15/1/68 ?sp.

Heracleum sphondylium: 23/6/68 Hogweed

Herb Gerard: 2/11/65 Ground elder *Aegopodium podograria* (Gout-weed, ashweed)

Herb Paris: 2/5/66 FS¶ *Paris quadrifolia*

Herb Robert: 29/4/66 *Geranium robertianum*

Herb two-pence: 29/8/66 FS Creeping Jenny *Lysimachia nummularia* (Money wort)

Hesperis matronalis: 25/5/66 FS Dame's violet

Hibiscus syriacus: 2/9/72 Hibiscus

Hieracium minus . . .: 13/9/66 FS (Yellow Devil's-bit) Autumn hawkbit *Leontodon autumnalis*

Hieracium murorum . . .: 21/5/66 FS, 16/7/68 Few-leaved hawkweed (Golden lungwort) *Hieracium murorum*

Hill, Dr: 22/10/60¶, 5/9/65¶

Hippobosca equina: 24/7/68¶ Forest fly (side fly)

Hippomyrmeces: 19/3/66 FS Horse-ants, great wood-ants ?*Formica rufa*

Hirundo agrestis: 14/4/66 FS House martin *Delichon urbica*

Hirundo apus: 5/8/66 Swift *Apus apus*

Hirundo domestica: 14/4/66 Swallow *Hirundo rustica*

Hirundo riparia: 19/4/68 Sand martin *Riparia riparia*

Hitt, T. A.: 6/2/58¶

Hoarhound, stinking: 16/10/65 Black horehound *Ballota nigra* (*Marrubium nigrum*)

Hoarhound, water: 16/10/65, 2/8/66 FS Common water horehound *Lycopus europaeus* (*Marrubium aquaticum; Lycopus palustris* . . .)

Hoarhound, white: 16/10/65 White horehound *Marrubium vulgare* (*Marrubium album*)

Hogs: 30/6/72¶ Hogsheads

Holly (berries sown): 6/1/55 *Ilex aquifolium* (*agrifolium*)

Holly-hocks, China: Variegated double hollyhock *Althaea rosea chinensis*

Holly-leaved oak: 1/5/56 Holly oak, holm oak *Quercus ilex*

Holy-oaks: 22/3/51 Hollyhocks *Althaea rosea*

Honey-suckels: 6/11/51 Honeysuckles *Lonicera* spp.

Honeysuckle: 3/3/66 FS Perfoliate honeysuckle *Lonicera caprifolium* (*caprifolium*)

Honeysuckle, Dutch (planted): 20/3/55 *Lonicera periclymenum* varieties

Honeysuckle, French: 5/3/52 *Hedysarum coronarium*

Hop: 6/3/66 FS Humulus lupulus

Hoop'd: 23/4/55¶

Horse-radish: 28/9/54 *Armoracia rusticana* (*Raphanus rusticanus*)

Horse-tail, great water: 2/11/65 Marsh horsetail *Equisetum palustre* or Water horsetail *E. fluviatile*

Hot-bed (esp. for melons): 12/3/54¶

Hot well: 1753¶

Hottonia paulustris: 12/5/69 Water violet

Humulus lupulus: 23/7/69 Hop

Hyacinthus muscari: 6/4/68 *Muscari* spp.

Hyacinthus non-scriptus: 19/4/68 Bluebell *Hyacinthoides non-scriptus*

Hyacinths: 3/3/66 FS *Hyacinthus* spp.

Hyacinthus Anglicus: 25/4/66 FS ?Bluebell *Hyacinthoides non-scriptus* (Hare's-bells)

Hyacinthus orientalis: 20/4/68 Common Hyacinth

Hybiscus syriacus: 30/8/68 *Hibiscus syriacus* syn. *Althaea frutex*

Hyoscyamus niger: 14/4/66 FS, 27/6/68 Henbane

Hypericum androsaemum: 6/8/89 Tutsan

Hypericum Constantinopolitanum: 7/8/68 ?Rose of Sharon *Hypericum calcinum*

Hypericum elodes: 22/7/68 Marsh St John's wort

Hypericum humifusum: 29/7/60 Trailing St John's wort

Hypericum perforatum: 26/6/68 Perforate St John's wort

Hypericum procumbens minus: 2/11/65 ?*Hypericum humifusum*

Hypericum pulchrum: 26/7/66 FS Slender St John's wort (Upright St John's wort)

Hypopitys lutea: 7/7/66 FS¶ Yellow bird's-nest *Monotropa hypopitys*

Hyssop: 21/7/66 FS *Hyssopus officinalis*

Ichneumon: 11/4/66 FS Family *Ichneumonidae* Flies and wasps whose larvae are parasitic

Ilex: 6/1/55 Holly *Ilex aquifolium* (*agrifolium*)

Impatiens balsamina: 13/4/51, 23/8/68 Balsam

Inula dysenterica: 2/8/68 Common fleabane *Pulicaria dysenterica*

Iris foetidissima: 18/11/65 Gladdon, Gladwin iris (Stinking flag flower, *Iris foetida*)

Iris palustris pallida: 11/6/66 FS, Yellow flag *Iris pseudacorus*
Iris pseudacorus: 11/6/66 FS, 2/6/68 Yellow flag (*Iris palustris pallida*)
Iris Xiphium: 19/6/68 Bulbous xiphium
Iulus terrestris: 2/4/70 Millipede
Ivy: 30/9/65, 18/9/72¶ *Hedera helix*
Ivy, ground-: 12/3/66 FS *Glechoma hederacea* (*Calamintha humilior . . .*)
Jacinth: 18/2/57 Hyacinth *Hyacinthus* spp.
Jacione montana: 11/7/68 Sheep's-bit scabious *Jasione montana*
Jack-by-the-hedge: 12/3/66 FS *Alliaria petiolata* (*hesperis allium . . .*)
Jakes: 17/10/66 FS Lavatory
Jasmin, dwarf-yellow: 7/6/66 FS *Jasminum humile* 'Revolutum' (*Jasminum humile luteum*)
Jasmine, Persian: 17/4/66 FS¶ ?Persian lilac *Syringa persica* or 22/3/56,¶ 24/10/59
      White jasmine *Jasminum officinale*
Jasmine, white: 2/8/66 FS, 24/10/59 *Jasminum officinale*
Jasmine, yellow: 24/10/59 Winter jasmine *Jasminum nudiflorum*
Jessamin, Persian: 9/3/51 Persian jasmine
Jobb: 21/2/63 Cartload
Jonquils: 24/10/57 *Narcissus jonquilla*
Judas tree: 5/4/56 *Cercis siliquastrum*
Juglans regia: 18/5/68 Walnut tree
Juniperus: 16/5/66 FS Juniper *Juniperus communis*
Jynx: 3/3/66 FS, 30/4/69¶ Wryneck *Jynx torquilla*
J. W, Mrs: 28/10/69 Mrs John White, GW's sister-in-law
Kelsey: 6/4/51 Selborne farmer
Kite: 13/11/71¶, 17/4/68¶ Red kite *Milvus milvus*
Kiver: 14/5/68¶ Wooden tub
Knapweed: 22/8/65 *Centaurea nigra*
Knapweed, greater: 17/6/66 FS *Centaurea scabiosa* (*Jacea major . . .*)
Knawel: 15/5/66 FS *Scleranthus annuus*
Knight's ponds, James: 6/7/66 FS Extensive ponds NW of Selborne village
Knotweed: 14/7/66 FS *Polygonum aviculare* (*Polygonum mas vulg:*)
Laburnum: 29/3/54 *Laburnum anagyroides*
Lacerta vulgaris: 4/4/68 ?Viviparous lizard *Lacerta vivipara*
Ladies-treaces: 5/9/65¶ Autumn lady's tresses *Spiranthes spiralis*
Lady-cows: 3/3/66 FS (*Scarabaei subrotundi*)
Ladypease: 23/5/51 Sweet peas *Lathyrus odoratus* (Painted Lady peas)
Ladysmocks, common: 2/5/66 FS see *Cardamine pratensis*
Lady's bedstraw: 27/8/65 *Galium verum*
Lamium album: 21/4/68 White dead-nettle
Lamium folio caulem . . .: 16/5/66 FS Henbit dead-nettle *Lamium amplexicaule* (Great hen-bit)
Lamium vulgare rubrum: 6/3/66 FS Red dead-nettle *Lamium purpureum*
Lampsana: 31/10/65 Nipplewort *Lapsana communis*
Lampyris noctiluca: 26/5/68¶, 2/6/73 Glow-worm (*Cantharis noctiluca*)
Land rail: 10/9/69¶ Corncrake *Crex crex*
Landsprings: 12/3/64¶
Lang de boeuf = ox's tongue: 16/10/65 Bristly ox-tongue *Picris echioides* (*Hieracium
      echioides . . .*)
Lanius minor ruffus: 21/5/68 Woodchat *Lanius senator*
Lanius excubitor: 15/2/72 Great grey shrike (*Lanius . . . cinereus major . . .*)
Lapwing: 24/4/66 *Vanellus vanellus* (*capella sive vanellus*)
Larch (sown): 21/3/55 *Larix* spp.
Lark, sky: 30/10/65 *Alauda arvensis*
Lark, wood: 30/10/65 *Lullula arborea* (*Alauda arborea*)
Larkspur: 23/4/51 *Delphinium consolida*

Larus maximus . . .: 11/4/72 Greater black-back gull *Larus marinus*

Larus ridibundus: 13/3/71 Black-headed gull

Lassam (Lasham): GW's manservant

Lathraea squammaria: 4/5/72¶ Toothwort *Lathraea squamaria*

Lathyrus Aphaca: 18/7/69 Yellow vetchling *Lathyrus aphaca*

Lathyrus earth-nut: 19/3/59 Everlasting pea *Lathyrus latifolius*

Lathyrus luteus . . .: 12/6/66 FS Yellow vetchling *Lathyrus aphaca* (common yellow bastard-vetchling)

Laurel: 10/4/54 *Prunus laurocerasus* (*lauro-cerasus*)

Laurel, wood: 22/10/54, 3/3/66 FS Spurge laurel *Daphne laureola*

Lauristines: 25/10/53 Laurustinus *Viburnum tinus*

Lavender: 21/7/66 FS *Lavandula* spp.

Lavender cotton: 22/3/56¶ *Santolina chamaecyparissus*

Lavants: 7/12/68¶

Leek: 22/3/51 *Allium porrum*

Leontodon autumnale: 18/8/68 Autumn hawkbit *Leontodon autumnalis*

Leontodon taraxacum: 16/1/68 Dandelions *Taraxacum* agg.

Lepismae: 14/1/68 Silverfish *Lepisma saccharina*

Lettuce, Coss: 5/3/52 Cos lettuce *Lactuca sativa*

Lettuce, wild: 31/10/65 Wall lettuce *Mycelis muralis* (*Lactuca sylvestris murorum* . . .)

Leucojum: 25/1/66 FS Wallflower *Cheiranthus cheiri*

Libellulae, libella: 22/5/66 FS, 25/5/68 Damselfly *?Agrion virgo*

Ligustrum vulgare: 20/4/66 FS, 3/7/68 Wild privet

Lilac: *Syringa* spp.

Lilac, privet-leaved: 17/4/66 FS¶ Persian lilac *Syringa persica* (Persian jasmine, *Syringa ligustrifolio*)

Lilium convallium: 12/5/66 FS Lily-of-the-valley *Convallaria majalis*

Lilium martagon: 1/7/68 Turk's cap lily

Limax argrestis: 24/2/68 Slug

Lithospermum officinale: 21/5/66 FS Common gromwell (Gromil, Gromel)

Lithrum salicaria: 22/7/66 FS, 6/7/68 Purple loose-strife *Lythrum salicaria* (*Salicaria vulg: purpurea*)

Loaf cabbage: 23/1/51¶ Sugar loaf cabbage *Brassica oleracea* varieties

Locusta: 28/3/66 FS Grasshopper family *Acrididae ?Locusta migratoria*

London pride: 25/6/66 FS *Saxifraga spathularis* × *umbrosa*

Long: 24/1/61¶ The mason who built the Ha-ha

Loose-strife, purple spiked: 22/7/66 FS, 6/7/68 Purple loose-strife *Lythrum salicaria* (*Salicaria vulg: purpurea* . . ., *Lysimachia purpurea*)

Loose-strife, yellow: 16/10/65 *Lysimachia vulgaris*

Lonicera periclymenum: 17/1/68 Honeysuckle

Lord Keeper: A title held by Sir Robert Henley, soon to become Lord Chancellor

Loti corniculatae major: 5/7/66 FS Greater bird's-foot trefoil *Lotus pedunculatus*

Lotus pentaphyllos . . .: 30/5/66 FS Bird's-foot trefoil *Lotus corniculatus*

Lovage: 3/6/66 FS *Ligusticum scoticum* (*levisticum*)

Love-lies-bleeding: 21/5/54 *Amaranthus caudatus* (Pendulous amaranths)

Loxiae curvirostrae: 5/10/70 Crossbill *Loxia curvirostra*

Lunaria . . .: 20/4/66 FS Honesty *Lunaria annua*

Lupi nigri: 8/3/66 FS Wolf spiders *Lupi negri*

Lupine: 23/5/51 Lupin *Lupinus perenne*

Luscinia: 17/4/66 FS Nightingale *Luscinia megarhynchos*

Lychnidea: 10/11/66 FS *Phlox* spp.

Lychnis sylvestris: 28/10/65 Red campion *Silene dioica*

Lychnis: 15/10/54 Scarlet lychnis, Maltese cross *Lychnis chalcedonica* or double ragged robin *L. flos-cuculi flore-pleno*

Lychnis flos cuculi: 29/5/68 Ragged robin *Lychnis flos-cuculi*
Lycoperdon borista: 17/6/68 Puff ball L*ycoperdon caelatum*
Lycoperdon tuber: 13/7/68 Puffball spp.
Lysimachia nemorum: 30/6/68 Yellow pimpernel
Lysimachia nummularia: 13/7/68 Creeping Jenny (Money-wort, herb two-pence *Nummularia major lutea*)
Lysimachia purpurea: 16/10/65 Purple loose-strife *Lythrum salicaria*
Lysimachia: 16/10/65 Yellow loose-strife *Lysimachia vulgaris* (Yellow willow-herb, *Lysimachia lutea*)
Madder (cultivated): 16/10/65 *Rubia tinctorum*
Madder, little field: 22/11/65 Field madder *Sherardia arvensis*
Mallow, common: 28/10/65 *Malva sylvestris*
Mallow, dwarf: 15/6/66 FS *Malva neglecta* (*Malva sylvestris folio rotundo*)
Mallow, marsh: 16/7/66 FS, 4/8/66 FS *Althaea officinalis* (*Althaea vulgaris*)
Mallow, oriental: 6/3/52 ?sp.
Mallow, tree: 26/4/57 *Lavatera arborea*
Mallow, Venetian: 5/4/56¶
Mallow vervain: 3/5/66 FS ?Musk mallow *Malva moschata* (*Alcea vulgare*)
Malus armeniaca: Apricot
Malus persica: Peach
Malva moschata: 30/6/68 Musk mallow
Malva sylvestris rotundifolia: 28/10/65 Common mallow *Malva sylvestris*
Mareland: Bentley, nr Farnham, GW's brother Benjamin's house from Novr. 1792
Marigold, African: 23/5/51 *Tagetes erecta*
Marigold, corn-: 16/7/66 FS *Chrysanthemum segetum*
Marigold, French: 23/3/51 *Tagetes patula*
Marjoram: 30/9/65 *Origanum vulgare*
Marrubium aquaticum: 16/10/65 ?Gypsywort *Lycopus europaeus* (Water hoarhound)
Marrubium nigrum: 16/10/65 Black horehound *Ballota nigra* (Stinking hoarhound)
Marrubium vulg: 23/7/68 White Horehound *Marrubium vulgare*
Martagon: 1/7/68 Martagon lily *Lilium martagon*
Martens: 24/8/65¶, 2/10/71¶, 3/11/72¶, House martins *Delichon urbica*
Martins, bank: 30/5/70, 19/4/68 Sand martins *Riparia riparia*
Marvel of Peru: 10/4/56 *Mirabilis jalapa*
Marygold, marsh-: 14/3/66 FS *Caltha palustris* (*Populago*)
Matricaria parthenium: 15/3/66 FS Feverfew *Chrysanthemum parthenium*
Matted: 23/4/55¶
Maudlin: 7/8/66 FS Ox-eye daisy *Chrysanthemum leucanthemum*
Mays-seed: 22/3/51¶ Maize or sweet corn *Zea Mays* (Indian wheat)
Mayweed, stinking: 28/10/65 Stinking chamomile *Anthemis cotula* (*Chamaemelum foetidum*)
Mazagon bean: 20/11/54¶ Broad bean variety *Vicia faba*
Meadowsweet: 14/3/66 *Filipendula ulmaria* (*Ulmaria*)
Medica: 16/5/66 FS Lucerne *Medicago sativa*
Medlars: 26/10/64¶ *Mespilus germanica*
Melampyrum sylvaticum: 9/7/68 Crested Cow-wheat
Melissa nepeta: 7/7/68 Lemon balm *Melissa officinalis*
Melon: 22/3/51, 4/4/54¶ *Cucumis melo*
Melvus aeruginosus: 18/7/69 Marsh harrier (moor buzzard) *Circus aeruginosus*
Mentha aquatica: 18/9/66 FS Water mint
Mentha longifolia: 5/8/69 Horse mint
Mentha vulgaris: 13/3/66 FS ?Corn mint (Common mint) *Mentha arvensis*
Menyanthes trifoliata: 16/5/66 FS Bogbean
Meonstoke: Village on R. Meon 4m E of Bishops Waltham. John Mulso lived at the Rectory there from 1771.

Mercurialis: 24/9/65 Annual mercury *Mercurialis annua* (French mercury)
Mercurialis perennis: 9/3/66 FS Dog's mercury (*Cynocrambe*)
Mercury, French: 24/9/65 Annual mercury *Mercurialis annua*
Merula torquata: 25/9/68¶, 13/4/69¶ Ring ouzel *Turdus torquatus*
Merula vulgaris: 8/3/66 FS Blackbird *Turdus merula*
Mespilus German: 11/4/66 FS Common or Nottingham medlar *Mespilus germanica*
Mezereon: 4/8/60¶ *Daphne mezereum*
Mice, field: 1/12/67¶ Harvest mice *Micromys minutus*
Mignonette: 8/7/66 FS¶ *Reseda odorata* (*Reseda aegyptiaca* . . .)
Milkwort, common: 5/566 FS *Polygala vulgaris*
Miller, Philip: 21/11/54¶ Celebrated gardener at the Chelsea Physic Garden and author of *The Gardener's Dictionary*
Miller's thumb: 19/11/66 FS Fish *Cottus gobio*
Milvus aeruginosus: 18/3/73¶ Red kite *Milvus milvus*
Mint, corn: 16/8/66 FS *Mentha arvensis* (*Mentha sive calamintha* . . .)
Mint: 28/9/54 *Mentha* spp.
Missel-bird: 5/3/66 FS Mistle thrush *Turdus viscivorus* (Shrite, storm-cock)
Mole: 1/2/66 FS *Talpa europaea*
Monedula: 7/3/66 FS Jackdaw *Corvus monedula*
Money-wort: 29/8/66 FS Creeping Jenny *Lysimachia nummularia* (Herb two-pence)
Moor buzzard: 18/7/69 Marsh harrier *Circus aeruginosus*
Moor hen: 10/6/74 *Gallinula chloropus*
Morel, stinking: 1/7/66 FS, 21/9/66 FS Stinkhorn fungus *Phallus impudicus*
Moreton Pinkney: Northamptonshire parish of which GW was absentee Curate from 1757
Moschatel: 17/3/66 FS, 7/4/68 *Adoxa moschatellina*
Motacilla atricapilla: 10/4/67 Blackcap
Motacilla phoenicurus: 10/4/67 Redstart *Phoenicurus phoenicurus*
Motacilla trochillus: 4/4/67¶, 15/4/68¶ Chiff-chaff and other leaf warblers *Phylloscopus collybita* etc. (Willow wren)
Mother of thyme: 28/10/65 Wild thyme *Thymus serpyllum*
Motherwort: 16/7/66 FS *Leonurus cardiaca* (*Cardiaca*)
Mountain-elder: 28/2/56 Red-berried elder *Sambucus racemosa*
Mouse, field: 4/12/67 Harvest mouse *Micromys minutus*
Mouse-ear, creeping: 29/10/65 Mouse-ear hawkweed *Pilosella officinarum*
Mugwort: 12/8/66 FS *Artemisia vulgaris*
Mulberry: 15/3/51, 25/7/53¶ *Morus nigra*
Mullein: 28/10/54 *Verbascum thapsus*
Mullein, moth: 16/10/65 *Verbascum blattaria*
Mullein, great white: 25/6/66 FS *Verbascum lychnitis* (High taper, cow's lungwort)
Mullein, moth: 16/10/65 *Verbascum blattaria*
Mulso, Edward: 13/7/63 Brother of GW's friend John Mulso
Mulso, John: Contemporary of GW at Oriel College, Oxford, and a lifelong friend
Mulso, Hester: John Mulso's sister
Mulso, Mrs: 27/9/57¶
Mulso, Thomas: 7/7/66 Eldest brother of John Mulso
Murdoch Myddleton: 22/3/57 Nurseryman – many plants GW bought from him failed
Musca apiformis . . .: 17/10/66 FS Fly ?sp.
Musca bipennis . . .: 17/10/66 FS Fly ?sp.
Musca bombyliiformis: 12/4/66 FS Hoverfly *Eristalis intricarius*
Musca Caesar: 2/6/71 Fly sp. Green-bottle *Lucilia caesar*
Musca carnaria: 27/4/66 FS Flesh fly *Sarcophaga carnaria*
Musca meridiana: 18/9/67 *Mesembrina meridiana*
Musca mystacea: 4/8/69 Hoverfly *Volucella bombylans*
Musca stercoraria: 6/3/69 Yellow dung fly *Scathophaga stercoraria*

Musca tenax: 8/4/68 Drone fly *Eristalis tenax* (Jakes fly)

Musca vomitoria: 19/5/71 Flesh fly *Sarcophaga carnaria*

Mustard, hedge: 9/6/66 FS ?*Sisymbrium officinale* or ?Treacle mustard *Erisimum cheiranthoides*

Mustard, white: 27/4/51 *Sinapis alba*

Myosotis arvensis: 30/10/65 Field forget-me-not (Mouse-ear scorpion grass)

Myosotis scorpiodes: 20/4/66 FS ?Field forget-me-not *Myosotis arvensis*

Myosotis scorpioides palustris: 16/10/65 Water forget-me-not *Myosotis scorpioides*

Narcissus jonquilla: 20/4/68 Wild jonquil

Narcissus pseudonarcissus: 25/3/68 Wild daffodil

Nasturtium: 13/4/51, 11/11/72¶ *Tropaeolum minus*

Natrix torquata: 17/10/66 FS Grass snake *Natrix natrix*

Necessary: 21/3/55¶ Euphemism for lavatory

Nepeta major: 16/6/66 FS, 9/7/68 Catmint *Nepeta cataria* (*Nepeta vulg:*)

Nettle, common: 25/6/66 *Urtica dioica*

Nettle, dead: 28/10/65 *Lamium* spp.

Nettle, red dead-: 6/3/66 FS *Lamium purpureum* (*Lamium vulgare rubrum*)

Nettle, white dead-: 6/3/66 FS *Lamium album*

Nettle, yellow dead-: 27/4/66 Yellow archangel *Galeobdolon luteum*

Nettle, hedge: 12/12/65 Hedge woundwort *Stachys sylvatica* (*Galeopsis legitima* . . .)

Newton, Newton Valence: 27/5/69 Village 2m from Selborne. Edmund White became Vicar 1784.

Nigella: 28/6/66 Love-in-a-mist *Nigella damascena* (Devil in a bush) or *N. hispanica* (*Nigella romana*)

Nightshade, deadly: 9/9/65 *Atropa belladonna*

Nightshade, enchanters: 3/10/65 *Circaea lutetiana*

Nightshade, garden: 26/7/66 FS Black nightshade *Solanum nigrum* (*Solanum vulg:*)

Nightshade, woody: 1/6/66 FS *Solanum dulcamara*

Nipplewort: 31/10/65, 28/6/66 FS *Lapsana communis* (*Lampsana*)

North Warnboro': 23/10/51 North Warnborough, a village nr. Odiham

Nummularia major lutea: 29/8/66 FS Creeping Jenny *Lysimachia nummularia* (Money wort, herb two-pence)

Nuthatch: 10/12/67 *Sitta europaea*

Nux juglans: 13/5/66 FS Walnut *Juglans regia* (Wallnut)

Nymphaea lutea alba: 1/7/66 FS White water lily *Nymphaea alba*

Odiham: 5/3/69 Hampshire village 7m E of Basingstoke

Oedicnemus: 16/8/65¶ Stone curlew: *Burhinus oedicnemus*

Oenanthe fistulosa: 23/7/68 Tubular water dropwort

Oenanthe: 12/9/69 Wheatears *Oenanthe oenanthe*

Oenas sive vinago: 8/12/68 Wood pigeon (NHS) *Columba palumbus*

Oenas sive vinago: 10/11/69 Stock dove *Columba oenas*

Oenothera biennis: 16/7/68 Evening primrose

Oestrus bovis: 3/8/68¶ Cattle warble fly *Hypoderma bovis*

Oestrus sive curvicauda: 8/8/70¶ ?Horse-bot fly *Gasterophilus intestinalis*

Onagra: 6/7/66 FS Broad-leaved tree-primrose *Oenothera* spp.

Onion: 22/3/51 *Allium cepa*

Oniscus asellus: 23/1/68 Woodlouse

Onobrychis viciifolia: 9/6/66 FS, 20/4/68¶ Sainfoin

Ophioglossum vulgatum: 17/5/66 FS Adder's-tongue

Ophrys apifera: 4/7/70 Bee orchid

Opulus: 22/10/54 Guelder rose *Viburnum opulus*

Orange, mock: 7/6/66 FS (*Syringa*)

Orchis alba . . .: 21/6/61 Lesser butterfly orchid *Platanthera bifolia*

Orchis, butterfly: 13/6/66 *Platanthera bifolia* (*Orchis alba bifolia minor* . . .)

Orchis conopsea: 3/6/69 Fragrant orchid *Gymnadenia conopsea*
Orchis, female handed-: 14/6/66 FS *Dactylorhiza maculata (Orchis palmata . . . folio maculato)*
Orchis . . . maculatis: 29/4/66 FS Early-purple orchid *Orchis mascula*
Orchis morio: 16/5/66 FS Green winged orchid (Female fools-stones)
Orchis. . . . pyramidali: 8/7/66 FS Pyramidal orchid *Anacamptis pyramidalis*
Origanum vulgare: 26/7/68 Marjoram
Ornithogalum umbellatum: 29/4/66 FS Common star-of-Bethlehem
Orobanche major: 4/7/68 Greater broomrape *Orobanche rapum-genistae*
Orobus sylvaticus . . . glabris: 19/4/66 FS Bitter vetchling *Lathyrus montanus* (Wood pease)
Orpine: 29/4/66 FS *Sedum telephium (Anacampseros . . .)*
Ortygometra: 6/9/68 Land rail, Corncrake *Crex crex*
Osprey: 10/4/73 *Pandion haliaetus*
Outlet: Field, garden or enclosure attached to a house.
Owl, barn: 9/9/65¶ *Tyto alba*
Ox's tongue: 16/10/65 Bristly ox-tongue *Picris echioides (Hieracium echioides)*
Oxys: 13/3/66 FS Wood sorrel *Oxalis acetosella*
Painted Lady peas: 16/4/52 Sweet pea *Lathyrus odoratus*
Palumbus torquatus: 17/3/68 Wood Pigeon *Columba palumbus*
Pansy: 19/5/66 FS Wild pansy *Viola tricolor*
Pansy, small flowered: 22/11/65 *Viola arvensis (V. bicolor arvensis)*
Paper, oiled: 13/4/51¶
Papilio Atalanta: 3/9/69, 15/9/72¶ Red Admiral *Vanessa atalanta*
Papilio brascicae: 28/4/71 Large white *Pieris brassicae*
Papilio c album: 25/5/70 Comma butterfly *Polygonia c-album*
Papilio cardamines: 14/5/70 Orange-tip *Anthocharis cardamines*
Papilio cinxia: 3/8/69 Glanville fritillary *Melitaea cinxia*
Pap: Hyale: 4/9/69 Pale clouded yellow *Colias hyale*
Papilio Io: 30/12/69 Peacock butterfly *Inachis io*
Papilio Machaon: 14/9/69¶ Swallowtail
Papilio maera: 2/6/70 Large wall *Lassiommata maera*
Pap: paphia: 30/8/69 Silver-washed fritillary *Argynnis paphia*
Papilio Phlaeas: 29/8/69 Small copper *Lycaena phlaeas*
Papilio rhamni: 4/3/69 Brimstone *Gonepteryx rhamni*
Pap: semele: 15/8/69 Grayling *Hipparchia semele*
Papilio sulphureus: 8/3/66 FS ?Brimstone butterfly *Gonepteryx rhamni* or ?Clouded yellow *Colias croceus*
Papilio urticae: 2/4/68, 27/1/70¶ Small tortoiseshell *Aglais urticae*
Parnassia: 9/9/65, 2/11/65 Grass of Parnassus *Parnassia palustris*
Parsley, corn: 4/8/66 FS *Petroselinum segetum (sium arvense . . .)*
Parsley, small corn-: 1/10/66 FS Spreading hedge-parsley *Torilis arvensis (caucalis segetum minor)*
Parsley, Dutch: 22/3/51, ?Hamburg parsley *Carum petroselinum fusiformis*
Parsley, fool's: 6/3/66 FS *Aethusa cynapium (Cicutaria tenuifolia)*
Parsley, hedge: 22/7/66 FS Upright hedge-parsley *Torilis japonica (Caucalis minor . . .)*
Parsley piert: 21/5/66 FS *Aphanes arvensis (Percepier anglorum)*
Parsons, Farmer: 22/4/55 A Selborne farmer who may have been a tenant of GW's
Parsnep: 22/3/51 Parsnip *Pastinaca sativa*
Parsnep, wild: 9/7/66 FS *Pastinaca sativa (Pastinaca sylvestris . . .)*
Parson: 6/4/56 Farming tenant of GW
Partriges: 24/8/65, 6/3/66 FS Partridges *Perdix perdix*
Parus ater: 1/8/67 Coal tit (Colemouse)
Parus caeruleus: 3/3/69 Blue tit (Tom-tit, titmouse)
Parus caudatus: 3/3/66 FS Long-tailed tit *Aegithalos caudatus* (Long-tailed titmouse)
Parus major: 1/2/66 FS Great tit (Great titmouse)
Parus palustris: 6/3/70 Marsh tit

Passer arundinaceus minor: 13/5/69¶ Sedge warbler *Acrocephalus scirpaceus* (less reed-sparrow)
Passer torquatus: 13/5/69, 28/11/71¶ Reed bunting *Emberiza schoeniclus*
Passer troglodytes: 6/3/66 FS Wren *Troglodytes troglodytes*
Passion-flower: 24/1/51 *Passiflora* spp.
Paconia officinalis: Paeony This species is now rare
Papaver rhoeas: 24/6/68 Common poppy
Pastinaca sylvestris: 12/7/68 Wild parsnip *Pastinaca sativa*
Pease, everlasting, wild: 14/7/66 FS *Lathyrus sylvestris* (*Lathyri majoris* . . .)
Pease, everlasting: 5/8/52 Broad-leaved everlasting pea *Lathyrus latifolius*
Pease, lady: see Painted Lady pease
Pease, wood: 29/4/66 FS¶/ Bitter vetch *Lathyrus montanus* (*Orobus sylvaticus* . . .)
Pease, marrow-fat: 1/4/51¶ Marrow fat peas *Pisum sativum*
Pedicularis palustris: 2/5/66 FS Marsh lousewort
Pedicularis sylvatica: 15/4/68 Lousewort
Penny-cross: 11/6/66 FS Field penny-cress *Thlaspi arvense* (*Thlaspi Dioscoridis*)
Pennyroyal (mint): 28/9/54 *Mentha pulegium*
Peony: see Piony
Perdix cinerea: 6/3/66 FS Partridge *Perdix perdix*
Periwinkle, lesser: 12/3/66 FS¶ *Vinca minor*
Persian-jessamin: 9/3/51 See Jasmine, Persian
Persicaria: 24/10/54 ?*Polygonum persicaria*
Petrifactions: 8/10/71 Fossils
Pewit-gull . . .: 28/12/71¶
Peziza acetabulum: 5/3/66 FS, 23/11/68 Fungus of order *Pezizales*, a smallish cup fungi
Phalaenae: 14/12/69 Moths
Phalaena pacta: 31/8/69 Moth ?sp.
Phalaena russula: 1/9/69 Moth ?sp.
Phallus impudicus: 1/7/66 FS Stinkhorn fungus
Pheasant: 3/5/66 FS *Phasianus colchicus*
Philadelphus coronarius: 5/6/68 Mock orange, orange blossom 22/3/56¶ (syringa)
Phlomis fruticosa: 15/6/66 FS, 25/6/68 Jerusalem sage
Phryganea nigra: 3/6/68 Caddis fly (Cadew fly)
Phlox: 7/8/66 FS *Phlox* spp. (*Lychnidea, Phlox folius lineari* . . .)
Phlox maculata: 31/7/68 Species from eastern USA
Phyllitis scolopondrium: 31/10/65 Hart's-tongue fern
Physic Garden: 26/3/68¶
Phyteuma orbicularis: 16/7/66 FS, 5/11/71¶ Round-headed rampion *Phyteuma tenerum* also
    Rapunculus scabiosae
Picris hieracioides: 4/8/68 Hawkweed Ox-tongue
Pignut: 17/3/66 FS *Bunium bulbocastanum*
Pimpernel, red: 24/10/66 FS see *Anagallis arvensis*
Pimpernel, yellow: 30/5/66 FS *Lysimachia nemorum*
Pimpinella saxifraga: 8/9/66 FS Burnet saxifrage
Pilewort: 25/11/65 Lesser celandine *Ranunculus ficaria* (*Chelidonium minus*)
Pine, Weymouth: 2/5/66 FS *Pinus strobus*
Pines: 22/12/68¶ Pineapple *Ananas comosus*
Pinks: 21/10/54 *Dianthus* spp.
Pinks, Double China: 11/4/58 ?*Dianthus chinensis*
Pinks, Indian: 26/5/58 ?*Dianthus sinensis*
Pinks, meadow: 11/6/66 FS Ragged Robin *Lychnis flos-cuculi* (*Lychnis plumaria* . . .)
Pinks, pheasant-eyed: 27/7/63¶
Pinus abies: 24/5/73 Common spruce *Picea abies*
Pinus larix: 14/4/68 Larch
Pinus sylvestris: 2/5/66 FS Scots pine

Piony: 19/3/66 FS Peony *Paeonia officinalis*

Plantago lanceolata: 29/4/66 FS Ribwort plantain

Plashed: 10/3/52¶ Pleached

Plies: 6/2/58 Bends

Podura fimetaria: 4/3/69 Springtail *Folsomia fimetaria*

Polemonium caeruleum: 17/6/66 FS Jacob's ladder (Greek Valerian)

Polyanths: 4/8/56, 2/10/58¶ Polyanthus *Primula polyantha*

Polygala vulgaris: 5/5/66 FS Common milkwort

Polygonatum: 4/4/66 FS *Polygonatum multiflorum* Common Solomon's seal (*Polygonatum vulgare*)

Polygonum fagopyrum: 28/7/66 FS, 21/7/68 Black bindweed *Polygonum convolvulus* (*Fegopyrum scandens sylvestre*)

Polypody, common: 18/11/65 *Polypodium vulgare*

Pondweed, broad-leaved: 19/5/66 FS *Potamogeton nutans*

Poppy: 10/3/52

Poppy, corn: 6/6/66 FS *Papaver rhoeas* (*Papaver erraticum* . . .)

Poppy, Venetian: 17/4/55 ?*Papaver orientale*

Populus tremula: 12/3/73 Aspen

Potamogiton latifolium: 19/5/66 FS Broad-leaved pondweed *Potamogeton natans*

Poterium sanguisorba: 29/5/68 Salad burnet

Prenanthes muralis: 2/7/68 Purple lettuce *Prenanthes purpurea*

Primrose: 22/2/66 FS¶ *Primula vulgaris* (*Primula veris*)

Primula veris: 22/2/66¶, 8/4/66 FS Cowslip

Primula vulgaris: 22/2/66 FS¶ Primrose

Prunella vulgaris: 29/10/65 Self-heal

Prunus armeniaca: 25/3/68 Apricot

Prunus avium: 24/4/68 Wild cherry

Prunus cerasus: 18/4/68 Dwarf cherry

Prunus domestica: 19/4/68 Plum

Prunus lusitanica: 25/6/68 Portugal laurel

Prunus spinosa: 19/3/66 FS Blackthorn, sloe (*Prunus sylvestris*)

Ptinus pectinicornis: 7/8/70 Woodworm *Anobium punctatum*

Pulmonaria officinalis: 14/4/66 FS, 16/4/68 Lungwort (bugloss-cowslips)

Pulex irritans: 21/2/68, 4/6/70¶ Human flea

Purslain: 13/4/51¶ Purslane *Portulaca oleracea*

Pyram: Camp: 14/6/63 Pyramidal campanula, bellflower *Campanula pyramidalis*

Pyrus communis: 26/4/69 Wild pear

Pyrus malus: 3/5/68 Crab apple *Malus sylvestris*

Pyrus sativa: 21/4/68 ?Pear

Quaking grass: 28/5/66 FS *Briza media* (*Gramen tremulum*)

Quercus robur: 15/5/68 Pedunculate oak

Quince: 26/10/51 *Cydonia oblonga*

Quincunx: 5/3/52¶ Pattern like a 5-dot domino

Radishes: 24/1/51, 16/4/52¶ *Raphanus sativus*

Ragged Robin (double form in garden): 15/10/54 *Lychnis flos-cuculi*

Ragweed: 12/3/66 FS Ragwort *Senecio jacobaea* (*Jacobaea*)

Ragwort, hoary perennial: 17/6/66 FS Hoary ragwort *Senecio erucifolius*

Ragwort, water-: 18/7/66 FS *Senecio aquaticus* (*Jacobaea latifolia* . . .)

Ragwort, wild/common: 28//8/65 *Senecio jacobaea*

Rail, land: 10/9/69¶ Corncrake *Crex crex*

Rampion, with scabious head: 16/7/66 FS Sheep's-bit *Jasione montana* (*Rapunculus scabiosae*)

Ramson: 9/4/66 FS *Allium ursinum*

Rana bufo: 28/3/68 ?Common toad *Bufo bufo*

Rana temporaria: 13/3/66 FS Common frog

Ranunculus aquatilis . . .: 24/4/66 FS Water crowfoot ?*Ranunculus aquatilis*

Ranunculus aquatilis hederaceus: 24/4/66 Ivy-leaved water crowfoot *Ranunculus hederaceus*
Ranunculus arvorum echinatus: 22/7/66 FS Corn buttercup *Ranunculus arvensis* (Corn-crow foot)
Ranunculus flameus minor: 24/4/66 FS, 3/6/68 Lesser spearwort *Ranunculus flammula*
Ranunculus pratensis erectus acris: 14/3/66 FS Meadow buttercup *Ranunculus acris* (Upright meadow crowfoot)
Ranunculus pratensis repens: 3/6/66 FS Creeping buttercup *Ranunculus repens* (Creeping crowfoot)
Ranunculus repens bulbosus acris: 30/5/68 Bulbous buttercup *Ranunculus bulbosus*
Raven: 21/4/66 FS¶ *Corvus corax*
Raspberry: 21/1/53 *Rubus idaeus*
Red-breast: 13/1/66 Robin *Erithacus rubecula* (*Rubecula*)
Redstart: 8/5/66 FS *Phoenicurus phoenicurus*
Redwing: 13/1/66 *Turdus iliacus*
Reed, common: 23/8/66 FS *Phragmites communis* (*Arundo vallatoria*)
Reed-sparrow: 28/11/71¶ Reed bunting *emberiza schoeniclus*
Regulus cristatus: 12/3/69 Goldcrest *Regulus regulus*
Regulus non-cristatus: 2/7/66 FS¶, 4/4/67¶, 15/4/68¶, Chiff-chaff and other leaf warblers *Phylloscopus collybita* etc.
Regulus non-crist (cristatus) minor (minimus): 4/4/67¶ 15/4/68¶ Chiff-chaff *Phylloscopus collybita* (Willow wren *Motacilla trochillus*)
Regulus non cristatus cantat voce stridula locustae: 30/4/68¶ Wood warbler *Phylloscopus sibilatrix*
Reseda Aegyptiaca . . .: 8/7/66 FS¶ Garden mignonette *Reseda odorata*
Rest harrow: 22/8/65 *Ononis repens* (*Anonis* . . .)
Rest-harrow, prickly: 20/9/65 *Ononis spinosa* (*Anonis spinosa* . . .)
Rhamnus catharticus: 17/6/66 FS Buckthorn
Rhubarb: 16/9/52 *Rheum raponticum*
Ribes grossularia: 5/4/68 Gooseberry *Ribes uva-crispa*
Ribes rubrum: 19/3/68 Red currant *Ribes rubrum* agg.
Ribbon-grass: 22/3/56 Gardener's garters *Phalaris arundinacea* var. *picta*
Ringmer: 8/4/52 S. Downs village in E. Sussex where GW's aunt Mrs Rebecca Snooke lived
Ring Ouzel: 25/9/68¶, 13/4/69¶ *Turdus torquatus* (*Merula torquata*)
Rocket: 24/10/57 Sweet rocket *Hesperis matronalis*
Rocket, base: 20/6/66 FS¶
Rocket, water-: 4/8/66 FS *Rorippa sylvestris* (*Nasturtium sylvestre*)
Rod hedge: 13/4/52¶
Roman, Mr: Rector of Faringdon
Rook: 7/3/66 FS *Corvus frugilegus* (*Cornus frugilega, Cornix frugilega*)
Rorella: 9/9/65¶ Sun-dew *Drosera* spp.
Rosa alba: 15/6/68 The 'white rose of York'
Rosa canina: 15/6/66 FS Dog rose
Rosa cinnamoniea: 6/6/68 The cinnamon rose (Miller)
Rosa centifolia: 13/6/66, 18/6/68 Moss rose, or Provence rose
Rosa gallica: 18/6/68 French rose
Rosa pimpinellifolia: 17/9/65¶ Burnet rose (*Rosa spinosissima*)
Rosa spinosissima: 17/9/65 FS, 16/6/66 FS Burnet rose *Rosa pimpinellifolia*
Rose, Austrian: 5/6/66 FS ?Austrian briar *Rosa foetida* (*Rosa sylveestris* . . .)
Rose, Burnet: 17/9/65¶ *Rosa pimpinellifolia*
Rose, dog: 15/6/66 FS Rosa canina
Rotherfield Park: 15/2/72 Lies to the east of East Tisted
Rubecula: 13/1/66 Robin *Erithacus rubecula* (Red-breast)
Rubus idaeus: 24/1/53 Raspberry
Rue: 9/7/66 FS *Ruta graveolens*
Ruscus aculeatus: 19/3/66 FS Butcher's broom
Ruticilla: 8/4/68 Redstart *Phoenicurus phoenicurus*

Sage: 14/6/66 FS *Salvia officinalis*
St. foin: 9/6/66 FS, 20/4/68¶ Sainfoin *Onobrychis viciifolia*
Saint foin fly: 17/6/92 ?sp (*Sphynx filipendulae*)
St John's wort: 26/6/68 Perforate St John's wort *Hypericum perforatum* (*Hypericum vulgaris*)
St John's wort, small procumbent: 2/11/65 Trailing St John's wort *Hypericum humifusum*
St Peter's wort: 24/10/54¶, 11/6/66 FS Square-stemmed St John's wort *Hypericum tetrapterum*
    (*Hypericum ascyron . . .*) or ?*Hypericum maculatum* Imperforate St John's wort
St Peter's wort, marsh: 11/8/67 Marsh St John's wort *Hypericum elodes* (*Ascyron supinum . . .*)
Salicaria: 13/5/69, 13/5/69¶ Sedge warbler *Acrocephalus scirpaceus* (Reed-sparrow *Passer
    arundinaceus*)
Salicornia: 23/8/66 FS Marsh samphire, glassworts *Salicornia* spp.
Salsafy: 6/4/51¶ Salsify *Tragapogon porrifolius* (*Tragapogon purpureum*)
Salix: 6/3/66 FS Willow spp.
Salix Babylonica: 17/3/66 FS¶ Weeping willow
Salvia pratensis: 7/768 Meadow clary
Sambucus: 3/2/66 FS Elder *Sambucus nigra*
Sambucus ebulus: 21/4/66 FS Dwarf elder (Danewort)
Sambucus nigra: 20/3/68 Elder
Sanicula sive diapensia: 10/5/66 FS Sanicle *Sanicula europaea*
Sanicle: 17/3/66 FS¶ *Sanicula europaea* (*Sanicula sive diapensia*)
Saponaria: 19/3/66 FS Soapwort *Saponaria officinalis*
Savoy: 15/4/55 Savoy cabbage *Brassica oleracea*
Saxifraga rotundifolia alba: 21/5/66 FS Meadow saxifrage *Saxifraga granulata* (White saxifrage)
Saxifrage, golden: 11/4/66 FS *Chrysosplenium spp.*
Saxifrage, meadow: 2/7/66 FS *Saxifraga granulata* (*Seseli pratense nostras*)
Saxifrage, white: 21/5/66 FS Medow saxifrage *Saxifraga granulata* (*Saxifraga rotundifolia alba*)
Scabiosa arvensis: 21/6/68 Field scabious *Knautia arvensis*
Scabiosa columbaria: 30/7/68 Small scabious (Less field scabious)
Scabiosa succisa: 29/8/66 FS, 17/8/68 Devilsbit scabious *Succisa pratensis* (*Scabiosa radice succisa*)
Scabiuss, blue: 2/9/65 *Scabiosa* spp.
Scandix semine rostrato: 14/4/66 FS Shepherd's needle *Scandix pecten-veneris*
Scarab, green: 23/5/66 FS ?Rose chafer *Cetonia aurata* (Rose fly)
Scarabaeus arboreus . . .: 16/5/66 FS Chafer ?*Phyllopertha horticola*
Scarabaeus auratus: 2/6/69 Rose chafer *Cetonia aurata*
Scarabaeus magnus . . .: 19/11/66 FS Dor beetle *Geotrupes stercorarius*
Scarabaeus melolontha: 22/5/68 Cockchafer *Melolontha melolontha*
Scarabaeus solstitialis: 30/6/68 Summer chafer *Amphimallon solstitiale* (fern chafer)
Scarabaeus stercorarius: 23/1/70 ?Dor beetle *Geotrupes stercorarius*
Scarabaei subrotundi: 3/3/66 FS Ladybirds family *Coccinellidae* (Lady-cows)
Scolopax: 9/9/65, 1/10/66 FS Woodcock *Scolopax rusticola*
Scolopendra forficata: 16/3/68 ?Centipede *Lithobius forficatus*
Scrophularia nodosa: 31/5/68 Common figwort
Scorpion grass, mouse-ear: 30/10/65 Field forget-me-not *Myosotis arvensis*
Scorpion grass, water: 16/10/65 Water forget-me-not *Myosotis scorpioides*
Scorpion senna: 6/11/51¶ Crown vetch *Coronilla emerus* (*Colutea scorpiodes*)
Scorzonera: 6/4/51¶ *Scorzonera hispanica*
Scrophularia: 11/10/65 Common figwort *Scrophularia nodosa*
Scutellaria galericulata: 23/7/68 Skullcap
Scutellaria minor: 1/8/69 Lesser skullcap
Sea-cale: 6/4/51¶ Sea Kale *Crambe maritima*
Sea pie: 10/4/73 Oystercatcher *Haematopus ostralegus*
Seacales cereale: 2/6/68 Barley *Hordeum* spp.
Sedum minus haematoides: 22/6/66 FS Biting stonecrop *Sedum acre* (Yellow stone-crop, prick
    madam)

Sedum, pyramidal: 3/6/66 FS ?sp.
Self-heal: 29/10/65 *Prunella vulgaris*
Senecio: 1/3/66 FS Groundsel *Senecio vulgaris*
Senecio jacobea: 12/3/66 FS Ragwort (Ragweed, *Jacobaea*)
Serapias latifolia: 6/8/68 Broad-leaved helleborine *Epipactis helleborine*
Serratula arvensis: 1/7/68 Creeping thistle ?*Cirsium arvense*
Service, wild: 20/10/66 FS, 26/12/61¶ *Sorbus torminalis*
Seseli carvifolia: 24/7/68 Cambridge milk parsley *Selinum carvifolia*
Seseli pratense nostras: 2/7/77 FS Meadow saxifrage *Saxifraga granulata*
Shepherd's needle: 14/4/66 FS *Scandix pecten-veneris* (*Scandix semine rostrato*)
Shepherd's purse: 29/3/66 FS *Capsella bursa-pastoris* (*Thlaspi bursa pastoris*)
Sherardia arvensis: 7/7/68 Field madder
Silverweed: 9/4/66 FS *Potentilla anserina* (*Pentaphylloides argentina . . .*)
Sitta: 10/12/67 Nuthatch *Sitta europaea*
Sinclus: 11/7/69 Little stint *Calidris minuta* (Stint or summer snipe)
Sium erectum . . .: 29/8/66 FS Greater water-parsnip *Sium latifolium*
Sium nodiflorum: 20/7/68 Lesser water-parsnip *Berula erecta*
Skie-lark: 30/10/65 Skylark *Alauda arvensis* (*Alauda vulgaris*)
Skillings: 26/4/65¶ Lean-tos.
Skirret: 6/4/51¶ *Sium sisarum*
Sliped: 6/4/51¶
Slips: 24/1/51 Cuttings
Sloe: 19/3/66 FS Blackthorn *Prunus spinosa*
Slow worm: 17/10/66 FS *Anguis fragilis* (Blind worm)
Smatch: 8/11/64 Taint, under the influence of
Snap-dragon: 30/8/65 *Antirrhinum* spp.
Sneeze-wort: 26/7/66 FS *Achillea ptarmica* (*Ptarmica*)
Snipe: 4/6/68¶ *Gallinago media*
Snooke, Henry: Husband of GW's Aunt Rebecca, died 1763
Snooke, Mrs Rebecca: GW's aunt who lived at Ringmer, Sussex
Snow-drop: 22/2/66 FS *Galanthus nivalis*
Soapwort: 22/10/54 *Saponaria officinalis* (*Lychnis saponaria*)
Soberton: 21/5/54 Hampshire village 2m S of Meonstoke
Solanum dulcamara: 11/6/68 Bittersweet
Solanum tuberosum: 16/7/66 FS Potato
Solidago canadensis: 1/9/72 Golden rod
Solidago virgaurea: 13/9/69 Golden rod
Solomon's seal: 24/10/57 *Polygonatum multiflorum*
Sorbus aucuparia: 27/4/68 Rowan
Sorrel, sheep's: 9/4/66 FS *Rumex acetosella* (*Lapathum acetosum . . .*)
Sorrell, wood-: 13/3/66 FS *Oxalis acetosella* (*Oxys*)
Southern wood: 9/9/65 *Artemisia abrotanum* (*Abrotanum*)
Sonchus arvensis: 3/8/68 Perennial sow-thistle
Southton: 18/6/66 Southampton
Sow-thistle, ivy leaved: 31/10/65 Smooth sow-thistle *Sonchus oleraceus*
Spanish beans: 7/1/51¶ Broad beans (long pod var.) *Vicia faba*
Sparganium erectum: 14/6/66 FS, 22/7/68 Branched bur-reed
Sparganium ramosum: 14/6/66 FS Branched bur-reed *Sparganium erectum* var. *erectum*
Sparred-on: 20/2/59 Fastened down
Sparrow, hedge: 9/3/66 FS *Prunella modularis*
Spear-worth, small: 30/8/65 Lesser spearwort *Ranunculus flammula* (*Ranunculus flammeus*)
Speedwell-chickweed: 4/3/66 FS ?Wall speedwell *Veronica arvensis*
Speedwell, ivy-leaved: 25/11/65 *Veronica hederifolia* (Small henbit, *Veronica flosculis . . .*)
Speedwell, male: 11/6/66 FS Heath speedwell *Veronica officinalis* (Fluellin, *Veronica mas*

supina . . .)

Speedwell, thyme-leaved: 7/5/66 FS *Veronica serpyllifolia* (*Veronica pratensis serpyllifolia*)

Speedwell, wall: 4/3/66 FS¶ ?*Veronica arvensis* (Speedwell chickweed)

Spergula arvensis: 21/7/68 Corn spurrey

Sphinx filipendula: 13/6/71¶ Six-spot burnet moth (*Zygaena filipendula*)

Spiderwort, Virginian: 10/6/66 FS *Tradescantia virginiana* (*Ephemeron*)

Spikenard, plowmans: 12/8/66 FS *Inula conyza* (*Baccharis Monspeliensium*)

Spinage: 12/9/51 family *Chenopidiaceae*

Spipola prima: 3/7/67 Whitethroat *Sylvia communis*

Spiraea filipendula: 9/7/68 *Filipendula ulmaria*

Spiraea frutex: 24/10/54 Willow-leaved spiraea *Spiraea salicifolia*

Spiraea ulmaria: 28/6/68 *Filipendula ulmaria*

Spleen wort, rough: 12/12/65 ?*Polypodium interjectum* (*Lonchitus aspera*)

Spurge, broad-leaved: 7/8/66 FS *Euphorbia platyphyllos* (*Tithymalus platiphyllos* . . .)

Spurge, corn: 22/7/66 FS *Euphorbia* spp. (*Tithymalus segetum longifolius*)

Spurge, dwarf: 29/10/65 *Euphorbia exigua* (*Tithymalus pumilus angustifolius*)

Spurge, petty: 22/7/66 FS *Euphorbia peplus* (*Tithymalus parvus annuus* . . .)

Spurge, sun: 2/11/65 *Euphorbia helioscopia*

Spurge, wood: 2/11/65 *Euphorbia amygdaloides*

Spurrey: 18/11/65 Corn spurrey *Spergula arvensis* (*Alsine spergula* . . .)

Squash: 22/3/51 ?sp.

Stachys fuchsii: 20/10/67¶ Downy woundwort *Stachys germanica* (base horehound)

Stachys germanica: 20/10/67¶, 2/8/73 Downy woundwort (base horehound)

Stachys palustris: 17/7/68 Marsh woundwort

Stachys sylvatica: 10/6/68 Hedge woundwort

Stares: 30/9/68 Starlings *Sturnus vulgaris*

Stellaria graminea: 16/10/65 Lesser stitchwort

Stellaria holostea: 20/4/66 FS, 29/5/68 Greater stitchwort

Stickleback: 19/11/66 FS *Gasterosteus aculeatus* (three-spined) or *Pungitius pungitius* (nine-spined)

Stinking flag: 18/11/65 Stinking iris *Iris foetidissima*

Stint: 11/5/69 Little stint *Calidris minuta*

Stitchwort, lesser: 16/10/65 *Stellaria graminea* (*Caryophyllus* . . .)

Stock-gilliflowers: 5/10/51¶ Stocks *Matthiola incana*

Stocks: 16/4/52 *Matthiola incana*

Stone curlues: 16/8/65¶ Stone curlew *Burhinus oedicnemus* (*Oedicnemus*)

Stoparola: 16/5/66 FS, 3/7/67 Spotted flycatcher *Muscicapa striata*

Storax: 29/4/55 Snowbell *Styrax* spp.

Strawberries, pine and Chili: 20/3/55¶ *Fragaria chiloensis*

Strawberries, pine-: 1/9/55 ?*Fragaria virginiana*

Succory, wild: 28/10/65 Chicory *Cichorium intybus*

Sumach, myrtle-leaved: 25/4/66 FS *Rhus* spp. (*Coriaria*)

Sumach, Venice: 20/6/66 FS Smoke tree *Cotinus coggygria* (*Coccygria* – *Rhus folius simplicibus* . . .)

Sundew: 9/9/65¶ 24/4/66 FS Round-leaved *Drosera rotundifolia* (*Ros solis*)

Sun-flowers: 13/4/51 *Helianthus* spp.

Sunflower, perennial: 1/7/66 FS *Helianthus rigidus* (*Helianthus radice perenni*)

Swallows: 9/4/58¶, 30/8/65 *Hirundo rustica*

Swan's egg: 31/10/69¶ A variety of pear

Swarraton: 17/3/55 Village 3m NW of New Alresford. Uncle Charles White was Vicar of Swarraton & Bradley

Swarth: 20/3/64¶

Swedish juniper: 1/5/56 *Juniperus suecica*

Sweet bryar: 13/3/66 *Rosa rubiginosa*

Sweet William: 25/4/57 *Dianthus barbatus*

Sycamore: 6/3/66 FS *Acer pseudoplatanus* (*Acer majus*)

Sycamore, variegated: 10/3/62 Variegated sycamore *Acer pseudo-platanus* var. *albo-variegatum*

Symphylus offic.: 13/6/68 Comfrey *Symphytum officinale*

Synocrambe: 11/10/65 Dog's mercury *Mercurialis perennis*

Symphytum magam: Comfrey *Symphytum officinale*

Syringa: 22/3/56¶ Common name for *Philadelphus coronarius*

Syringa ligustri folio: 17/4/66 FS¶ Persian lilac *Syringa persica* (Persian jasmine, privet-leaved lilac)

Tabanus bovinus: 19//71 ?Horsefly *Tabanus bromius*

Tamus communis: 8/6/68 Black Bryony

Tanzy: 2/11/65 Tansy *Chrysanthemum vulgare* (*Tanacetum*)

Tare, tine: 28/7/66 FS Tufted vetch *Vicia cracca* (*Cracca minor* . . .)

Taxus: 6/3/66 FS Yew *Taxus baccata*

Termes pulsatorium: Death watch beetle ?sp.

Teucrium scordonia: 28/7/68 Wood sage

Thalictrum flavum: 14/8/68 Common meadow-rue

Thistle, carline: 6/9/66 FS *Carlina vulgaris* (*Carlina sylvestris* . . .)

Thistle, dwarf carline: 16/7/66 FS Dwarf thistle *Cirsium acaulon* (*Carlina acaulis*)

Thistle, marsh: 24/10/66 FS *Cirsium palustre*

Thistle, musk: 15/7/66 FS, 24/10/66 FS *Carduus nutans*

Thistle, red star-: 16/7/68 *Centaurea calcitrapa*

Thistle, sow: 28/10/65 *Sonchus* spp.

Thistle, star: 23/8/66 FS Red star thistle *Centaurea calcitrapa* (*Carduus stellatus*)

Thlaspi bursa pastoris: 3/3/69 Shepherd's purse *Capsella bursa-pastoris*

Thorn: 22/3/56 ?Double hawthorn *Crataegus monogyna*

Throat-wort, cluster-flowered: 28/10/65¶ Clustered bellflower *Campanula glomerata*

Throatwort, great: 29/10/65, 22/7/66 FS *Campula trachelium* (Canterbury bells, nettle-leaved bellflowers *Campanula vulgatior folius urticae* . . .)

Throat-wort, little: 29/10/65 Clustered bellflower *Campanula glomerata*

Throatwort, nettle-leaved: 29/10/65 Nettle-leaved bellflower *Campanula trachelium* (Canterbury bells *Trachelium*)

Throat-worts: 30/9/65, 28/10/65¶ *Campanula* spp.

Thum: 16/8/65 Tuft, tassle

Thyme, mother of: 28/10/65 Wild thyme *Thymus serpyllum*

Thymus serpillum: 28/10/65 Wild thyme *Thymus serpyllum* (Mother of thyme)

Tilia Europaea: 2/5/66 FS Common lime

Tinea vestianella: 26/2/70 ?Clothes moth *Tineola bisselliella*

Tinea vestivora: 6/3/66 FS Moth ?sp.

Tipulae: 27/8/68 Crane flies *Tipula paludosa*, *T. maxima*

Titlark (. . . sings like a grasshopper): 3/7/67, 9/4/68¶, 26/3:21/4/73¶ Grasshopper warbler *Locustella naevia*

Titlark: 11/7/67, 21/4/73¶ Meadow pipit *Anthus pratensis* and Tree pipit *Anthus trivialis*

Titmice: 9/1/68¶

Titmouse, great: 1/2/66 FS Great tit *Parus major*

Titmouse, marsh: 6/3/70¶ Marsh and willow tits *Parus palustris* and *Parus montanus*

Toadflax, ivy-leaved: 16/10/65 *Cymbalaria muralis*

Toad flax, yellow: 30/8/65 Common toad flax *Linaria vulgaris*

Tom-tit: 2/2/72 Blue tit *Parus caeruleus*

Toothwort: 4/5/72¶ *Lathraea squamaria*

Tormentil: 14/6/66 FS *Potentilla erecta*

Tormentil, creeping: 10/10/65 Creeping cinquefoil *Potentilla reptans* (Tormentilla)

Tormentilla reptans: 5/5/66 FS Creeping cinquefoil *Potentilla reptans*

Torquilla: 3/3/66 Wryneck *Jynx torquilla*

Tortoise: 4/4/66 FS *Testugo graeca ibera* (*Testugo terrestris*)

Tragopogon luteum: 1/6/66 FS Goatsbeard *Tragopogon pratensis*

Tree mallow: 26/4/57 *Lavatera arborea*
Tree primroses: 16/7/68 Evening primrose *Oenothera biennis*
Tremella nostoc: 14/8/65¶
Trifolium arvense: 1/7/66 FS Haresfoot clover
Trifolium fragiferum: 29/8/66 FS Strawberry clover (Strawberry trefoil)
Trifolium pratense luteum . . .: 9/9/66 FS Hop trefoil *Trifolium campestre*
Trifolium pratense . . .: 19/5/66 FS Red clover
Trig: 6/3/59¶ To prop
Tringa minor: 29/4/66 FS Sand-piper *Tringa hypoleucos*
Tringa ochrophys: 10/8/69 Green sandpiper (white-rumped sand-piper)
Triticum hybernum: 17/6/68 Wheat
Tropaeolum majus: 20/7/68 Nasturtium
Trotta fluviatilis: 19/11/66 FS Trout *Salmo trutta fario*
Tulip tree: 16/4/55 *Liriodendron tulipifera*
Tulipa Gesneriana praecox: 3/4/68¶ Early-flowering tulip
Tull, Robin: Local man, sometimes employed in GW's garden
Tunn'd: 11/10/59 Put into barrels
Turdus iliacus: 13/1/66, 24/10/72¶ Redwing
Turdus pilaris: 15/10/65 Fieldfare
Turdus simplicitur dictus: 22/2/66 FS Thrush
Turdus torquatus: 25/9/68¶, 13/4/69¶, 4/9/70 Ring ouzel (*Merula torquata*)
Turdus viscivorus: 5/3/66 FS Mistle thrush (Missel-thrush, shrite)
Turnep: 29/7/52 Turnip *Brassica rapa* (*Rapa sativa*)
Turnep fly: 22/8/72 ?Flea beetle *Phyllotreta nemorum* family *Chrysomelidae* (*Chrysomelae oleraceae . . .*)
Turnip-radishes: 27/8/51 Round radishes
Turritis, oval-leaved: 12/12/65 Tower mustard *Turritis glabra*
Turtur: 17/5/70 Turtle dove *Streptopelia turtur*
Tussilago farfara: 17/3/66 FS Coltsfoot
Tutsan: 9/6/66 FS *Hypericum androsaemum* (*Hypericum maximum*, *Androsaemum vulgare*)
Twayblade, common: 2/5/66 FS *Listera ovata* (*Ophris*)
Typha latifolia: 23/8/66 FS, 6/7/68 Bulrush (Great cat's-tail, *Typha palustris*)
Ulmus: 29/4/66 FS Elm
Ulmus campestris: 4/4/68 English elm *Ulmus procera*
Ulmus glabra: 5/4/68 Wych elm
Valantia cruciata: 9/7/68 Crosswort *Galium cruciata*
Valerian, red: 12/10/65 Red valerian, *Centranthus ruber*
Valeriana dioica: 2/5/66 FS Common Valerian (*V. sylvestris*)
Valeriana floribus rubris caudatis: Red valerian *Centranthus ruber*
Valeriana locusta: 29/4/69 Valerian ?Marsh valerian *Valeriana dioca*
Valeriana officin: 7/7/68 Common valerian *Valeriana officinalis* agg.
Valerianella locusta: 7/4/66 FS Cornsalad, Lamb's lettuce
Vanellus vanellus: 24/4/66 FS Lapwing
Venus-Lookinglass: 17/4/55 Venus looking-glass *Legousia speculum-veneris*
Veratrum rubrum: 28/7/72 ?False hellebore *Veratrum nigrum*
Verbascum nigrum: 6/7/68 Dark mullein
Verbascum phoeniceum: 16/8/68 Purple mullein; Hybrid form *V. phoenicium* and forms of sp. now known as *V. hybridum*
Verbascus thapsus: 18/6/68 Great mullein *Verbascum thapsus*
Verbena offic: 24/6/68 Vervain *Verbena officinalis*
Veronica agrestis: 10/3/68 Green field speedwell
Veronica chamaedrys: 27/4/66 FS Germander speedwell
Veronica flosculis . . . hederulae . . .: 25/11/65 Ivy-leaved speedwell *Veronica hederifolia* (small henbit speedwell)

Veronica flosculis . . . cauliculis . . .: 4/3/66 FS ?Wall speedwell *Veronica arvensis* or green speedwell *V. agrestis* (Speedwell-chickweed)

Veronica pratensis serpyllifolia: 7/5/66 FS Thyme-leaved speedwell *Veronica serpyllifolia*

Vervain: 9/7/66 FS *Verbena officinalis* (*Verbena vulg.*)

Vespa communis: 6/5/68, 20/8/73 Common wasp *Vespula vulgaris*

Vespa vulgaris: 6/5/68 Common wasp *Vespula vulgaris*

Vespertilio altivolans: 6/8/71 Noctule bat *Nyctalus noctula*

Vespertilio auribus: 22/4/69¶ Long-eared bat *Plecotus brevimanus*

Vespertilio murinus: 4/4/68¶, 22/4/69¶ Pipistrelle bat *Pipistrellus pipistrellus*

Vetch, kidney: 13/6/66 FS *Anthyllis vulneraria* (*Vulneraria rustica*)

Vetch, tufted: 7/7/66 FS *Vicia cracca* (*Cracca multiflora*)

Viburnum lantana: 30/5/66 FS Wayfaring tree

Viburnum opulus: 26/5/68 Guelder rose

Vicia cracca: 10/7/68 Tufted vetch

Vicia sepium: 15/5/66 FS Bush vetch

Vicia sylvatica: 10/7/68 Wood vetch

Vinca pervinca minor: 12/3/66¶ Lesser periwinkle *Vinca minor*

Viola bicolor: 12/12/65 *Viola arvensis* or *Viola tricolor*

Viola canina: 14/4/66 FS, 9/4/68 Heath dog violet

Viola martia . . .: 14/4/66 FS, 9/4/68 Heath dog violet *Viola canina*

Viola odorata: 14/3/66 FS, 13/3/68 Sweet violet

Viola tricolor . . .: 19/5/66 FS Wild pansy

Violet, blue and white: 14/3/66 FS ?Sweet violet *Viola odorata*

Viper: 9/3/66 FS Adder *Vipera berus*

Viscum album: 9/4/66 FS Mistletoe

Vitis vinifera: Grape vine

Wagtail, white: 1/12/73¶ Water wagtail/pied wagtail *Motacilla alba yarrellii*

Wagtail, yellow: *Motacilla flava*

Wagtail, yellow, water: 21/11/73¶ Grey wagtail *Motacilla cinerea*

Walnut: 13/5/66 FS *Juglans regia* (*Nux juglans*)

Waltham: 21/5/54 Bishops Waltham: Hampshire town 7m N of Fareham where GW lodged while he was Curate at Durley.

Water-cress: 17/6/66 FS *Rorippa nasturtium-aquaticum* (*Nasturtium aquaticum vulgare*)

Water-cress, early flowering: 24/4/66 FS *Rorippa microphylla* (*Nasturtium aquaticum . . .*)

Water eft: 15/9/68 Newt *Triturus* sp.

Water-parsnip, creeping: 18/7/66 FS Lesser water parsnip *Berula erecta* (*Sium umbellatum repens*)

Water parsnip, upright: 29/7/66 FS Greater water-parsnip *Sium latifolium*

Water-plantain, great: 19/5/66 FS Common water-plantain *Alisma plantago-aquatica* (*Plantago aquatica*)

Water wagtail: 20/8/65 Pied wagtail *Motacilla alba yarrellii*

Wells: Selborne farming family

Weyhill: 12/10/73 Village 3m W of Andover

Wheat, Indian: 7/3/52¶ Maize, sweet corn *Zea mays* (Mays-seed, Indian corn)

Wheatear: 12/9/65 *Oenanthe oenanthe*

Whitchurch: 11/7/69 near Pangbourne: Mr Etty's living 1768

White, Anne: 1731–1807 GW's sister, married to Thomas Barker

White, Benjamin: 1725–1794 GW's brother, a London publisher. Married Ann Yalden, then Mary, widow of Revd Richard Yalden

White, Edmund: 1758–1838 Son of Benajmin White and Ann Yalden. Vicar of Newton Valence after death of Revd Richard Yalden

White, John: 1688–1758 GW's father

White, John: 1729–1780 Brother of GW, Chaplain to the garrison at Gibraltar, then moved to Blackburn, Lancs.

White, John (Jack): Son of GW's brother John

White, Henry: 1733–1788 GW's youngest brother. Rector of Tidworth, then Fyfield
White, Rebecca: 1726–1771 GW's sister, married Henry Woods
White Sampson: 1765–1825 Eldest son of GW's brother Henry
White, Thomas F.R.S.: 1724–1797. GW's brother, a wholesale merchant in London. Married
    Wm. Yalden's widow
White, U.: 7/3/51¶ Charles White, GW's uncle, Rector of Bradley and Swarraton
Whitethroat: 3/7/67 *Sylvia communis* (*Spipola prima, Ficedulae affinis atricapella*)
Whitlow-grass, common: 7/4/66 FS *Erophila verna* (*Paronychia*)
Whitlow-grass, rue: 27/4/66 FS Rue-leaved saxifrage *Saxifraga tridactylites*
Whortleberry: 21/7/66 FS Bilberry *Vaccinium myrtillus* (*Vitis idaea angulosa*)
Willow, French: 24/10/59¶ *Epilobium* sp., possibly *Epilobium dodonaei*
Willow, weeping: 17/3/66 FS¶
Willow-herb, greater smooth-leaved: 6/6/66 FS *Epilobium montanum* (*Lysimachia siliquosa . . .*)
Willow-herb, hooded: 12/8/66 FS ?*Scutellaria galericulata* (*Cassida palustris . . .*)
Willow-herb, narrow-leaved: 4/8/66 FS ?sp. (*Lysimachia siliquosa glabra . . .*)
Willow-herb, rosebay: 11/4/66 FS *Chamaenerion angustifolium* (*Lysimachia . . .*)
Willow herb, small flowered, hairy: 22/7/66 FS Hoary willow herb *Epilobium parviflorum*
    (*Lysimachia siliquosa*)
Willow wren: 4/4/67¶, 15/4/68¶ Chiff-chaff and other leaf warblers *Phylloscopus collybita* etc.
    (*Motacilla trochillus*)
Winter aconite: 22/2/66 FS *Eranthis hyemalis*
Wire-drawn: 12/4/54 Drawn out, weak, etiolated
Witney: John Mulso was Vicar and Rector there in 1767 (April)
Woodcock: 9/9/65 *Scolopax rusticola*
Woodpecker: 13/2/72¶
Woods, John: 1/4/71¶ of Chilgrove: old Mr Woods, Harry Woods's father
Woods, Henry (Harry): Of Chilgrove, husband of GW's sister Rebecca
Woodsage: 1/7/66 FS *Teucrium scorodonia* (*Scorodonia*)
Wormwood: 10/3/66 FS *Artemisia absinthium* (*Absinthium vulgare*)
Wornils: 7/7/10¶ Warbles
Worting: 11/10/73 Village 2m W of Basingstoke
Wren: 20/8/65 *Troglodytes troglodytes*
Wulmere-pond: 28/12/71 Woolmer pond (archaism)
Wryneck: 3/3/66 FS, 30/4/69¶ *Jynx torquilla*
Xyphium (planted): 24/10/54, 10/9/57¶ Bulbous xiphium *Iris xiphium* (bulbous iris)
Yalden, Ann: Sister of Revd Richard Yalden, married GW's brother Benjamin
Yalden, Revd Edmund: Vicar of Newton Valence, father of Richard, William and Ann Yalden
Yalden, Richard: 4/10/73 Revd Richard Yalden, Vicar of Newton Valence, a parish adjacent to
    Selborne
Yalden, Will: 24/4/55¶ Son of Revd Edmund Yalden and business partner of GW's brother
    Thomas White
Yarrow: 28/10/65 *Achillea millefolium*
Yellow centory: 17/9/67¶ Yellow wort *Blackstonia perfoliata*
Yellow hammer: 14/8/65 *Emberiza citrinella*
Zig-zag: The steep path up Selborne Hanger

BIBLIOGRAPHY

Bunyard, Edward	*A Handbook of Hardy Fruits* (2 vols., 1920)
Britten, J. & Holland, Robert A.	*A Dictionary of English Plant Names* (1886)
Chinery, Michael	*A Field Guide to the Insects of Britain and Northern Europe* (Collins, 1973)
	Collins Guide to the Insects of Britain and Western Europe (Collins, 1986)
Clapham, A. R., Tutin, T. G. & Warburg, E. F.	*Excursion Flora of the British Isles* (3rd ed., 1981)
	Flora of the British Isles (2nd edition, 1962)
Galpine, John Kingston	*The Georgian Garden – An Eighteenth-Century Nursery-man's Catalogue.* Introd. by John Harvey (Dovecote Press, 1983)
Harvey, John	*Early Nurserymen* (Phillimore, 1974)
	Early Gardening Catalogues (Phillimore, 1972)
Hitt, Thomas	*A Treatise of Fruit Trees* (1757)
Miller, Philip	*The Gardener's Dictionary* (1731 etc.)
Parkinson, John	*Paradisi in Sole Paradisus Terrestris* (1629)
Ray, John	*Catalogus Plantarum Anglicae* (1677)
	Historia Plantarum (1686–1704)
	Synopsis Methodica Stirpium Britannicarum (3rd ed. by J. J. Dillenius, 1724)*

Rye, Anthony	*Gilbert White and his Selborne* (1970)
Smith, A. W. revised by Stearn, William T.	*A Gardener's Dictionary of Plant Names* (1972)
South, Richard	*The Moths of the British Isles* (Frederick Warne, 1961)
Stearn, William T.	*Botanical Latin* (2nd ed., 1973)
Vilmorin-Andrieux	*The Vegetable Garden* (1905)
White, Rashleigh Holt	*Life and Letters of Gilbert White* (1901)

The following editions of Gilbert White's works have been consulted or referred to:

Natural History and Antiquities of Selborne edited by R. Bowdler-Sharpe (1900–01), Sir William Jardine (1890), E. M. Nicholson (1929), Richard Mabey (1977).

Gilbert White's Journals edited by Walter Johnson (1931).

The Garden Kalendar included in the Bowdler-Sharpe edition of the *Natural History of Selborne* (see above).

---

*Facsimile edition with Introduction by William T. Stearn, published by the Ray Society 1973.